INDUCTIVE LOGIC

PROBABILITY AND STATISTICS

DAVIS BAIRD
University of South Carolina

PRENTICE HALL
Englewood Cliffs, New Jersey 07632

Library of Congress Cataloging-in-Publication Data

Baird, Davis.
Inductive logic : probability and statistics / Davis Baird.
p. cm.
Includes bibliographical references and index.
ISBN 0-13-539685-9
1. Induction (Logic) 2. Statistics. I. Title.
BC91.B25 1992
161--dc20 91-27074
CIP

Editorial/production supervision and
interior design: Marielle Reiter
Cover design: Patricia Kelly
Manufacturing buyer: Patrice Fraccio
Prepress buyer: Herb Klein
Acquisitions editor: Ted Bolen
Editorial assistant: Diane Schaible
Copy editor: Barbara Zeiders

A Simon & Schuster Company
Englewood Cliffs, New Jersey 07632

Printed in the United States of America
10 9 8 7 6 5 4 3 2 1

ISBN 0-13-539685-9

PRENTICE-HALL INTERNATIONAL (UK) LIMITED, *London*
PRENTICE-HALL OF AUSTRALIA PTY. LIMITED, *Sydney*
PRENTICE-HALL CANADA INC., *Toronto*
PRENTICE-HALL HISPANOAMERICANA, S.A., *Mexico*
PRENTICE-HALL OF INDIA PRIVATE LIMITED, *New Delhi*
PRENTICE-HALL OF JAPAN, INC., *Tokyo*
SIMON & SCHUSTER ASIA PTE. LTD., *Singapore*
EDITORA PRENTICE-HALL DO BRASIL, LTDA., *Rio de Janeiro*

To L. W.

CONTENTS

Part I Four Statistical Methods of Induction

CHAPTER 2 SURVEY SAMPLING

CHAPTER 3 DECISION THEORY IN MEDICINE

CHAPTER 4 FACTOR ANALYSIS AND HUMAN INTELLIGENCE

CHAPTER 5 EXPERIMENTAL DESIGN

Part II Some Technical Apparatus

CHAPTER 6 DESCRIPTIVE STATISTICS

CHAPTER 7 INTRODUCTION TO PROBABILITY

CHAPTER 8 CONDITIONAL PROBABILITY

CHAPTER 9 BINOMIAL PROBABILITIES

Part III Statistical Inference and Induction

CHAPTER 10 CONFIDENCE INTERVALS AND INFERENCE

CHAPTER 11 BAYESIAN PROBABILITY AND RATIONALITY

PREFACE

This book is an introduction to four statistical/probabilistic methods of inductive inference. Statistical methods, because of their increasingly wide domain of application, have come to exert a substantial impact on contemporary society. Reports of statistically based studies—such as poll taking and drug screening—fill many pages of the popular press. IQ tests and a variety of their cousins play a significant role in determining the schools and jobs each of us has access to. Those who understand the strengths and weaknesses of these methods will be better equipped to read these reports and draw appropriate conclusions from them. I do not aim to teach students how to be statisticians, but to teach "statistical literacy."

I also aim to introduce these methods to philosophy students interested in the problem of induction. Besides much else, statistical methods must be seen as a partial offering toward an inductive logic. The text introduces students to the variety of contributions that probability and statistics make to solving the problem of induction, and should help set out the lay of the land of contemporary discussion of probability, statistics, and induction. I do not advocate a single philosophical approach to probability, statistics, and induction. I would be surprised if there was a fully satisfactory and theoretically unified approach to inductive inference; the field encompasses too many different contexts. I hope that this introductory text invites further study of statistics by students of the problem of induction.

The book is divided into three parts and an introduction. In the first part I present, nontechnically, four different statistical methods. Each is presented in the context of particular practices that employ them. I present the logic of interval estimation as a fundamental part of the practice of poll taking, Bayesian inference and decision theory in the context of medical decision making, factor analysis in its original role as the statistical foundation for intelligence measurement, and significance tests in the context of experimental design. What these methods claim to accomplish is remarkable, given the conceptual and practical challenges they face. This part of the text does not provide a technically detailed understanding of these methods. It does provide, I hope, an appreciation for these methods.

This part of the text also serves to examine statistics in practice. It is important to see just how far the practices that employ statistical methods differ from the specific presuppositions of the methods. It is also important to understand these practices and their impact on contemporary society. Although the text does not provide an in-depth analysis of, for example, the impact of public opinion polling on the democratic process, it should provide a good critical introduction to these practices.

To appreciate why these statistical methods work, one needs an elementary understanding of some technical matters. In the second part of the book I present the elements of probability and statistics. I introduce students to the computation and interpretation of some summary statistics, including averages, measures of spread, and correlation. I present some of the elements of measurement theory; I show how the scale of measurement employed can affect the summary statistics one can use. I prove the simplest rules of probability mathematics, including the multiplication rule, the theorem on total probability, Bayes' rule, and the formula for binomial probabilities. I discuss but do not prove Bernoulli's theorem and the central limit theorem. I introduce the idea of a probability density function.

In the third part of the book I use the technical apparatus developed in the second part to examine in greater detail the statistical methods introduced in the first part. In particular, I present derivations of confidence intervals for a large sample binomial trials. I present the basics of Bayesian inference and decision theory, including the determination and interpretation of personal degrees of belief, learning from experience by Bayes' rule, and assessing the value of information and experimentation. I show how factor analysis "finds for us" such properties as "IQ." I show how significance tests, such as the *t*-test and the chi-squared test, test for artifactual chance fluctuations in experimental data. I also consider a variety of foundational criticisms of each of these methods. I detail the pros and cons of several interpretations of probability in the context of their implications for Bayesian and classical statistical inference. I consider the difficulties that confront significance testing. I present some of the arguments that have been offered against the possibility of a logic of discovery such as factor analysis claims to be. Each method can be used to develop "good" inductive inferences; but what counts as "good" differs in each case, and many contest these "goods."

The different parts of the book, and the different statistical methods, are relatively independent of each other. While I hope the book as a whole paints a compelling picture of the—desirable—disunity of inductive logic in general, and statistical inference in particular, one need not read the entire book or read it in the order in which I have put the chapters. Figure 0.1 gives some idea of the relationships of the chapters. Each of the four chapters in the first part can be read independent of the others. The three probability chapters build on each other, but they do not require

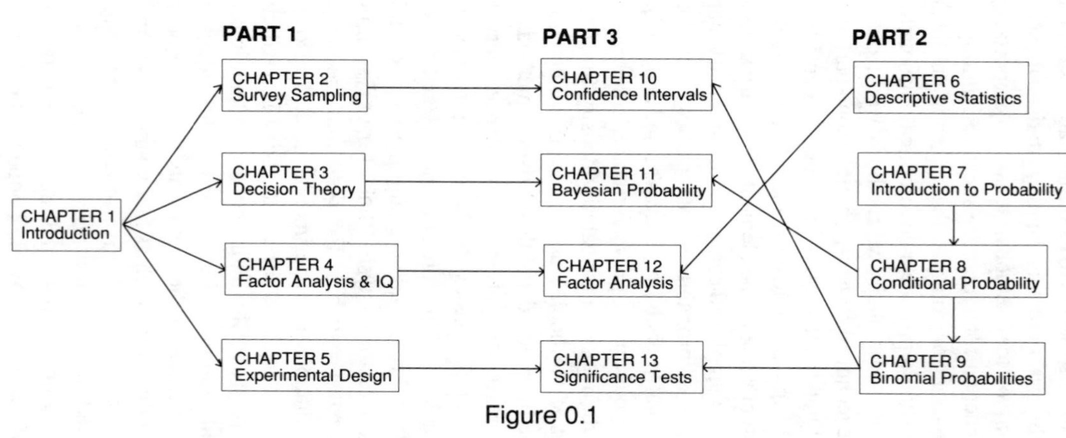
PART 1
PART 3
PART 2
CHAPTER 1
Introduction
CHAPTER 2
Survey Sampling
CHAPTER 3
Decision Theory
CHAPTER 4
Factor Analysis & IQ
CHAPTER 5
Experimental Design
CHAPTER 10
Confidence Intervals
CHAPTER 11
Bayesian Probability
CHAPTER 12
Factor Analysis
CHAPTER 13
Significance Tests
CHAPTER 6
Descriptive Statistics
CHAPTER 7
Introduction to Probability
CHAPTER 8
Conditional Probability
CHAPTER 9
Binomial Probabilities

Figure 0.1

the chapter on descriptive statistics; it can be read independently. The four chapters in the third part of the book can be read independent of each other, although where appropriate, I try to point out some of the important relationships among these methods. The chapters in the third part do build on earlier material, but one need not be familiar with all the material in the second and first parts to understand each chapter in the third part. For exmple, one need not be fully familiar with binomial probabilities to benefit from either Chapter 11, on Bayesian inference and decision theory, or Chapter 12, on factor analysis.

By selecting and organizing the chapters in different ways, the book can serve for a variety of courses. One kind of course, which focuses exclusively on statistical literacy, might use only the first five chapters. Another kind of course, aimed to emphasize the pros and cons of Bayesian and classical approaches to statistical inference, might use Chapters 1, 2, 3, 7, 8, 9, 10, and 11. A third kind of course might start with the technical material and then show how it is applied; Chapters 6, 7, 8, 3, 11, 4, and 12 could be used in this manner. The third part of the text can also serve to provide introductory material for a more advanced course on statistical and probabilistic concepts of evidence. Appropriate chapters can also be selected to supplement other courses; Chapters 4, 6, and 12, for example, provide a good introduction to IQ and factor analysis.

This is not a comprehensive introduction to probability, statistics, and induction. In the interests of keeping the technical demands of the book to a minimum, most of the technically interesting results have been omitted or summarized. Bayes' rule may be very important conceptually, but it is not of great technical interest. Similarly, in the interests of presenting some methods in detail, I have skipped many other methods of statistics. Factor analysis is but one method of data reduction and analysis. The four methods that are presented in detail were chosen for the variety of strategies they employ toward inductive inference. Nor should one think that probability and statistics provide the only important or interesting approach to induction. Finally, this book lacks any serious discussion or even appreciation of the historical development of probability and statistics; (Gigerenzer et al., 1989) is a nice antidote.

Many people have helped me in many ways to write the book. I have taught an introductory course based on material that grew into this book. Much of the ability of the book to serve as a textbook must be attributed to the criticisms and praise my students have had for the notes they have had to use as a textbook. Five graduate students, Dale Smoak, Mark Moller, Rod Rebuck, Peter Hager, and Leila Batarseh were particularly helpful in relaying student reactions to the text and in suggesting better ways to say "what the notes really mean." Several undergraduate students, most particularly Pam Hatfield, are to be thanked for their help ferreting out typos and other indiscretions. In the early 1970s, Jim Oliver, then Chair of the Department of Philosophy at USC, had the foresight to create a freshman introduction to inductive logic; had he not done so, and had I not been hired in part to teach this course, this text would not have been written. He also, gently but unflaggingly over several years, encouraged me to write the book. Several of my colleagues have read and commented on portions of the book at various stages of its preparation. Barry Loewer, Ferdy Schoeman, Jerry Wallulis, and Zeno Swijtink deserve special thanks. Bob Janarone, of the Center for Machine Intelligence at USC, helped with the material on factor analysis. Howard Harriott, Alfred Nordmann, and Eric Folley deserve special thanks for being the first to teach from the notes that grew into this book. Their reactions to both coverage and treatment were very helpful. The text has benefitted from much help provided by the editorial expertise of Prentice Hall; I would particularly like to thank Joe Heider and Andy Karr for originally encouraging me to pursue my idea of a text on probability, statistics, and induction; Joe Heider for helping the text reach production; and Marielle Reiter and Barbara Zeiders for doing such a fine job of making the text read and appear so well. I also wish to acknowledge those who reviewed this manuscript at various stages and provided helpful suggestions, criticism, and comments. These include Theodore Messenger, University of North Dakota; Ron Bombardi, Middle Tennessee State University; Mark Bedau, Dartmouth College; and Leslie Burkholder, Carnegie Mellon University. I would also like to thank my teacher, Ian Hacking, who introduced me to probability, statistics, and induction. Finally, I would like to thank Linda Weingarten, who prepared the figures—from rather sketchy drawings—helped with writing the text, and put up with a sometimes grumpy and sometimes frantic husband.

CHAPTER 1

INTRODUCTION

1. INFERENCES AROUND US

The October 31, 1983 issue of the *Wall Street Journal* reports that 74% of middle-level business executives from large businesses say that they take office supplies home from work; 80% have driven while intoxicated. Reading further we find that these percentages are based on a study conducted by the Gallup organization. Gallup obtained information about such matters from 396 business executives and claims that the reported percentages are accurate to plus or minus 5% (page 33).

Is it not remarkable that Gallup can boast such accuracy about *all* business executives based on information from only 396 executives? Yet, typically, polls or sample surveys contact only a minuscule fraction of the population about which they make an inference. One of the largest surveys conducted regularly, the monthly employment survey conducted by the Bureau of the Census, contacts approximately 120,000 people; from this they determine the percentage of unemployed persons in the entire work force of roughly 100,000,000 people. Most polls get information from at most 2,500 people. Then they tell us, for example, about the political preferences of the entire population of U.S. voters.

The March 8, 1986 issue of *Science News* reports the following item:

> There are five words that, if used properly, can tap into powerful unconscious wishes shared by many adults, provoke several types of improvement in behavior and possibly enhance the effects of psychotherapy, according to psychologist Lloyd H. Silverman of

> New York University. Which words? MOMMY AND I ARE ONE. . . . In 68 studies (representing 2,443 subjects) employing MOMMY AND I ARE ONE, Richard A. Hardaway of the University of Southern California in Los Angeles uncovered clear-cut but modest behavioral improvements for people exposed subliminally to the message (page 156).

One can imagine installing such subliminal messages at appropriate points in television programming. A world with a "better-behaving populace" may be just around the corner.

The same issue of *Science News* reports that women who regularly get breast lumps are at no greater risk of developing breast cancer than are women who do not regularly get breast lumps. This finding is based on biopsy tissue examined from 3,303 women with benign lumps; 70% of these cases were found to face no higher risk of forming a malignancy than the risk in the population as a whole. Most breast lumps are benign and the presence of benign lumps is not predictive of malignant lumps.

As with the Gallup Poll of business executives, these inferences are based on information collected from a small number of people. We make an inference about all women based on examinations of 3,303 women. We reach a conclusion about the salutary effects of MOMMY AND I ARE ONE based on data from 2,443 subjects. The conclusions concern vastly larger populations. These inferences can alter how we think about ourselves and the world around us. They can affect us materially; a spokesperson for Aetna Insurance has indicated that insurance premiums may be altered in light of the lump study.

We are regularly confronted with claims based on polling studies or experimental studies. Some of these claims are trivial and amusing and some are full of profound implications for our own lives. All of these claims are generalizations from information obtained about a small group of people or, in the case of many studies, experimental animals such as rabbits and chimpanzees.

This book is about the reasons we have to place confidence in such generalizations. Put simply, we reach a *conclusion*—"MOMMY AND I ARE ONE" subliminally presented, improves behavior—based on information acquired through experiments or polls or whatnot. We can call this acquired information the *premises* from which we draw the conclusion. The question is: Why is it reasonable to make the further claim, the conclusion, given the information presented in the premises? Such questions, in their general form, are part of logic, and this is where we can begin our investigation. When we finish we may have a clearer understanding about these inferences and a broader notion of logic.

2. WHAT IS LOGIC?

We can begin by asking, "What is logic?" The dictionary tells us that logic is the science of correct reasoning. There are two parts to this definition, "correct reasoning" and "the science of." Let's consider these briefly in turn.

Correct reasoning. Reasoning comes in units called *arguments*. An "argument," as we shall use the term, should not be confused with an emotional disagreement between two people. While such "verbal fights" occasionally include bits of reasoning, the arguments we shall be concerned with, generally, are not emotional. As far as we are concerned, an argument is a bunch of sentences that together are a bit of reasoning.

All arguments have parts called *premises* and another part called the *conclusion*. Sometimes premises and conclusion are brought together as phrases in a single sentence (It's raining out, so the game surely will be canceled.), sometimes they occur as separate sentences (The car's exhaust is blue and the car has been losing a quart of oil a week. Probably, the car needs an engine overhaul.). We can describe an argument schematically:

$\mathbf{P_1}$	The car's exhaust is blue.
$\mathbf{P_2}$	The car has been losing a quart of oil a week.
.	
.	
.	
$\mathbf{P_n}$	
So **C.**	So, probably, the car needs an engine overhaul.

The $\mathbf{P_i}$s, numbered 1 to *n* (*n* might be any number, even one for an argument with only one premise), are the premises of the argument and **C** is the conclusion. The $\mathbf{P_i}$s and **C** provide a schema for an argument; the real argument to the right of the $\mathbf{P_i}$s is one example where $\mathbf{P_1}$ and $\mathbf{P_2}$ are replaced by particular sentences; **C** is replaced by another sentence.

We can easily find examples of correct reasoning—or "good arguments"—and incorrect reasoning—or "bad arguments." Here is a good argument. I have a fish pond in my backyard. Recently, all the fish disappeared; strangely, I did not find their corpses floating on the surface. However, I did discover a new tenant of my pond, a frog. Since frogs eat fish and there has been no other change in the pond that might cause my fish to disappear, I inferred that my fish were disappearing inside the frog:

$\mathbf{P_1}$	All the fish in my fish pond have been disappearing.
$\mathbf{P_2}$	A frog recently took up residence in my pond.
$\mathbf{P_3}$	Frogs eat fish.
$\mathbf{P_4}$	There is no other change in the pond that plausibly could cause my fish to disappear.
So **C.**	So, probably, the frog is eating my fish.

The premises of this argument *support* its conclusion. Believing the premises is good reason to believe the conclusion. There also are bad arguments:

P_1 The Earth circles the Sun every 365 days.

P_2 The digital clock in my study is cream color.

So **C.** So it will probably snow tonight.

Here the premises are irrelevant to the conclusion. Whether or not it snows tonight has nothing to do with the color of my digital clock.

There are other bad arguments whose premises appear to be relevant to the conclusion, but which still fail to support the conclusion:

P_1 If I have no gas in my car's gas tank, it will not start.

P_2 My car is broken and will not start.

So **C.** So it is out of gas.

The premises are related to the conclusion, but there are many other reasons that might explain why my car doesn't start. Perhaps the battery is dead. Bad arguments that have the appearance of good arguments, like this example, are called *fallacies*.

The science of. Since logic is the science of correct reasoning, we must understand how a discipline is a science. Among the many goals that all sciences have in common, three are particularly important for our purposes. One goal of science is to *describe* correctly the particular bit of the world relevant to the science. A second goal is to *explain* why this particular bit of the world is the way it is. A third goal is to *predict* the unknown.

Consider psychology: Much psychology consists of attempts to describe human behavior or the mind accurately. Presented subconsciously, the sentence "Mommy and I are one" improves behavior. But psychology also offers explanations of known facts: "Mommy and I are one" is important *because* many adults are motivated by an unconscious wish for a state of fusion with another nurturing protective person—such as one's mother. Finally, a good psychological theory should be able to predict future human behavior: Subliminally presenting "Mommy and I are one" in psychotherapy sessions should relieve schizophrenic symptoms.

What about logic? We can think of a big box containing every possible argument (Figure 1.1). The business of logic, as a science, is to describe, explain, and predict correct reasoning. Which are the good arguments and which are the bad arguments? We should be able to sort out the arguments in the box (Figure 1.2). We should be able to say which arguments go in the left-hand part of the box and which in the right-hand part. But we want to know more. Why are the good arguments good and the bad ones bad? Why is the line separating good from bad drawn where it is drawn? Finally, we should be able to predict of a new argument whether or not it

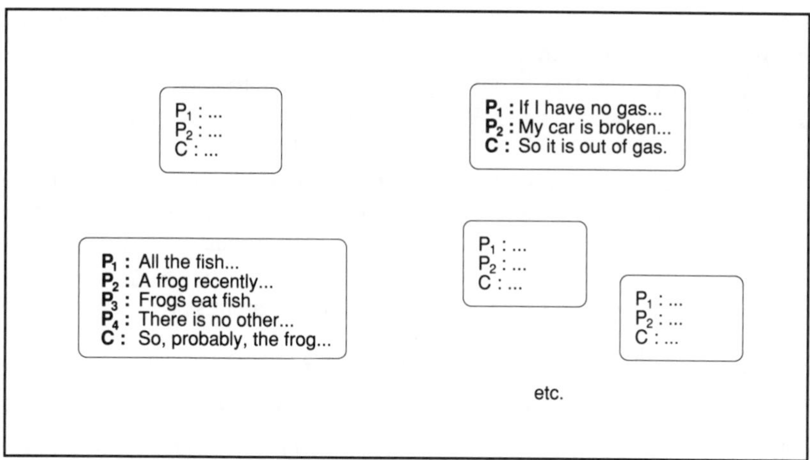

Figure 1.1

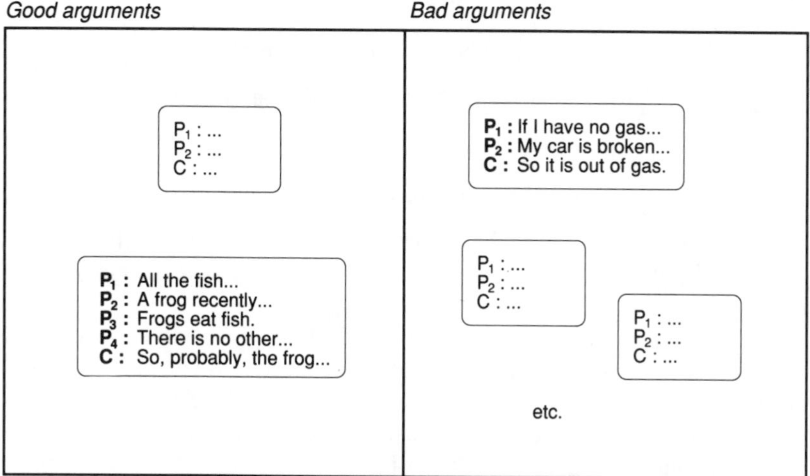

Figure 1.2

is a good argument. For example, all arguments of the form—**A**, **A** $\rightarrow$ **B**, so **B**—will be good arguments.

3. DEDUCTIVE AND INDUCTIVE ARGUMENTS

It is common to think of arguments as either deductive or inductive, although it is a bit difficult to say in detail which are which. We can perhaps best think of deductive arguments as those arguments where the premises provide the greatest possible support for the conclusion. Such arguments are frequently found in mathematics and logic itself, although they are also found elsewhere.

We can draw the line between *good deductive* arguments and other arguments—good or bad—in a particularly nice way. One concept, *validity*, allows us to draw this line. Deductively valid arguments are those for which, *if* the premises are true, the conclusion *must be* true. Put another way, it is impossible to imagine the premises to be true and the conclusion false in a deductively valid argument.

It is difficult to appreciate this definition. The "must be true" can easily confuse. Both the premise and the conclusion of the following argument are true. But *must* the conclusion be true given the truth of the premise?

P_1 Lyndon B. Johnson was elected President of the United States.

So **C.** So Lyndon B. Johnson served as President of the United States.

It is possible to imagine that Johnson was elected and that he died before he took the oath of office. A maniac who disliked Johnson but liked Humphrey might have relied on this *possibility*. This is not a deductively valid argument.

In contrast, the following argument is valid:

P_1 Every person is either a man or a woman.

P_2 Aspirin relieves any headache that a man might have.

P_3 Aspirin relieves any headache that a woman might have.

So **C.** So aspirin relieves any headache that any person might have.

If all of the premises are true—they are not, but suppose they were—the conclusion would have to be true as well. It is impossible to imagine all the premises to be true and, simultaneously, the conclusion false.

The requirement that the conclusion *must be* true, given true premises, is very strong. To ensure that an argument is valid, we must consider not only how the world actually is but all the ways it might be as well. If the premises of a valid argument are true, the truth of the conclusion is guaranteed to be true as well. No other kind of argument provides this kind of guarantee. An important goal of deductive logic is to find out what kinds of arguments are valid—what kinds of arguments provide this kind of guarantee.

Inductive arguments can most *un*informatively be characterized as all the good arguments that are not valid. The fish pond argument is not valid. One can imagine that a bird or a neighbor's cat ate my fish. I did not consider these plausible explanations of my fishes' disappearance because they fail to account for why my fish started to disappear just when the frog appeared. This could have been a coincidence, but a good initial inference given the information at my disposal blames the frog. Nonetheless, we can imagine a false conclusion and true premises; the argument is not valid. Yet it is a good argument.

The examples at the beginning of the chapter also are good arguments that are not deductively valid. Given only information about 396 executives, it is *possible* that the percentage of *all* executives who drive while intoxicated is not even close to the inferred estimate of 80% ± 5%. Given only information about 3,303 women, it is possible that benign breast lumps *are* symptomatic of future malignancies among most other women in the population. These are *possibilities*, but we have better reason to believe the results of the studies. The studies *support* but do not *guarantee the truth* of the conclusion; they are not deductively valid arguments.

There is no single concept, like validity, with which to describe all good inductive arguments. The fish pond example is quite different from the unemployment survey. Roughly, in the case of the fish pond we seek a plausible explanation for an established fact—the disappearance of the fish. Surveys, such as the unemployment survey, seek to generalize an established description of a small sample to a larger population from which the sample is taken. The use to which established information is put differs in the two cases. To date, there is no satisfactory theory that can account for both kinds of argument as two particular species of a general form.

Thus inductive logic is a messier business than deductive logic. We will study several different kinds of inductive arguments in this book. Some, like those used to produce survey sample estimates, are concerned primarily with generalizing a result observed in a sample to a larger population from which the sample was taken. Others, like those used to produce probable medical diagnoses from a variety of symptoms, are concerned primarily with selecting the most plausible explanation for what is known to be true. We will study some others as well.

Inductive logic faces a second harder problem not faced by deductive logic. In an important sense, deductive arguments alone cannot teach us anything new about the world. Inductive arguments can, but this makes the problem of understanding and explaining how they work difficult.

Consider an example. The following is not too great a simplification of an argument urged by some economists early in the Reagan Presidency:

$\mathbf{P_1}$	If taxes are cut, there will be more money available to individuals.	$\mathbf{A \rightarrow B.}$
$\mathbf{P_2}$	Individuals can do only two things with their money: They can spend it, or they can save it.	$\mathbf{B \rightarrow (C \vee D).}$
$\mathbf{P_3}$	If individuals spend their money, the increased consumer spending will spur the economy.	$\mathbf{C \rightarrow E.}$
$\mathbf{P_4}$	If individuals save their money, the increased savings available for loans will reduce interest rates and spur the economy.	$\mathbf{D \rightarrow E.}$
So **C.**	So cutting taxes will spur the economy.	$\mathbf{A \rightarrow E.}$

This is a valid argument. Students familiar with introductory deductive logic can show this themselves with a truth table test. It appears that the conclusion of the argument does teach us something about the world. Yet this appearance is deceptive.

The premises of this argument are far from certain. What happens if people spend their money on foreign products, and the third premise, $\mathbf{P}_3$, is false? What happens if the federal government borrows so much that despite a greater supply of available funds to borrow, interest rates do not come down, and the fourth premise, $\mathbf{P}_4$, is false? What if the tax cuts are more than compensated for by tax increases on the state or local level, and the first premise, $\mathbf{P}_1$, is false? There are plenty of ways that this argument fails to provide a sure-fire reason to believe its conclusion.

Such deductive arguments are important. They help us figure out what is *necessary* for "Reaganomics," for example, to work. *If* the premises are true, the conclusion must also be true. Deductive logic guarantees this much. But such arguments by themselves cannot show us that Reaganomics will work. To infer that Reaganomics will work we must have reason to believe the premises of the argument.

This further work is typically provided by inductive arguments. Perhaps there is strong evidence that enough of the savings from a tax cut will not be spent on foreign goods. Perhaps the federal government will not borrow so much money that interest rates will fail to decline. For each way in which a premise of a nice deductive argument might fail, an inductive argument is needed to support that premise. Of course, it is entirely possible that no such inductive argument is available.

Deductive logic is attractive because the support the premises of a valid argument provide for the conclusion is of the strongest sort possible. The truth of the premises guarantees the truth of the conclusion. But this strength is achieved at a price. All the deductive arguments we use either do not teach us anything beyond clarifying what we already know to be true—an important goal, to be sure—or they have premises of which we cannot be certain. Since the support a deductive argument provides its conclusion is derived from the truth of its premises, having uncertain premises diminishes a deductive argument's power to persuade.

Valid deductive arguments are said to be *nonampliative*. They can clarify what we know about the world, but they do not expand what we know about the world. To learn more, we must use *ampliative* arguments. This poses a major problem, which we can appreciate with a more extended example.

4. BODE'S LAW

Johannes Kepler (1571–1630) is remembered for his discovery of three laws that describe the motion of the planets around the Sun. Kepler's first law states that each planet orbits the Sun in an elliptical path with the Sun at one focus of the ellipse. Kepler's second law describes the velocity with which a planet takes its elliptical course: If one connects the planet with the Sun by an imaginary line, the area swept out by this line in a given amount of time is the same no matter where in the orbit the planet is; when the planet is closer to the Sun, it goes faster, when farther, it goes slower. Kepler's third law relates the time it takes a planet to completely orbit the Sun—its period—**P**, with the mean distance between the planet and the Sun, **D**. Kepler showed that (using appropriate units of measurement) the square of the mean distance is equal to the cube of the period of rotation: $\mathbf{D}^2 = \mathbf{P}^3$.

Roughly eighty years later, in 1687, Isaac Newton (1643–1727) showed how Kepler's laws could be derived from his inverse-square law of universal gravitation. Prior to Newton, Kepler's laws were purely numerical wonders. There was no known reason why squaring the mean distance should produce the same number as cubing the period. But these numerical wonders both accurately described the solar system, and ultimately helped to establish Newton's fundamental achievement.

It was a sensible project to seek other precise numerical relations that accurately describe other aspects of the solar system. In particular, astronomers sought such a relation describing the sequence of mean distances between the planets and the Sun. Until 1781, when Uranus was discovered, there were six known planets (Table 1.1). (When talking about large distances such as those between planets and the Sun, it is useful to adopt a unit of measurement astronomers call *astronomical units*—A.U. One A.U. is the mean distance between the Earth and the Sun.)

Johann Titius (1729–1796), pursuing some ideas of Christian Wolf (1679–1754) and Immanuel Kant (1724–1804), discovered a numerical regularity. Start with the sequence

$$0,\quad 3,\quad 6,\quad 12,\quad 24,\quad 48,\quad 96,\quad 192,\quad \ldots.$$

To each of these numbers add 4:

$$4,\quad 7,\quad 10,\quad 16,\quad 28,\quad 52,\quad 100,\quad 196,\quad \ldots.$$

Finally, divide each of these numbers by 10:

$$0.4,\quad 0.7,\quad 1.0,\quad 1.6,\quad 2.8,\quad 5.2,\quad 10.0,\quad 19.6,\quad \ldots.$$

With one exception, this sequence of numbers compares favorably with the distances of the planets from the Sun in astronomical units (Table 1.2). This fact was first announced in 1772; it was brought to general notice by Johann Elert Bode (1747–1826) and has since been called "Bode's law."

TABLE 1.1

Planet	Distance
Mercury	0.38 A.U.
Venus	0.72 A.U.
Earth	1.00 A.U.
Mars	1.52 A.U.
Jupiter	5.20 A.U.
Saturn	9.53 A.U.

TABLE 1.2

Planet	Distance	Bode's Law
Mercury	0.38 A.U.	0.40
Venus	0.72 A.U.	0.70
Earth	1.00 A.U.	1.00
Mars	1.52 A.U.	1.60
—	—	2.80
Jupiter	5.20 A.U.	5.20
Saturn	9.53 A.U.	10.00

Here is an inductive argument. The close agreement between the simple series described by Bode's law and the actual distances between the planets and the Sun argues for Bode's law. Indeed, astronomers used this fact to urge that there must be another, yet undiscovered, planet between Mars and Jupiter.

In 1781, Sir William Herschel (1738–1822) began what he hoped to be a complete inventory of the major and minor stars in the sky. One night he found a new pinprick of light. However, when looking for it on the following night, he found that it had moved relative to the other stars; it could not be a star. At first Herschel thought it was a comet. But, after obtaining a series of positions and plotting its movement, it became apparent that it was a planet. ("Planet" is derived from the Greek for "wanderer." The planets can be distinguished from the stars by the fact that they do not stay in the same position relative to the other stars, they wander among them.) We now call the planet Herschel discovered "Uranus."

Herschel's discovery of Uranus was a major victory for Bode's law. Uranus's distance from the Sun is 19.10 A.U.—close to the distance one would predict on the basis of Bode's law:

$$\frac{(96 \times 2) + 4}{10} = 19.60 \approx 19.10.$$

Twenty years later, on the first day of 1801, Giuseppe Piazzi discovered an asteroid, Ceres, orbiting the Sun between Mars and Jupiter. While the history concerning the asteroids is somewhat more complicated, Ceres's mean distance from the Sun is also close enough to count as confirming Bode's law. Ceres fills the blank in the fifth element of Bode's series.

Here is another inductive argument for Bode's law. The foregoing argument for Bode's law, which employs only the close agreement between Bode's predicted distances and the known distances, is not very persuasive. Many sequences could be constructed that give numbers as close as Bode's predictions. Few of these other sequences, however, would correctly predict both Uranus's and the asteroid's distance from the Sun. Correct predictions count in favor of the law from which the predictions are made.

P_1 The agreement of Bode's law with the six known planetary distances.

P_2 The agreement between Bode's prediction and Uranus's distance.

P_3 The agreement between Bode's prediction and the asteriod's distance.

So **C.** So Bode's law is a correct description of the planetary distances.

Clearly, Bode's law could be false while each premise is true; an undiscovered eighth planet *could* be closer or farther from the Sun than the distance predicted by Bode's law. Yet these two successes of Bode's law were, in fact, quite persuasive.

Uranus's orbit is not normal; it wiggles around the orbit predicted by Newton's law of gravity. Instead of taking this divergence as evidence that Newton's theory was wrong, it was supposed that there was another, eighth, planet beyond Uranus which was heavy enough to pull Uranus away from a simple elliptical orbit.

To find this supposed eighth planet, astronomers tried to calculate a probable orbit for it. The position and mass of the planet had to be such that it would account for the irregularity in Uranus's orbit. This information alone was not enough to determine an orbit for the planet. But according to Bode's law, the distance between the Sun and this new planet should be about

$$\frac{(192 \times 2) + 4}{10} = 38.80 \text{ A.U.}$$

With this new constraint, and with a lot of hard mathematical work, two astronomers, John Adams (1819–1892) in England and U. J. J. Leverrier (1811–1877) in France, independently calculated orbits for the supposed eighth planet. Leverrier convinced a German astronomer, J. G. Galle (1812–1910), to look for this planet using information provided by the hypothesized orbit. On September 23 and 24, 1846, Galle saw the new planet: Neptune. Galle's observation was a triumph for Adams and Leverrier.

Despite the fact that both Leverrier and Adams used Bode's law to help calculate an orbit for Neptune, Neptune's discovery was not a triumph for Bode's law. Neptune is much closer to the Sun than Bode's law predicts. According to Bode's law, Neptune should be about 38.80 A.U. from the Sun; in fact, Neptune is about 30.07 A.U. from the Sun. Neptune's discovery was a fatal blow for Bode's law.

5. THE PROBLEM OF INDUCTION

We believe we have a good idea of what the future will be like. We believe that the Sun will rise tomorrow as it has in the past; we believe that the bread we eat tomorrow will not poison us. Our beliefs may be based on the best evidence available; we may, without knowing it, employ the most powerful and persuasive arguments to conclude that the Sun will rise and that bread will nourish. But we may be surprised; the future may turn out radically different than we suppose.

Adams and Leverrier had reason to believe that Neptune would be about 38.80 A.U. from the Sun. But Neptune is not 38.80 A.U. from the Sun. Even the most powerful inductive arguments cannot guarantee the truth of their conclusions. The argument for Bode's law is not the most powerful inductive argument imaginable, but it was sufficiently powerful to convince many astronomers. Yet Bode's law is false. Kepler's laws could have suffered a similar fate. Indeed, all our beliefs about the future, no matter how well convinced we are of them, *could* turn out to be false. It is *possible*. Inductive arguments cannot guarantee the truth of their conclusions, and deductive arguments cannot tell us how the future will be without some doubtful premise.

The future *may* be radically different from how we imagine it will be. This remains possible in the face of the most powerful inductive argument. This fact about the world and inductive arguments poses severe difficulties for inductive logic. In the first place, if an inductive argument does not guarantee the truth of its conclusion—given the truth of its premises—what other kind of guarantee can it provide instead?

We will find that there are many different concepts, or guarantees. Some arguments guarantee a specified probability of a true conclusion—given true premises. Other arguments guarantee a true probability of the conclusion. Subsequently, we will have to sort out the differences between these two kinds of probabilistic guarantees. Other arguments offer yet other kinds of guarantees not so explicitly probabilistic in character; concepts such as significance level, or variance reduction through factorial causation, help endorse different kinds of inductive arguments. A main aim of this book is to examine these alternative guarantees to the deductive guarantee of truth.

Our first problem is to appreciate the nature of these alternatives. Our second problem is to see how one can justify the desirability of these alternative guarantees. Little was said explicitly about the argument for Bode's law based on its successful predictions for Uranus and Ceres. People simply accepted it to be a good argument; but is it a good argument, and why? A *logic* of inductive inference must do more than *describe* which arguments are good inductive arguments. It must *explain* why certain inductive arguments are good arguments; it must describe the guarantees these arguments come with and justify the desirability of these guarantees. We may be able to describe the guarantees, but a skeptic about induction can pose powerful arguments against the desirability of the guarantees offered.

Some have argued, on completely general grounds, for a skeptical position regarding the possibility of justifying inductive arguments. One argument goes like this: Suppose that one wants to justify an inductive argument; call the argument **I**. There are only two ways to justify **I**: One can justify it deductively or one can justify it inductively. But neither the deductive nor the inductive justification is possible. Here is why.

Suppose that we use a deductively valid argument to justify an inductive argument. In schema we have two arguments, the inductive argument, **I**, which is being justified by some valid deductive argument; call this argument **D**. **D** must have premises whose truth is beyond any doubt and a conclusion which states that **I** is a valid argument:

Inductive Argument, I	*Deductive Argument, D, Justifying I*
$\mathbf{IP_1}$: . . .	$\mathbf{DP_1}$: . . .
$\mathbf{IP_2}$: . . .	$\mathbf{DP_2}$: . . .
$\mathbf{IP_3}$: . . .	$\mathbf{DP_3}$: . . .
:	:
:	:
$\mathbf{IP_n}$: . . .	$\mathbf{DP_m}$: . . .
So **C**	So **I** is a valid argument.

We need not worry about what the specific premises, $\mathbf{DP_1}$ through $\mathbf{DP_m}$, are in this argument. What we must know is that we can be certain of their truth and that we can validly infer the conclusion—**I**, is a valid argument—from them. But we combine these two arguments to form a new argument:

New Combined Argument

$\mathbf{DP_1}$: . . .

$\mathbf{DP_2}$: . . .

:

:

$\mathbf{DP_m}$: . . . , and

$\mathbf{IP_1}$: . . .

$\mathbf{IP_2}$: . . .

:

:

$\mathbf{IP_n}$: . . .

So **C** . . . .

This new argument must be valid: From $\mathbf{DP_1}$ through $\mathbf{DP_m}$ we can validly infer that we can validly infer **C** from $\mathbf{IP_1}$ through $\mathbf{IP_n}$; we infer that we can validly infer **C**. Since we suppose that all of these premises are beyond doubt, we can conclude **C** and be certain of its truth as well. To put matters another way, we could not imagine all these premises to be true and the conclusion false. If all the premises are true, then, because of $\mathbf{DP_1}$ through $\mathbf{DP_m}$, we know that we can validly infer **C** from $\mathbf{IP_1}$ through $\mathbf{IP_n}$. Since we additionally suppose that $\mathbf{IP_1}$ through $\mathbf{IP_n}$ are true, **C** must be true as well.

Thus, it would seem, a deductive justification of an inductive argument allows us to turn an inductive argument into a valid deductive argument. But it seems totally implausible that we could turn an important inductive argument into a valid deductive argument with premises whose truth is beyond question. If this were possible, we would have constructed an *ampliative deductive* argument. But since there is good reason to think that there are no such ampliative deductive arguments, it does not seem that any such deductive justification for an inductive argument will work.

Suppose, on the other hand, that we used an *inductive* argument to justify our inductive argument. Such an approach seems implausible from the start. A skeptic who doubted the goodness of any inductive argument is not going to be convinced of the goodness of an inductive argument because some other—suspicious—inductive argument justifies it. The skeptic would simply deny that our justifying inductive argument is any good. If it is not any good, it certainly cannot provide a good justification for the original inductive argument whose goodness is in question. This approach is viciously circular. Thus, it appears that no argument—deductive or inductive—could justify an inductive argument.

However, we do not need to answer the skeptic before we look in detail at the logic of particular kinds of inductive arguments. We will find arguments that justify inductive arguments, but they do not show that the inductive arguments in question are *valid*. Inductive arguments offer some other kind of guarantee. Thus we cannot simply use a justifying argument to turn an inductive argument into a valid deductive argument. Of course, a skeptic can question whether the guarantees offered are worthwhile. No one doubts that guaranteeing the truth of the conclusion of an argument—given the truth of its premises—is a worthwhile guarantee. But many will question the other kinds of guarantees offered by inductive arguments. In what follows we do not directly refute the skeptic.

It is possible that the guarantees offered for the particular kinds of inductive arguments we consider will not satisfy an unrelenting skeptic. But in coming to appreciate these guarantees, we will come to a better appreciation of what such a skeptic must deny. Put another way, one might be more skeptical about general skeptical arguments than about particular criticisms of the guarantees provided for specific kinds of inductive arguments.

A close understanding of the guarantees offered by the particular kinds of inductive arguments we study softens the impact of the skeptic's arguments. We have a new forum for examining inductive arguments. Instead of arguing on entirely general grounds, a skeptic must argue on more detailed grounds. Skeptical complaints must focus on the particular guarantees offered by these inductive arguments. Such complaints can be met by modifying the forms of inductive argument involved and the details of the guarantees claimed for these arguments. No doubt new complaints can be lodged. But the important fact to notice is that the forum of discussion is a detailed and potentially progressive critique of particular forms of inductive argument. General skepticism about inductive arguments may not be possible to refute head-on. But general skepticism may not lend itself to a detailed and potentially progressive critique of particular forms of inductive arguments. A forum of progressive critique is surely a more sensible forum to participate in than a simple general skeptical argument of questionable merit.

The most general consequence of this approach to induction is that the nature of the inductive arguments we examine does not quite fit the confines of the picture of logic we have been using so far. Arguments tell us what to believe given our other beliefs. But they also tell us what to do. With deductive logic it is easier to separate these two functions. With inductive logic this becomes much more difficult.

6. PROBABILITY, STATISTICS, AND INDUCTION

The variety of good inductive arguments makes the task of inductive logic demanding. In this book we examine four different kinds of good inductive arguments and the different guarantees each comes with. The arguments and their guarantees are different, but they do have one thing in common: they are based in probability and statistics. It should be clear, however, that the arguments we examine do not include every different kind of good inductive argument. Many kinds of good inductive argument are statistical in character, but there are many other kinds of good inductive argument that are not statistical in character; nor can the arguments discussed be claimed to include every good statistical argument.

There are several reasons for my choice of arguments to examine, and it is worth mentioning some of these reasons at the outset. There are two kinds of reasons, practical and theoretical; let me mention the practical reasons first.

Many statistically based arguments—from political polls to drug approval experiments to legal testimony—have become common and influential in the conduct of our lives. This point needs little elaboration for the evidence is all around us. The results of polling studies can be read in almost every edition of almost every newspaper. The federal government requires statistically based tests of efficacy and safety for every drug that a manufacturer wants to bring to market. In many cases the results of SAT tests and similar measures of intellect influence what educational opportunities are available to us as individuals; in a perhaps more insidious fashion, these measures can fundamentally affect how we think about ourselves and how we fit into the world. Again, such tests are based in statistics.

Despite how frequently they occur, statistical arguments can be quite deceptive. This is perhaps the point of the quip that there are three kinds of lies: lies, damn lies, and statistics. Consider the following attractive fallacy. According to the 1986 *Statistical Abstract of the United States*, a 29-year-old white male has a life expectation of 44.1 years. We will suppose that John is a 29-year-old white male. Thus, it seems, John can "expect" to live for another 44.1 years. Consequently, John can "expect" to die at age 73.1, or, supposing that John was born in April 1957, in May or June of the year 2029.

Of course, if John is to live to age 73, he must, at some point, be 49 years old. If the life expectations stay the same for the next 20 years (most likely they will not, but we need not quibble over this point), then, according to the *Statistical Abstract*, John will have a life expectation of 26.0 years. Consequently, he would *then* expect to die at age 75, or in roughly March or April of 2031—a gain of nearly 2 years. Of course, if he is to live until age 75, he must, at some point, be 70 years old. He would then have a life expectation of 11.3 years; he would *then* expect to die at age 81.3, or in roughly July or August of 2037—a gain of 6 more years. This maneuver can be iterated. Since the life expectation for white males older than 85 is 5.5 years, one could argue that John has an indefinite life expectation.

It would not be correct to conclude from this that anything goes as far as statistical arguments are concerned. There are good statistical arguments. Las Vegas and Atlantic City are founded on good statistical arguments. Life insurance companies keep from going bankrupt by the correct use of life expectation tables such as those above. Our problem is to find out what is right about statistical inference and to learn to avoid such sophistry as this argument.

Because of the prevalence and deceptive nature of statistical arguments, they merit our study on practical grounds. But there are theoretical reasons to study statistical arguments in a course on inductive logic.

I cannot hope in an introductory inductive logic text to discuss all the different kinds of good inductive arguments and the various guarantees these different kinds of arguments offer. But the particular statistical arguments I do discuss cover a range of possibilities that is reasonably representative of many of the different kinds of inductive arguments. The kinds of arguments I do not discuss, in many cases, will offer similar guarantees to one or another of the kinds I do discuss.

Perhaps more important is the fact that statistical methodology is relatively explicit. There are many arguments that we employ with little thought. Only by searching for a simple humdrum example was I forced to make my reasoning about the frog and my fish relatively explicit. In fact, I hardly thought about it; I saw the frog and knew (or so I believed) what was happening to my fish. When there is little explicitly said about an argument, it is difficult to appreciate what makes it a good argument. Statistical arguments are relatively new; the arguments we will examine did not exist a century ago. Because of this and because they are prone to abuses like my statistical argument for immortality above—and considerably more subtle abuses—there are extensive explicit justifications for statistical arguments. This helps a great deal in our project to explain why certain inductive arguments are good arguments.

Statistical arguments are important to study because they are common, influential, and easily misunderstood and misapplied. What follows is not a statistics text. We will not dwell on each particular technical detail that helps to construct each particular statistical argument. Our focus will be on the underlying logic of these arguments. We will come to appreciate this logic through a study of a few particular kinds of statistical argument which are common and illustrative of the general logic used in statistics. Since much statistical information is presented to all of us as members of the public, an appreciation of the logic underlying this information can be quite useful. An appreciation of this logic also serves as an introduction to the science of inductive logic.

7. SUMMARY

1. Logic is the science of correct reasoning.
   - **(a)** Reasoning comes in units called arguments. An argument is a sequence of sentences. One of these sentences is the conclusion of the argument, and the other sentences are premises of the argument.
   - **(b)** Arguments can be good or bad. In a good argument, the premises support the conclusion.
   - **(c)** Logic is a science, and as such it has the task of describing, predicting, and explaining which arguments are good and which are not.
2. There are two general kinds of good arguments.
   - **(a)** Good deductive arguments are called valid.
     - **(1)** A valid argument is one where the truth of the premises guarantees the truth of the conclusion.
     - **(2)** It is impossible to imagine a situation where the premises are true and the conclusion is false in a valid argument.
     - **(3)** For this reason valid arguments are commonly said to be "truth preserving"; the truth of the premises is preserved in the conclusion.
     - **(4)** A valid argument is nonampliative; the conclusion contains no more information than is already contained in the premises.
     - **(5)** Valid arguments may clarify what we know, but they do not teach us about what we don't know.
   - **(b)** There are many different kinds of good inductive arguments.
     - **(1)** Some good inductive arguments conclude with the most plausible explanation of a known fact.
     - **(2)** Other good induction arguments generalize known properties of a sample group to the whole population in which the sample resides.
3. Inductive logic faces several problems.
   - **(a)** The future may be radically unlike what we expect based on our past experience.
   - **(b)** Any inductive argument that tells us about the future based on information about the past must be ampliative.
   - **(c)** Since the future may be unlike the past, the conclusion of an inductive argument with true premises may still be false.
   - **(d)** Thus, inductive arguments cannot guarantee the truth of their conclusions given the truth of their premises.
   - **(e)** Different kinds of good inductive arguments provide different kinds of guarantees—in place of deductive validity.
     - **(1)** A skeptic may challenge whether any of the guarantees offered by various good inductive arguments are sufficient to justify their use.
     - **(2)** But skeptical challenges of particular claims made for particular kinds of inductive argument will probably be more productive than skeptical challenges to the entire enterprise of inductive logic.

4. There are several reasons to focus the study of good inductive arguments on a variety of statistical arguments.
   (a) Two reasons are practical.
      (1) Statistical arguments—from opinion polls to drug screening studies—are frequently used.
      (2) Statistical arguments can be deceptive; it is difficult to understand what they guarantee for their conclusions, and it is easy to abuse statistical arguments to produce absurd conclusions.
   (b) Two reasons are theoretical.
      (1) The variety of statistical arguments represents well the overall variety of good inductive arguments; thus, the guarantees provided for statistical arguments are similar in many cases to guarantees offered by other good inductive arguments.
      (2) Because they are relatively new and can be deceptive, extensive explicit justifications have been developed for statistical arguments; thus they are easier to study than are many other good inductive arguments.

8. REFERENCES

Examples have been taken from the *Wall Street Journal* and *Science News*. There are many good introductory logic texts; most emphasize or even focus exclusively on deductive arguments. Two are (Jeffrey, 1967) and (Thomas, 1977); (Copi, 1961) provides a somewhat more elementary and general treatment. Three sources provided information for the brief history of Bode's law: (Grosser, 1979), (Berry, 1961), and (Banville, 1981). The problem of induction has been discussed in numerous places. It is generally attributed to (Hume, 1978)—a reprint of Hume's 1739 *Treatise*. (Salmon, 1967) provides a nice contemporary treatment with a careful discussion of probabilistic attempts to solve the problem of induction. The *Statistical Abstract of the United States* provides a wealth of information from which to construct statistical fallacies as well as well-founded statistical arguments.

9. PROBLEMS

1. Find an example of an argument from some standard printed source—newspaper, magazine, and so on. Copy it and, by some means, identify the premises and conclusion of the argument.
2. Give an example of a valid argument.
3. Is the following argument valid?

   P_1 Five out of 10 people in a certain group are male.

   P_2 Eight of 10 people in the same group are taller than 5 feet 4 inches.

   So **C.** So two women in the group are shorter than 5 feet 4 inches.

   Why or why not?

4. Is the following argument valid? Does the argument persuade you of its conclusion?

$\mathbf{P_1}$	$5 = 6$.
$\mathbf{P_2}$	$6 = 7$.
So **C**.	So, $5 = 7$.

Why or why not?

5. What lessons might one draw from the failure of Bode's law to predict correctly Neptune's distance from the Sun? Was it pure luck that Adams and Leverrier found Neptune? Discuss.

6. Why does it make sense to say that valid arguments do not teach us anything new about the world. Surely valid mathematical proofs teach us new things about mathematics. Discuss.

7. Why might one be very worried about a general skeptical attack on any inductive argument. Are inductive arguments necessary? Discuss.

8. Is the following argument valid? Is it a good argument?

$\mathbf{P_1}$	Every clock in my house today is 47 minutes behind the correct time.
$\mathbf{P_2}$	There was a severe lightning storm near my house last night.
$\mathbf{P_3}$	Lightning storms can disrupt electrical service.
$\mathbf{P_4}$	There was no other change recently which plausibly could disrupt the electrical service at my house.
So **C**.	So probably, the lightning storm disrupted electrical service at my house last night.

Why or why not?

CHAPTER 2

SURVEY SAMPLING

1. INTRODUCTION TO SURVEY SAMPLING

In this chapter we look into a very commonly used method of inductive inference: survey sampling, or polling studies. Not only is survey sampling commonly used, its results are widely distributed and discussed by most segments of the U.S. population. Everyone has heard of the Gallup or Yanklovich or Harris polls, to name a few major polling firms. Survey sampling is perhaps the only method of explicit probability-based inductive inference with which most everybody has some familiarity.

Typically, pollsters ask a small number of people—from 10 to 2,500—questions about various subjects—from politics to economic status. On the basis of the responses to these questions pollsters hope to learn about a much larger population of people; sometimes they make inferences about all the people in the United States.

For example, a pollster might ask 1,500 people who they intend to vote for in the next presidential election. On the basis of these 1,500 "intended votes," the pollster hopes to be able to say something, in terms of *all* potential voters, about the relative standings of those running for office.

It is entirely possible for the 1,500 people interviewed to represent the population as a whole inadequately. Of the 1,500 people interviewed, 1,400 might favor one candidate for re-election, while 65,000,000 of the 100,000,000 voters might well favor someone else. Consequently, it is entirely possible for the pollster's conclusions to be wrong. The Gallup Poll in the Truman election of 1948 is an example. According to the poll, Truman's opponent, Dewey, was strongly favored to win. In fact, early editions of newspapers were sold announcing that Dewey had won. But Truman won; the polls were wrong.

Yet polling studies frequently do contain useful information. If the group of people polled is picked properly to *represent* the entire population, we should be able to learn something about people's preferences regarding the candidates. The problem, of course, is to find a way to pick *representative* groups of people.

Thus, the pollster's method is inductive. The conclusion of a poll is not guaranteed to be true by the results of the poll; polling conclusions are not based on deductively valid arguments. But the pollster's argument is persuasive; we do learn something of value from the results of a poll. So whatever the arguments used to sustain the conclusions of a poll, they are *good inductive arguments*.

Suppose that we are interested in the current political preferences for the next presidential election. The *population* of interest is the group of people eligible to vote in the next election. (It might be argued that the group we are interested in actually includes only those people who will in fact vote in the next election.) On the other hand, if we are interested in the state of housing in Columbia, South Carolina, then the group we are interested in includes the houses in Columbia.

The population is made up of *units*. Frequently, units are individual people. But units can be other sorts of things. The Bureau of the Census has measured the quality of housing by determining the *average* number of full bathrooms in houses in a particular area; in this case units are houses.

There are many things one might want to know about units in a population. If our units are people, we may want to know about each person's gender or about a physical characteristic such as height. If our units are houses, we may want to know about the number of rooms in the house, the number of stories, the lot size, and so on. The characteristic of the units of a population that is of interest is called the *variable* of interest. It is called a variable because different units are different with respect to the characteristic of interest. Different people have different heights; different houses have different numbers of rooms.

Suppose that we are interested in the average income of residents of Lexington, Massachusetts. The *population* is the group of wage earners in Lexington. The *variable* of interest is the income of these wage earners. Since there are so many different exact wages that a person might earn, we might simplify our project and look only into wage categories:

Category 1:	\$0–\$5,000
Category 2:	\$5,001–\$10,000
Category 3:	\$10,001–\$15,000
Category 4:	\$15,001–\$20,000
⋮	⋮
Category 11:	over \$50,000

Finally, the people whose income we actually determine constitute our *sample*. It is very tempting to suppose that our sample is taken from *all* residents of Lexington. Sometimes, however, this is not so. For example, we might take our sample from those residents listed in the Lexington phone book. Since some people either do not subscribe to phone service or have unlisted numbers, the people from which we choose our sample in such a case would not include all the residents of Lexington; they would only include those listed in the phone book. The group of units from which our sample is chosen is called the *sampling frame* (see Figure 2.1).

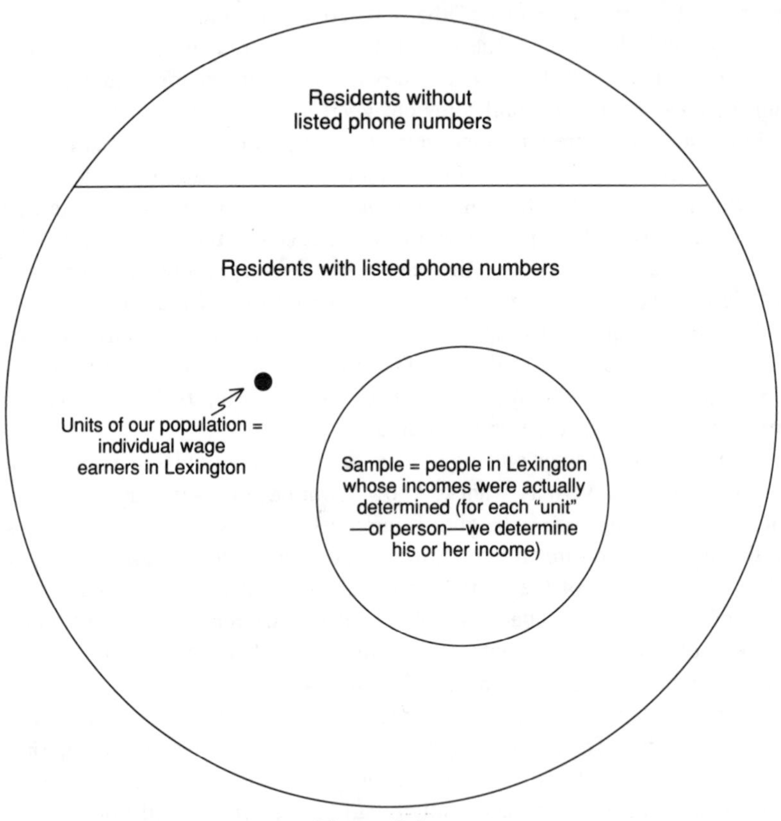

Figure 2.1

2. THE CURRENT POPULATION SURVEY

Perhaps the largest survey conducted on a regular basis is the Current Population Survey (CPS) conducted monthly by the Bureau of the Census for the Bureau of Labor Statistics. This survey provides such information as the unemployment rate and the rate of population migration from one part of the country to another. Each month, Bureau of the Census employees contact approximately 60,000 households.

They gather information about 120,000 people. Despite the relatively large number of people about which information is obtained, it is still only a tiny fraction of the 108,700,000 people (as of 1982) in the labor force.

What population does this survey attempt to find information about? It is easy to say "U.S. citizens." But the unemployment rate does not consider newborns in the labor force; they are not part of the population under consideration. Who is in the labor force? According to the Bureau of Labor Statistics *Handbook*, persons 16 years old or older who are employed civilians, persons in the armed forces, or unemployed persons comprise the labor force. This is not very informative.

Who is employed? Anyone who either did any work as a paid employee, or who worked more than 15 hours in their own business or profession, or who did not work but had jobs or businesses from which they were temporarily absent.

Who is unemployed? Unemployed persons include those who did not work and were available *and looking* for work. Unemployed persons also include those who are waiting to be called back to a job from which they have been laid off temporarily.

Persons who are engaged in housework, are in school, are unable to work, are retired, or a variety of other possibilities, are not counted as being in the labor force. Among other things, if a person is not employed and does not seek work, he or she is not in the labor force.

There is such a large variety of ways for humans to engage themselves that it is not easy to define the *population* of interest. Nor is it easy to define the *variables* of interest—the properties of the *units* in the population about which we gather information. Some of the decisions about who to include in what group, and who not to include, can seem rather arbitrary and perhaps pernicious. Is house*work* not work after all? Some of the decisions about who to include in what group have strong political ramifications. The unemployment rate dropped at one point during the 1980s because persons in the armed forces were included in the labor force when previously they had been excluded. Such a drop looks good in the press even if it represents no underlying change in employment.

The procedure for selecting households for this survey excludes those people who do not have something that could count as a permanent residence. People who live in the mountains with no clear address or location cannot be included in the sample. Also, people do not have to provide information; people whose households are selected may decline to participate in the survey, and roughly 2% of selected households do refuse. Thus, the *sampling frame* is somewhat different from the population. All of this information can be represented in a diagram similar to Figure 2.2.

3. METHODS OF SAMPLING

Clearly, the problem facing the pollster is to find a sample *representative* of the population of interest. There are many different ways to obtain a sample; some are better than others. By choosing units in a random way, a pollster can provide a

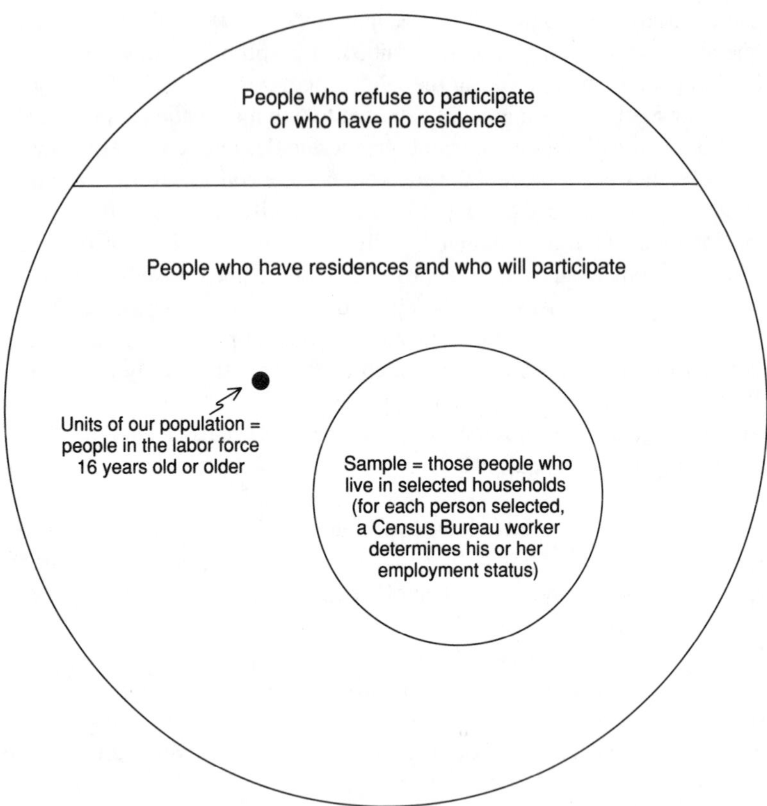

Figure 2.2

certain kind of guarantee that the result will be representative. To appreciate this, it is useful to consider other methods of sampling first.

The most obvious way to sample is to take a *census:* ''look at'' each unit in the population. This method would surely be able to produce the information desired. If we ''look at'' every person in the labor force, we would know exactly what proportion of persons in the labor force is employed.

But there are substantial difficulties with taking a census. In many cases it is simply not possible to obtain information about every unit in a population without changing the population. For example, we may wish to determine what percentage of a population of light bulbs will burn for 5,000 hours. We might sample the population and let the bulbs burn until they were burned out and see what percentage of the bulbs sampled burned for more than 5,000 hours. If we took a census sample, we would not have any bulbs left!

In other cases it is simply too costly or time consuming to obtain information about every unit in the population. Suppose that we wanted to determine how many people use a certain brand of hand soap. Suppose it took half an hour—on average—to contact and question people. If we contacted every person in the United States—to obtain a census of soap usage—it would take 240,000,000/2 = 120,000,000 labor-hours to conduct the survey. That is, it would take 1,000 people 5,000 days working 24 hours a day just to conduct the census. If each of these 1,000 workers were paid a wage of $4.00/hour, the census would cost 480 million dollars! It is very unlikely that information about the use of soap could possibly be worth this much time and cost. This should give you some appreciation for the difficulty that must be surmounted in undertaking the constitutionally required 10-year census of the United States.

Finally, information from censuses can be incorrect. For example, in the 1970 census it is reported that there are 69 women under the age of 15 with 11 or more children. I suppose that this is possible, but it is highly unlikely. It is much more likely either that there was a mistake in registering the answers of respondents, or that the respondents misunderstood the question. Because census information is so extensive, it is virtually impossible to avoid such errors.

There are other ways to collect samples. *Convenience sampling* is one way. Consider the incomes-in-Lexington example again. Suppose that the pollster has an office in Lexington. One easy way for the pollster to obtain a sample is to walk out of the office and talk to the first 200 Lexingtonians that he or she runs across. Such convenience sampling has the advantage that it is easy to do and requires little advance preparation.

In 1936, the *Literary Digest* predicted that Alfred Landon would defeat Franklin Roosevelt in the presidential election. The prediction was based on 2,376,523 returned questionnaires that were mailed to registered telephone and automobile owners. These lists provided a convenient source of people to contact. Despite the large size of the sample, the prediction failed because the sample systematically favored wealthier people—those with telephones or automobiles—who were willing to respond to the questionnaire. As it happened, these people tended to be Republicans and not Democrats.

In a nutshell, convenience sampling is *biased*. We would expect convenience samples to overrepresent certain portions of the population and underrepresent other portions of the population. We may not know *how* a given method of convenience sampling is biased, but we would guess that it would be biased in some way or another. It was only after the failed prediction of Landon's defeating Roosevelt that people realized that the convenience sample used systematically favored Republicans—and hence Landon. This source of bias was not obvious until the sample proved to be substantially unrepresentative of the population.

Bias is a property of the *method* of sampling. Occasionally, a *biased method may* produce a single sample that happens to represent well the whole population. But for the most part a biased method will yield samples that either systematically overestimate or systematically underestimate the average unemployment rate—or whatever is of interest.

Consider a silly method of sampling: We might choose exactly one unit from the population. We might choose this unit by randomly selecting it from the set of all units in the population. By "random selection" I mean that each unit in the population has the same *chance* of being selected. Exactly what is intended by this notion of chance will occupy us in the second and third parts of the book. For now, think of chances like the outcomes of rolling a die. Here we imagine a die with as many faces as there are units in the population. This method at least has the advantage that we do not waste time and money gathering information.

Obviously, however, letting one unit represent the entire population can result in wildly different results. Were we to sample Lexington wage earners this way, the person selected might be one of the biggest wage earners on some occasions, one of the smallest wage earners on other occasions, and on yet other occasions this unit might earn the average wage for Lexington. This method of sampling does not provide any guarantee that our "sample" is anything like the population of Lexingtonian wage earners.

Curiously, such a method of sampling is not biased. This method would not systematically overestimate one segment of the population. That is, if we took many such "one-samples" we would not always or for the most part get a person who earned more than the true average wage, nor would we always or for the most part get a person who earned less than the true average wage. We would get results that sometimes were higher and sometimes were lower than the true average wage. The sample statistic—the wage of the person selected—would not always or for the most part be larger than the true population parameter—the average wage of all Lexington wage earners; nor would it always or for the most part be smaller than the true population parameter. Taking one-person samples produces no systematic tendency to overestimate or systematic tendency to underestimate the true population parameter. Such a method is not biased.

But this method of sampling *lacks precision.* The precision of a method of sampling can be understood as the tightness with which a bunch of different possible sample results group together. Having one person represent the entire population is one of the least precise methods possible. The results of the different possible one-samples will vary all over the map, covering the entire spectrum of different wages that are earned in Lexington.

Consider another silly method of sampling. Suppose that we picked one resident, Frank Sands, to be the sample. That is, we "sample" by picking Frank Sands. Were we to repeat this method of sampling over and over, we would always have a sample that included just Frank Sands. This is obviously a silly method of sampling. But it is not silly because it is imprecise. Every time we sample we would get the same sample statistic—whatever Frank Sands' wage happened to be. These results group together as closely as possible—they are all identical—and consequently, this method of sampling is very precise. However, this method of sampling is biased. If Frank Sands earned more than the average wage, this "method" of sampling would systematically overestimate the true population average wage; if Frank Sands earned less than the average wage, this method would systematically underestimate the true average wage. Both lack of bias and precision are necessary for a good method of sampling.

As with bias, it is important to recognize that precision is a property of the *method* of sampling. One cannot even make sense of how tightly a "bunch of a single sample" is grouped together. There is only one member of the "bunch." When we imagine repeating the "one-random-wage-earner-sample" many times, we know that the results of all these repetitions will vary a lot. Thus this *method* of sampling is not precise.

4. ACCURACY = LACK OF BIAS + PRECISION

When we conduct a survey we desire to know about averages. For example, what is the average income in Lexington? Frequently, we seek a proportion. For example, what proportion of the labor force is unemployed? Such a description of the population of interest is called a *population parameter*. Population parameters do not describe individual members of a population; they describe average properties of the whole population.

We use information from a sample to help determine the true value of the population parameter. For example, if the unemployment rate in the sample is 6.5%, we might infer that the unemployment rate in the population is *roughly* 6.5%. The unemployment rate in the sample is called the *sample statistic*. Sample statistics do not describe individual members of the sample, nor do they describe the population of interest; they describe the average properties of the sample.

Consider another example: Suppose that we are interested in the relative proportions of men and women enrolled at the University of South Carolina. The *population parameter* of interest is the percentage of women (or equivalently of men) enrolled at USC. The *sample statistic* that we would look at is the percentage of women in our sample of USC students.

The variable of interest describes individual units in the population. A given USC student selected to be part of our sample might be a male or a female. We combine information about the variable of interest for each unit in our sample to determine a sample statistic. This sample statistic describes some "average" property of our sample. Perhaps 54% of our sample of USC students are female. We then use this sample statistic to help us to infer a value of the population parameter of interest: Roughly 54% of all USC students are female. If we use a good method of sampling, we can make some fairly definite and useful claims about this inference from sample statistic to population parameter.

Thinking of population parameters—what we want to know—in terms of averages helps us to understand bias and precision graphically. Keep in mind that bias and precision are properties of a method of sampling. They describe what would happen if we took a sample over and over using the same method to select units for the sample.

A *biased method of sampling* is one where sample statistic values from different samples—each selected with the same method—are predominantly on one side or predominantly on the other side of the true population parameter. A biased method of sampling *can* produce a sample statistic that is ''right on the money'' — being exactly equal to the population parameter—but for the most part, samples from a biased method of sampling will be on one side or the other of the true value.

Recall the incomes-in-Lexington example. Suppose that we used a method of convenience sampling that happened to pick predominantly wealthy people; perhaps we interviewed people at an expensive clothing store that happened to be close to ''our office.'' Very likely our sample would include mostly relatively wealthy people, and the average income of our sample—the sample statistic—would be higher than the true average income in Lexington. Of course, we might happen to get a low average in our sample, but this would be unusual. If we imagined repeating this method of selecting a sample over and over, the ''typical'' result would be a sample statistic higher than the true population parameter (see Figure 2.3).

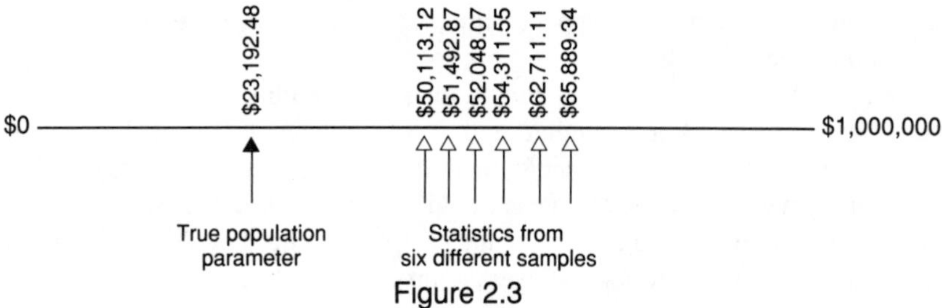

Figure 2.3

In this imagined example, the true average income in Lexington—the true population parameter—is $23,192.48. One time when we sampled the population we got an average income of those in our sample—the sample statistic—of $50,113.12. Another time we got a sample statistic of $51,492.87. All of the six sample statistic values—one value for each different sample—are higher than the true population parameter. In this sense, such a method of sampling is biased. If we were to use this method over and over again, we would consistently or for the most part get samples that produced sample statistics which are too high—as in the current example—or too low.

A *precise method of sampling* is one where sample statistic values are all clumped together. They need not be clumped near the true value. In the example above sample statistic values varied between a low of $50,113.12 and a high of $65,889.34. If they all were between $50,113.12 and $51,482.90, we would be using a more precise method of sampling. If, on the other hand, they varied between a low of $1,769.04 and a high of $94,444.93, we would be using a less precise method of sampling. Some examples are shown in Figure 2.4.

When we develop the notion of precision more technically in Chapter 10, we will measure the degree to which sample results clump together with what is called the ''sampling variance.'' The variance is just a measure of how closely clumped values are; the smaller the variance, the more closely values are clumped together (see Chapters 6 and 10).

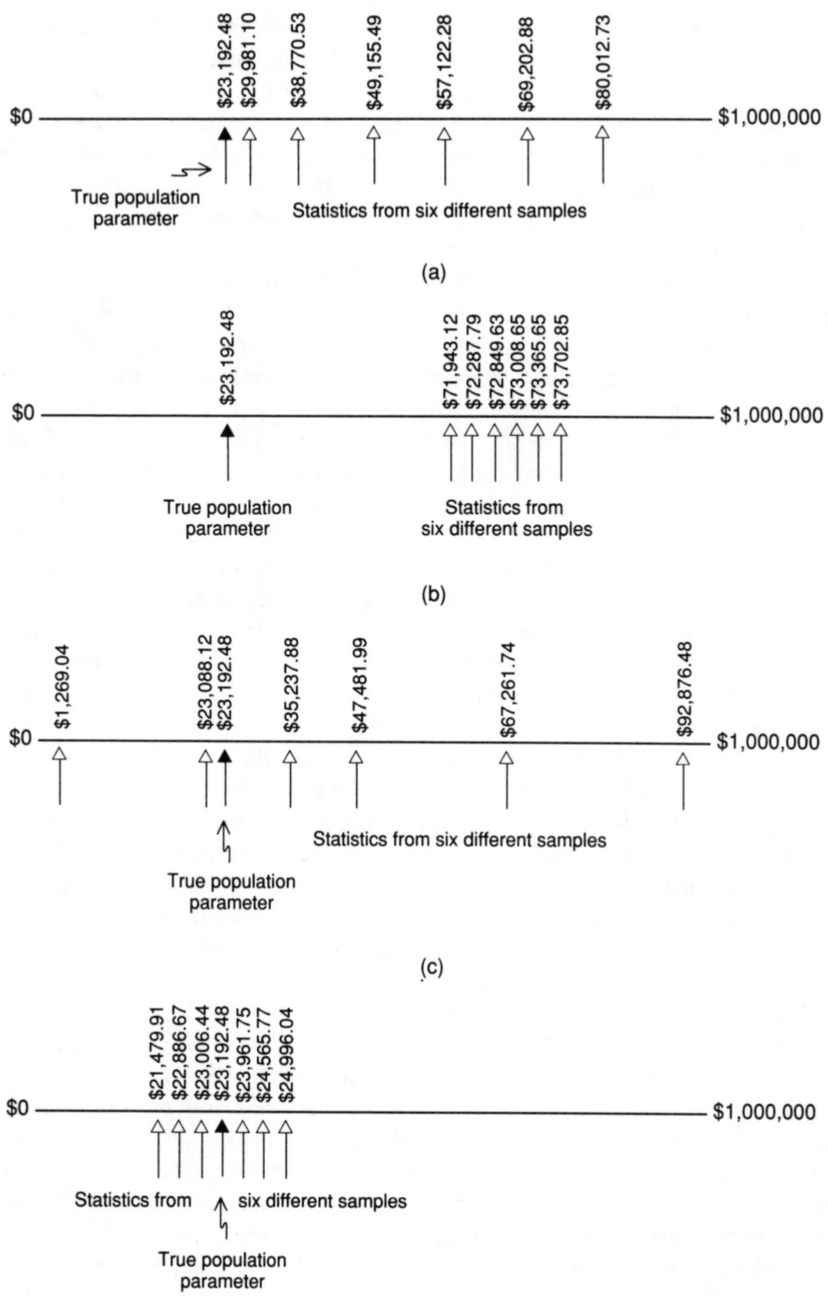

Figure 2.4 (a) Imprecise and biased; (b) precise and biased; (c) imprecise and unbiased; (d) precise and unbiased.

Obviously, what we want is a method of sampling that is neither biased nor imprecise. We would like the results of sampling to yield sample statistic values that tend to clump together right around the true value of the population parameter. That is, we want an *accurate* method of sampling. An accurate method of sampling is precise *and* unbiased. Such a method of sampling will tend to produce sample statistic values clumped right around the true value of the population parameter. If we can guarantee accuracy, we can guarantee results near the truth.

We can understand accuracy metaphorically in terms of an archer. Our sample statistic is like an arrow shot at the true population parameter: We want to shoot accurately in order to hit close to the true population parameter. There are two important aspects to accuracy: *precision and bias*. A *biased* method of sampling is like an archer who consistently shoots to one side of the bull's-eye. The archer perhaps is not correcting for the prevailing wind conditions, so the arrows consistently get blown downwind of the target. To avoid this sort of problem we want a method of sampling that does not favor one side or the other; that is, we want an unbiased method of sampling. The *precision* of a method of sampling is like the basic skill of the archer to get arrows in the same place time and time again. A skillful archer who neglects wind conditions will consistently get arrows about the same distance downwind of the target; to correct this fault, the archer must adjust aim to account for the prevailing wind. Thus, a precise method of sampling is one where the sample statistics, from many different samples, are all near each other—whether or not they are near the true value of the population parameter.

Ideally, we want both precision and lack of bias. Such a method of sampling produces sample statistics that are generally near each other (precise) and are not consistently to one side or the other of the true population parameter (unbiased). If you think about it for a moment, it will be clear that such a method will be *accurate:* The results of such a method of sampling will consistently be near the true value of the population parameter. If they were not near the true value and they were clumped together in a precise way, they would have to be to one side or the other of the true value; but this would be bias of one kind or another. So when we put lack of bias and precision together, we get accuracy.

It is important to bear in mind that this concept of accuracy is a feature of the method of sampling. It is *not a feature of a specific sample*. An accurate archer may occasionally miss the mark. We call the archer accurate because most of his or her shots land close to the desired target, but no archer is always right on target. Similarly, an accurate method of sampling can produce bad, unrepresentative samples. Conversely, an inaccurate archer may occasionally get lucky and hit the bull's-eye; an inaccurate method of sampling may produce a sample where the sample statistic is very close to the true population parameter. The kind of accuracy we are interested in concerns the ability of a method of sampling to produce mostly good results over the long haul.

5. RANDOM SAMPLING

There is a method of sampling that has the virtues of lack of bias and precision. It is *random sampling many units in the population*. Earlier we considered one method of random sampling where we selected *one* person from Lexington to represent the entire town. This method was not biased, because each member was as likely to be represented in the sample as each other member. But this method was not precise; results could vary all over the map, because individual incomes in Lexington could vary all over the map. But when we *randomly* select a larger number of Lexingtonians, we can keep the virtue of lack of bias and substantially increase the precision of the sample. Technically, we say that the variance of random sampling decreases—the results clump more closely together—when there are more units in the sample.

Selecting a sample by the method of *random sampling* gives each unit in the population a predetermined chance of being in the sample. In simplest cases, each unit in the population gets the same chance of being selected as each other unit. If there are 100,000 units in the population and we randomly choose a sample of 100, each unit in the population has the same chance as every other unit of being in the sample chosen—roughly 100/100,000 = 1/1,000.

We can select a random sample by using a random number table. Random number tables are lists of numbers with two characteristics: (1) each digit, 0 through 9, occurs with the same frequency; and (2) there is no way to predict the next digit from a knowledge of the preceding digits in the table. Thus the numbers in a random number table are like a list of outcomes from tosses of a fair 10-sided die. Table 2.1 is a small piece of a random number table. The random numbers are presented in groups of five digits each. This grouping is purely cosmetic; it is there to help us read the table and refer to it. Strictly speaking, a random number table is just a string

TABLE 2.1

	Column				
Row	**1**	**2**	**3**	**4**	**5**
0	10097	32533	76520	13586	34673
1	74945	37542	04805	64894	74296
2	00822	91665	08422	68953	19645
3	34767	35080	33606	99019	02529
4	88676	74397	04436	27659	12807
5	36653	98951	16877	12171	76833
6	54876	80959	09117	39292	24805
7	24037	20636	10402	09303	23209
8	02560	15953	09376	70715	38311
9	31165	99970	80157	36147	64032

of digits, 10097325337652013586346737494537542048056489474296 . . . , such that each digit, 0 through 9, occurs equally frequently, and it is not possible to predict future digits from knowledge of past digits.

We can read numbers from a random number table and get a random sample of five people from a group of 10 people. First we label each of the 10 people in the group with a distinct digit 0 through 9. Then we read five digits from a random number table. Suppose that the following 10 people were labeled with digits as follows:

Gene—0 Lisa—1 Chris—2 Billie—3 Dennis—4

Leslie—5 Louis—6 Rhonda—7 Alan—8 Brenda—9.

Using the small random number table above, we can select a sample of five. We select people whose assigned numbers are in the first five different numbers read from the table. Suppose that we enter the table above at some arbitrary row, say ***3***, column ***1***, we read off the following digits: 34767 35080 .... We would select the following people for our sample 3, 4, 7, 6, ~~7~~, ~~3~~, 5:

Billie—3 Dennis—4 Leslie—5 Louis—6 Rhonda—7.

When a number comes up a second time before we have finished filling out our sample, we simply drop it; thus, the second 7 and 3 are crossed off above.

If the population we wish to take a random sample from has more than 10 individuals, we can read numbers from a random number table more than one digit at a time. For example, if the population had 99 individuals, we could read off *pairs* of digits. Entering Table 2.1 at row ***0***, column ***1***, we get 10, 09 (=9), 73, 25, 33, 76, 52, 01, 35, 86, and so on. Each pair of digits has the same chance of turning up as any other pair. There are 100 different pairs of digits, so each has a probability of 1/100. Of course, we can similarly use triples (or quadruples, quintuples, etc.) of digits from a random number table to get random numbers between 0 and 999 or 9999 or higher.

Suppose that we want a random sample of 10 units from a population of 1,000,000 units. First we assign each unit in the population a number. Since we can use the number 0, each unit can be assigned a six-digit number (where we use 000,000 in place of 0, 000,076 in place of 76, etc.). Then we turn to a random number table, enter it at some arbitrary place, and record the first 10 six-digit numbers to come up (reading left to right and down lines as we normally do). For example, entering the table above at row ***2***, column ***1***, we get the following 10 six-digit numbers:

Pick 1: **008,229** *Pick 2:* **166,508** *Pick 3:* **422,689** *Pick 4:* **531,964**

Pick 5: **534,764** *Pick 6:* **350,803** *Pick 7:* **360,699** *Pick 8:* **019,025**

Pick 9: **298,867** *Pick 10:* **674,397**

We then find those units in the population that were initially assigned these numbers. These units, then, constitute our random sample.

Most of the time, the population we will be interested in will contain fewer units than just enough to make use of all the available digits we must use to label units. For example, suppose that the population contained 20 units. We would have to use pairs of digits to label units because there are more than 10 units in the population. But with only 20 units in the population we will use only 20 of the 100 available pairs of digits. In principle this does not matter. We can pick a random sample by reading pairs of digits from the table until we come across pairs that correspond to units in the population. Thus, if we labeled units 00 through 19 and we started reading the table on row ***2***, column ***1***, we would use the following pairs:

00 ~~82~~ ~~29~~ **16** ~~65~~ **08** ~~42~~ ~~26~~ ~~89~~ ~~53~~

19 ~~64~~ ~~53~~ ~~47~~ ~~35~~ ~~08~~ **03** ~~36~~ **06** ~~99~~

01 ~~90~~ ~~25~~ ~~29~~ ~~88~~ ~~67~~ ~~67~~ ~~43~~ **97** **04**

~~43~~ ~~62~~ ~~76~~ ~~59~~ **12** ~~80~~ ~~73~~ ~~66~~ ~~53~~ ~~98~~

~~95~~ **11**

Or, eliminating all of the unusable crossed-off pairs,

Pick 1: **00** *Pick 2:* **01** *Pick 3:* **03** *Pick 4:* **04** *Pick 5:* **06**

Pick 6: **08** *Pick 7:* **11** *Pick 8:* **12** *Pick 9:* **16** *Pick 10:* **19**.

Many of the pairs of digits have to be thrown out—crossed off the list—because they are higher than 19 and hence do not correspond to any unit in our population. Also, the second occurrence of 08 had to be dropped. There is a lot of waste with this approach to using random number tables.

There are several ways to avoid such waste. We need not worry about them in detail here for these are technical points that will take us away from the central conceptual issues. It is worth mentioning the basic idea. We can use repeated labels. We could label each unit in our population of 20 units with five different numbers between 00 and 99. What used to be simply unit 00, could be unit 00 *and* 20 *and* 40 *and* 60 *and* 80 all at once; what used to be unit 01 could be unit 01 *and* 21 *and* 41 *and* 61 *and* 81; and so on. Thus, we would not have to discard so many numbers. The second pair above, 82, had to be discarded. Now we use it to select the unit that before had simply been labeled 02. We would get the following random sample:

Pick 1: **00** *Pick 2:* **02** (=82 − 80) *Pick 3:* **09** (=29 − 20)

Pick 4: **16** *Pick 5:* **05** (=65 − 60) *Pick 6:* **08**

Pick 7: **06** (=26 − 20) *Pick 8:* **13** (=53 − 40) *Pick 9:* **19**

Pick 10: **04** (=64 − 60)

Here many fewer numbers have to be discarded, only 42, because it refers to the same unit as a unit that has already been selected (namely, unit 82 = unit 02), and 09—for the same reason.

When we use repeated labeling, we must be sure that each unit gets the same number of labels (in this example each unit gets five different labels) and that no label refers to more than one unit. Then we can use repeated labels to use numbers more efficiently in a random number table.

Random sampling has many virtues. (Later, we will see some of its faults.) Over the long run, random samples are *not biased*. This should be intuitively obvious. Each unit in the population is given the same chance to be part of the sample as each other unit. Consequently, there is nothing intrinsic to the method of sampling that would tend to favor units with values higher than average or to favor units with values lower than average.

Random sampling also gives us control over the precision of our method of sampling. It does this by means of the probabilities introduced in taking a *random* sample. When we choose a random sample we choose a sample so that each unit in the population has the same *probability* of being part of the sample. Since our method of sampling introduces probabilities into our project, we can calculate with the rules of probability. In Chapter 10 we show how to use these rules to calculate values for the precision of a method of sampling.

When we randomly select units from a population we can say, in detailed terms, how our method is precise. We make statements like the following: "There is a 95% chance that the observed sample statistic plus or minus 4% will include the true population parameter." For example, suppose that we want to know what percentage of USC students are in-state residents. We could sample 1,000 students and determine a percentage of this sample that were in-state residents. If we use a random method to select students for our sample, we can be sure that "there is a 95% chance that the observed sample statistic plus or minus 4% will include the true population parameter." These numbers are made up. The important point here is not how to calculate these numbers, but how such numbers describe the precision of a method of sampling.

The precision of random sampling is understood in terms of two different percentages. The "plus or minus 4%" part is the *margin of error* of our method of sampling. We do not claim that our sample statistic will exactly equal the population parameter. Instead, we adopt a "margin of error" around our sample statistic and say that the population parameter is somewhere in this area. This is the detailed sense of "roughly" when we say that the population parameter is *roughly* equal to our sample statistic.

In fact, we do not make quite this strong a claim. We only claim that "there is a 95% chance" that the population parameter is roughly equal to our sample statistic. The "95% chance" is the *level of confidence* of our method of sampling. We are admitting at the outset that our poll might produce a result that is wildly wrong. But there is a high probability (perhaps 95%) that the poll will not be wildly wrong.

Ideally, we would like there to be a 100% chance that our sample statistic *exactly* equals the population parameter we want to know. But usually we cannot get such an ideal result. We must abandon the ideal certainty and we must allow for some margin of error. Still we will be able to get serviceable conclusions. In Chapter 10 (Section 3) we show that a random sample of 1,500 units can give very accurate results. Such a sample can give us a 95% level of confidence with a 3% margin of error, no matter how many units in the population—20,000 or 200,000,000. And the result will not be biased. This is the result that makes survey sampling both efficient and informative.

We can adjust the precision of our sample. We would like a high level of confidence and a small margin of error. We can increase our level of confidence and decrease our margin of error by increasing the number of units in our sample. Alternatively, if it costs too much to get information from more units, we can increase our level of confidence by allowing a larger margin of error (with the same number of units in our sample). Alternatively, we can get a smaller margin of error if we are willing to accept a lower level of confidence (with the same number of units in our sample). The details of all of these manipulations are controlled by the probability relations we introduce when we use random sampling.

There is one other very important result of random sampling: We can show that in any situation where a poll would be appropriate, the precision of the method of random sampling does not depend on the percentage of the population sampled; it depends on the number of units in the sample. Thus a sample with 1,000 units from a population with 100,000,000 units will have the same precision as a sample of 1,000 units from a population of 1,000,000 units.

For example, suppose that we were interested to know the proportion of married couples with children. In one instance we might be interested in this proportion among married couples in South Carolina; in another, we might be interested in this proportion among all couples in the United States. The precision of a sample of 500 couples chosen randomly from all the couples in South Carolina *is the same as* the precision of a sample of 500 couples chosen randomly from all the couples in the United States. This is true despite the fact that our 500-couple sample is roughly 0.2% of the population of couples in South Carolina and a tiny fraction—0.0009%—of the population of couples in the United States.

Once we have some probability mathematics behind us, we can see just how random sampling has these virtues:

1. It is not biased.
2. It gives us control over the precision of our method of sampling in terms of two detailed concepts: margin of error and level of confidence.
3. The precision of our method depends on the absolute number of units in the sample, it does not depend on the percentage of the population in the sample.

6. KINDS OF WORRIES ABOUT RANDOM SAMPLING

Before we leave the general topic of survey sampling, it is worth our while to consider some of the problems with random sampling. There are three kinds of worries that we might consider. I can put them in order of generality:

1. Practically, how difficult is it to obtain random samples?
2. Suppose that we can obtain a "for real" random sample from a population. Is the kind of accuracy ensured by random sampling the kind of accuracy we want or need?
3. Suppose that we can obtain "for real" random samples and that the information we obtain from these samples is accurate. Is having this information a good thing; can it be destructive?

In this section I explain these kinds of worries very briefly. We consider them in more detail further on.

Regarding (1): It is easy to imagine picking random numbers from a random number table and then determining an income category for each person whose number was drawn. But it is not as simple with a human population. Human beings cannot simply be picked out of a random number table; they must be contacted somehow and they must be available and willing to provide the information sought. It is not always easy, nor is it proper in all cases, to obtain information from real, live people. Consequently, there are significant limitations to our ability to obtain honest random samples from human populations.

Regarding (2): It may seem a bit perverse to question the kind of accuracy we get with random samples. After all, we went to some trouble to see how to understand accuracy in terms of lack of bias and precision. *Then* we saw that this kind of accuracy can be had by taking random samples. But there are important worries about this kind of accuracy. Very briefly, there may be situations where we do not want to come close to the true value *in the long run;* we want to come close *on this very trial*. By analogy, we may very well not be happy with a sharpshooter who blows the one chance to shoot out the tires of a getaway car at the scene of a crime. The fact that this sharpshooter has a good long-run record is of little consolation if he or she misses at some crucial juncture. And so it is with our method of sampling. There may well be cases, assessing nuclear power plant safety, for example, where we do not want to miss on a particular trial. We will discuss this kind of worry when we finally look at some of the details for how we control precision with the aid of probability.

Regarding (3): There are good reasons to question the entire enterprise of taking polls. Even if we convince ourselves that this procedure gives us accurate information, is this information particularly useful or important information? An example: Suppose that 90% of the U.S. population (as estimated by an extremely accurate survey) favors building up our nuclear arsenal. Certainly, there is information which those in the government have that most of the rest of us do not have. It is not unreasonable to suppose that this information might be pertinent to the advisability of building up our nuclear arsenal. Perhaps, those people with this information are in a better position to judge than the 90% of the U.S. population who favor building up the nuclear arsenal. Of course, in a democratic society a strong case can be made for the opposite point: It is up to the majority to say what policies are desirable.

I consider the first and third of these kinds of worries in the remainder of this chapter. The second sort of worry is a symptom of a more general philosophical worry regarding this whole way of thinking about and using probability to solve inductive problems. We return to this question in Chapter 10.

7. WHAT POLLING CAN REALLY BE LIKE

To appreciate the kind of information that polling provides us, I will quote an extended passage from Michael Wheeler's book, *Lies, Damn Lies, and Statistics* (Dell Publishing Co., 1976, pages 103–118). I quote:

> On a Tuesday morning in June, Diane went to a working-class section of New Haven, Connecticut, where she had to complete ten interviews. Some [polling] firms tell their interviewers to start at a certain house and work in a particular direction, but this day she was simply given a map of the neighborhood and told to begin wherever she wanted.
>
> "If I get to choose, I like to drive around the area a bit. I look for parked cars, toys in the yard. That means that it's more likely people are around and I don't have to waste time at empty houses."
>
> Judged by Diane's standards, the neighborhood did not look very promising, but she managed to find a street where there were a few cars. The first house she tried was surrounded by a chain link fence. The occupants, one guessed, were conservative in their politics, but no one answered the door, so whatever their views, they went unrecorded.
>
> Next door was a rather run-down two-family house. No one was home on one side. An older man answered Diane's knock on the other side and she was pleased, as it is harder to find men at home during the day. Her pleasure was brief, however, because the man spoke so little English that an interview was impossible. Diane tried to explain what she had wanted, but her attempt left him confused and her embarrassed.
>
> Diane has interviewed all over Connecticut, in rich areas and very poor ones. Her one real phobia is dogs. She walked by one house without hesitating; a large German shepherd was sleeping on the porch.

> Diane finally succeeded at the sixth house. A woman returning from the supermarket with two large bags of groceries said she would be willing to talk for a little while. . . .
>
> Diane said she just wanted "your reaction to these questions—it doesn't have to be something you would stand by." . . .
>
> As the interview went on, however, the woman got increasingly impatient. "Everything you're asking me is yes or no, black or white. I just don't think that way." She felt trapped by a question which asked her to agree or disagree with the statement, "Since Henry Kissinger failed to make peace between Egypt and Israel it looks as though he is losing his touch as a peacemaker."
>
> She said she had never liked Kissinger. Were she to take the question literally, she must answer no, for she believed he never had had a touch as a peacemaker. But that answer, as she could plainly see, would be taken as an endorsement of Kissinger. On the other hand, she could not bring herself to say yes, as that implied that she had until recently supported him. . . .
>
> The woman still could not subscribe to either of the two offered alternatives. Diane eventually put her down as "not sure" when in fact the woman had a clear and strong opinion about Kissinger.

8. PROBLEMS GETTING RANDOM SAMPLES

The really nice feature of Wheeler's work is that he makes clear how difficult it is to make the world work like homogeneous units selected with the help of a random number table. There are essentially two kinds of problem: (1) sampling frame problems, and (2) ambiguities in the questions—what I call "color clarity problems."

The first thing to notice is the lack of randomization! Apparently, the polling company figured that a *random enough* sample could be obtained if Diane Bentley simply interviewed the first 10 available people in the area she was sent to. The company may have randomized over small neighborhoods and then allowed the interviewer to conduct convenience sampling within the randomly chosen neighborhoods. There is good practical reason to do this: It is much easier to find people available to be interviewed within a neighborhood than to require interviewers to interview people at a specific address; it can take many return visits to find a family at home. Perhaps little accuracy is lost and much time, effort, and money is saved introducing this little bit of convenience sampling.

But whenever we depart from strict randomization two things happen: (1) We lose some control over the accuracy our methods can claim, and (2) our sampling frame differs from the population in some more or less systematic ways.

In the example above, the sampling frame differs from the population in several ways: People who happen to live on a street with cars and toys about have a much greater chance of being interviewed. People who do not speak English well enough are not interviewed. People who are busy and do not want to be interviewed are not interviewed. People with big dogs are not interviewed. No doubt other people are excluded systematically by Diane Bentley's predilections.

As a result, the sampling frame differs from the entire population in several systematic ways. And the various ways in which the sampling frame differs from the population are explicitly understood only incompletely. The exact effect of these differences on the sample is not fully known.

There are other kinds of sampling frame difficulties. In some instances more complete randomization is attempted. Sometimes, interviews are conducted by telephone instead of person to person. It is much easier to keep trying a number that does not answer than it is to return in person to a house where no one has been home. Consequently, it is easier to select a more fully random sample: Pick the phone numbers randomly and call them until one gets a response.

But telephone interviewing requires several things to work: (1) The person interviewed must subscribe to telephone service; (2) the phone number must be listed, or a device that dials random digits must be used to dial the numbers—and this, inefficiently, will produce many wasted phone numbers; (3) the person must be home at some time when the interviewer calls; and (4) the person must be willing to be interviewed over the telephone.

Then there are other, more complicated issues with obtaining a random sample. Occasionally, the subject matter of the poll is controversial—so much so that it would be inappropriate to ask any randomly selected person if he or she would be willing to answer some questions about (for example) medical problems or (for another example) sexual habits. In such cases, it is more appropriate to use volunteer subjects. But volunteers clearly do not provide a random—or representative—sample of the population.

Summarizing, the following practices change the sampling frame from what it, ideally, should be—the entire population about which information is desired:

1. Introducing convenience sampling after some amount of randomization
2. Using readily available lists of "*most*" of the population—such as telephone directories
3. Relying on volunteer subjects

All of these differences introduce departures from the theoretical ideal. We always have to cope with situations that are not exactly as theory says they should be—theories just are not that good. The real problem in the case of polling is that it is unclear how these departures affect the conclusions reached by the polling.

The other kind of difficulty I call "color clarity" problems. In Chapter 10 we compare selecting a sample to drawing a bunch of balls from a large container of balls. People's opinions or incomes or what not—the variable of interest—is analogous to the colors of the balls. When a person is selected to be in a sample, the important aspect of that person is his or her "color" with respect to the question of interest. For example, when we want to determine incomes in Lexington we can think of the income categories as colors:

Category 1:	\$0–\$5,000	''color'' : blue
Category 2:	\$5,001–\$10,000	''color'' : red
Category 3:	\$10,001–\$15,000	''color'' : orange
Category 4:	\$15,001–\$20,000	''color'' : yellow
⋮	⋮	⋮

When we survey real people, however, determining their ''color'' is a more complicated matter than the analogy of looking at a ball makes it seem.

The ''Diane Bentley poll'' suffers from several color clarity problems. In the first case, what are we to make of the two kinds of nonresponse: (1) not at home for an interview, and (2) refuse to be interviewed. Both kinds of nonresponse are treated the same way—that is, they are both ignored. But refusing is different from being unavailable. And both are different from not being selected to be interviewed.

The second sort of problem results from forcing people into predetermined categories. For example, ''agree strongly,'' ''disagree strongly,'' and ''no opinion'' make up three nice categories, but actual people's opinions are more complicated than such categories allow. How can we be sure that the way we group people's responses will not obscure important features of the population? The ''Henry Kissinger, peacemaker?'' question is a good example of this problem.

Finally, there is a worry about truth. How can we be sure that the ''colors'' we see, when we interview subjects, are their ''true colors?'' People will fail to tell the truth for many different reasons. People will tell falsehoods without knowing or intending to do so. Sometimes people will lie: Some people may not take polls seriously and answer one way or the other just because that is the way they feel like answering—not because it is a true representation of their opinion. Other times, people will knowingly lie to avoid embarrassment—''Who is Henry Kissinger anyway?'' Still other times, people will lie by virtue of not thinking about the question carefully enough; this could easily happen at the end of a long questionnaire.

The list of color clarity problems could be drawn out even more, but I have noted three sorts of problems: (1) different kinds of nonresponse, (2) ambiguous or badly worded questions, and (3) various forms of lying. In short there is a large degree of difficulty in accurately designing categories for people's opinions to fit in and for ensuring that the information obtained is reliable.

9. EVEN IF THE INFORMATION IS ACCURATE . . .

Even if it works perfectly, there are several reasons not to be happy with the results of polling studies. I do not submit these reasons as conclusive arguments favoring the elimination of polling. My purpose here simply is to emphasize that even if we gain control of a new tool like polling, we must still resolve important and difficult issues about policy and implementation. Following is a brief potpourri of the kinds of problems polling presents.

First, opinions change. This has two important consequences: (1) the facts revealed by a poll are representative of the population only at the specific time the poll was conducted, (2) if multiple polls are conducted in sequence—as occurs during political campaigns—the outcome of one poll can itself affect opinions; people may hold beliefs just so that the next poll will show this. Polling outcomes affect people's opinions, which in turn affects subsequent polls. The fact that polls only provide information about a specific time is a severe limitation. It is also an easy limitation to quietly forget.

We use polls to help us decide how to resolve various issues. For example, potential contributors to a candidate for elected office will watch polls to see if the person they are considering supporting "has a chance." If he or she does not, why waste one's money? But how important are polling results early in an election race? Such early polls may only reflect the candidates' name recognition; they may not reflect informed or considered opinion. So we have a mechanism for determining campaign funding on the basis of name recognition and not potentially more important matters.

A last problem with using information supplied by polls is simply that the information a poll provides can be low-quality information. Nothing in the outcome of a poll represents either (1) the importance various people attach to the views they express, or (2) the amount of information they have used to come to their views. Some argue that we would be better off having policy decided by people who both know and care about the issues at stake. Polling seems to be at odds with this kind of attitude.

10. SUMMARY

1. Survey samples employ some special terminology.

(a) The *population* includes all of the "objects," be they individual people, individual voters, married couples, households, and so on, about which information is sought.

(b) Each *unit* in the population is one individual member of the population.

(c) The *sample* is the group of units taken from the population from which information is obtained. This information is used to make inferences about the whole population.

(d) Generally, the important information in the sample relates to the relative proportions of different values of the *variables measured*. These proportions, called *sample statistics,* serve as estimates for the population proportions, called *population parameters*.

(e) The *sampling frame* is the collection of units in the population from which the sample is chosen. All members of the sample must also be members of the sampling frame.

2. There are several different methods for selecting a sample from a population.
   (a) Taking a *census* requires getting information from each unit in the population. Taking a census can alter the population in important respects—since each unit is looked at. It is also very time consuming and expensive if the population is large. It is also difficult to ensure the accuracy of information obtained through a census since there is so much information to keep track of.
   (b) *Convenience sampling* is a method of selecting a sample where those units that are easiest to examine are selected. This can be done in an active way by examining the first 500 (say) units one comes across. It can be done in a passive way by letting the units come to the researcher, as in the case of "call-in" newspaper polls. There is no reason to suppose that information from a convenience sample will consistently represent the entire population.
   (c) *Random sampling* is a method of selecting a sample where each unit is given a predetermined probability of being selected. Selection occurs by using a random number table, or some such device, where units can be so chosen to ensure that each has the same chance. Random sampling copes well with the difficulties of the other methods of sampling.

3. There are two fundamental components to an *accurate method of sampling*.
   (a) *Bias* is a feature of a method of sampling, where different samples predominantly overrepresent certain portions of the population or, alternatively, underrepresent portions of the population. Accurate methods of sampling are not biased.
   (b) *Precision* is a feature of a method of sampling where different samples give similar results. Samples obtained from a precise method do not vary much from each other. Accurate methods of sampling are precise.
   (c) *Accuracy* is a feature of a *method of sampling*. Specific individual samples may misrepresent the entire population even if they result from an accurate method of sampling. Accurate methods, however, should result in fewer misrepresentative samples in the long run.

4. Random sampling has many virtues.
   (a) Since each unit in the population has a predetermined chance of being selected, we can ensure that over the long run, random sampling is not biased.
   (b) Since probability is introduced in the process of selecting a random sample, we can both calculate and control the precision of random sampling.
   (c) The precision of random sampling is measured in terms of two values. The *margin of error* measures how close a polling study result should usually be to the population parameter in question. The *level of confidence* measures how frequently polling studies will get as close as the margin of error.
   (d) Thus, the result of a polling study is a statement like this: "There is a 95% chance—the level of confidence—that the sample statistic plus or minus 3%—the margin of error—will include the true population parameter."
   (e) The precision of a random sample *does not depend* on the proportion of the entire population included in the sample. The precision of a random sample depends on the *absolute number of units in the sample*.

5. There are three kinds of worries about random sampling.
   (a) Actual random samples are difficult to obtain when dealing with human populations.

(b) It is not clear that the kind of accuracy that randomization provides is the kind of accuracy that we want. It would be nice to know of a specific sample that it was close to the truth—not just that it came from a method that erred only infrequently.

(c) Accurate information from polls may not be as useful as we like to think. Perhaps the mass of not very well informed opinion is not as important as a small amount of very well informed opinion.

6. There are two major kinds of problems with obtaining random samples, sampling frame problems, and color clarity problems.
   (a) It is difficult to fully randomize down to individual units, because individual units frequently "are not home." So randomization is rarely done "all the way down." It is frequently only down to fairly small groups within which convenience sampling takes place.
   (b) Randomization is much easier from readily available lists of "most of the population" such as telephone directories. Using such lists is a lot easier, but it results in a sampling frame that differs from the population.
   (c) Some types of polls, because of the nature of the questions involved, must rely on volunteer subjects.
   (d) People's opinions are not so easily observed as the colors on a ball.
   (e) We treat "nobody at home" the same as refusal to respond; but they are different—two different "colors" treated the same.
   (f) People's opinions frequently cannot be accurately represented in a simple categorization—represented by a small number of different "colors." Different "shades" of opinions must be ignored.
   (g) People do not always tell the truth when polled.

7. We might not find the information a poll contains useful.
   (a) Uninformed opinion, perhaps, is not as valuable or useful as informed opinion.
   (b) Opinions change over time.
   (c) People frequently modify their opinions in light of the outcomes of polls to produce a "bandwagon" effect. Thus polls not only describe what opinions *are*, they alter these opinions.

11. REFERENCES

An excellent introductory text covering, among other things, survey sampling is (Moore, 1985). A slightly more technical, but still concise, introduction to survey sampling is (Kalton, 1983). Information about the Current Population Survey comes from the 1982 edition of the *Bureau of Labor Statistics Handbook of Methods*. A series of arguments criticizing the use of opinion polling is in (Wheeler, 1976). (Gallup, 1978), in (Tanur et al., 1978), defends the use of opinion polling; several other essays in (Tanur et al., 1978) concern survey sampling. (Kruskal, 1978) provides a fascinating discussion of the problems posed by large amounts of data.

12. PROBLEMS

1. A dental clinic considering opening a new office near the University of South Carolina wants to know what percentage of USC students visit the dentist regularly. They survey the students by randomly selecting a residence hall—as it happens, a female residence hall is selected—and conducting 93 in-person interviews with students at this residence hall during their dinner.
   (a) What is the population of interest?
   (b) What variable is measured of the units in the population?
   (c) What is the sample, and how was it selected?
   (d) Is there any source of bias in this survey study? Explain.
2. Find a report of a polling study in a current publication such as a newspaper or magazine. Answer questions (a) through (d) about this study from Problem #1.
3. Use the bit of a random number table in Section 5 to select 10 people from the following list:

Francis	Robbin	James	Michael	Rudolf	Terri
Sheila	Ian	Suzanne	Deborah	Ellie	Tom
Ingrid	Yetta	George	John	Yvonne	Mark
Luther	Laura	Leyla	Edward	Bruce	Eric
Brian	Delar	Carol	Dave	Lezlie	Carte
Ginger	Lynn	David	Kathryn	Jenifer	Troy

4. The Bureau of Labor Statistics intends to take a random sample of residents in each state to estimate the proportion of people who use public transportation to commute to work. States vary in population from California with a population of 23,668,000, to Alaska with a population of 402,000. Will the precision of the sample proportion vary from state to state if a random sample of 0.5% of the state's population is taken in each state? Explain your answer.
5. A news article on a Gallup Poll noted that "28% of the 1,548 adults questioned felt that those who were able to work should be taken off welfare." The article also said (this information is usually cut out by editors): "The margin of error for a sample size of 1,548 is plus or minus three percentage points." Explain carefully what "margin of error" means here.
6. A poll, with a margin of error of 4%, is conducted to determine which of the two candidates, Rhett Brawley or Pat Jacobs, is likely to win election for county clerk. Although 52% of the sample say they will vote for Jacobs, the polling organization announces that the election is too close to call. Why is the conclusion proper?
7. A random sample of adult Americans is taken for a poll with a 3% margin of error and a 95% level of confidence. Of those asked, 63% respond "yes" to the question, "Are you afraid to go out at night within a mile of your home because of crime?" Make a 95% confidence statement about the percentage of all adult Americans who fear to go out at night because of crime.
8. What kind of results does a method of sampling that is both precise and biased produce?

9. I have described the properties of bias, precision, and accuracy as properties of a *method* of sampling; they are not properties of a particular sample. Now consider an argument that looks like this:

P_1 1,000 adults were randomly selected from a population of 100,000.

P_2 673 of these adults responded "yes" to the question, "Have you been to the dentist in the last 6 months?"

So, **C** So 67% plus or minus 4% of the adults in the population of 100,000 have been to the dentist in the last 6 months.

(a) Is this a deductively valid argument? Why or why not?
(b) Is this a good argument? Why or why not?
(c) What attitude of belief should one adopt toward the conclusion of this argument (assuming that the premises are true)? Why?

10. Recently, a poll was conducted of faculty opinions at the University of South Carolina. Faculty were asked about the importance of the university's emphasis on international educational programs. Faculty were asked to respond to statements on a scale from 1, "strongly agree," to 5, "strongly disagree." Here are some of the statements:
(a) "Faculty cannot benefit professionally from conducting research or teaching outside the United States through the faculty exchange programs of the institution."
(b) "Students benefit educationally from the opportunity to study abroad."
(c) "Gaining knowledge and/or experience in international education does not increase the decision-making and problem-solving ability of graduates."
Discuss whether such questions can be used to measure faculty opinion about the importance of international educational programs. Write questions that you think might do the job better.

CHAPTER

3

DECISION ANALYSIS IN MEDICINE

1. INDUCTION AND DECISIONS

In Chapter 2 we saw the appeal of an argument such as the following:

P_1	1,000 adults were randomly selected from a population of 3,000,000 South Carolinean adults.
P_2	583 of these adults responded "yes" to the question, "Have you been to the dentist in the last 6 months?
So, **C**	So 58% (plus or minus 4%) of the population of South Carolinean adults have been to the dentist in the last 6 months.

Such an argument clearly is not valid; it is possible for the conclusion to be false while the premises are true. Yet we saw that such arguments do provide reason—if not infallible reason—to believe their conclusions. They are candidates for good inductive arguments.

In practice, one usually seeks confidence in the conclusions of arguments to help decide on some action or another. Perhaps a statewide association of dentists is trying to determine the demand for dentists in South Carolina. They are interested, not out of idle curiosity, but to decide whether or not to advertise for new dentists from out of state.

This distinction between conclusions which are sought for their informative value and those which are sought to direct subsequent action is important. We need not approach induction simply through seeking good *arguments*. In this chapter we consider induction as an inseparable component to directing *action*. Instead of seeking relationships between premises and conclusions so that the premises provide good, but not valid, reasons for the conclusions, we seek reasons to choose certain courses of action. Typically, one chooses certain courses of action because of two different kinds of considerations. One considers how things will probably turn out and one considers how desirable different outcomes are. Both kinds of consideration are important in finding preferable courses of action.

Consider an example. Suppose that you are having an allergy attack. You are sneezing 20 times a minute, your eyes itch, you feel terrible. Sometimes your allergy attacks subside after an hour; other times, they can last all day. You consider taking an allergy pill, but you know that it will make you sleepy for the rest of the day. What should you do?

There are three possible outcomes here:

1. No pill, long attack, miserable all day
2. Pill, sleepy all day
3. No pill, short attack, miserable for an hour, fine for the rest of the day

If being sleepy all day is no worse than being miserable for an hour and fine for the rest of the day, there is no reason *not* to take the pill. On the other hand, if being sleepy all day is no better than being miserable all day, there would be no point to taking the pill.

Here is an important point: When we are concerned with acting, the desirability of the outcomes makes a difference; sometimes the desirability of an outcome is all that matters. Whatever you might conclude about the likely duration of your allergy attack, if you would rather be miserable all day than sleepy all day, you should not take the allergy pill.

Most of the time, however, one must weigh both the desirability and the likelihood of the different outcomes to reach a "recommended" course of action. For many people, being miserable for an hour and fine for the rest of the day is preferable to being sleepy all day, and being sleepy all day is preferable to being miserable all day; (3) is preferable to (2), and (2) is preferable to (1). For such people, the question of whether or not to take the pill cannot be answered without giving some thought to how long the allergy attack is *likely* to last. If it was extremely likely that your allergy attack would be short-lived, then unless you really did not mind being sleepy all day, you probably should not take the pill. But some people do not mind being sleepy all day and would prefer it to even a small chance of being miserable all day; they probably should take the pill. Decision analysis provides a way to weigh together considerations about both desirability and likelihood to reach a "recommended" course of action.

Thinking about induction one way, it makes little sense to consider decision analysis as a method of inductive inference. We are not going to find good but not valid *arguments* from decision analysis. Thinking about induction another way, however, decision analysis is central. The recommendations of decision analysis are not guaranteed to lead to the best result. You might decide not to take an allergy pill because you think it unlikely that your attack will continue all day and you dislike being sleepy all day. Clearly, it is possible for the attack to continue; your decision can result in an undesirable outcome *even if it was a good decision.* We would say that it was a good decision because you sensibly weighed both how likely and how desirable the different outcomes were. Unfortunately, things did not turn out well.

There is a parallel with good but not valid arguments. One can reach a conclusion, which turns out to be false, from a good inductive argument. Here we consider a method of deciding what to do that cannot guarantee to produce the outcome one desires most. But the course of action taken may still have been the right course to take. In this chapter we develop a sense in which decisions are right. Stated roughly, the right decision guarantees the best overall average outcome.

2. MEDICAL DECISIONS

Decisions are made by everyone in a virtually unlimited variety of contexts. We can better understand the principles behind decision analysis if we pick a particular context. While the examples that we explore in this chapter are taken from medicine, do not think that decision analysis is used only in a medical context. You should also be aware that the medical examples discussed below are simplified for the purpose of this introduction to decision analysis. The ''medical recommendations'' that follow are illustrative only; actual cases invariably are more complicated and require a correspondingly more thorough analysis. A good physician is indispensable.

With that in mind, we can start with the following simplification. There are two kinds of medical decisions: A doctor can decide to do a certain *procedure* (e.g., a surgical procedure) hoping to improve the condition of the patient. Alternatively, a doctor can decide to give a certain *test* (e.g., a white blood cell count) hoping to obtain information about what is going on in the patient. In typical cases both are involved.

Unfortunately, medical procedures do not always work; surgery to remove a cancerous tumor may fail to get all of the tumor. And worse, many medical procedures have undesirable side effects. Thus, with many medical procedures there are costs as well as benefits—not to mention the literal dollar costs of medical procedures. Much the same can be said for tests. Most tests can mislead. A pregnancy test can mistakenly report that a woman is pregnant when she is not. Such a test may only tell us that there is a high chance that the woman is pregnant. Decision analysis is designed to cope with weighing the costs and benefits of proposed procedures in the context of diagnoses that are not certain, but only probable to a greater or lesser extent.

Consider an example. A 15-year-old boy enters the hospital with pain in his lower right abdomen. Given information from a variety of tests, a physician estimates that there is a 30% chance that the boy has acute appendicitis. He might have severe gas pains. Unfortunately, there is a small chance, 0.1%, that the boy would not survive surgery to remove the appendix. On the other hand, if the decision to operate is delayed and the boy has appendicitis, there is a small but larger chance, 1%, that the boy would not survive. Is an appendectomy called for?

There are four different possibilities:

1. Boy does not have appendicitis—no surgery.
2. Boy does not have appendicitis—surgery.
3. Boy has appendicitis—no surgery.
4. Boy has appendicitis—surgery.

We can represent these outcomes, and all the information that accompanies them, in a tree (Figure 3.1). Read the tree from left to right. The first two branches correspond to the two possible actions available at this time—surgery or no surgery. The numbers on the four right-hand branches are the chances that the boy has appendicitis. The numbers in the boxes are the chances of dying in the four different cases.

Suppose, for the sake of simplicity, that we are concerned only with minimizing the boy's chance of dying. Performing the surgery results in a 0.001 chance of dying. Waiting to perform the surgery, however, is a gamble: if the boy does not

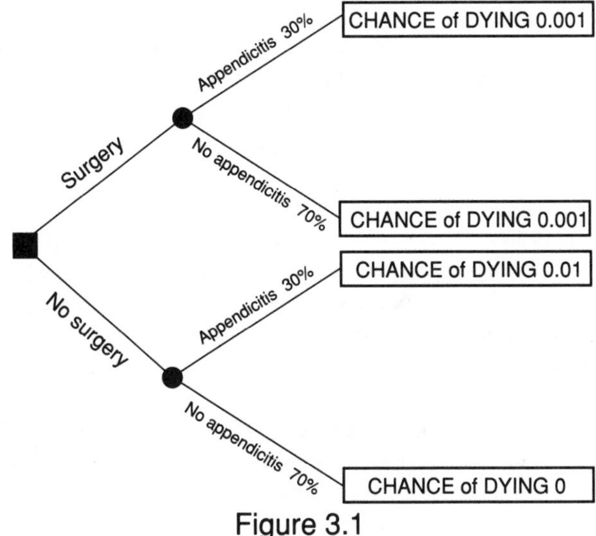

Figure 3.1

have appendicitis, there is no chance of dying; if he does have appendicitis, however, there is a 0.01 chance of dying. Neither option *minimizes* the boy's chance of dying.

Clearly, the appropriate decision depends on whether the boy has appendicitis, but unfortunately, we do not know whether he does. The decision to operate must be based on the *chance*s that the boy has appendicitis. If it were virtually certain that all the boy had was severe gas pains, it would not make sense to operate. On the other hand, if it were virtually certain that the boy had appendicitis, it would not make sense not to operate. Decision analysis helps to determine a sensible cutoff point by weighing the values of the different outcomes with the chances that the boy has appendicitis.

3. UTILITIES AND DEGREES OF BELIEF

Decisions are made by decision makers. Corporations, neighborhood associations, political parties, governments, and a wide variety of other social entities are decision makers. Here we study decisions made by individual people. The right decision for one person may not be the right decision for another person. Two people may reasonably decide to order different flavors of ice cream. This can happen simply because they have different preferences. When we analyze a decision problem we must employ the individual decision maker's preferences; otherwise, the analysis may well recommend actions that are best for another person.

Usually, it is the preferences of the decision maker that matter. *I* might pick chocolate ice cream because *I* like chocolate ice cream. Sometimes, however, I make choices for my 2–year-old child. Sometimes doctors make choices for their patients. Thus, although we say that it is the preferences of the decision maker that matter, it is really the preferences of the person for whom the decision is made that matter. There are many situations where a decision maker has to attempt to determine what these preferences are. For the sake of simplicity, I will write as if it is the preferences of the decision maker that matter; you should understand that it is the preferences of the person for whose benefit the decision is made that should matter.

As we saw in Section 2, it is not only the preferences of the decision maker that matter, their beliefs about how likely the various possible outcomes are also matters. I might decide to buy one kind of car because I have had good experience with such cars; I think it likely that another car by the same maker will be just as reliable. Someone else may judge differently. Both of us may dislike having our cars break down. We decide to buy different cars because we judge the likelihood of a breakdown differently.

Sometimes data are available to help us judge the chances of different outcomes. We used the fact that approximately 0.1% of otherwise healthy 15-year-old boys who have an appendectomy die. This number, 0.1%, summarizes studies of many such operations. As such, it recommends itself to us as a reasonable estimate of the chance that this particular 15-year-old boy will die under similar circumstances.

Frequently, however, such data merely point to a reasonable number. In the same example the doctor estimated that there was a 30% chance that the boy had acute appendicitis. This number was not based simply on data. There were no statistics which reported that exactly 30% of 15-year-old boys with exactly these symptoms and these test results do have appendicitis. Rather, this is the doctor's belief about the chance that the boy has appendicitis. The number is based on the doctor's knowledge of the statistics, the doctor's knowledge of the particular boy's particular symptoms, and the doctor's trained judgment.

As with preferences, I will write in terms of the beliefs of the decision maker, while it is the beliefs of the person for whose benefit the decision is made that matters. Commonly, particularly so in the case of medical decisions, the patient's beliefs about the likelihood of different outcomes will be largely determined by a doctor's judgment. We should not forget, however, that it is the patient's beliefs that should count in the final analysis.

Thus, when we do a decision analysis, we tailor it to both the preferences and beliefs of the decision maker. "Preference" and "belief" are vague concepts. Decision analysis requires more refined versions of these concepts. *Utility* and *degree of belief* serve this purpose.

Some things we are sure of, some things we are less sure of. We can represent this variation in our certainty with *degrees of belief.* I am sure that the low temperature tonight will be above 40 degrees—it is July and I am in Columbia, South Carolina. I have a *high degree of belief* that the low temperature will be above 40 degrees tonight. I believe there is virtually no chance that it will snow tomorrow. I have a *low degree of belief* that it will snow. Some things are more chancy: There *might* be a thunderstorm this afternoon. I have a middling degree of belief that there will be a thunderstorm this afternoon.

We will assume that these degrees of belief behave like probabilities, and in the second part of the book we examine with greater mathematical care how such probabilities work. For now it will suffice to note a few central properties of degrees of belief. The scale of degrees of belief goes from zero to 1. The closer a degree of belief is to 1, the more likely "the believer" believes the outcome is. The doctor who says that there is a 30% chance that a 15-year-old boy has appendicitis believes it more likely that the boy has the disease than a doctor who says there is a 5% chance. If a person is certain that something will happen, he or she would assign it probability 1. If a person is certain that something will not happen, he or she would assign it probability zero. In many cases we can use frequency data—0.1% of patients who undergo appendectomy die—to give us a sense for how likely we ought to believe something is.

There is a major assumption here. A person's degrees of belief may not behave like probabilities. Indeed, a person may not have *degrees* of belief. Nonetheless, there are many instances when it is very natural to speak of the *degree* to which someone believes something, and there are good reasons to think that it is not too great an idealization to model these degrees of belief as probabilities. We will, however, examine this assumption in Chapter 11.

We will also use a numerical scale of *utility* to represent a person's preferences. In contrast to degrees of belief, there is no single scale of utility. Usually, the higher the utility value, the more desirable the outcome, but on occasion, it may make sense to use an ''upside-down'' scale. In the appendicitis example, we used the chance of dying to measure the utility of the different outcomes. The larger the chance of dying, obviously, the less desirable the outcome.

While we will employ many different utility scales, they all share some characteristics. Within a given analysis, the ''orientation'' of the scale must be fixed—higher numbers will either represent more desirable outcomes or less desirable outcomes, not both. We will be able to compare any two outcomes in a given problem in terms of the scale of utility adopted. Within any given decision problem we will be able to say of any two outcomes that one is ''better than'' the other or that they are equally preferable. Indeed, we will be able to make even more precise numerical comparisons.

Here again, there is a major assumption in the use of any numerical scale of utility to measure preference. Many people doubt whether all outcomes in some decision problems are comparable, let alone that they can be compared with the kind of numerical precision a utility scale presupposes. On the other hand, there are many benefits to using such a scale of utility, and some decision problems seem to lend themselves to such a use. We will, however, examine this assumption as well in Chapter 11.

4. DECISION TREES

The first step to analyzing a decision problem is to understand the various things that might happen, and how they might happen. Decision trees are useful for modeling the various courses events might take—for modeling what might happen. Decision trees are made up of nodes, branches, and leaves. *Branches sprout from nodes.* Each branch that sprouts from a given node represents one different course that events could follow—if they ''got to'' the node from which the branch sprouted. The set of all branches sprouting from a given node must accommodate all the possible courses events might take from that node. There are two different kinds of nodes: *round nodes,* ●, and *square nodes,* ■. Round nodes represent situations where the decision maker cannot control what happens. Square nodes represent situations where the decision maker can control what happens. A branch either ends in another node or in a *leaf.* Leaves represent the different outcomes that each path through the tree can result in.

Recall the allergy example from Section 1. You are having an allergy attack and are contemplating taking an allergy pill. At the outset, you can choose to take the pill or not. Thus, a tree representing this decision problem starts with a square node from which two branches sprout (Figure 3.2). If you did not take the allergy

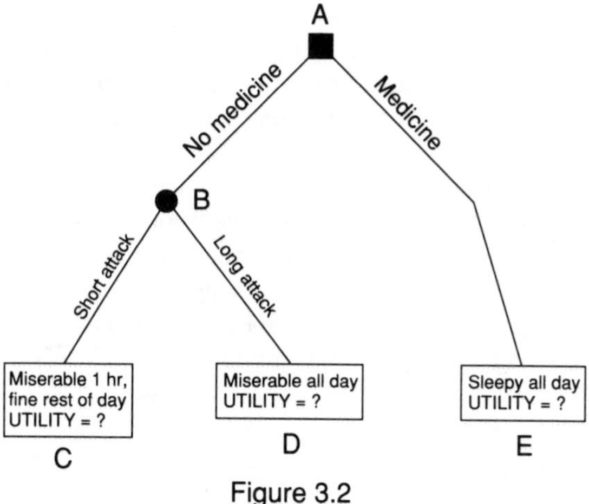

Figure 3.2

pill, the allergy attack might be long or short lived. Thus the branch for this choice ends in a round node from which two more branches sprout—one for a short-lived attack and one for a long-lived attack. If you did take the pill, you would be sleepy all day, and that would be the end of things.

A decision tree is supposed to represent all of the different courses that events relevant to the decision problem could follow. Many allergy sufferers do not consider the current price of IBM stock relevant to their allergies; thus, different possible prices of IBM stock would not be represented in their decision trees. On the other hand, many allergy sufferers do consider their proximity to pollinating plants relevant to their allergies; such information should be included in their decision trees. For the sake of simplicity, I have ignored such factors.

The structure of the resulting tree should represent the order in which one would learn about the course that events take. The tree for the appendicitis example (see Figure 3.1) has the branches for deciding whether or not to perform surgery before the branches for whether or not the boy has appendicitis. Of course, the boy either has or does not have the disease before the surgery is performed. But we will not know which is the case until later. Thus, the surgery/no-surgery distinction comes before the appendicitis/no-appendicitis distinction.

Once you have the basic structure of the decision tree straight, you can add numerical values for your degrees of belief and your utilities. Degrees of belief attach to branches that sprout from round nodes. When you can choose what will happen, what happens is not a matter of chance. Thus, degrees of belief are not attached to branches that sprout from square nodes. Round nodes, however, represent cases where you cannot control what happens; so to speak, "nature controls" what happens. But you can predict or estimate what will—or did, but you do not know yet—happen. You can estimate which possibilities are more likely. The doctor in the appendicitis example estimated that there was a 30% chance that the boy had appendicitis. Based on your past experience, you might estimate that there is a

20% chance that your allergy attack will go away in an hour. There would then be a corresponding 80% chance that your allergy attack will not go away in an hour. The degrees of belief of all of the branches sprouting from a given round node must add up to 1, because this collection of branches represents all the courses events could take from this node.

Utilities attach to the leaves at the end of the tree. Here you look at each different way that things might turn out and give them a numerical rank representing your relative preferences. For example, you might be the kind of person who really dislikes being sleepy all day, but you prefer being sleepy all day to being miserable all day, and, you might much prefer being miserable for an hour and fine for the rest of the day. You might assign the following utilities:

1. Miserable all day; utility 0
2. Sleepy all day; utility 1
3. Miserable for an hour, fine for the rest of the day; utility 10

You would then insert these degrees of belief and utilities into the decision tree (Figure 3.3).

To determine a recommended action we must find out what action is best. Mechanically, this is a straightforward—although at times tedious—matter of arithmetic. We start at the end of the tree—the leaves—and successively "filter" the leaf utilities inward toward the root of the tree.

Proceed one node at a time. If the node is a round node, we first multiply the degree of belief for each branch by the utility at the end of that branch; then we add all these products together. If one or more branches does not have a utility at its end, we must start with a node farther out in the tree.

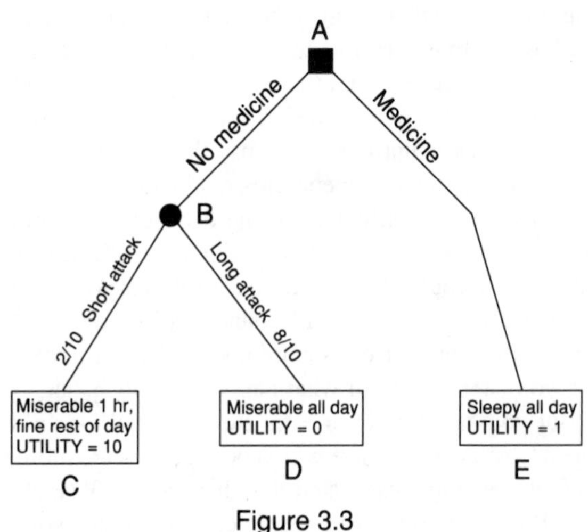

Figure 3.3

Consider the allergy example. We cannot start with node A because the left branch from node A does not have a utility at its end. We first have to find a utility for node B. We compute the utility for node B from the degrees of belief attached to the branches sprouting from B, and the utilities in leaves C and D. We multiply each branch degree of belief by the branch's leaf's utility, and we add these products together:

$$\left(\frac{2}{10} \times 10\right) + \left(\frac{8}{10} \times 0\right) = 2.$$

This is called the *expected utility* of node B. The utility assigned to square nodes is the highest utility of all the utilities at the end of the branches sprouting from the node. This is because one can choose what to do at a square node, and presumably one would choose the course of action with the highest utility. So the highest available utility is the utility of the square node.

Completing the allergy example: Square node A has two branches. At the end of its left-hand branch is node B, which we have just determined has utility 2. At the end of its right-hand branch is leaf E, which has utility 1. Two is the highest value, so node A is assigned utility 2, (Figure 3.4).

What action is recommended? Decision analysis "recommends" an action for each square node in the tree. Whenever you can choose—at each square node—you should choose the branch that has the highest utility. The decision maker *chooses* this branch, and consequently, the decision maker "gets" (or better perhaps, "takes") its utility. In the allergy example, you should not take the pill. The branch for taking the pill has a lower utility, 1, than does the "take-your-chances" branch, with utility 2.

The arithmetical procedure used to compute expected utilities is a kind of average. Each branch's probability is multiplied by the utility at the end of the

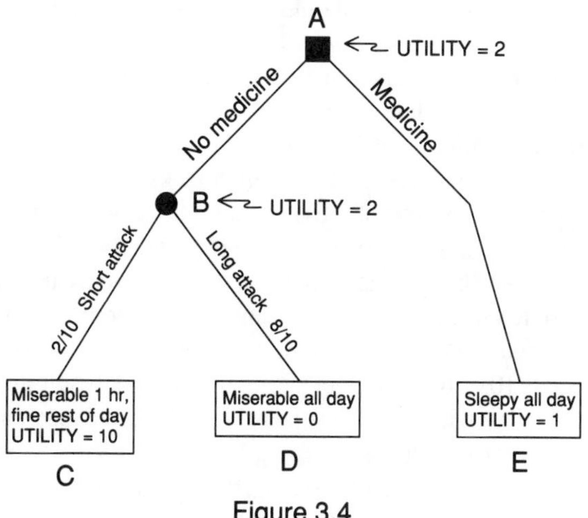

Figure 3.4

branch, and these products are added. In the allergy case, if you do not take a pill, you take your chances. You may be lucky—your attack may go away in an hour—or you may be unlucky. One or the other of these possibilities will occur. Thus, if you do not take a pill, you will get utility zero or 10. The value we compute for node B is a *weighted average* of these two utilities. Most of the time, the allergy attack will stick around and you will be miserable all day. Some of the time the allergy attack will be short-lived. We average the two utilities, zero and 10, but we give zero more weight than 10 because we think it more likely that the attack will be long-lived. The degrees of belief, 8/10 and 2/10, represent the degree to which you believe either outcome, respectively, will occur.

Consider another use of weighted averages. Suppose that you had a can of cola everyday for lunch. Some days you remember to bring a can from home. Some days you forget and buy a can from a vending machine. By shopping carefully, you buy six-packs of cola at a discount price of $1.89; each can costs 31½ cents. When you buy from a vending machine each can costs 50 cents. Suppose that you forget two days in five. Two days you pay 50 cents for a can of cola; three days you pay 31½ cents. The amount you pay *on average* for a can of cola is

$$\left(\frac{3}{5} \times 31\frac{1}{2}\right) + \left(\frac{2}{5} \times 50\right) \approx 0.19 + 0.20 = 39 \text{ cents.}$$

This is a weighted average of the two cola prices, 31½ and 50 cents. The weights, 3/5 and 2/5, reflect the proportion of instances you pay one price, 31½ cents (3/5 of the time), or the other price, 50 cents (2/5 of the time).

It can make sense to use weighted averages as a guide to action. Suppose that a member of the group of people you regularly have lunch with proposes to buy cola each week for everyone in the group. However, the group buyer does not want to spend the time searching for discounts. Six-packs of cola will cost the group $2.70, or 45 cents a can. Cola from the group would be cheaper than the machine but more expensive than from your home. Should you join the group? If you really do remember to bring cola from your home three days a week and you are concerned primarily with minimizing the amount you spend, you should not join the group. Your average cost per can is less than the group's average cost per can. Over the long run you will save money not joining.

Most allergy sufferers have many allergy attacks. It makes sense to do whatever will minimize the discomfort of these attacks. If we assume that there really are only three possible outcomes: (1) long attack and miserable, (2) pill and sleepy, and (3) short attack and fine for the rest of the day—and if we assume that the utilities assigned to these outcomes really are 0, 1, and 10, respectively, and if we assume that long attacks occur 8/10 of the time, *then* not taking the pill makes sense. Sometimes, indeed 8/10 of the time, not taking the pill will result in a miserable day; 2/10 of the time, the day will be the best possible. However, each attack will "cost less on average" by not taking the allergy pill.

In most examples, there will be some arbitrariness in the specific degrees of belief and utilities used. It is worthwhile to investigate the extent to which the action that the analysis recommends depends on these particular values. Many times the analysis would recommend the same action for a wide range of degrees of belief and utilities. In the allergy example, the probability that the attack will be short-lived would have to be less than 1/10 for the pill route to be preferable—assuming that the utilities are right. Only then would the utility of node B be less than the utility of leaf E.

5. PULMONARY EMBOLISM

Consider a more detailed example. A 30-year-old woman enters the hospital with severe pain in her chest. After a variety of tests, her doctor concludes that there is a 50% chance that she has a pulmonary embolism—a blood clot lodged in her lungs—which is a dangerous condition if other clots form. Alternatively, she might have a virus which is not dangerous and that would take care of itself.

If the pain was caused by a pulmonary embolism, it should be treated by administering anticoagulants to "thin the blood" and reduce the chance of future clots. If the woman is not treated with anticoagulants, and she does have a pulmonary embolism, there is a 50% chance of future embolisms; of those who have subsequent embolisms, 50% die of the disease. Unfortunately, treatment with anticoagulants can produce undesirable side effects, most notably a bleeding episode serious enough to require hospitalization. This occurs in 5% of cases. Moreover, the treatment does not eliminate the possibility of future embolisms; it reduces the chance of a subsequent embolism to 15%.

Whether or not anticoagulants are appropriate depends on the utilities that this woman attaches to the various possible outcomes. We can see just what these possibilities are from a decision tree. The first node of the decision tree is a square node representing the decision to administer the treatment or not. At the end of either of these branches is a node for whether the woman had a pulmonary embolism (Figure 3.5). Now we focus on each of these possibilities individually.

Suppose that no anticoagulants are given; what could happen? That is, suppose we arrive at node A in Figure 3.6, how does the tree continue? If she did not have an embolism, that is the end of matters. On the other hand, if she did have an embolism, there is a 50% chance of a subsequent embolism, and if she does have a subsequent embolism, there is a 50% chance that she will die of this disease. The probabilities assigned to these branches are taken from the frequencies stated above. Since there is a 50% chance that the pain was caused by an embolism, we assign each branch leaving node A probability 1/2. Similarly, since there is a 50% chance of future embolisms, we assign each branch leaving node B probability 1/2.

A similar line of reasoning is appropriate for the case where she is given anticoagulants, except in this case there is the additional possibility of a serious hemorrhage, but a reduced chance of subsequent embolisms. Thus two branches sprout from node E, one for the case where no hemorrhage occurred and one for the

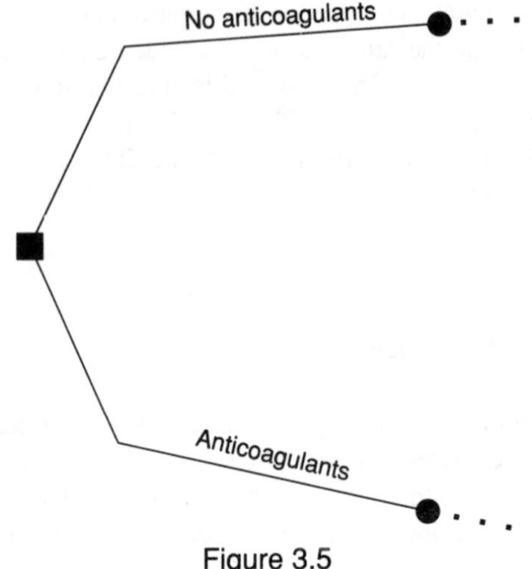

Figure 3.5

case where a hemorrhage did occur (Figure 3.7). The probability assigned to each branch follows from the fact that hemorrhage occurs in 5% of all cases. Figure 3.8 shows this decision tree.

The utilities in this tree are based on the following considerations. Clearly, the worst outcome is the patient's dying. The best outcome is no pulmonary embolism being present to begin with and no treatment being given. We can assign death utility zero and no embolism/no treatment utility 100. This establishes a scale within which to rank the other outcomes. We might assume that the pain and anxiety associated with a reembolization is equivalent to the pain and anxiety of a serious hemorrhage. Clearly, either outcome is much more desirable than dying. For most people, there is some disutility in having to undergo such a treatment as proposed here (one must remember to take the medicine, and there is some anxiety associated with the possibility of a hemorrhage side effect). Cases where the woman had a pulmonary embolism but there were no subsequent embolisms and no hemorrhaging are no different from the best outcome—treatment aside—for in such cases the woman experiences the same pain and anxiety with no further complications. We can summarize these considerations in Table 3.1. These utilities are meant only to be suggestive. We can use them to see how the analysis gets carried through. In a real case, more thought would have to go into the construction of a utility scale—and some care would have to be taken to ensure that the scale is used correctly (see Chapter 6, Sections 2 and 3, and Chapter 11, Section 6).

To determine a ''recommended'' course of action we need to ''filter'' the utility assignments in the leaves back to the root of the tree. We cannot start at the top of the tree with *outcome 1* because node A has a branch that does not end in a leaf—it ends in node B—and we do not yet have a utility assigned to node B. For such reasons we must start with node C, whose branches end in *outcome 3* and

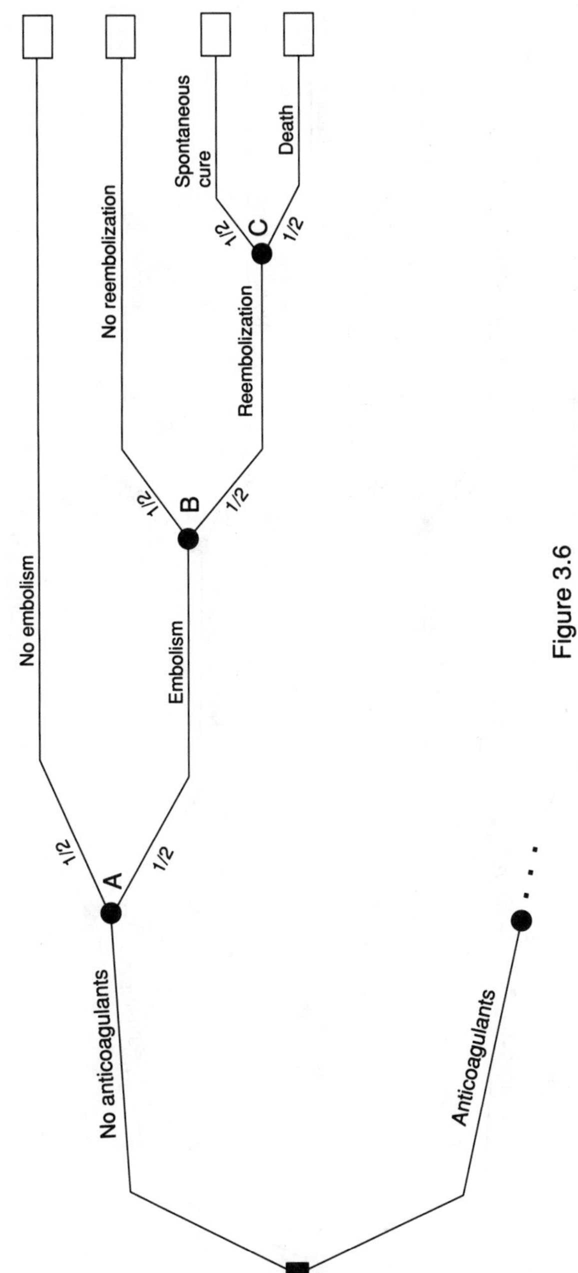
No anticoagulants
Anticoagulants
A
1/2
1/2
No embolism
Embolism
B
1/2
1/2
No reembolization
Reembolization
C
1/2
1/2
Spontaneous cure
Death

Figure 3.6

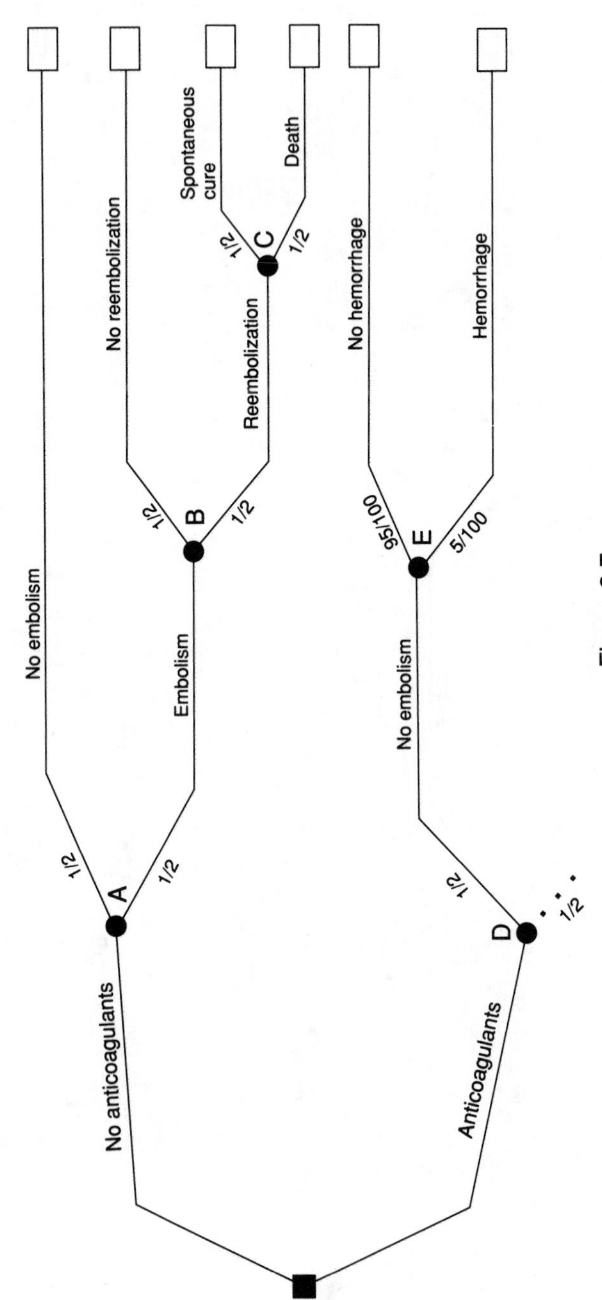
No anticoagulants
Anticoagulants
A
1/2
1/2
No embolism
Embolism
B
1/2
1/2
No reembolization
Reembolization
C
1/2
1/2
Spontaneous cure
Death
D
1/2
1/2
No embolism
E
95/100
5/100
No hemorrhage
Hemorrhage

Figure 3.7

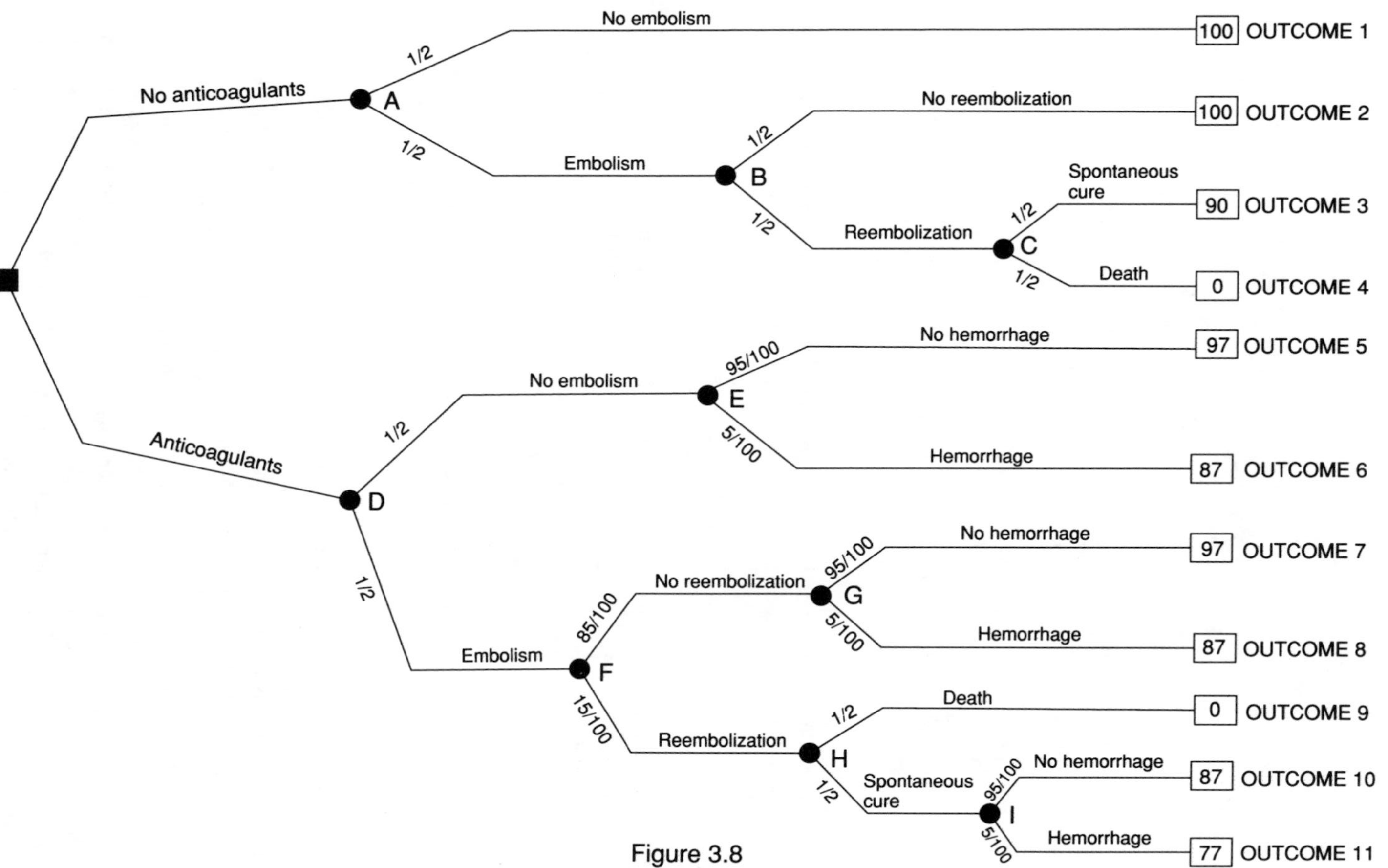

No anticoagulants
A
1/2
No embolism
100 OUTCOME 1
1/2
Embolism
B
1/2
No reembolization
100 OUTCOME 2
1/2
Reembolization
C
1/2
Spontaneous cure
90 OUTCOME 3
1/2
Death
0 OUTCOME 4
Anticoagulants
D
1/2
No embolism
E
95/100
No hemorrhage
97 OUTCOME 5
5/100
Hemorrhage
87 OUTCOME 6
1/2
Embolism
F
85/100
No reembolization
G
95/100
No hemorrhage
97 OUTCOME 7
5/100
Hemorrhage
87 OUTCOME 8
15/100
Reembolization
H
1/2
Death
0 OUTCOME 9
1/2
Spontaneous cure
I
95/100
No hemorrhage
87 OUTCOME 10
5/100
Hemorrhage
77 OUTCOME 11

Figure 3.8

TABLE 3.1

Outcome	Anticoagulant	Embolism	Re-embolization	Hemorrhage	Death	Utility
1	N	N	N	N	N	100
2	N	Y	N	N	N	100
3	N	Y	Y-10	N	N	90
4					Y	0
5	Y-3	N	N	N	N	97
6	Y-3	N	N	Y-10	N	87
7	Y-3	Y	N	N	N	97
8	Y-3	Y	N	Y-10	N	87
9					Y	0
10	Y-3	Y	Y-10	N	N	87
11	Y-3	Y	Y-10	Y-10	N	77

outcome 4. The utility of node C is the product of the chance assigned to each of its branches and the utilities of the leaves at the end of the branches:

$$\left(\frac{1}{2} \times 90\right) + \left(\frac{1}{2} \times 0\right) = 45.$$

Now we can calculate a utility for node B. One of node B's branches ends in outcome 2, with utility 100, and the other ends in node C, with utility 45. Thus, the utility of node B is

$$\left(\frac{1}{2} \times 100\right) + \left(\frac{1}{2} \times 45\right) = 72\frac{1}{2}.$$

We can now, similarly, compute the utility of node A:

$$\left(\frac{1}{2} \times 100\right) + \left(\frac{1}{2} \times 72\frac{1}{2}\right) = 86\frac{1}{4}.$$

In a similar manner we compute the utilities of all of the rest of the nodes on the tree. Figure 3.9 is a completed tree with the utilities calculated for each node. The best course of action is to give the anticoagulants. This choice has utility 92½, whereas not giving anticoagulants has utility 86¼.

While these utilities are somewhat arbitrary, as far as deciding what to do, this is not too important. The "recommended" action is remarkably resilient to changes in the utilities. With a little bit of algebra (see Chapter 11, Section 6) we can show that the decision to do the procedure depends almost entirely on the disutility of the procedure itself. Given the disutilities for hemorrhage and reembolization used (10 each), we would opt for anticoagulants unless the disutility of this treatment was greater than nine and a half—much more than the value of 3 used. If hemorrhage

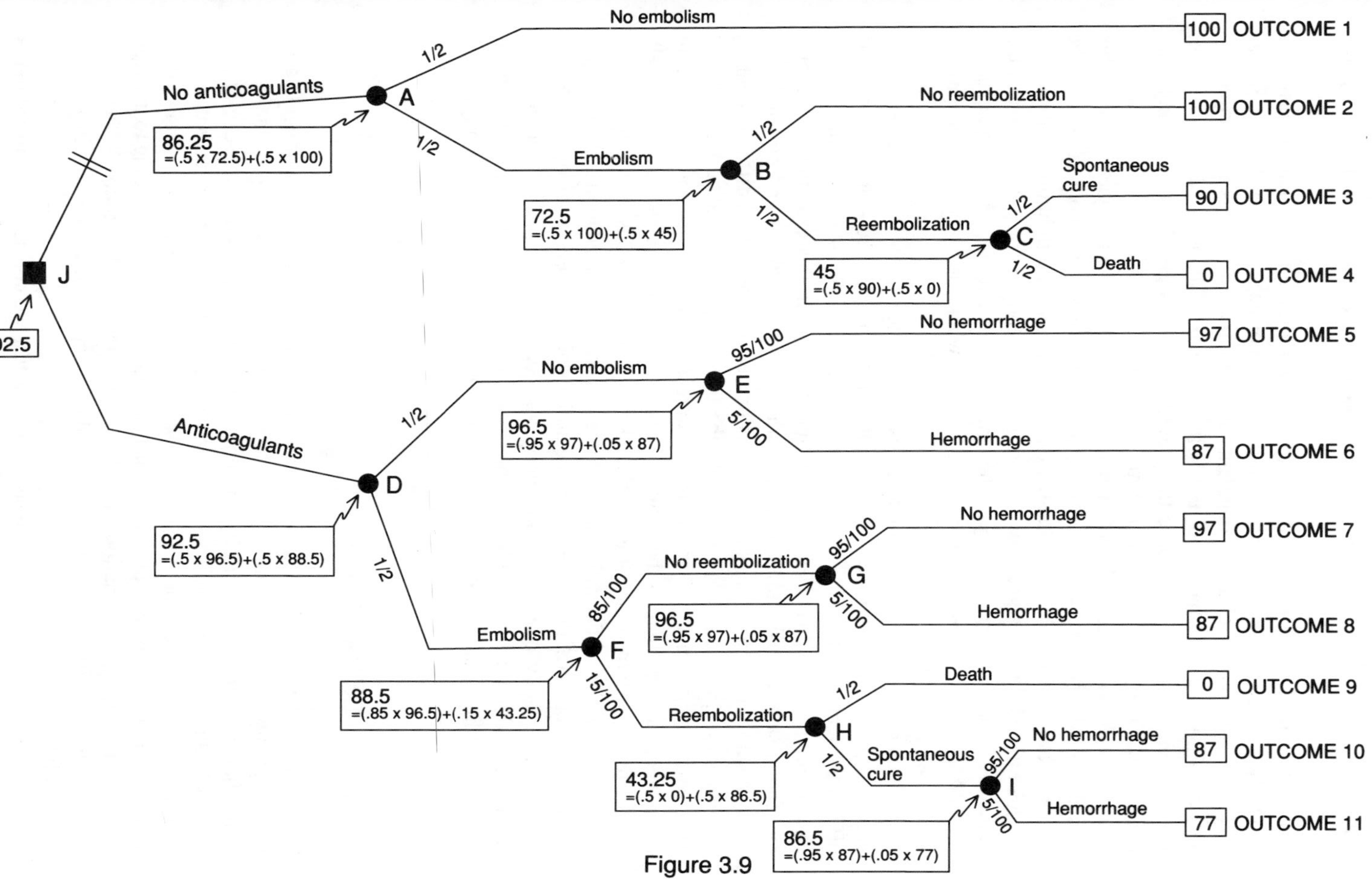

J
92.5
No anticoagulants
Anticoagulants
A
86.25
=(.5 x 72.5)+(.5 x 100)
1/2
No embolism
1/2
Embolism
100 OUTCOME 1
B
72.5
=(.5 x 100)+(.5 x 45)
1/2
No reembolization
100 OUTCOME 2
1/2
Reembolization
C
45
=(.5 x 90)+(.5 x 0)
1/2
Spontaneous cure
90 OUTCOME 3
1/2
Death
0 OUTCOME 4
D
92.5
=(.5 x 96.5)+(.5 x 88.5)
1/2
No embolism
E
96.5
=(.95 x 97)+(.05 x 87)
95/100
No hemorrhage
97 OUTCOME 5
5/100
Hemorrhage
87 OUTCOME 6
1/2
Embolism
F
88.5
=(.85 x 96.5)+(.15 x 43.25)
85/100
No reembolization
G
96.5
=(.95 x 97)+(.05 x 87)
95/100
No hemorrhage
97 OUTCOME 7
5/100
Hemorrhage
87 OUTCOME 8
15/100
Reembolization
H
43.25
=(.5 x 0)+(.5 x 86.5)
1/2
Death
0 OUTCOME 9
1/2
Spontaneous cure
I
86.5
=(.95 x 87)+(.05 x 77)
95/100
No hemorrhage
87 OUTCOME 10
5/100
Hemorrhage
77 OUTCOME 11

Figure 3.9

and reembolization had zero disutility, we would opt for anticoagulants unless their disutility was greater than 9. If the disutility of hemorrhage and reembolization was 40 (each), we would opt for anticoagulants unless their disutility was greater than 11. The disutility of hemorrhage and reembolization makes almost no difference here. Roughly speaking, this is because the procedure reduces the chance of dying from 0.125 to 0.0375, and this is what is most important.

Most of the degrees of belief in this example are based on frequencies available in the medical literature. However, judgment was necessary to pool results of all the tests and estimate a probability that the pain was caused by a pulmonary embolism. With a little additional algebra, we can show that as long as the probability that the pain was caused by a pulmonary embolism is greater than 2⁄10, anticoagulants are preferable. And ½ is not even close to a point where not taking anticoagulants would be preferable.

Such probing of the decision analysis "recommendation" is called *sensitivity analysis*. We vary the utilities—keeping the probabilities fixed—and see how this affects the recommendation. We also vary the probabilities—keeping the utilities fixed—and see how this affects the recommendation. In this example, the recommendation stands for the most sensible combinations of utilities and probabilities.

What we have done here is use a decision tree to organize the different courses that events might follow. We build into the tree the possibilities we have control over—with square nodes—and those "nature controls"—with round nodes. In cases where nature controls the course of events, however, we estimate how likely are the different turns that nature might take. These likelihoods, then, are used to weight the utilities of the different outcomes. The recommendation for anticoagulants is based on a weighted average of the utilities of the different outcomes. While, in the end, exactly one of the outcomes will occur (if the tree is accurate), the recommendation for anticoagulants is the "best" course to follow in the sense that it combines utilities and degrees of belief to find the highest weighted average.

6. PERFECT INFORMATION

The pulmonary embolism example focuses on the decision of whether or not to give anticoagulants. It is, of course, desirable to obtain the best estimate of the probability that the pain was caused by a pulmonary embolism. To do so, a doctor typically will administer a variety of *tests*. However, as with procedures, tests can have undesirable side effects, and they do not always provide a true sign of what is wrong with the patient. Thus, two questions must be considered before deciding to undergo a test. First, is the information provided by the test worth the cost—due to an undesirable side effect? Second, how should we cope with the unreliability of test information?

We consider two kinds of tests. The first test we consider in this section is very reliable. We will assume that it gives perfect information. But it is dangerous.

The second test we consider in the next section is not dangerous, but it is not reliable. We consider both in the context of the pulmonary embolism example.

A pulmonary angiogram is a test where an x-ray-sensitive dye is injected into the lungs. An x-ray is then taken of the lung. A radiologist can then determine whether or not a pulmonary embolism is lodged in the lungs. While this test, in fact, is not perfect, it is extremely reliable. On the other hand, a variety of complications are possible. For the sake of illustration, we will suppose, first, that no errors can result from this test, and second, that 1% of patients who undergo this test have an undesirable side effect as bad as a hemorrhage caused by anticoagulant treatment.

Suppose that all of the degrees of belief and utilities used in the pulmonary embolism example in Section 5 apply in this case. Would it be appropriate first to give the woman a pulmonary angiogram, and only if it showed an embolism, to treat with anticoagulants?

Here we have another decision problem. We start the decision tree for this problem with a square node with two branches—one for giving the pulmonary angiogram and one for not giving the pulmonary angiogram. If we do not give the pulmonary angiogram, we are in the situation analyzed in Section 5. If we do give the pulmonary angiogram, there is the possibility of an undesirable side effect, which we represent with a round node with two branches. With or without the side effect, the test can either show a pulmonary embolism present or not. If it is present we give anticoagulants; otherwise, we do not. Thus, we have the decision tree shown in Figure 3.10. The upper part of this tree—node J—is an abbreviated form of the tree we constructed in the preceding section. Here we only need to represent the two options—giving anticoagulants and not doing so—with the expected utilities we calculated for each case—92.5 and 86.25. The double-hatch mark on the upper branch is used to show that that choice is less desirable and consequently not to be taken.

The utilities for *outcomes 12* through *15* are based on the following considerations. Suppose that the test is negative for a pulmonary embolism and there is no undesirable side effect from the test, *outcome 15*. In this case no anticoagulants would be given and there would be no chance of further undesirable side effects. This is the same as the best possible outcome from the previous analysis, except that the patient had to undergo a pulmonary angiogram. We might suppose that the disutility of undergoing the test is 3, so we would subtract 3 from 100, for a utility of 97. If, on the other hand, the test was positive for a pulmonary embolism, we would give the anticoagulants and suffer both the (reduced) risk of reembolization and the risk of hemorrhage. This is just the situation the woman would be in had she arrived at node F in Figure 3.9. We calculated this utility, 88½, in Section 5. Since she also had to undergo a pulmonary angiogram, the utility of *outcome 14* is 3 less, or 85½. To account for a disutility of an undesirable side effect of the pulmonary angiogram, the utilities of *outcome 12* and *outcome 13* are 10 less than *outcome 14* and *outcome 15*, respectively.

These utilities are filtered back through the tree toward nodes K and N in the same manner as in the preceding section. The result is a utility of 91.15 for node K.

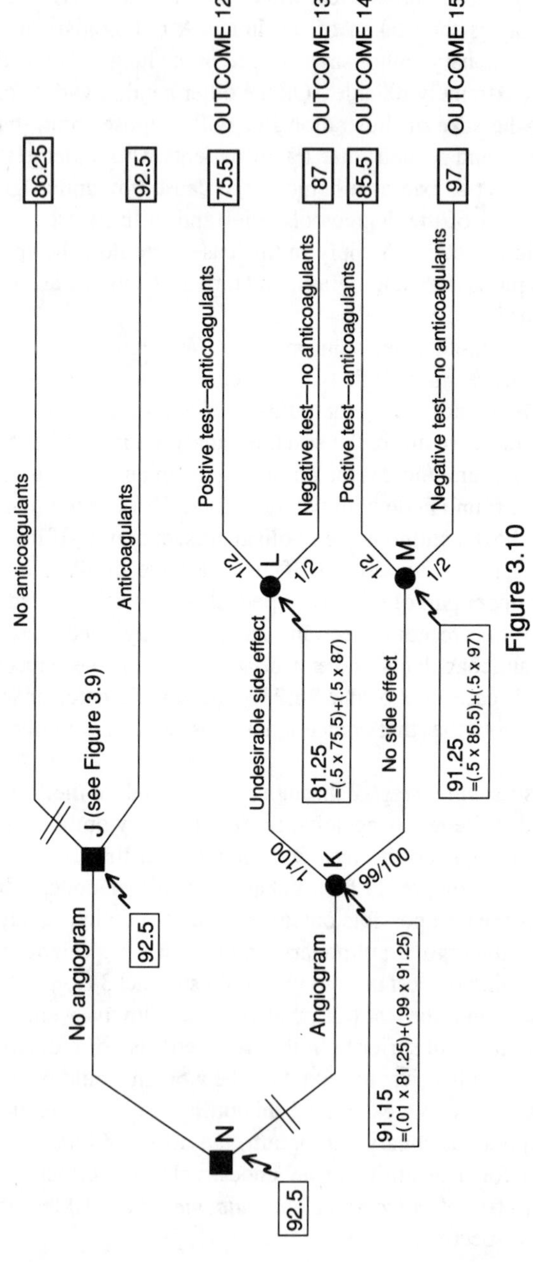

92.5
N
No angiogram
Angiogram
J (see Figure 3.9)
92.5
No anticoagulants
86.25
Anticoagulants
92.5
K
1/100
99/100
91.15
=(.01 x 81.25)+(.99 x 91.25)
Undesirable side effect
No side effect
L
81.25
=(.5 x 75.5)+(.5 x 87)
M
91.25
=(.5 x 85.5)+(.5 x 97)
1/2
1/2
1/2
1/2
Postive test—anticoagulants
75.5
OUTCOME 12
Negative test—no anticoagulants
87
OUTCOME 13
Postive test—anticoagulants
85.5
OUTCOME 14
Negative test—no anticoagulants
97
OUTCOME 15

Figure 3.10

This is slightly less than the utility of 92.5 (at node J) for just giving the anticoagulants. Consequently, this test does not provide valuable enough information to warrant its use. In the context of the entire decision tree, we should first decline to give a pulmonary angiogram and then administer the anticoagulants.

Similar to the analysis of Section 5, the recommendation against pulmonary angiogram depends primarily on the disutility of the test itself. For example, if there were no disutility associated with undergoing the procedure itself, doing the test would have a higher utility, 94.15, than simply giving the anticoagulants. The disutility of the undesirable side effects associated with the test have almost no impact on the calculation. They reduced the utility 1/10, from 91.25 to 91.15. If these side effects were extremely serious with a disutility of 40, they would still only reduce the utility 4/10, from 91.25 to 90.85. This is because they are so unlikely.

7. FALLIBLE INFORMATION

Most tests do not give perfect information, and indeed it is an artificial assumption to assume that the pulmonary angiogram gives perfect information. The point of the analysis above is that even when we can get perfect information, it may not be appropriate to seek it. Information has a cost, and there are times when it is not worth the cost.

Consider another test for pulmonary embolism, a lung scan. Here, by injecting a small amount of radioactive protein into the patient's blood, the flow of the blood through the lungs can be observed. This test is essentially without side effects. However, it can produce misleading results. Some patients with a pulmonary embolism will not show it with this test; sometimes the test gives a *false negative* result. Some patients may test positive when they do not have a pulmonary embolism; sometimes the test gives a *false positive* result. In practice, these tests can provide varying degrees of intermediate indications that a pulmonary embolism is present. For the sake of simplicity, however, we suppose that the test is either definitely positive for pulmonary embolism, or definitely negative, but it may be falsely positive or negative.

For many tests, and this lung scan is no exception, there is fairly reliable statistical information about the frequency of false negatives and false positives. For the sake of this example, we can assume that these frequencies are the following: The test will detect 90 out of 100 pulmonary embolisms; it will produce a *false negative* report 10 times in 100 uses. 70 out of 100 cases without a pulmonary embolism will be correctly labeled by the test; the test will produce a *false positive* for pulmonary embolism 30 times in 100 uses.

Our problem is to interpret a positive result from such a test. Given a positive result, what is the chance that a pulmonary embolism is present? To answer this, we need to know the chance that the patient had a pulmonary embolism to begin with. Consider a population of 10,000 people administered this test. Of these 10,000, suppose that 1,000 have a pulmonary embolism. We can use a tree to look at the effect of the test's false positive and false negative rates on this population (Figure 3.11). In this population 1,000 people have a pulmonary embolism. Since the test detects 90 out of 100 cases of pulmonary embolism, 900 of the 1,000 people with a pulmonary embolism will test truly positive for a pulmonary embolism; 9,000 people in this population do not have a pulmonary embolism. Since the test produces a false positive in 30 cases out of 100, 2,700 of the 9,000 people without a pulmonary embolism will test falsely positive for a pulmonary embolism. There are 90 100s in 9,000; each of these 90 100s will produce 30 false positives. So there are $30 \times 90 =$ 2,700 false positives from this group of 9,000 people without a pulmonary embolism. In all, 3,600 people in the population of 10,000 will test positive for a pulmonary embolism, 900 truly and 2,700 falsely. Since 900 of these 3,600 will be true positives, the chance that a person from this population has a pulmonary embolism, given a positive test, is 900/3,600 or 0.25.

Now consider a different population of 10,000 people, 5,000 of whom have a pulmonary embolism. If the test works in the same way, we would have 6,000 positive outcomes, of which 4,500 would be true positives and 1,500 would be false positives (see Figure 3.12). The chance that a person from this population has a pulmonary embolism, given a positive test, would be 4,500/6,000, or 0.75.

On the other hand, if we used this test in a population of 10,000 people, only 100 of whom had a pulmonary embolism, we would get yet another result. In this case there would be 90 true positives and 2,970 false positives. The chance that a person from this population has a pulmonary embolism, given a positive test, would be a tiny 90/2,970, about 0.03.

There is a significant difference in the interpretation of the test results in these three cases. In the second case, the chance that a person has a pulmonary embolism, given a positive test result, is 0.75; in the last case it is only 0.03. Arithmetically, the source of this difference is not hard to find. It comes from the vastly larger number of false positives in the last case. While the test produces 30 out of 100 false

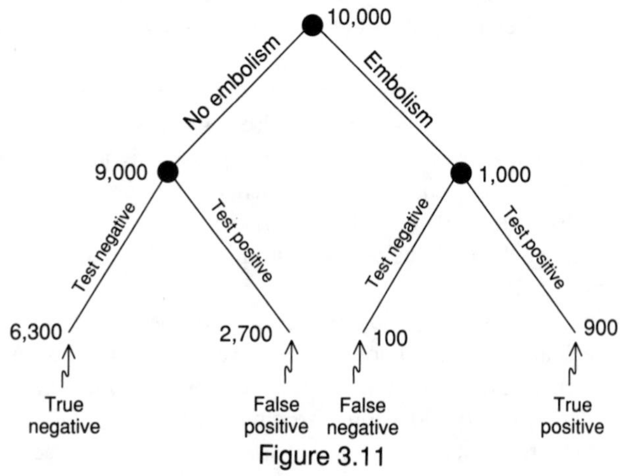

Figure 3.11

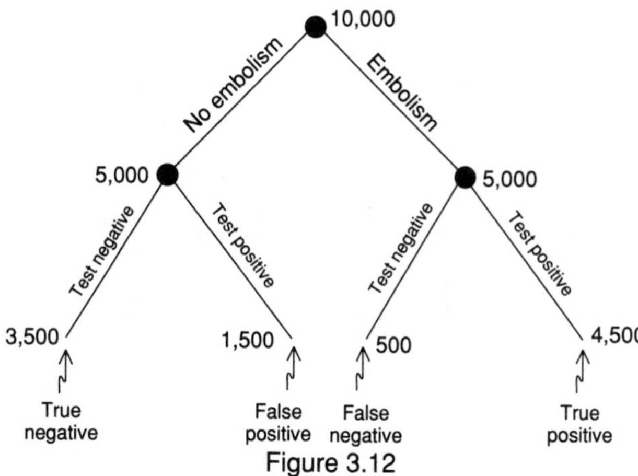

Figure 3.12

positives in all cases, in the last case there are 9,900 people who do not have a pulmonary embolism, and who *could be* falsely positive. In the second case, there are only 5,000 people who do not have a pulmonary embolism, and who *could be* falsely positive.

Should the woman from the example in the preceding section have a lung scan? We use a tree that is structurally similar to that in Figure 3.10. In this case, however, there is no problem with an undesirable side effect. There is a problem with false positive and negative test results (Figure 3.13). Finding appropriate branch degrees of belief is a little tricky. After the initial battery of tests, the doctors estimated that there was a 50% chance that the woman was suffering from a pulmonary embolism. Consequently, we can usefully consider a hypothetical population of 10,000 people, 5,000 of whom had a pulmonary embolism (see Figure 3.12). Suppose that the test was positive for a pulmonary embolism. The probability that there is an embolism is 4,500/(4,500 + 1,500) = 3/4. The chance that no embolism is present is 1/4. Suppose, on the other hand, that the test was negative for a pulmonary embolism. The probability that there is an embolism—that the test produced a false negative—is 500/(500 + 3,500) = 1/8; the probability that there is no embolism is 7/8. The probability that the test is positive at all is (1,500 + 4,500)/10,000 = 6/10; the probability that the test is negative is 4/10. All these calculations can be done with ratios of values taken from Figure 3.12.

The utilities can be determined relatively easily. We can assume that this test is relatively painless and has no disutility associated with it. If the test was positive—anticoagulants were given—and there was an embolism present, the situation is like node F from Figure 3.9. The utility we calculated for this case is 88½. If the test was positive—anticoagulants were given—but there was no embolism present, then "we are at" node E from Figure 3.9; the utility is 96½. On the other hand, if the test was negative—no anticoagulants were given—and a pulmonary embolism

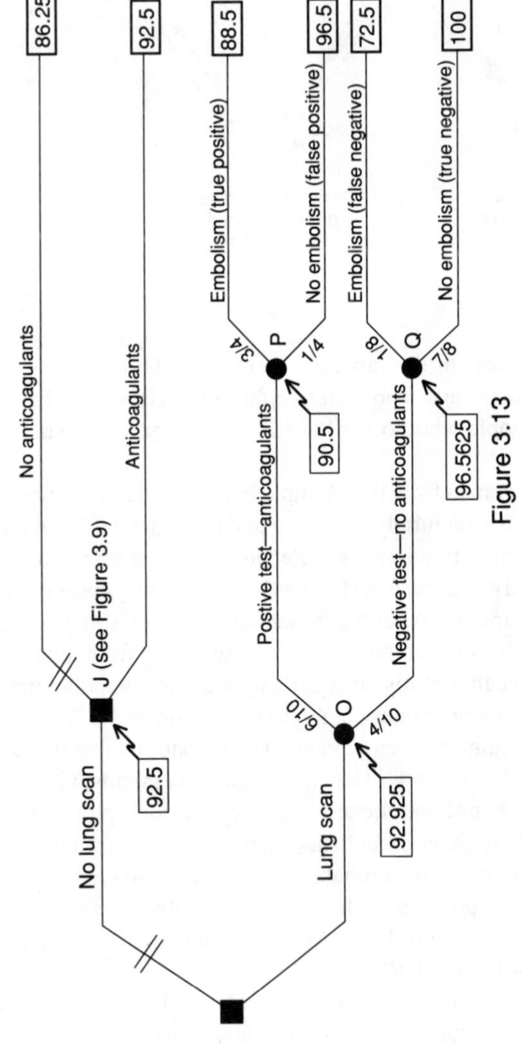

No lung scan
92.5
J (see Figure 3.9)
No anticoagulants
86.25
Anticoagulants
92.5
Lung scan
92.925
O
6/10
Postive test—anticoagulants
90.5
P
3/4
Embolism (true positive)
88.5
1/4
No embolism (false positive)
96.5
4/10
Negative test—no anticoagulants
96.5625
Q
1/8
Embolism (false negative)
72.5
7/8
No embolism (true negative)
100

Figure 3.13

was present, we are at node B, with utility 72½. If the test was truly negative, the situation is ideal, utility 100.

We filter the utilities back toward the root of the tree as in the previous examples. The utility for performing a lung scan is 92.925, slightly higher than the utility for not giving the lung scan and just giving anticoagulants. The lung scan is appropriate in this case.

As with all of the other examples, the recommendation depends on the utilities and degrees of belief used. Here we have used an idealized description of the results of a lung scan, to make the impact of false positives and false negatives clearer. We have also assumed that this test has no disutility associated with it. As always, the effects of modifying these assumptions should be examined.

8. BENEFITS OF DECISION ANALYSIS

Here we have a general proposal for making decisions. We lay a decision problem out in a tree diagram which displays the possible paths the course of events might follow. We distinguish between cases where we can control which alternative comes about—square nodes—and cases where nature controls which alternative comes about—round nodes. We estimate how likely we think the different things that can happen are, and we represent these judgments with numerical probabilities. To represent relatively how much we prefer the various things that might occur, we add numerical utilities at the leaves of the tree. We filter these utilities inward toward the root of the tree by taking weighted averages of utilities—expectations—at each round node. Decision analysis recommends that we act to maximize our *expected utility*—"expected" in the sense of taking expectations. At each square node we should choose the branch with the greatest utility at its end; conversely, the utility of a square node is the greatest utility at the end of all the square node's branches.

Perhaps the most important benefit of decision analysis is how it extends our ability to conceptualize complex decision problems. It provides a framework for organizing the factors that ought to enter into making a complex decision, and it allows us to analyze a complex problem into simpler component problems that are easier to think about.

Doing a decision analysis urges us to consider a variety of alternative courses of action. Life is not completely determined in advance. Different courses of action are, in most circumstances, open to us, even when we do not think of them. A theory that helps us recognize these options can be very liberating. Decision analysis also urges us to recognize that nature can evolve in different ways. Understanding the variety of things that might happen, and how likely these possibilities are, is important in reaching a sensible plan of action.

In the end we do make choices, whether we think about them or not. Decision analysis urges us to consider how desirable different outcomes are. It may seem morbid or wholly artificial to compare one's death with the pain and anxiety of a serious hemorrhage. But in deciding to undergo anticoagulant treatment, for example, such a comparison is made, if only implicitly. Decision analysis makes such comparisons explicit. Consequently, we have more control over such comparisons and the decisions they underwrite; we can tailor choices to our individual preferences. But we need a theory that accommodates individual preferences, and we need to understand what these preferences are.

Decision analysis provides a framework for evaluating information. Only rarely is information definitive. Tests can mislead. Thinking about test results in terms of false positives and false negatives provides a way to evaluate the results of fallible tests. Information is rarely free. In medical contexts, tests can have undesirable side effects, not to mention their dollar cost. Decision analysis provides a framework for determining whether or not the benefit of the information a test might provide outweighs its cost.

Decision analysis provides a slick "end-run" solution to the problem of induction. We no longer are forced to find good, but not valid, arguments that aim to allow us to make some definite assertion, while recognizing that the assertion may be false. Instead, we "quantify our ignorance" in terms of numerical degrees of belief. When we add numerical utilities to the possible results of a decision, we can reach a definite recommendation for what to do. Our need for a definite conclusion is satisfied by definite recommendations for action, not definite recommendations for what to believe. Here again, we *may* make the right decision and end up with an undesirable outcome.

9. KINDS OF WORRIES ABOUT DECISION ANALYSIS

Decision analysis employs a variety of concepts. We must construct decision trees with degrees of belief for branch probabilities, leaf utilities, and expected utilities. We use a decision rule that advocates maximizing expected utility. Worries arise with all of these concepts at a variety of levels. Here I briefly mention three kinds of worries: (1) practical worries, (2) conceptual worries, and (3) ethical worries.

Regarding (1). There are many practical worries. How can we find reasonable degrees of belief, a reasonable structure for the decision tree, reasonable utilities? Recalling the allergy example, you may not have kept track of how long your allergy attacks last. They seem to last forever, but you know that this reflects your biased memory of their unpleasantness. So it may be difficult to know what degree of belief you have (or should have) that the attack will be a long one.

Surely the decision tree for the allergy example is incomplete, for all of the possible remedies have not been included as possibilities. There is more than one kind of allergy pill. Perhaps you believe that any allergy pill will make you sleepy, perhaps not. It may be difficult to construct a complete decision tree which one can have confidence in.

Frequently, decisions are made for what turn out to be irrelevant reasons. The market for electric calculators was ill anticipated. A friend reports moving from upstate New York to Arizona. His reasons—better job, better pay, better co-workers—turned out to be irrelevant compared with the basic advantage of Arizona, which he had not considered: He was "allergic" to the cold damp weather in New York; Arizona's hot dry climate made him a happier and healthier man. Doing a decision analysis may seem irrelevant when we have every reason to believe unanticipated factors will largely determine how we feel about the outcome.

Regarding (2). Other worries focus on the value of decision analysis setting aside practical issues. Decision analysis recommends actions on the basis of the utilities and degrees of beliefs. These utilities and degrees of belief are presumed to be measurable with a numerical scale of utility and numerical probabilities. But many theorists question the very existence of such degrees of belief and utilities. Such a description may not be appropriate for a person's state of mind.

Even if we can suppose that people have utilities and degrees of belief, the inputs to a decision analysis are *just* the beliefs and utilities of the person. Decision analysis may not make a good recommendation for a person who is radically misinformed or has utilities which later, in the fullness of experience, he or she would regret having had.

Decision analysis recommends doing whatever maximizes one's expected utility. Why is *expected* utility desirable? Utility, by definition, represents relatively how desirable different outcomes are. Why should expected utility do the same? Consider the pulmonary embolism example. We computed a utility of 86¼ for not taking anticoagulants. This was based on a small (1/8) chance of dying, equally small chances of reembolization and a spontaneous cure, and of no reembolization, and a relatively large (1/2) chance that there was no pulmonary embolism in the first place. Dying, however, is not the kind of outcome one can risk over and over, sometimes getting unlucky, sometimes not. This is not like the allergy example, nor is it like the lunch cola example. One cannot suffer the worst outcome in this example more than once. Why, then, should one be moved by a rule that guarantees the best overall average outcome were one confronted with such a decision many times?

Regarding (3). There are an assortment of essentially ethical worries. Decision analysis recommends doing that which maximizes expected utility. *Whose* utility? I have assumed in the medical examples that it is the patient's utility that should be maximized. No doubt the patient's preferences are very important. But medical services are provided in a larger social context. The limited supply of organs for organ transplant operations makes the point most clearly. A decision analysis done for 10,000 similarly ill patients might recommend an organ transplant in each case. Society may not have the resources to accommodate. How is utility to be maximized in such a circumstance; whose utility should be maximized in such a circumstance?

Ought each of us aim to fulfill our preferences to the greatest degree possible? Perhaps there are other, more important values that need to figure more prominently in a person's deliberations over what to do. A doctor's lying to his or her patient about the severity of the patient's illness might make the patient happier. Indeed, the patient may be the kind of person who does not want to know the "awful truth." Even if such an action maximizes the patient's preferences, it may not be the right thing for the doctor to do.

10. OBJECTIVE RULES AND SUBJECTIVE JUDGMENT

Two general problems hamper the use of decision analysis in medicine. Decisions, of course, must be made in medicine—as in most parts of life. Decision analysis makes specific recommendations for how to go about making these decisions. Instead of relying on the *implicit judgment* of a physician, decision analysis requires the *explicit presentation* of possible courses of events, their chances of happening, and their desirability. The first problem is that making matters explicit, like any procedure or test, takes time and effort. The second problem is that implicit medical judgment may result in better recommendations than an explicit decision analysis.

Consider the first problem, that decision analysis takes time and effort. Many emergency situations simply do not allow the leisure for such an analysis. And even when there is time, producing a careful, individually tailored analysis has both a dollar cost and a psychological cost. The dollar cost may be prohibitive in many more or less routine cases. The psychological cost may be prohibitive in other cases. It is one thing to recognize in a vague way that a given procedure comes with a small (perhaps 0.001) chance of a serious complication or of dying. It is quite another thing to focus on such outcomes and attempt to assign them numbers representing their relative worth. Doing so requires imagining dire outcomes vividly, and this can make it difficult to keep their small chance in perspective.

Consider the second problem, decision analysis may take the place of sound implicit medical judgment. Decision analysis makes certain presuppositions about the structure of decision making. It *may* ignore components of implicit medical judgment, and thus *could* result in disastrous recommendations. Of course, if we knew what the missing ingredient was, we could (in principle) develop an improved decision analysis to accommodate it. But we may not know either whether an ingredient is missing or, if one is, what it is. Consequently, a blind reliance on explicit decision analysis may produce worse results than implicit subjective judgment. Worse, if decision analysis becomes the accepted way to make medical decisions, the ability to make subtle subjective judgments could atrophy.

These two problems can conspire together. One can imagine medical decision specialists developing a catalog of decision trees for standard situations. It would save time, energy, and money to adapt these trees to individual cases as they arose. The result could lose the advantages of both explicit decision analysis and implicit medical judgment. Decisions would not be properly individualized and subtle implicit judgments would no longer be pursued.

While these problems should be kept in mind, the benefits of decision analysis should also be kept in mind. Decision analysis can keep medical costs down by making it clear that certain tests cannot provide usable information. Decision analysis can provide a widely recognized framework within which alternative courses of treatment can be discussed. Decision analysis can provide a widely recognized justification for opting for a particular course of treatment. Decision analysis makes a place for the individual preferences of each patient. Decision analysis forces explicit recognition of the varying degrees with which different aspects of a medical situation are known. All of these are salutary consequences for the practice of medicine.

11. SUMMARY

1. One way to approach induction is to focus on criteria for making good decisions.
   - **(a)** Inferences may be used to help gather and clarify information. They also may be a part of a process aimed at directing future action.
   - **(b)** Decision analysis provides recommendations for how to act, given incomplete information, and the preferences of the decision maker regarding the various possible outcomes.
   - **(c)** Decision analysis cannot guarantee the best outcome. In a similar manner, a good inductive inference cannot guarantee the conclusion's truth.
   - **(d)** But decision analysis can guarantee decisions that are best on average.
2. Decision analysis employs two central concepts, *utility* and *degree of belief.*
   - **(a)** Decision analysis provides recommendations in the context of incomplete information. Such beliefs are represented numerically as *degrees of belief.*
   - **(b)** These numerical degrees of belief behave like probabilities: They vary between zero and 1; the more likely a decision maker believes something is, the closer the decision maker's degree of belief in it is to 1.
   - **(c)** Decision analysis provides recommendations in the context of the preferences of the decision maker. These preferences are represented numerically as *utilities.*
   - **(d)** Usually, the higher a utility value, the more preferable the outcome associated with it is. Sometimes, for convenience, an "upside-down" scale of utility is used.
3. Decision analysis represents decision problems in terms of *decision trees,* which contain nodes, branches, and leaves.
   - **(a)** A *branch* sprouts from a node and terminates in a node farther down the tree or in a leaf. The collection of branches that sprouts from a given node represents all of the possible different courses events might take given that events "got to" the node.
   - **(b)** There are two kinds of nodes. *Round nodes* represent cases where the decision maker cannot control what course events take. *Square nodes* represent cases where the decision maker can control what course events take.
   - **(c)** The *leaves* represent the various final outcomes as far as the decision problem is concerned.
   - **(d)** The order of tree branchings should represent the order in which the decision maker would come to know what course events are taking.

(e) The decision maker's degrees of belief represent how likely the decision maker believes each branch is—given that events "got to" the node.
(f) The decision maker's utilities represent relatively how preferable each outcome is.

4. To determine preferred actions, leaf utilities are "filtered" inward toward the root of the tree.
   (a) The utility assigned to a round node is computed as follows: The probability of each branch is multiplied by the utility at the branch's end. These products are then added together. The result is the *expected utility* of the round node. It is a weighted average of all the utilities that could be accrued from the round node.
   (b) At each square node where the decision maker can control the direction of the course of events, the decision maker should opt for that branch with the highest utility at its end. Thus, the utility assigned to a square node is the highest utility of all its branches.

5. Information can, but need not always, help the decision maker make better decisions.
   (a) Information usually has a cost. In the case of medical decisions, tests used to get information can subject a patient to potentially undesirable side effects.
   (b) Information is usually fallible. Medical tests can produce both *false positive* results and *false negative* results.
   (c) To determine whether it is worthwhile to collect information, the cost of the information and its fallibility must be taken into account. This is another decision problem.
   (d) Three things must be known in order to interpret fallible information: (1) the frequencies with which the method of collection produces false positive results, (2) the frequency of false negative results, and (3) the initial chance that the condition being tested for is present.

6. There are many benefits to decision analysis.
   (a) Decision analysis provides a framework within which to conceptualize complex decision problems. Thus a complex problem can be analyzed into simpler components.
   (b) Decision analysis urges decision makers to contemplate alternative courses of action, and to recognize the variety of ways that things could evolve.
   (c) Decision analysis urges decision makers to be explicit about preferences, to think seriously about which outcomes are preferred to others and to what extent they are preferred.
   (d) Decision analysis provides a framework for evaluating costly and fallible information.

7. Three kinds of worry plague decision analysis, practical worries, conceptual worries, and ethical worries.
   (a) Practically, it can be difficult to determine the several ingredients necessary for a decision analysis.
   (b) Doing a decision analysis itself has a cost.
   (c) Conceptually, the existence of degrees of belief and numerical utilities has been called into question. Furthermore, the adequacy of the recommended action depends on the adequacy of these utilities and beliefs.

(d) Decision analysis recommends that action with the greatest expected utility. This would produce the best net result were a decision maker confronted with such a decision problem many times, but some problems are one-time affairs. Why prefer the action with the greatest expected utility in such cases?
(e) Decision analysis recommends that action with the greatest utility for the decision maker. But decisions are not made in a social vacuum. What is best for the decision maker may not be best for the rest of society.
(f) Decision analysis seems to present human beings as purely self-interested. Perhaps other values should be more central to choosing what to do.
(g) Decision analysis makes certain assumptions about the nature of decision making. It is possible that important, but implicit, aspects of medical decision making are ignored by decision analysis. Decisions where such aspects were important would be better made informally by a doctor with well-trained medical judgment.

12. REFERENCES

(Resnik, 1987) is a primarily philosophical introduction to decision analysis. (Raiffa, 1970) is an excellent introduction to the mathematics of decision analysis. (Hill et al., 1979) provides a nice discussion of decision analysis in a variety of different contexts; its chapter on "Decision Making in the Practice of Medicine" is particularly good. (Bunker et al., 1977) discusses at greater depth a decision theoretic approach to a variety of medical examples. The appendicitis example in Section 2 is adapted from information appearing in the *New England Journal of Medicine* in an article entitled "Therapeutic Decision Making: A Cost-Benefit Analysis" (Pauker and Kassirer, 1975, Volume 293, Number 5, p. 230). The pulmonary embolism example used in Sections 5 and 6 is adapted from information appearing in the *New England Journal of Medicine* in the same article (Pauker and Kassirer, 1975, Volume 293, Number 5, pp. 231–2), (Pauker and Kassirer, 1978), and (Hill et al., 1979). (Ransohoff and Feinstein, 1976) discusses some of the problems with using decision analysis in medicine. (Nisbett and Ross, 1980) is a good introduction to some of the sticky psychological questions that decision analysis must confront.

13. PROBLEMS

1. Consider the allergy example discussed in Sections 1 and 4.
   (a) Suppose that you assign different utilities to the three outcomes in the example. For you, being sleepy all day has utility 5. Being miserable all day still has utility zero, and being miserable for an hour and fine for the rest of the day still has utility 10. You still think that there is an 80% chance the allergy attack will last all day. Given these utilities and degrees of belief, would decision analysis recommend that you take an allergy pill?
   (b) Now suppose you assign the same utilities to the three outcomes in the example in Section 4. However, you think there is a 50% chance the allergy attack will last all day. Given these utilities and degrees of belief, would decision analysis recommend you take an allergy pill?

(c) Given the new utilities from (a) and the new degrees of belief from (b), would decision analysis recommend that you take an allergy pill?

2. Imagine you own a car that needs a new battery. The best place in town for batteries sells two varieties. One is a "3-year" battery, the other is a "5-year" battery. On reading the fine print, you find that a 3-year battery has an equal chance of wearing out during the second, third, or fourth year of use; the probability in each case is 1/3. The 5-year battery has an equal chance of wearing out in the fourth, fifth, or sixth year of use—1/3 each. The 3-year battery costs \$30.00 and the 5-year battery costs \$50.00. Which battery should you buy so that your expected cost per year of use is the smallest possible? Be sure to construct a decision tree inserting the proper round and square nodes, the proper number of branches and branch probabilities, and the proper utility values for the ends of each branch. Then calculate the expectation of each possible choice, to determine which battery has a lower expected cost per year of use.

3. Suppose that the following artificial deck of cards is created. It contains 10 cards, nine hearts, ace through nine, and the ace of spades. It is shuffled well and you draw a card. If the card is the ace of spades, you win \$20.00; otherwise, the deck is reshuffled and you draw again. If you get the ace of spades on this second draw, you lose \$50.00; otherwise, you lose \$100.00. What is your expected monetary gain from this game?

4. Suppose that you are offered the following gamble on the toss of a fair die. If it comes up 1 or 6, you are paid \$10.00; if it comes up anything else, you are paid \$5.00. You can play this game over and over—as long as you like. But you must pay the expected monetary value each time you play.
   (a) What is the expected monetary value for this game?
   (b) In what sense and why is the expected monetary value a *fair price* for this game?

5. Suppose that a psychologist develops a test for 6–month-old babies that allows one to predict the "handedness" of a baby as an adult. Unfortunately, the test is not perfect. It will properly label 90% of all babies; 10% of the time it mislabels a baby. Suppose that the psychologist used this test on 1,000 babies in 1980. Now that we can determine their handedness, we know that there were 750 right-handed babies in the group and 250 left-handed babies in the group.
   (a) How many babies did the test label right-handed?
   (b) How many of those babies that were labeled right-handed turned out to be right-handed?
   (c) How many babies did the test label left-handed?
   (d) How many of those babies that were labeled left-handed turned out to be left-handed?

6. Consider a pregnancy test that claims to detect 99% of all pregnancies it is used on; it will produce a false positive report 5% of the time.
   (a) Suppose that to begin with there is a 99% chance that a woman is not pregnant—because she has been using a method of birth control which claims to be 99% effective. Suppose she uses this pregnancy test and it says that she is pregnant. What is the chance that she is pregnant, given this result?
   (b) Suppose that a man uses this test and it shows that he is pregnant. What is the chance that he is pregnant? What does this mean about how to interpret the results of such tests? Discuss

7. Consider the following example: A 49–year-old woman is 6 weeks pregnant. She is worried that her unborn child might have Down's syndrome. She considers undergoing a

test, amniocentesis, where a small quantity of amniotic fluid is taken from her uterus. Fetal cells from this fluid are then cultured and examined for chromosomal abnormalities. If this test showed an abnormality such as Down's syndrome, she would abort the pregnancy. Unfortunately, the test can cause a spontaneous miscarriage 5 times in a 1,000. Assume that the test gives perfect information.

(a) Suppose the chance that a pregnant 49–year-old woman is carrying an affected fetus is 1/12. Build a decision tree which, given the necessary utilities, could be used to determine whether or not the woman should undergo amniocentesis.

(b) Add the following utilities to your tree from part (a): live, full-term birth of a child with Down's syndrome—0; live, full-term birth of an unaffected child—100; miscarriage subsequent to procedure—15; elective abortion—5. Given these utilities, should the woman undergo amniocentesis

8. Unfortunately, amniocentesis does not give perfect information. It will correctly detect 99% of affected fetuses; it will correctly fail to detect 99.9% of unaffected fetuses. Do Problem 7 under these new conditions.

9. Many people believe that abortion is murder and, consequently, immoral.

(a) Could such views be accommodated in the amniocentesis decision tree discussed above? Why or why not? Be as specific as you can with your answer.

(b) In your opinion, then, is decision analysis of the sort considered here *value neutral*? Why or why not? Again, be as specific as you can with your answer.

10. Is the fact that decision analysis uses the utilities and degrees of belief which might be wildly out of whack—for some "radically misguided decision maker"—a valid criticism of the analysis? Why or why not?

11. Consider the following argument adapted from an early decision-theoretic argument—the "wager"—by Blaise Pascal (1670). Ought one believe in God? There are two possibilities: God exists or God does not exist. One may believe in God and act piously, or not.

(a) Construct a simple decision tree for this problem as it is stated here.

(b) If one has even a tiny degree of belief that God exists, what recommended course of action should one take?

(c) What are some of the problems with this argument for belief in God? Discuss.

CHAPTER 4

FACTOR ANALYSIS AND HUMAN INTELLIGENCE

1. BEGINNING TO MAKE SENSE

In this chapter we examine a kind of induction that is different from both confidence intervals and decision analysis. Factor analysis helps us construct new, potentially fruitful, concepts out of confused data. Here we find how a more precise—although perhaps not more accurate—psychological concept of human intelligence was extracted from a variety of confusing measurements of different kinds of intellectual abilities. While the factor analysis of human intelligence is our main example, factor analysis has been used in a wide variety of contexts—from chemical analysis to the sociology of voter preference. Perhaps more important, factor analysis is not the only way to begin to make sense. And so we start with a different, more historically distant, example to appreciate the kind of induction factor analysis aims to be.

Around the year 1600, Galileo invented a primitive thermometer. It consisted of a vertical tube with a glass bulb attached to its top end. The bottom end was immersed in an open container of water so that some water would extend up into the tube. As the air in the glass bulb warmed, it expanded down into the tube and so lowered the water level in the tube, thereby indicating the "temperature." This "thermometer" was sensitive to barometric pressure. There were no established reference temperatures with which to calibrate different such thermometers. The tubes did not have uniform bore. Indeed, it was entirely unclear what this curious device measured. There was no doubt that it measured something related to *sensed* warmth. But the relation was not a simple one. Consider the following discovery—described in a February 1615 letter to Galileo from one of his students, Sagredo: "With the instrument I see clearly that the water of our fountain is colder in winter than in summer, and I imagine that the same is true of springs and subterranean places, although our feelings seem to indicate the contrary" (quoted in Bolton, 1900). Without special training, the human being is not a reliable measuring instrument of temperature. Many factors beside temperature influence how warm something feels to a person: the ambient temperature, the humidity, the heat conductivity of the material, the person's state of physical exertion, the person's expectations, the person's habitual climate, the time of day, and so on. In order to produce reliable thermometers, scientists had to sort out this variety of factors that contribute to sensed warmth, on the one hand, and "natural temperature" on the other.

Given the contemporary notion of temperature, all of this makes good sense. But this notion had to be developed and isolated from sensed warmth. Now we can say, "It may feel cold to you, but it is really 70 degrees out." It was not until nearly 1740 that reliable, consistently calibrated thermometers were available. It was not until nearly 1850 that anything like our contemporary understanding of heat and temperature was developed. Before the concept of natural temperature was available there simply was a mess of different opinions about how warm things were. The early thermometers simply added another source of "opinions," and there were as many different "thermometer opinions" as there were thermometers.

A central aim of data analysis in general and factor analysis in particular is to begin the process of sorting out such different sources of "opinion." Ideally, all of the various factors that contribute to how something seems would be isolated. In this way, instruments could be built to measure in a reliable and consistent manner each of the various factors contributing to the mass of conflicting and confusing "opinions." In most cases, however, data analysis alone cannot succeed in this. It can help our understanding by distinguishing what could be important and separable contributing factors to some mess of opinions. It can suggest future lines of research. Rarely can it supply a final dissection of a complex of factors contributing to a mess of confusing and contradicting "opinions." It can lead to mistakes and fruitless directions for further investigation.

Factor analysis takes a large collection of confused measurements of some ill-defined and ill-understood property and *re*-presents them in a more orderly way. The production of such a *re*-presentation depends on uncovering statistical regularities hidden in the mass of data. It also depends on guidance from the data analyst, who may impose constraints on how the data are to be re-presented and may try a variety of different constraints until something that could be sensible or "interpretable" is produced. The goal is to find regularities in the confused data that make some sense of the data.

We cannot be *certain* that the structures identified through a factor analysis will prove to be enduring and important parts of nature. Factor analysis is not a deductively valid form of argument. But factor analysis does provide another kind of guarantee. Stated roughly, it guarantees to produce the smallest number of structures that can "formally account" for the interrelationships between the various explicitly measured features of the data.

2. INTELLIGENCE TESTING

Factor analysis originally was developed by psychologists for the analysis of intelligence test data. Many people have a sense that individuals differ with respect to intelligence. Some people seem "sharp" or "quick" others seem "dull" or "slow." But exactly what intelligence is and how it could be measured are difficult to discern from such vague descriptions. The variety of items used to "measure intelligence" is truly astounding. They have included items like the following:

- Bill is taller than John. Ralph is shorter than Bill. Who is the tallest?
- "Today is worth two tomorrows." is most like which of the following?
  "Time is an herb that cures all diseases."
  "A bird in the hand is worth two in the bush."
  "To speed today is to be set back tomorrow."

These, and an astonishing variety of other questions, some probing pattern recognition (see Figure 4.1), have been used to measure intelligence. All these different types of questions seem to skirt a more basic ability.

For many researchers, underwriting the diversity of different approaches to testing intelligence is the view that a person's ability to answer such questions is based on some more basic latent trait(s). People do not simply have the ability to

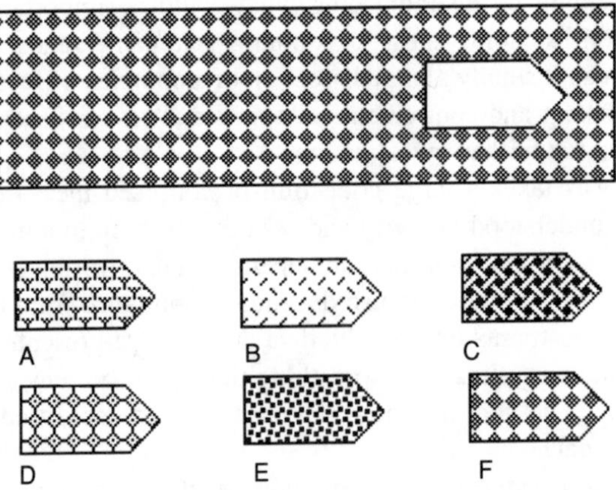

Which of A through F is most appropriate to fill the blank space?

Figure 4.1

recognize patterns, they have basic abilities that manifest themselves in the human faculty to recognize patterns, understand proverbs, or reason. It is in these basic abilities that a precise concept of intelligence is to be found. Given this general view of human intellect, the problem is to find a more precise concept of intelligence from the diversity of tests of intelligence. This is where factor analysis plays a role.

Scores on all of the variety of intelligence tests tend to be highly correlated: someone who scores high on one intelligence test usually scores high on other intelligence tests. Factor analysis has been used to provide one kind of "formal account" for these correlations. The idea is this: Test scores are highly correlated *because* those people who tend to do well on all the tests are basically smarter. Factor analysis is used to tease out from the mess of intertest correlations specifically what the features of such basic smarts are. Perhaps there is verbal intelligence, numerical intelligence, and geometric intelligence. Some analysts have found the suggestion of an overarching "general intelligence," dubbed "*g*" when it was first analyzed from a bunch of intertest correlations in 1904.

3. VARIATION AND CORRELATION

To achieve any understanding of how factor analysis made general intelligence a possible object for study and controversy, we need some understanding of two central concepts: variation and correlation. While each is defined precisely mathematically, we concern ourselves here with the basic concepts of which the mathematics makes sense. The mathematical details are pursued in Chapter 6.

Variation. Consider a population of people, perhaps all adult female residents of Lakewood, Colorado. We can speak of many properties of each resident. Each has a particular height and weight. Each is a particular age. Each first moved to Lakewood (or was born there) in a particular year. We call such properties *variables* because different members of the population vary with respect to such properties. One resident lives at 1048 Valentine Way; she first moved to Lakewood in 1959; in 1988 she was 36 years old; and so on. Another resident will have different *values* for these variables.

Some of these variables come with a numerical sense of order. *Age* is a variable with numerical order. The *year the resident first arrived in the state* is another. On the other hand, *street address* is not a variable that has a numerical order; there is no sense in which 1123 East Hampton St. is bigger than 1038 Wheat St. The variables we are concerned with have a built-in numerical order.

Within a given population, some variables "vary a lot" and some "vary little." Consider the population of entering freshmen at the University of Arizona. The vast majority of them are 18 years old. Some are 19; fewer are 20, and fewer still are 21, or older. There is some variation in the age of entering freshmen, but relatively little. On the other hand, there is more variation in the ages of the faculty at the University of Arizona. Some faculty members are relatively young, perhaps

25 years old, and some are relatively old, perhaps 70 years old, and many are some age between.

We can get some sense for the degree to which a population varies with respect to some variable graphically. We can plot the relative number of entering freshmen against their ages (Figure 4.2). Such graphs are called *histograms*. The height of each bar represents how many freshmen entered at that "bar's age." Compare this histogram to a similar plot of the relative ages of the faculty (Figure 4.3). The columns in Figure 4.2 are much more sharply peaked than they are in Figure 4.3. So we have one way to make sense of the claim that the age of entering freshmen varies less than the age of the faculty.

In Chapter 6 we learn to compute the *variance* of a population of measurements. This is a measure of the variation of a population with respect to a given variable. For now we need only note a few general characteristics of variance. The variance of a given variable (in a given population) is always zero or greater. The larger the variance, the more the population varies with respect to the given variable. If the variance is zero, the population does not vary at all with respect to the variable—all the members of the population have the same *value* of the variable.

Correlation. The second central concept underlying factor analysis is *correlation*. Correlation is a measure of the degree to which two variables tend to "vary together." Consider height and weight. Were we to measure the heights and weights of each male resident of Half Moon Bay, California, we would find that tall residents "tended" to be heavier than short residents. Height and weight are *positively correlated*. Of course, some people are short and heavy and some are tall and light, but typically, the taller someone is, the heavier that person is.

Sometimes two variables vary in "reverse tandem." Consider, for example, the age of a male resident of Half Moon Bay and the number of hairs on his head. Older men tend to have fewer hairs on their heads. As age increases, the number of hairs on a male's head typically decreases. Such variables are *negatively correlated*.

Sometimes two variables do not vary "in tandem." Suppose that we compared the heights of adult male residents of Half Moon Bay with the number of times each has left the city limits in the last week. A 5-foot 4-inch resident of Half Moon Bay may have left Half Moon Bay 42 times during the last week or he may not have left once. There is no reason to suppose that as heights go up, the number of times leaving Half Moon Bay will go up as well. These two variables are not positively or negatively correlated.

Again, graphs can give us some sense of how two variables are correlated. We could measure the height and shoe size of each resident of East Thetford, Vermont. For each resident we would obtain two numbers—his or her height and his or her shoe size. We could mark a graph with an **X** in the appropriate spot for each resident (Figure 4.4). The result is called a *scatter plot*. The distance the **X** is above the horizontal axis represents the person's shoe size. The distance the **X** is to the right of the vertical axis represents the person's height. We can see from such a graph that

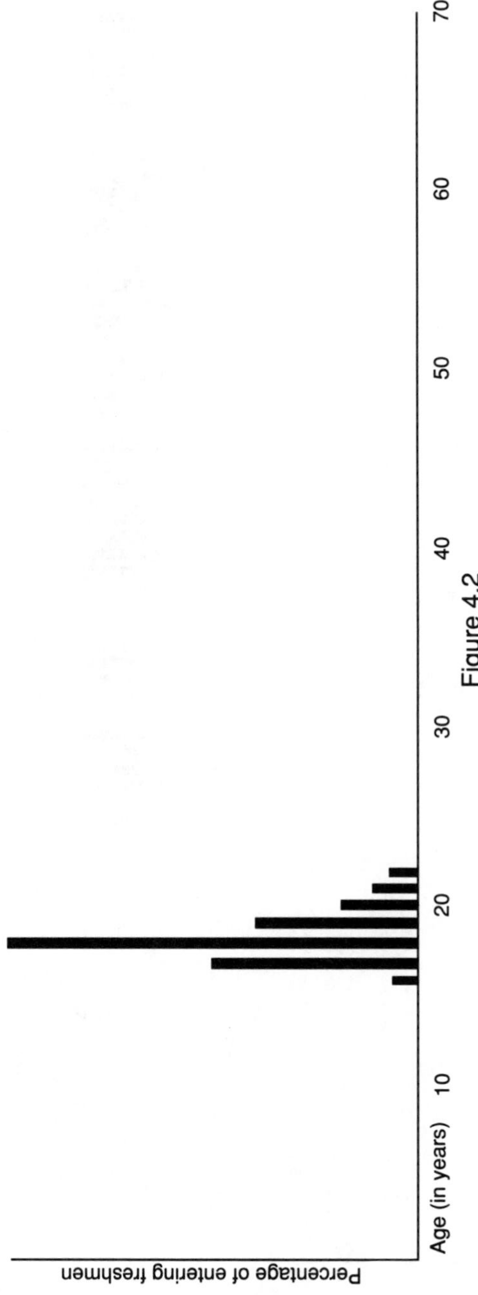

Percentage of entering freshmen
Age (in years)
10
20
30
40
50
60
70

Figure 4.2

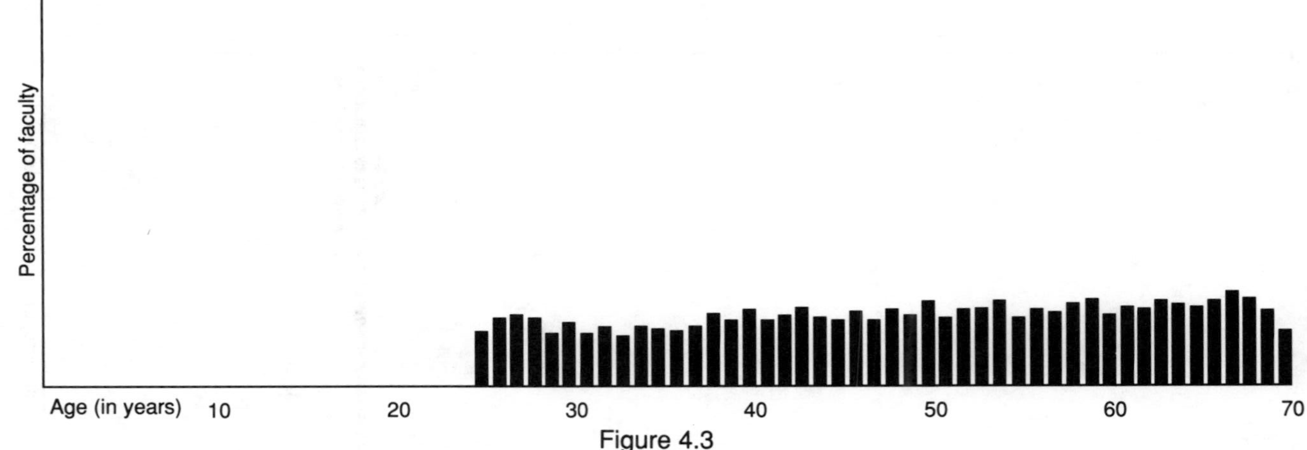

Figure 4.3

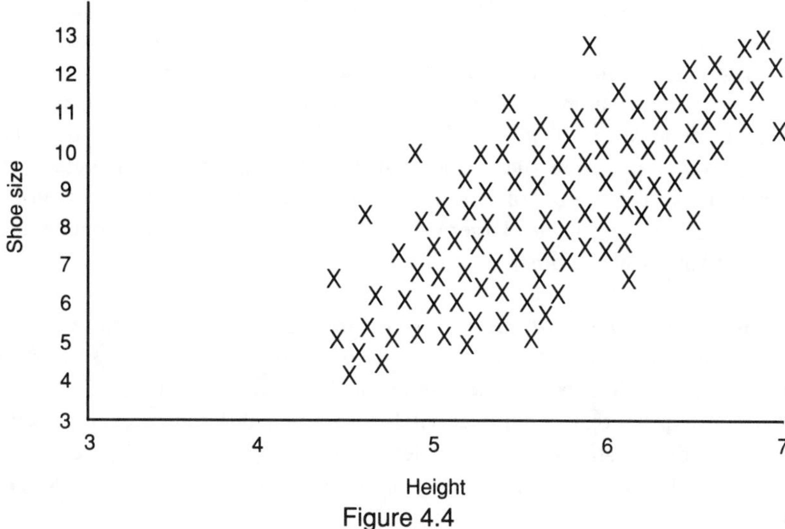

Figure 4.4

for the most part, as height increases, so does shoe size. There is a "swarm" of **X**s that starts in the lower left and moves toward the upper right.

Some variables are less closely related. A scatter plot of age and height for adult residents of East Thetford might look something like the plot shown in Figure 4.5. For the most part there is little relationship between age and height. There might be some slight tendency for older people to be shorter, as their spines "settle." But one could not well predict how tall someone was knowing his or her age alone.

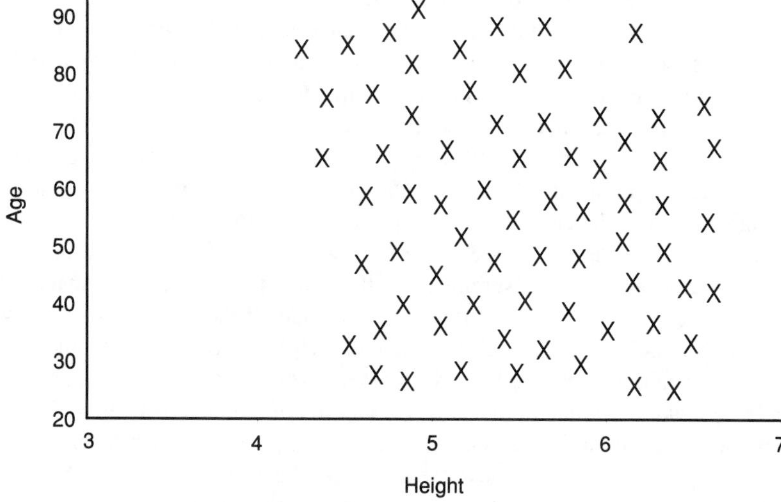

Figure 4.5

As with variation, we will learn to compute the *correlation* between two variables in Chapter 6. Here we need only note a few general characteristics of correlation. The correlation of two variables lies between -1 and $+1$. Two variables have a positive correlation when larger values of one of the variables are associated with larger values of the other variable—such as height and weight. Two variables have a negative correlation when larger values of one of them are associated with smaller values of the other—such as age and number of head hairs. Two variables have a correlation of zero when larger values of one are associated with neither larger nor smaller values of the other.

Correlation reduces variation. At the most general level, variation and correlation are important to factor analysis for two complementary reasons. If there is too much variation in a population, we are inclined to postulate some underlying difference in causes that could account for observed differences. Conversely, if there is too little variation, if the variables are all strongly correlated, we are again inclined to postulate some underlying similarity of causes that could account for observed similarities.

In the case of intelligence testing, people who do well on one test tend to do well on other tests. Scores on all of these tests are positively correlated. Here, then, is a source of similarity that might be explained in terms of some underlying "factor" or "factors." A person does well on all of the tests *because* this person has a "high IQ." The single property—high IQ—is used to account for the person doing well on all the different tests. Conversely, different people can have different scores on a single intelligence test. Such differences might also be explained by individual differences in an underlying factor, such as IQ. One person may have a high IQ and another a low IQ; this single difference would account for the observed differences in their scores on an intelligence test.

At this general level of discussion, "IQ" is just a vague fantasy. It is some postulated kind of property that might account successfully for two facts about intelligence test scores. However, we do not know anything in particular about the nature of this IQ. Factor analysis is used to help determine in greater detail what IQ might be like, to determine what cognitive capacity or capacities are primarily responsible for human intelligence in general and the test-score data in particular.

The basic relationship which makes factor analysis work is that the variation in one variable can be reduced by "fixing" the value of a correlated variable. Consider all the heights of adults living in Santa Fe, New Mexico. There would be a large amount of variation in the measurements of the heights of all the individuals in this population. Suppose, however, that we only considered the heights of people who weighed 182 pounds—we "fixed" the value of weight to 182. There would still be some variation in the heights of Santa Fe residents who weigh 182 pounds, but there would be less variation than in the entire population of Santa Fe residents. To put it another way, one would have an easier time guessing what a person's height was if his or her weight were known in advance. Because these two variables are positively correlated, knowing the value of one reduces the variance in the other.

4. FORMAL FACTORS

With factor analysis we mathematically construct new variables, called *factors*. Initially, these new variables have only a formal meaning; they do not provide a scale for some more or less well understood property—such as height or pattern recognition or number of head hairs. Instead, they have a meaning only in the sense that values of the original test variables are related to values of these constructed factors by mathematical equations: for example,

$$(0.5 \times \text{constructed factor 1}) + (0.7 \times \text{constructed factor 2}) = \text{pattern recognition}.$$

There is no reason to suppose that these mathematical constructions are anything more than formal objects; they may identify no real aspect of the units under study.

These constructed variables, however, have several important properties. Factors are constructed to reduce the variation in the original test variables to the greatest degree with the fewest number of constructed factors. That is, fixing the values of the constructed factors reduces the variation in the original test variables. This happens because the constructed factors are correlated with the original test variables. These two connected relationships—reducing the variation because of correlation—directs the initial construction of factors. The fact that the constructed factors are highly correlated with the original test variables provides the most important property of the constructed factors.

The constructed factors can formally account for the correlations between the original test variables. The constructed factors can do this because of their correlations with the original test variables. If a variable, **F**—think of it as a constructed factor—is correlated with two other variables, $\mathbf{T}_1$ and $\mathbf{T}_2$—think of them as original test variables—then $\mathbf{T}_1$ and $\mathbf{T}_2$ will be correlated as well. Their correlation with **F** is what $\mathbf{T}_1$ and $\mathbf{T}_2$ have in common to make them correlated. $\mathbf{T}_1$ is correlated with $\mathbf{T}_2$ because $\mathbf{T}_1$ is correlated with **F** and **F** is correlated with $\mathbf{T}_2$.

Ultimately, factor analysts want factors that identify real aspects of the units they study. These real aspects should play causal roles in producing the observed values of the original test variables. Ideally, the correlations that the constructed factors have with the original test variables should arise from causal relations between the constructed factors and the original test variables. The correlations the original test variables have with each other would then be explicable as the result of the causal relations the original test variables have with the constructed factors. A high value on one observed test is associated with a high value on another test *because* both are the product of a high value of the constructed factor

Thus, ultimately, the constructed factors must bear more than a formal meaning; they must be interpretable in terms of real aspects of the units under study. Finding such interpretable factors requires manipulating the initially constructed factors. This manipulation is known as ''factor rotation.'' But before they are rotated, they must be constructed—or *extracted*—from the correlations between the original test variables.

5. EXTRACTING FACTORS

Factor analysis constructs or extracts factors in roughly the following way. Since the variables we use with factor analysis have an associated numerical order, they establish axes—such as those for height and shoe size. Extracted factors similarly establish axes, and sometimes factors are referred to as "axes." Recall the scatter plot showing how shoe size and height were correlated (Figure 4.4). Factor analysis would extract the best-fitting straight line drawn through this swarm of points (Figure 4.6).This extracted factor is a variable in the same sense as the original variables—different units in the population have different values of the extracted factor.

The original variables establish axes. When only two variables are involved, we can graph the relationship between values of the different variables. Factor analysis constructs new axes that can also be used to express the possible values that measurements of the original variables might have. The trick is to reproduce the original test scores with fewer axes, or variables.

In the height/shoe size example, two axes, one for height and one for shoe size, are used to express all of the possible values these two variables might have. But we can express most of this information with one extracted factor. If we knew the value of a person's "shoe size/height extracted factor," we could predict both shoe size and height reasonably well. There is some loss of information, but because of the high correlation between height and shoe size, very little information is lost.

Figure 4.6 gives an idea of how the "shoe size/height extracted factor" accounts for variation in the observed scores. Suppose that we fix the height variable at 5½ feet. The length of line A represents how much variation is left—fixing the value of the height variable. Line B represents how much variation is left if we fix the value of the extracted factor (at the value that corresponds to 5½ feet). Line B is

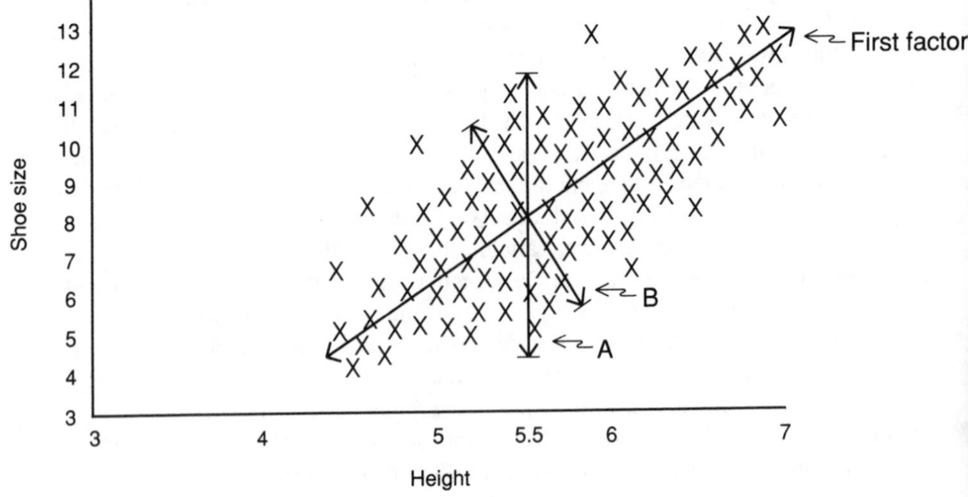

Figure 4.6

shorter than line A, so the amount of variation remaining after fixing the value of the extracted factor is smaller than after fixing the value of the height variable. Of course, we wish to reduce the variance generally, not just at the single value of 5½ feet. We need to measure the overall variation at *all* values and seek a reduction in the total variation from extracted factors.

A simple factor analysis of these two variables can also be pictured by a *path diagram* (Figure 4.7). If the factor analysis has worked right, the arrows show causal connections. Thus, the extracted factor is a common cause of both height and shoe size, and we have an explanation for why large shoe sizes are associated with high heights. Both are caused by high extracted factor values. No doubt, in this case, the extracted factor would identify an aspect of whatever regulates body growth to keep people proportioned in typically human shapes.

The path value, or *factor loading*, on the paths that connect extracted factors with observed variables measures the strength of the connection between these variables. In simple cases, factor loadings are numerically identical to the correlations between the variables they connect. Thus the path values use a correlation scale from -1 to $+1$ to represent the nature and strength of the connection between variables. The closer a path value is to $+1$, the more strongly do high (low) values of the extracted factor bring about high (low) values of the observed variable. For instance, the extracted factor in this example plays a larger role in producing height than it does in producing shoe size, $0.8 > 0.7$.

Associated with both of the original variables, shoe size and height, are "remainder" variables, $\mathbf{U}_1$ and $\mathbf{U}_2$. These variables are unique (hence "**U**") to their respective original variables, and are responsible for whatever variation remains that is not accounted for by the extracted factor. For instance, there may be some gene or complex of genes that regulates body growth. The fact that there is *one* gene or gene complex accounts for the correlation between height and shoe size. But there are other causes that affect growth, and these may not affect shoe size and height in the same way. The unique variables are catch-all variables designed to cover whatever

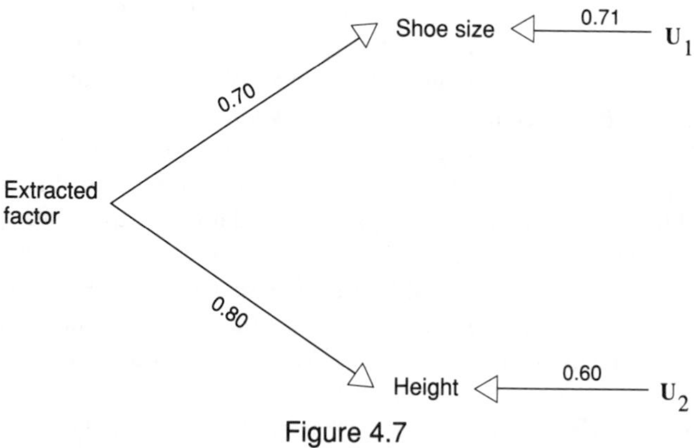

Figure 4.7

other causes outside the common factors might affect the values of the observed variables.

The sources of variation for any given variable can be "read off" such a path diagram. Shoe size has two sources of variation, the extracted factor and $\mathbf{U}_1$. Height also has two sources of variation. One might think of springs connecting $\mathbf{U}_1$ and the extracted factor to shoe size. The "vibrations" in both the extracted factor and $\mathbf{U}_1$ are communicated to the shoe size variable, causing it to "vibrate," or vary. Extending the metaphor, one could imagine springs along all the paths. By "pulling" on the underlying variables—the extracted factor, $\mathbf{U}_1$ and $\mathbf{U}_2$—one produces variations in the observed variables—height and shoe size.

The relations between variables are given by equations:

$$\text{shoe size} = 0.70(\text{extracted factor}) + 0.71(\mathbf{U}_1);$$
$$\text{height} = 0.80(\text{extracted factor}) + 0.60(\mathbf{U}_2).$$

That is, given the value of the three variables, $\mathbf{U}_1$, $\mathbf{U}_2$, and the extracted factor, we could calculate the value of both the height and shoe-size variables. For example, if a given person had values of 9.15, 2.92, and 5 for $\mathbf{U}_1$, $\mathbf{U}_2$, and the extracted factor, respectively, that person would wear size 10 shoes and would be 5 3/4 feet tall:

$$10 = 0.70(5) + 0.71(9.15);$$
$$5.75 = 0.80(5) + 0.60(2.92).$$

In general, we cannot directly measure values for a person's $\mathbf{U}_1$, $\mathbf{U}_2$, and extracted factor. We measure their shoe size and height directly. The point of these calculations is to clarify the nature of the relationships between these variables. Factor analysis extracts factors that relate to directly measurable variables by means of such equations: the extracted factor values are multiplied by their "loadings," and these products are summed to give the value of the variable observed. Such relationships are called *linear;* factor analysis assumes that the relationships between extracted factors and observed variables are linear in this sense.

When we are dealing with just two observed variables, such as height and shoe size, it is difficult to see the point of factor analysis: Why not stick with shoe size and height and call it a day? Factor analysis makes sense when there are many observed variables. There are many different intelligence tests, and it would make sense to describe a person's intelligence in terms of the values of one or two constructed factors instead of 68 different intelligence test values.

To give a more realistic example, then, we need to start with more observed test variables. Suppose that we start with measurements of 10 different tests of physical abilities on each individual in a given population: softball throw, hand grip, chinning, 50-yard dash, 100-yard dash, and so on. We need not worry here about exactly what each test measures, and how each is scored. After each test is given to each member of the population, we can compute the degree to which scores on one test correlate with scores on another test. We can compute such a correlation for each pair of tests. The result is a *correlation matrix* (Table 4.1). We can see, for example, that the correlation between softball throwing and chinning is 0.78. The

TABLE 4.1

	Softball throw	Hand grip	Chinning	50-yard dash	100-yard dash	One-leg balance	Tracing	Tracking	1-mile run	5-mile run/walk
1. Softball throw	1									
2. Hand grip	0.70									
3. Chinning	0.78	0.93								
4. 50-yard dash	0.32	0.47	0.39							
5. 100-yard dash	0.32	0.47	0.39	0.84						
6. One-leg balance	0.29	0.00	0.00	0.00	0.13					
7. Tracing	0.30	0.00	0.00	0.32	0.28	0.00				
8. Tracking	0.44	0.00	0.00	0.32	0.48	0.38	0.63			
9. 1-mile run	0.12	0.14	0.15	0.28	0.65	0.27	0.09	0.48		
10. 5-mile run/walk	0.16	0.19	0.20	0.22	0.62	0.28	0.05	0.47	0.93	

correlation between speed in the 50-yard dash and the 100-yard dash is 0.84. Such a correlation matrix is the starting point for a factor analysis. We see from such a correlation matrix that many test scores are positively correlated. Perhaps there are some basic underlying physical abilities that could account for these correlations. Factor analysis seeks to expose what underlying factors could sensibly account for this matrix of correlations.

Factors are extracted one by one. The first factor is extracted so as to account for the largest amount of the variation in the observed tests' scores than any one factor could account for (Figure 4.8). Here we have one factor, **I**, which is highly positively correlated with the 10 original test variables. In this case, even after fixing the value of this first factor, the remaining 10 variables are still highly correlated. A second common factor can be extracted (Figure 4.9). The second factor accounts for the largest remaining amount of variation—given the first factor. Still there is variation left to be accounted for. The third factor accounts for the largest remaining amount of variation given the first two factors; and so on. We keep extracting factors until whatever variation remains could be accounted for by errors of measurement alone (a concept with a precise probabilistic sense discussed in Chapters 12 and 13).

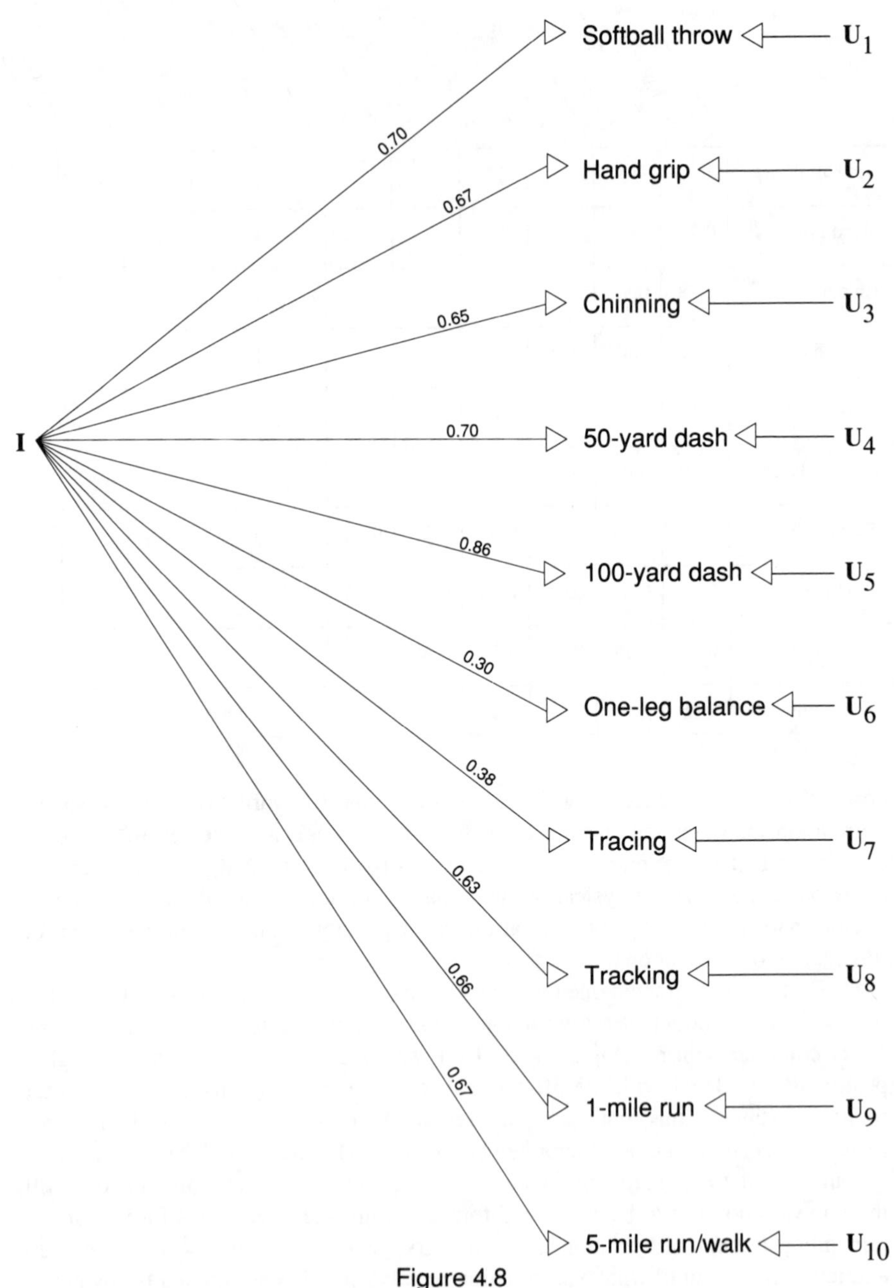

Softball throw
Hand grip
Chinning
50-yard dash
100-yard dash
One-leg balance
Tracing
Tracking
1-mile run
5-mile run/walk
U1
U2
U3
U4
U5
U6
U7
U8
U9
U10
I
0.70
0.67
0.65
0.70
0.86
0.30
0.38
0.63
0.66
0.67

Figure 4.8

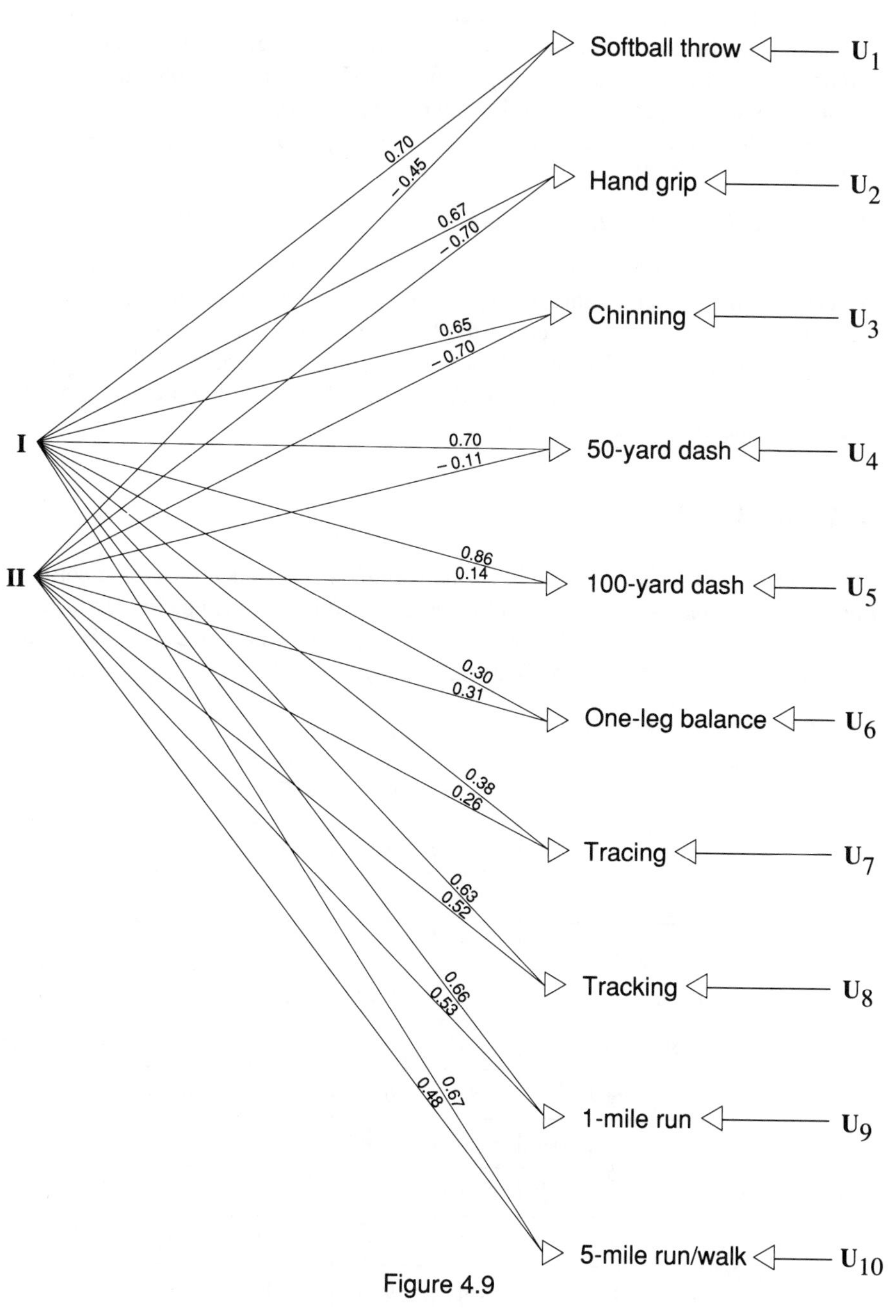
I
II
Softball throw
U1
Hand grip
U2
Chinning
U3
50-yard dash
U4
100-yard dash
U5
One-leg balance
U6
Tracing
U7
Tracking
U8
1-mile run
U9
5-mile run/walk
U10
0.70
−0.45
0.67
−0.70
0.65
−0.70
0.70
−0.11
0.86
0.14
0.30
0.31
0.38
0.26
0.63
0.52
0.66
0.53
0.67
0.48

Figure 4.9

In the case of the 10 tests of physical abilities, four factors can be extracted. These four factors account for 89% of the variation in the original 10 scores. The results can be tabulated as shown in Table 4.2. We can imagine that each person has certain values for the extracted factors **I** through **IV**, which—in combination with the unique factors representing all the other sources of variation—''produces'' the observed values on the 10 tests. In terms of linear equations, we find, for example, that

$$\text{chinning} = 0.65(\mathbf{I}) + -0.70(\mathbf{II}) + -0.13(\mathbf{III}) + 0.11(\mathbf{IV}) + \mathbf{U}_3.$$

Alternatively, the result can be expressed in terms of a path diagram (Figure 4.10). We can imagine 50 ''correlation springs'' hooked up to the 10 observable measurements of physical ability. By setting the ''spring-i-ness'' properly on each spring and pulling on **I** through **IV** and $\mathbf{U}_2$ through $\mathbf{U}_{10}$, we would produce the observed variations in the 10 observed test scores. We would also thereby produce the correlations in the 10 observed test scores.

6. ROTATING FACTORS

The process of extracting factors is virtually entirely mechanical. Given a correlation matrix, factors can be extracted by computer. But, there is nothing intrinsic to the idea of correlation that the factors extracted in this way must be causes. We need not think that factors **I** through **IV** actually bring about the 10 physical abilities.

TABLE 4.2

	Initially Extracted Factors			
	I	II	III	IV
1. Softball throw	0.70	−0.45	0.27	0.42
2. Hand grip	0.67	−0.70	−0.13	0.04
3. Chinning	0.65	−0.70	−0.13	0.11
4. 50-yard dash	0.70	−0.11	0.14	−0.52
5. 100-yard dash	0.86	0.14	−0.11	−0.38
6. One-leg balance	0.30	0.31	−0.03	0.73
7. Tracing	0.38	0.26	0.80	−0.14
8. Tracking	0.63	0.52	0.47	0.17
9. 1-mile run	0.66	0.53	−0.45	−0.02
10. 5-mile run/walk	0.67	0.48	−0.48	0.05

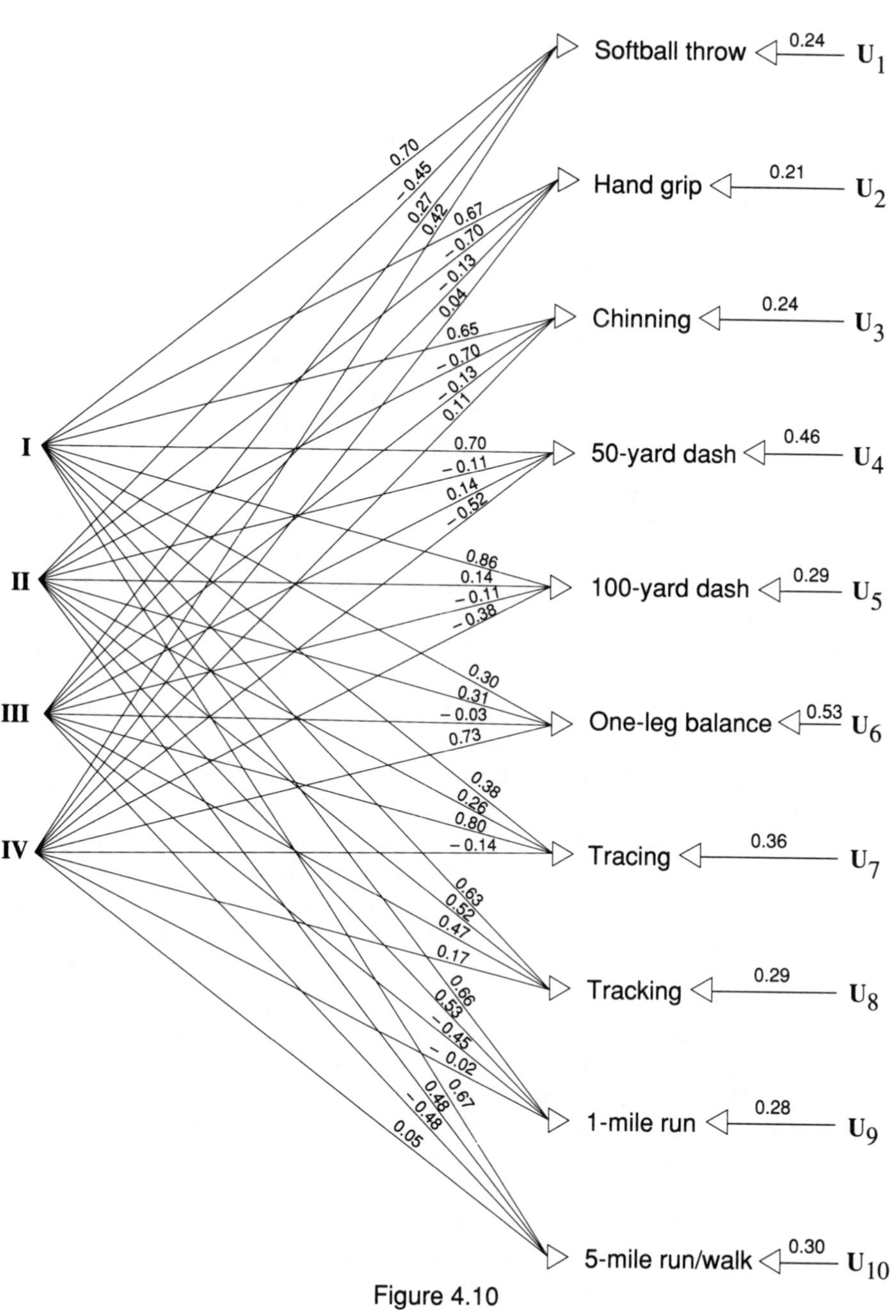
Softball throw
0.24
U1
Hand grip
0.21
U2
Chinning
0.24
U3
50-yard dash
0.46
U4
100-yard dash
0.29
U5
One-leg balance
0.53
U6
Tracing
0.36
U7
Tracking
0.29
U8
1-mile run
0.28
U9
5-mile run/walk
0.30
U10
I
II
III
IV
0.70
−0.45
0.27
0.42
0.67
−0.70
−0.13
0.04
0.65
−0.70
−0.13
0.11
0.70
−0.11
0.14
−0.52
0.86
0.14
−0.11
−0.38
0.30
0.31
−0.03
0.73
0.38
0.26
0.80
−0.14
0.63
0.52
0.47
0.17
0.66
0.53
−0.45
−0.02
0.67
0.48
−0.48
0.05

Figure 4.10

Part of the point of factor analysis is to reveal regularities in the data that arise from causally efficacious structures in the individual test takers. We factor analyze scores of the tests of 10 physical abilities in order to find some simpler underlying causal order for human physical abilities. If we find true underlying causes, we should be able to construct more direct ways to measure and interact with these underlying causes. To find these more direct ways to engage real underlying causes, factor analysts must be able to interpret the factors that presumably identify these underlying causes. Factor identification and interpretation are part of the key to finding real underlying causes.

Factors that are found through factor extraction account for variation in the observed variables. They may be averages of underlying causally efficacious factors. So further work must be done to modify—or *rotate*—extracted factors to find potentially meaningful and, ideally, causally efficacious factors. This is called factor rotation because, as noted above, we can think of factors geometrically as axes, just as we can think of the originally measured variables. Geometrically, factor rotation consists of rotating these extracted factor axes to new orientations—and hence new factors. (Figure 12.10 should help explain the general idea here.)

We can rotate the original factors found in the factor analysis of 10 physical abilities to produce factors that are easier to interpret. When we do, the first rotated factor no longer accounts for the largest amount of variation in the observed scores that is possible; the second factor accounts for some of the variation that the first factor had accounted for. The same total amount of variation in the observed scores is accounted for by rotated factors. But the amounts are apportioned differently. We can interpret these four rotated factors by looking at the collection of observed variables with which each is most strongly connected. The first rotated factor, $\mathbf{I}^R$, is most strongly connected with softball throw, hand grip, and chinning—these path values are circled in Table 4.3. We could interpret this factor as a hand- and arm-strength factor. The second factor, $\mathbf{II}^R$, has large loadings on the 100-yard dash, the 1-mile run, and the 5-mile walk/run; it represents running or leg strength. $\mathbf{III}^R$ has large loadings on tracing and tracking; it is a hand/eye coordination factor. $\mathbf{IV}^R$ has only one large loading, on one-leg balance; it represents body balance.

One rotates factors so that each factor has large loadings on a few of the observed variables and small loadings on the rest of the observed variables. Simultaneously, one seeks to minimize the number of factors loading on each observed variable. Suppose, for example, that two factors were extracted from six observed variables. Ideal rotated factors would appear as shown in Figure 4.11. Factor loadings that look like this are said to have *simple structure*. Rotated factors allow us to express the same amount of information as the original extracted factors, but because of their simple structure, they hold more hope of interpretation.

So far in our discussion, factor analyses require that all of the factors extracted from a correlation matrix be mutually uncorrelated. The correlation between any pair of the four factors extracted in the tests of 10 physical abilities above (Figure 4.10) is zero. Relaxing this constraint provides even more latitude for finding an interpretable, simple-structured, factor analysis. In terms of the geometric picture of

TABLE 4.3

	Rotated Factors			
	I^R	II^R	III^R	IV^R
1. Softball throw	(0.86)	0.00	0.34	0.32
2. Hand grip	(0.90)	0.14	−0.05	−0.11
3. Chinning	(0.96)	0.11	−0.07	−0.04
4. 50-yard dash	0.43	0.42	0.43	−0.50
5. 100-yard dash	0.37	(0.76)	0.35	−0.29
6. One-leg balance	0.08	0.23	0.13	(0.80)
7. Tracing	0.01	−0.02	(0.93)	−0.06
8. Tracking	0.03	0.39	(0.81)	0.33
9. 1-mile run	0.02	(0.94)	0.07	0.16
10. 5-mile run/walk	0.07	(0.93)	0.02	0.21

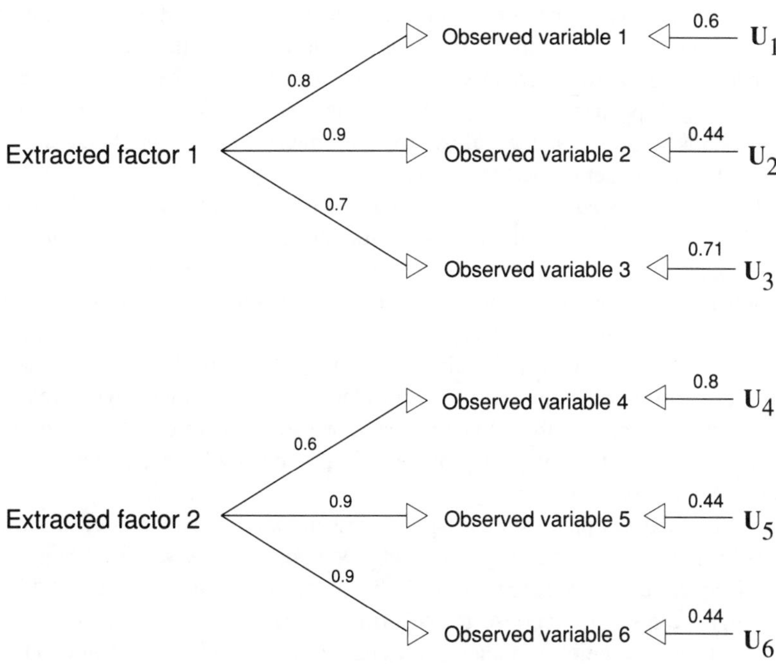

Figure 4.11

factors as axes, factors are uncorrelated when the factor axes meet at right angles. Factors are correlated when factor axes meet at other angles. Consequently, factor analyses where the factors are mutually uncorrelated are called *orthogonal* (right-angled). Rotations that allow factors to be mutually correlated with each other are called *oblique*.

7. BENEFITS OF FACTOR ANALYSIS

One important benefit of factor analysis is its ability to help us begin to make sense of a mess. Much of psychology suffers from an overabundance of variables. Human behavior presents itself to us with great variety. The point of factor analysis is to organize this variety. The drastically smaller number of extracted factor variables provide principles for such organization. The choice of these extracted factors is directed by two primary desiderata. In the first place, factor analysis reduces the data. Factor analysis seeks the smallest number of extracted factors that still allow the representation of as much of the variation in the original variables as possible. In the second place, the extracted factors should reveal something about the underlying sources of variation in the original test measurements.

The factors extracted in a factor analysis can predict values of observed variables. There is no guarantee that the prediction will be right on the money, but in a manner similar to survey sample predictions, a prediction based on such a factor score will be within a margin of error most of the time. Much of the justification for many intelligence tests lies in the fact that they allow researchers to predict reasonably accurately how well people will do in future circumstances that require intellectual skills. A primary reason that Scholastic Aptitude Tests (SATs) are used in college admissions is that they allow for reasonably accurate predictions about a student's future academic performance.

Factor analysis *can* isolate major sources of variation which underlie a system of varying measurements. The factor-analytic model for the source of variation in a batch of measurements must be close to correct for factor analysis to properly identify such hidden sources of variation. Thus, these sources of variation must be related to the measured variables in something close to the manner represented by the path diagram for the analysis. Pairs of variables that the diagram represents as having zero correlation must have zero correlation. Underlying sources of variation must affect observed variables linearly, or nearly so. And so on. When these conditions are met, factor analysis provides an efficient tool for uncovering hidden sources of variation.

Factor analysis has been used to suggest the kind of psychological variables which give rise to the surface behavior that psychologists observe. Such suggestions can usefully direct further research. L. L. Thurstone developed a specialized battery of intelligence tests in response to the primary mental aptitudes identified by his factor analysis (see below). Other researchers have looked for neurological correlates to general intelligence, g. Factor analysis gives order to a mass of confused variables and directs more detailed studies of what may be the causally efficacious variables underlying the mess. These detailed studies may not turn out to bear fruit, but an unsuccessful detailed study can teach us more than vague posturing about the nature of intelligence.

Thus factor analysis provides a means for making sense of many confused interacting variables. It orders the confusion and simplifies the data. Accurate predictions can be made from such simplified data. This is of value in its own right, but the fact that accurate predictions can be made is one (although, by no means infallible) reason to have confidence that little of importance is lost when data are ordered and reduced by factor analysis. Factor analysis can provide insight into the real causes of observed variations.

Factor analysis cannot guarantee to uncover the true causes behind a variety of correlated measurements. A factor analysis with the best imaginable simple structure may be no better than a fancy average. The factors may be interpretable, but the underlying variables they are interpreted to represent may not be real components of the units under study. The confidence one should place in a factor analysis will depend on independent corroboration of the analysis. A neurological correlate to general intelligence would give more reason to believe a theory of a unified one-dimensional concept of human intelligence. Factor analysis can begin an investigation; other methods are necessary to carry it forward.

8. WORRIES ABOUT FACTOR ANALYSIS

Despite these benefits, almost from its inception in 1904, factor analysis has been subject to considerable controversy. The kinds of criticisms that have been brought to bear against factor analysis have concerned a spectrum of problems from those which are entirely specific to factor analysis to those which address very broad issues in scientific methodology. Here I canvas these difficulties in order of increasing generality.

Statistical inference. Only rarely are the correlations used in a factor analysis *population* correlations. They are *sample* correlations. The factor analyses of intelligence test data are drawn from a sample of test takers. Researchers are interested in features of human intelligence in general, not the intellectual idiosyncrasies of those people in the sample of test takers. Thus inferences must be made from these sample correlations to population correlations and thence to a factor analysis appropriate for such population correlations. These inferences are conceptually like the sample survey inferences studied in Chapter 2, but because simultaneous estimates are being drawn about many correlations, these inferences are more complicated. Getting the mathematics and statistics of such inferences straight is a major hurdle.

Factor interpretation. Factor analysis does not create new concepts out of thin air; it creates new concepts out of combinations of old concepts. This introduces two sorts of worries. First, a poor or inadequately varied set of observed variables will limit the variety of interpretations that could be given to extracted factors. Second, the interpretation of the extracted factors can only be as good as the interpretation of the initial observed variables. If a variable, which is understood to test syllogistic reasoning, really tests something else, then any interpretation of a factor that loads highly on this variable will, to some extent, be misrepresented.

Factorial causation. Factor analysis seeks a causal analysis of correlational data. But there are great difficulties inferring causes from correlations—whether with factor analysis or some other method of data analysis. Indeed, there is considerable confusion about just how to define these causal relations.

Two variables may be correlated for many different underlying causal reasons. They may be correlated because both are brought about by a third variable. This is, indeed, a basic motivating principle of factor analysis. But this third variable may be entirely uninteresting or remote. There is a large positive correlation between the number of Churches of England during a given year and the number of divorces in England during the same year. Both, however, are caused by increasing values of a relatively mundane variable, the population of England. Two variables may be correlated because one is the cause of the other. There is a large positive correlation between the weight of a car and the number of gallons of gas it takes to drive from Boston to San Francisco. It takes more energy—supplied by these gallons—to move a heavier car a given distance. Two variables may be positively correlated in one population, but when the population is broken down into parts, these same two variables may be negatively correlated (or have zero correlation) in each part. A new drug may be positively correlated with cure rates among all people, whereas it is negatively correlated with cure rates among both men and women (see Chapter 6, Section 10, and Chapter 8, Section 6).

No logic of discovery. Some critics of factor analysis claim that there can be no privileged rules to scientific discovery. No automatic or quasi-automatic procedures can provide a golden road to scientific knowledge. Insofar as factor analysis appears to be such a procedure, it must be deceiving us. Critics note that the procedures embraced as factor analysis have changed as analysts have gained experience with the procedures. Thus, far from providing some automatic *a priori* sensible route to discovery, factor analysis at best provides one fallible means to explore large data collections.

In reply, some factor analysts point out that factor analyses can produce models that allow accurate predictions of observed (or observable) variables. But, the critics continue, the ability to predict observable variables is not the same thing as explaining them. We may be able to predict the onset of a thunderstorm from the dropping of barometric pressure. But such a change in barometric pressure is a symptom of the storm, not a cause of the storm. Explanation requires us to identify the causes, not the symptoms.

To such criticisms, some factor analysts have replied that it is not the business of science to uncover such "real" "causal" "structures." Those who reply in this manner are skeptical about such concepts. They claim, instead, that science is in the business of producing descriptions of measured (or measurable) data which promote successful predictions of future measurements. By uncovering variables that reduce the variance in observed variables, factor analysis does a good job of promoting economical descriptions and predictions of observable variables.

Here we have a web of deeply philosophical questions about the goals of science and the appropriate procedures for pursuing these goals. What, if anything, is there to an explanation over and above accurate prediction? Can there be a logic of discovery, or are all such methods on an equally poor footing. No method of discovery can provide reason to believe the results of using the method. We focus on some of these questions in Chapter 12.

Confirms prejudices. Related to the criticism that there can be no logic of discovery, but carrying additional social implications, some critics of factor analysis complain that it produces only what the analyst using it wants it to produce. On a cursory inspection factor analysis seems a more-or-less automatic procedure for turning confusing correlational data into an ordered factor structure. Both the extraction of variables in order to account for as much of the variance in the input data as possible, and the rotation of variables in the search for simple structure, can be automated in computer algorithms.

But doing a factor analysis involves making several decisions about transformations on the variables and transformations of factor axes. Factor analysis requires that the relationships between extracted factors and observed variables be linear. There are plenty of close relationships that are not linear. For example, the relationship between elapsed time of a rock's fall from the top of a tower and the distance the rock has traveled is not linear. Such a relationship would not be picked up by a standard factor analysis. To cope with this problem, analysts have developed a variety of transformations that can be applied to variables before they are analyzed. If the right transformation is used, a linear relationship can be created from a nonlinear relationship.

Analysts have also developed a variety of transformation procedures for implementing the search for simple structure. Allowing correlations between extracted factors, or constraining them to be mutually uncorrelated, is one source of this variety. In practice an analyst may try a variety of transformation procedures and pick the one with the most sensible and interpretable results.

The choice of variable transformations and the choice of rotation algorithms allows the factor analyst to exercise considerable judgment in producing a final analysis. Much of the value of a factor analysis depends on the ability of the analyst to pick a useful or interpretable final result from the variety of possibilities. In the case of intelligence measurement this concern that factor analysis only confirms prejudices is especially worrisome.

9. FACTOR ANALYSIS OF HUMAN INTELLIGENCE

There have been many factor analyses of tests of human intelligence. The early work of Charles Spearman (1904 and 1927) analyzed a central basic factor that Spearman called *g*. Spearman's analysis did not recognize the variety of options that are currently available to factor analysts. As researchers gained experience with factor analysis, they discovered that there was no intrinsic reason to trust the particular analysis Spearman produced. The ''rules'' were made more accommodating.

Thurstone (1938), for example, analyzed correlations between 60 different tests of human intelligence. With some amount of trial and error he ultimately produced an oblique rotated solution with seven factors. That is, he extracted seven underlying factors that accounted for most of the variation in the scores from the 60 original tests. He rotated these factors and allowed them to be correlated with each other to find an interpretable solution. He interpreted these factors in terms of the original tests on which they had large loadings. Thurstone's factors show human beings with basic capacities for (1) numerical thinking, (2) word fluency, (3) verbal thinking, (4) memory, (5) reasoning, (6) spatial thinking and (7) perceptual speed. He called these *primary mental abilities,* and he devised tests that could test each ability exclusively.

Thurstone did not find a single underlying intelligence factor; instead, he found his seven primary mental abilities. Hans Eysenck (1939) and more recently, Arthur Jensen (1980) have argued that the predominance of positive correlations between observed test scores is reason to seek a single underlying factor of basic or general intelligence, *g*. For example, Hakstain and Cattell gave a battery of 57 tests to a group of adults and found 19 interpretable factors using an oblique rotation. Jensen analyzed the correlations among these 19 factors and found a second-order *g* factor.

Critics of intelligence tests argue that intelligence researchers bend their factor analyses to conform to prior opinions about the structure of intelligence. Spearman believed all along in general intelligence, or *g*. His factor theory of intelligence (1904) was a product of his initial prejudice and not of an unbiased method of factor extraction which happened to extract a single general factor, *g*. Thurstone believed all along in a multidimensional view of human intelligence. His carefully extracted and rotated factor analysis (1938) again merely conformed to this belief. More recently, Jensen's extracting a second-order general factor (1980) reflects his prior inclination to such a view of the structure of human intelligence. Factor studies, in fact, are merely a more technical rendition of the prejudices of these researchers. The very facts that make up this history tend to confirm the critics' verdict. It seems that different analysts have been able to twist their factor studies of human intelligence in a variety of directions.

Still advocates of the factor analysis of intelligence reply that there is substantial evidence for *g* in the test data; all of the wide variety of batteries of intelligence tests that have been given can be analyzed to show a *g* factor that loads most strongly on the same kinds of skills: inductive reasoning, quickness at filling in incomplete patterns, and so on.

The controversy has significant political and social ramifications. Commonly, it is reported that the heritability of IQ is 70 to 80%. This would seem to imply that one could take a person's IQ and cut it into two unequal parts: 3/4 of it would come from that person's genes, 1/4 from that person's environment. This is not what the claim means. What it means is that 70 to 80% of the variation in IQs can be accounted for by genetic variation. The variation of IQs from people with the same genetic endowment—identical twins—is roughly 1/4 of the variation of IQs in the population at large.

It is easy to reach the conclusion that social programs are not likely to help the disadvantaged members of society given an understandable misinterpretation of the "fact" that the heritability of IQ is 70 to 80%. IQ seems central to socioeconomic advance in contemporary society. There is, in fact, a correlation between IQ and socioeconomic status. But if roughly 3/4 of the variation in IQ can be chalked up to hereditary factors, social programs designed to help those with predominantly low IQ scores would seem to be attempting to rearrange the "natural" state of society.

There are several mistakes behind this line of reasoning. First, there is a technical mistake. The "fact" that IQ has a heritability of 3/4 is no reason that environmental changes—brought about through social policies perhaps—cannot raise the distribution of IQ scores, all the while keeping the variation in scores the same. Consider another example. Different people have different visual acuity; some people have 20–20 vision, others can't read "the big E." This variation is almost entirely the consequence of hereditary factors. Yet suitable environmental changes—eye glasses—can help all but those with the most severe visual impairment.

Beside this technical error, this inference presupposes that social goods should be apportioned according to an essentially IQ-oriented meritocracy. The social goods available in society should be fought for in a fair fight where no members of society are given a privileged status through government programs. Since people with higher IQs will usually (although not always) win such fights, people with higher IQs will accumulate more of the social goods of society. This book is not the place to debate the merits of such a view of social policy. It is important to realize that the merit of arguments concerning the desirability of social programs depends on the social priorities of our society.

All scientific knowledge is provisional and can be abandoned when subsequent studies reveal problems and provide better solutions. Consequently, using the best available scientific knowledge to direct policy is always a risky venture. It is more risky when the scientists doing the work stand to gain or lose from the policies that might be implemented. The unconscious biases of those with vested interests in the outcome of the studies are difficult to detect and correct. This, coupled with the difficulties in properly interpreting the technical results of these studies make IQ studies, particularly vulnerable to abuse when they are applied. All methods of induction can produce mistakes; to pretend otherwise is a dangerous conceit.

In closing, two additional points need to be borne in mind. First, the detailed argument about *g* arose because of factor analysis. In a sense, factor analysis has supplied a series of possible structures that have focused debate both about the structure of the mind and about what we should do about individual and group differences in intelligence—if there are any. Second, it is clear that factor analysis on its own cannot substantiate the structure of human intelligence. More psychological theory and experiment is necessary. At its best factor analysis provides us with a possible way to read order out of a mess. It provides no guarantee that the order read is a real causally efficacious part of the world.

10. SUMMARY

1. Factor analysis provides an initial means for organizing and making sense of many confused measurements.
   - **(a)** Factor analysis constructs "factors" that organize the confused measurements by "accounting" for the variation in these measurements.
   - **(b)** These constructed factors may also identify real features of the units being measured which play a part in producing the measured values of the units.

2. The variation in a collection of measurements is one of the central concepts to data analysis in general and factor analysis in particular.
   - **(a)** Each unit in a particular population can be described in terms of many different properties.
   - **(b)** Some variables have a built-in sense of numerical order.
   - **(c)** The amount a population varies with respect to a variable is called the *variance* of the population with respect to that variable. This can be represented graphically with a histogram.

3. The correlation of two variables is another central concept to data analysis in general and factor analysis in particular.
   - **(a)** Two variables are positively correlated when larger values of one are usually associated with larger values of the other.
   - **(b)** Two variables are negatively correlated when larger values of one are usually associated with smaller values of the other.
   - **(c)** Two variables have zero correlation when there is no tendency for the values of one variable to "follow" values of the other.
   - **(d)** If two variables are correlated, knowing the value of one allows a better prediction of the value of the other.

4. Factor analysis constructs new variables from a collection of correlations between observed variables.
   - **(a)** The underlying motivation to factor analysis can be put simply as follows: Similar effects suggest similar causes, and different effects suggest different causes.

(b) Factor analysis constructs variables that reduce the variation in the original measurements. Fixing the value of the constructed factors to a specific value allows easier prediction of the values of the observed variables.
(c) Factors are constructed, or "extracted," one at a time. The first factor reduces the variation in the observed variables to the greatest extent that a single variable can. The second factor reduces the remaining variation—after fixing the value of the first factor—to the greatest extent that it can. This process continues until any remaining variation can be accounted for by errors of measurement.
(d) The relations between extracted factors and observed variables can be represented in a path diagram, where arrows connect variables that are causally connected.
(e) The strength of the relation between an extracted factor and an observed variable is expressed as a path value or factor loading.
(f) One can use values of extracted factors to predict values for observed variables by using the linear equations which specify the relationship between these variables.

5. To uncover factors that are more likely to represent causally efficacious properties of the units involved, factor solutions are rotated.
   (a) The factors constructed in order of their ability to account for variation in the observed variable scores may be only averages of real underlying variables. The real variables may not account for observed variation sequentially in this way.
   (b) Factors can be thought of as axes—dimensions—which organize a "space" of variation in observed variable scores. Rotating factors is like rotating axes: the space remains the same, but the axes that organize it are moved.
   (c) Rotated factors account for the same total amount of variation as do unrotated factors.
   (d) Rotated factors should be interpretable. Factors are interpreted in terms of the observed variables factors have large loadings on.
   (e) Factors with simple structure are sought through rotation: Each rotated factor should have large loadings on some variables and small loadings on the rest; each variable should be accounted for by as few factors as possible.
   (f) Sometimes more interpretable factors can be found by allowing factors to be correlated with each other.

6. There are a variety of worries about factor analysis.
   (a) Usually, the correlations used to start an analysis are sample correlations, not correlations from the entire population.
   (b) Factors are interpreted from the interpretations attached to the original observed variables. Consequently, any inadequate interpretation of these variables will distort the factor interpretation. Also, a narrow unrepresentative sample of observed variables may fail to include variables that would substantially effect the interpretation of extracted factors.
   (c) In the best cases, factor analysis should identify causally efficacious underlying variables. Thus, factor analysis aims to pick causal variables from correlations. Unfortunately, several problems confront such a project: no unique set of causal relations can be inferred from observed correlations.
   (d) Some have criticized factor analysis for attempting the impossible, to be a mechanical logic of discovery.

  (e) Since the factor analyst must make a variety of decisions regarding variable transformations and factor rotations, it is possible that the preconceived ideas of the analyst will prejudice these decisions.

7. Still, factor analysis offers several benefits.
   (a) Factor analysis provides an initial means to organize a large number of variables related in confusing diversity.
   (b) Values of extracted factors can be used to predict values of observed variables.
   (c) When the factor analytic assumptions are close to correct, factor analysis can uncover real causally efficacious sources of variation in observed variables.
   (d) Factor studies can make useful suggestions for future, more detailed, research.

8. The results of IQ studies provide no clear implications about which social policies should be preferred.
   (a) A variety of studies have shown that IQ is roughly 3/4 heritable. Even if the studies are assumed to be of uniformly high quality, there are difficulties drawing social policy recommendations from them.
   (b) The "fact" that the heritability of IQ is 3/4, does not imply that social intervention cannot raise IQs.
   (c) In addition to "facts" about IQ and its heritability, social policy depends on the desired social agenda.

11. REFERENCES

(Bolton, 1900) and (Roller, 1957) contain histories of the development of the thermometer. Many introductory psychology texts, such as (Lefton, 1985), have useful information about psychological intelligence testing. (Kim and Mueller, 1978a) is a nice concise introduction to factor analysis. (Cattell, 1952) and (Cattell, 1978) are introductions with considerably more depth. The factor analysis of 10 physical abilities in Sections 4 and 5 is adapted with permission of The Free Press, a Division of Macmillan, Inc. and Methuen and Co., from *Bias in Mental Testing* by Arthur R. Jensen, copyright © 1980 by Arthur R. Jensen (Jensen, 1980: Table 6.5, p. 206; Table 6.6, p. 207; Table 6.8, p. 213).

The first factor analysis of intelligence test scores is in (Spearman, 1904); (Spearman, 1927) extends and improves this analysis. (Thurstone, 1938) presents the seven-factor analysis of primary mental abilities. (Eysenck, 1939) argues that a factor of general intelligence still underlies Thurstone's primary mental abilities. (Thurstone, 1947) presents an expanded version of his work, along with a detailed introduction to oblique factor rotations. (Jensen, 1980) provides an introduction to factor analysis and its history in intelligence test analysis, with the primary aim of arguing for a basic underlying factor of intelligence, *g*.

(Gould, 1981) is a history of intelligence measurement, including a powerful critique of any factor-analytic argument for a unitary underlying factor of intelligence, such as *g*. (Block and Dworkin, 1976) is a useful collection of readings about the social and ethical implications of IQ measurement. (Eysenck and Kamin, 1981) is an interesting debate on the subject.

12. PROBLEMS

1. Explain why factor analysis might be considered a method of induction. How is factor analysis, as a method of induction, different from survey sampling? How is factor analysis different from decision theory?
2. Would the population of secretaries or the population of business executives vary more with respect to income?
3. Some frequency data are listed in Table 4.4.
   (a) Sketch two histograms to describe these data.
   (b) Describe what the numbers graphed represent—that is, 0.15 is a proportion of some population of Japanese men (aged 30 to 34) among some other population; the sizes of what two populations are divided to determine this proportion?
   (c) Which histogram shows more variation?
4. For each of the following pairs of variables, would you expect a substantial negative correlation, a substantial positive correlation, or a near-zero correlation?
   (a) The age of a coin (i.e., how many years it has been since the coin was minted) and the amount it is worth today (to a coin collector).
   (b) The year a coin was minted and the amount it is worth today.
   (c) The population of Mexico during a given year and George Bush's age during that year.
   (d) The number of leaves on an oak tree on a day and the day of the year (e.g., January 1, 1982 is the first day of the year; December 31, 1982 is the 365th day of the year).
   (e) The number of babies born in a given year and the total number of dollars in circulation 20 years later.
5. Find 50 leaves. Measure each leaf's length and width (at the longest and widest points on the leaf). Plot these measurements in a scatter diagram. Does the result show a positive correlation between leaf length and width?
6. Briefly explain what is meant by the sentence "Factor 1 accounts for more of the variance in the observed variables than any other factor."

TABLE 4.4 Marriage Rates in the Year 1950 (per Marriageable Man or Woman)

Age Group	Japanese Men	Japanese Women
15–19	—	0.01
20–24	0.04	0.09
25–29	0.14	0.09
30–34	0.15	0.04
35–39	0.10	0.01
40–44	0.06	0.01
45–49	0.03	—
50–54	0.02	—
55–59	0.01	—
60–	—	—

TABLE 4.5

Original Variable	Factor 1	Factor 2
Vocabulary	0.40	0.69
Sentence comprehension	0.40	0.69
Math word problems	0.65	0.72
Graphing equations	0.69	0.40
Arithmetic	0.61	0.35

TABLE 4.6

	Not Rotated		Rotated	
Original Variable	Factor 1	Factor 2	Factor 1	Factor 2
Digit recall	0.74	−0.30	0.79	0.17
Spelling	0.70	−0.26	0.73	0.17
Vocabulary	0.60	−0.18	0.60	0.19
Aesthetic judgment	0.43	0.36	0.15	0.54
Ideational fluency	0.50	0.60	0.08	0.78
Associative memory	0.54	0.25	0.31	0.50

7. Suppose that two factors can be extracted from correlations between five variables. The resulting factor loadings are given in Table 4.5.

(a) Construct a path diagram for this analysis.

(b) Which factor accounts for more of the variance in arithmetic problems? in graphing equations? in word problems? in sentence comprehension? in vocabulary?

8. Suppose that two factors can be extracted from correlations between six variables. The resulting factor loadings are given in Table 4.6 for an unrotated solution and a rotated solution.

(a) Which of these two factor analyses best approximates simple structure?

(b) Do either of these analyses suggest an interpretation? If so, what is it?

(c) What is it reasonable to infer about an interpretation based on this factor analysis?

9. What is the difference between an oblique rotation and an orthogonal rotation?

10. What is the problem of factor realism all about? Must factors be "real" to be useful? Discuss.

11. Can factor analysis alone prove that human beings possess a unitary property of intelligence? Why or why not?

12. Present and discuss one reason why we should be cautious when using the results of factor analysis to argue for or against implementing certain social policies.

CHAPTER

5

EXPERIMENTAL DESIGN

1. INDUCTIVE METHODS

Survey samples done with random samples allow us to estimate various features about a large population by inspecting a small number of units from the population. Decision analysis provides a framework for organizing various features that frequently play—or ought to play—a role in helping us reach decisions about what course of action to adopt. Factor analysis provides a means to examine large collections of data for regularities that are not evident on the surface and which may underlie concepts central to the domain from which the data are taken.

Each of these methods provides a certain guarantee. Survey sampling promises estimates that have a high probability of being close to the truth. Decision analysis recommends actions that have the highest expected utility. Factor analysis reorganizes data in such a way that the smallest number of variables account for the largest amount of variation.

These guarantees rest on certain assumptions, different in the three cases. Here is an analogy with deductive arguments. Valid deductive arguments only guarantee that the conclusion will be true *if* the premises are true; there is no guarantee that the premises are true. Similarly, survey samples only guarantee a high probability of being close to the truth if the sample was taken in a properly random way. The recommendations of decision theory are only as good as the utilities and degrees of belief on which they are based. But *if* a decision maker has these utilities and degrees of belief, *then* decision theory has some recommendations. *If* "linear common factor structure" contains the key to sensibly organizing many confused measurements, then factor analysis is a good tool for finding such organizing features.

Each of these methods *can* lead us astray. Survey samples only guarantee a high probability of a result near the truth; they do not guarantee the truth of the result. Decision analysis recommends courses of action with the highest expected utility, but such courses of action may not result in the outcome with the highest utility. The factors extracted in a factor analysis may not turn out to describe enduring and central features of the domain under investigation.

Despite their substantial differences, these inductive methods share two important properties. Each has its guarantee, and each is fallible. The guarantee calls attention to results obtained by the method. Thus survey sample results are better than sheer guessing because survey sampling can make certain guarantees that guessing cannot. Even so, survey sample results can be as far from the mark as the results of sheer guessing.

In this Chapter we examine one more inductive method, or better, related collection of methods: experimental design. Experimental design shares with the other methods we have studied two features: The results of well-designed experiments are better than sheer guessing—they come with their own kind of guarantee—but like these other methods, the results of well-designed experiments are still fallible. The results of well-designed experiments are said to be "significant" at a given numerical "level of significance" determined by the outcome of the experiment. One aim of this chapter and of Chapter 13 is to see just what this "level of significance" guarantee comes to.

2. POLIO VACCINE AND THE NEED FOR DESIGN

We can begin our discussion of experimental design by considering an example. Here is a brief history of large-scale experimental testing of the Salk polio vaccine. Polio has never been a major killer. Polio was, however, a scary disease. It struck in unpredictable epidemic waves. Children were the most frequent victims. And it seemed to be worse in areas of better hygiene. During polio epidemics entire public facilities might be closed down for fear of contagion.

By the early 1950s a vaccine had been developed that appeared effective for substantially reducing risk of contracting polio *in laboratory tests*. During the 1930s, however, another polio vaccine had been developed and used to some extent. Unfortunately, although this vaccine did reduce the risk of polio in some cases, it actually brought on the disease in a large number of other cases. The 1930s vaccine had to be withdrawn from use. For such reasons, convincing positive results from a field experiment were needed to justify recommending widespread vaccination with the new 1950s vaccine.

How should the effectiveness of this new vaccine be tested and evaluated? The simplest approach would be to administer the new vaccine to a large group of children and watch for a decline in the rate of polio in that group. Unfortunately, this method will not do. Since polio strikes in epidemics, there are wide swings in the incidence of polio from year to year. For example, in 1931 there were approximately 18,000 cases of polio, while in 1932 there were about 5,000 cases. The number of cases differed by a factor of 3 for no known reason. An observed decline in the rate of polio incidence could as easily be attributed to such a spontaneous decline; the vaccine might have nothing to do with the drop.

The next most obvious design would be to administer the vaccine to a specific group of children and *compare* the polio rate in this group with the rate of polio in another group that did not get the vaccine. A particular version of this kind of approach was used to substantiate the efficacy of the 1950s vaccine. A group of first- through third-graders were the subjects of the experiment. Some of the second-graders who were participating in the study were administered the vaccine. Polio rates among these second-graders were then compared with the polio rates for some of the first- and third-graders participating in the study.

Here is one element of experimental design. Instead of simply administering the drug and watching for an effect, we *compare effects* between two groups: One group, called the "experimental" group, gets the vaccine and another group, called the "control" group, does not get the vaccine. We compare the percentage of children contracting polio in the vaccinated—or experimental—group with the percentage of children contracting polio in the nonvaccinated—or control—group. Since being vaccinated is the major difference between members of the two groups, a smaller percentage in the experimental group would normally be attributed to being vaccinated.

This simple *comparative design* is necessary because of two features of polio:

1. The incidence of polio varies under normal conditions. Thus, a reduction in the incidence of polio could be due to "normal fluctuations" and not the vaccine.
2. We do not expect the vaccine to be 100% effective. Even with the best of conditions for administering the drug, some unlucky souls will still come down with polio.

Such a comparative design helps us to differentiate between a "normal fluctuation" and a reduction in the polio rate due to the vaccine. If the control group—those *not* administered the vaccine—has a higher incidence of polio than the experimental group—those administered the vaccine—we have some evidence that the vaccine is doing its job. Also, by comparing the amount of difference, we can get an idea of the amount of help the vaccine provides.

This kind of design also presents certain difficulties. A lower polio rate among second-graders, compared with the rate for first- and third-graders, might be due to something special about the second-graders. Many possibilities suggest themselves. A person at a second-grader's state of physical development might be less susceptible to polio. First- and third-grade classes might happen to go to places where polio is more easily contracted. A ''mini'' or ''local'' polio epidemic might run through the first- or third-grade classes because one or two children who were already infected happened to be first- or third-graders, and these ''seeds'' came into closer contact with the other first- and third-graders. An observed smaller polio rate among the second-graders might be due to something special about the second-grade classes other than the effects of the vaccine.

By introducing randomization into the design we can begin to surmount this difficulty. Here the deciding factor of whether or not a child is in the experimental group—and receives the vaccine—or the control group—and does not receive the vaccine—is determined randomly. This can be accomplished in several ways. For example, as children present themselves one by one to be vaccinated, a digit could be read off from a string of digits taken from a random number table. If a child's digit turns out to be an odd number, that child gets the vaccine, if an even number, no vaccine is given. As it happens, roughly half of the subjects in the polio study—those not treated in the second- versus first- and third-grader way—were sorted into experimental and control groups by a random process of this sort.

In this way, problems such as the special effects of being in the second grade would be avoided. It would be entirely unusual for only those children in the second grade to get vaccinated. Thus all of the possible reasons that might be offered to account for differences between the experimental group and the control group, other than being vaccinated, would not be available.

There is another difficulty. Doctors tend to diagnose the symptoms of children who have received a new and experimental treatment differently from the symptoms of children who have not received a new treatment. Similarly, patients who know they are receiving a new treatment may respond to their own physical feelings differently. One patient might ''shrug off'' a mild case of polio as a severe case of influenza. A lower polio rate in the experimental group compared to the control group might be blamed on faulty or biased diagnoses on the part of doctors and patients.

To avoid this problem, knowledge of who is in which group can be kept secret from both the participants of the experiment and the doctors performing the diagnoses. Children who do not get the vaccine are given a treatment that appears the same as the vaccination, but which contains no active chemicals. In this way, no one beyond the statisticians designing the experiment know who got the vaccine and who did not. Such experiments are called *double blind* because subjects (children) and experimenters (doctors) cannot ''see'' who is in the experimental and who is in the control groups.

This double-blind randomized design was the one used for about half the subjects of the polio vaccine study. Parents in some of the communities participating in the experiment objected to not knowing what drugs had been administered to what children. In these communities the second-grader versus first- and third-grader design was used instead.

The results of the double-blind part of the polio vaccine studies are outlined in Table 5.1. The results are nice. Those vaccinated still have a chance of contracting the disease. But their chances are considerably better than the chances for those who were not vaccinated. Overall, the rate of polio for all degrees of severity is 28 per 100,000 for those vaccinated and 71 per 100,000 for those not vaccinated. According to the study, the vaccine cuts the overall polio rate by more than half. Also, the improvement is greatest for the more severe forms of polio.

TABLE 5.1

	Type of Polio							
	Fatal		Paralytic		Nonparalytic		Total	
	Number	*Rate*	*Number*	*Rate*	*Number*	*Rate*	*Number*	*Rate*
Vaccinated of 200,745	0	0	33	16	24	12	57	28
Nonvaccinated of 201,229	4	2	115	57	27	13	146	71

Note: Rates are the number of cases per 100,000 subjects.

3. INDEPENDENT AND DEPENDENT VARIABLES

The basic idea of experiments is to see if doing something to a unit (giving a child polio vaccine) has an effect (reduces the child's chance for contracting polio). To see if what we do has an effect, we divide the general population into two groups—the "experimental" group of units, which we alter in some way (by vaccination), and the "control" group, which we leave alone. We then compare the two groups to see if the alterations that we introduced brought about a difference (Figure 5.1).

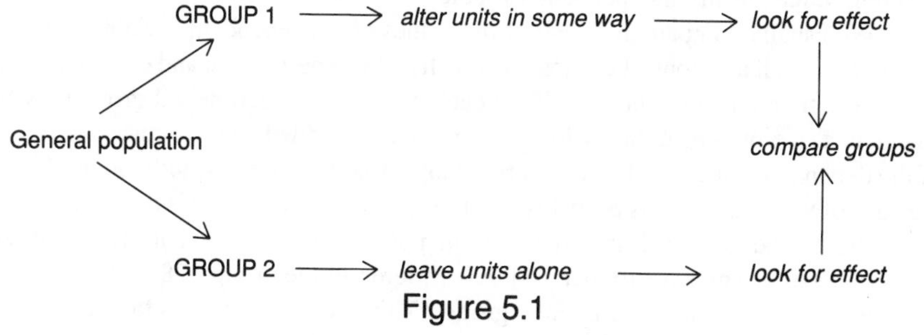

Figure 5.1

Some experiments require more complicated designs, but we can learn much about experimental design from this simple design.

Much of the special technical vocabulary that we have run across earlier in the book can be used here. The *population* is composed of *units*. The population in the polio study was composed of individual children. Many different properties, or variables, can be used to describe individual units. We can describe children in terms of their hair color, their gender, their height, their weight, whether or not they were vaccinated, whether or not they contracted polio, and so on. Each unit in the population has a *value* for each variable. Some children in the polio study had blond hair, some weighed 70 pounds, some received vaccine, some got polio.

In experiments we draw a distinction between two kinds of variables. *Independent variables* are those we manipulate. *Dependent variables* are those we hope to influence through our manipulation of the independent variables. We hypothesize that the value of a unit's dependent variable *depends on* the value of its independent variable. We run the experiment to test this hypothesis. We do this by causing certain units to have certain values for the independent variable and then watching for changes in the values of the unit's dependent variable. If there are changes in the values of the dependent variables, we have reason to think that the values of the dependent variables do depend on the values of the independent variables.

For example, whether or not a child received vaccine in the polio study was controlled by the experimenters. This is an independent variable. On the other hand, whether or not the child contracted polio was not directly controlled by the experimenter. This is a dependent variable. The experiment was run to determine whether or not contracting polio depends, at least in part, on being vaccinated or not. As things turned out, the experiment showed that whether or not one contracts polio *does depend* on whether or not one receives polio vaccine. This experiment confirmed the dependency between contracting polio and receiving vaccine.

We manipulate units in the experimental and control groups. We attempt to ensure that each unit in the experimental group has the same value of the independent variable, a value that differs from the value each unit in the control group has. We also attempt to ensure that the two groups are otherwise similar. If differences in values of the dependent variable arise between the experimental and control groups, we would be inclined to attribute it to the only other preceding difference—the different values of the independent variable.

We usually compare *averages* of the values of the dependent variable found in the experimental and control groups. Typically, the experimental and control groups have more than one unit apiece. While each unit in the experimental group may be vaccinated, it would be unlikely for each unit to respond with exactly the same value of the dependent variable. Furthermore, many variables are not strictly on or off. In the case of vaccination, it is probably fair to say that someone is or is not vaccinated. But polio can be more or less severe. In the polio study we note that there were 28 cases of polio of any severity per 100,000 children in the group. 28/100,000 is the average polio rate in the experimental group. This average compares favorably with 71 cases per 100,000 in the control group.

In short, we run experiments to see if the dependent variable depends on the independent variable. At its most basic level, the idea that justifies the conclusions we draw from experiments is this: Suppose that the only difference between units in the experimental group and units in the control group are the values of the independent variable. Suppose that units in the two groups have different values of the dependent variable. The only way to account for this difference would be in terms of the difference in values of the independent variable. The dependent variable must depend on the independent variable (Figure 5.2).

4. CONFOUNDED VARIABLES

Unfortunately, many experimental studies are difficult to interpret because of problems caused by *confounded variables*. For example, half of the population in the polio study was apportioned into control and experimental groups by grade level; second-graders were vaccinated, while first- and third-graders were not. When apportioning is done in this way, grade level becomes one way to distinguish membership in the control and experimental groups. Units in the experimental group are all in the second grade, while units in the control group are not in the second grade. The variable of grade level is *confounded* with the variable of being vaccinated or not.

When a variable is confounded with the independent variable, it is impossible to interpret the results of the experiment adequately. Subsequent differences between values of the dependent variable may be due either to the different values of the independent variable—being vaccinated or not—or to different values of the confounded variable—grade level. Much experimental design is devoted to avoiding confounded variables.

One can attempt to systematically divide units into experimental and control groups in such a way to avoid confounded variables. For example, researchers could balance the grade levels in the experimental and control groups. They could make

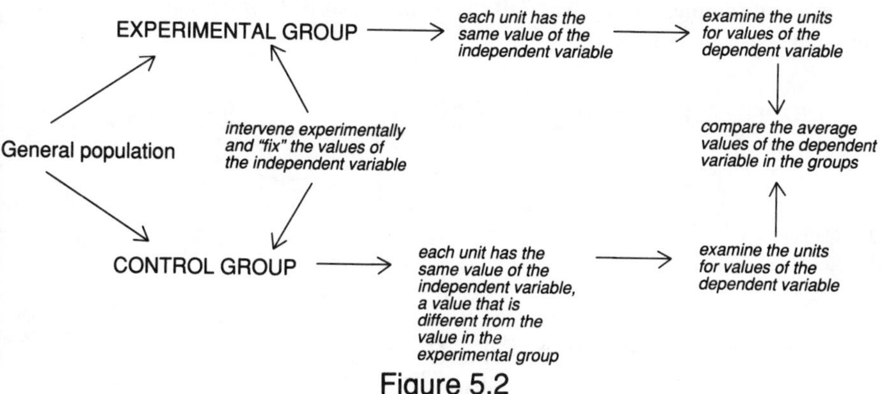

Figure 5.2

sure that half of each grade level was assigned to the experimental group and half to the control group.

Unfortunately, it is virtually impossible to ensure that systematically assigning units to groups in this way avoids confounded variables. Here is an example. An experiment was done in the 1930s to test the impact of feeding milk to public school children. Children in the experimental group were fed 3/4 pint of milk each school day for 4 months; children in the control group were not fed any milk. Each child's height and weight was measured before and after the study, and the average gain in the experimental group was compared with the average gain in the control group (Figure 5.3). Children were assigned to the experimental and control groups in two stages. Initially they were assigned randomly, then teachers shuffled the assignments to balance the number of well- and ill-fed children in the two groups. A careful analysis of the data revealed an unconscious bias on the part of the teachers to put more ill-nourished children in the experimental group, presumably so that each could get a little extra nourishment. Thus, despite a systematic effort to avoid this problem, the variable of being well- or ill-nourished thus was confounded with the independent variable—being fed milk or not.

Systematically assigning units to experimental and control groups always poses this danger. Some variable may be confounded with the independent variable because of unconscious bias on the part of the people doing the assigning. Consequently, assigning units by random selection is a common alternative. It is important to understand that random assignment is accomplished by using an objectively random method. Simply attempting to make the assignment haphazard will not do, for unconscious biases can influence what a person judges to be haphazard. A random number table of the sort discussed in Chapter 2, or a similarly objective randomizing device, is the source of a proper random assignment.

Using randomization to avoid problems with confounding variables is analogous to using randomization in sampling studies to avoid problems with bias. In sampling studies we choose our sample from the population in such a way that each unit in the population has the same chance of being included; our method of selection does not favor certain segments of the population. Over the long run, if we were to select many samples in this way, all the members of the population would be represented. So bias is avoided.

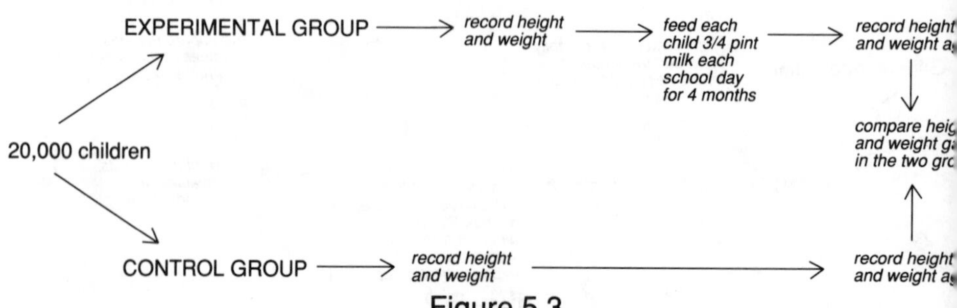

Figure 5.3

When we randomly assign subjects to different treatments our method of assignment does not systematically coordinate members of the experimental group with some other potentially important variable. Our selection *may*, ''by the luck of the draw,'' coordinate the experimental group with some important confounding variable in just the same way that we *may* choose a sample that grossly under- or overrepresents part of the population. But the chances of this happening are small. What is perhaps more important is that these chances can be calculated, but more on this in Section 5.

To see how this works, consider an absurdly small population of four people, Harry, Larry, Mary, and Terry. We are to use these four people to test the efficacy of a new sun block. For the sake of illustration, suppose—which is probably not true—that gender happens to be an important confounding variable. Women—Mary and Terry in this case—happen to burn more easily than men. If our experimental group consisted only of men, the new sun block would appear effective simply because it was harder for the men to get sunburned—new sun block or not. Having only men in the experimental group would make it difficult to interpret the results of the experiment because the variable of gender would be confounded with the variable of using the new sun block. Suppose that these four people are assigned to an experimental and a control group by a method of random assignment. There are six different ways that things could turn out:

1. *Experimental:* Harry, Larry *Control:* Mary, Terry
2. *Experimental:* Harry, Mary *Control:* Larry, Terry
3. *Experimental:* Harry, Terry *Control:* Larry, Mary
4. *Experimental:* Larry, Mary *Control:* Harry, Terry
5. *Experimental:* Larry, Terry *Control:* Harry, Mary
6. *Experimental:* Mary, Terry *Control:* Harry, Larry

Of these six different possible assignments, four have a balanced distribution of men and women in the control and experimental groups. Gender is confounded with the independent variable in only two assignments. Thus, by assigning subjects to the experimental and control groups randomly, the chance of confounding gender with the independent variable is only 1/3. If we had a much larger population, the chance of gender being confounded with the independent variable would be much smaller. This is for the same reason that increasing sample size increases the precision of a method of sampling.

It makes sense to wonder why we would not simply divide the population, making sure that the same number of men as women were in the experimental and control groups. If we knew in advance that gender had an effect on the dependent variable, it would make sense to do this. Usually, however, we do not know what other variables have an effect on the dependent variable. In the case of sunburn, the fairness of the skin is more likely to be a variable that has an effect on the dependent variable. But there may be other variables that we simply do not know about which are relevant. Since we do not know what these variables are, assigning subjects randomly to control and experimental groups is sensible. Doing so gives us some confidence that there is only a small chance that the independent variable will be confounded with some other variable that has an effect on the dependent variable.

Another way to make this point is this. Given enough resources, we could determine how susceptible to sunburn each person in the population is. We could then determine the ''average susceptibility'' to sunburn. Half the population would burn more easily than average and half would burn less easily than average. By assigning subjects to the experimental and control groups using a random process, we can be fairly sure that neither the control nor the experimental group will get a preponderance of easy- or hard-burners. Thus, no variable with a substantial effect on the dependent variable would be confounded with the independent variable.

5. HOW MUCH DIFFERENCE IS ENOUGH?

In the polio sutdy, 142 of the 201,229 children in the control group came down with polio; 57 of the 200,745 vaccinated children came down with polio. Apparently, the chances of getting polio are less for those that are vaccinated. But with chances of this sort it is possible for outcomes to differ even when the underlying mechanism is the same. With a *fair* coin we can easily imagine getting anywhere from 43 heads to 57 heads in 100 flips. How, then, can we be confident that the difference between 142 cases of polio *without* the vaccine and 57 cases *with* the vaccine represents an underlying difference in polio susceptibility? Why not conclude that the difference was like the difference between getting 43 heads or 57 heads in 100 flips of the same fair coin?

Consider the following contrasting experiment. If the pressure on a gas is kept constant, when the gas is cooled, its volume decreases. To show this we could do the following experiment. Take a large population of balloons, inflate them, and separate them into an experimental group and a control group. Measure the volume of each balloon and compute the average volume of the balloons in the two groups. Put each ''experimental balloon'' in a freezer for an hour. After the hour, measure the volume of all the balloons, and compare the average volume change in the experimental and control groups. We would find that the volume of each ballon in the experimental group decreased, while the volume of each ballon in the control group stayed about the same (assuming that the room's temperature stayed the same and the balloons were well tied). The difference is marked and universal. The shrinking of a balloon when it is put in a freezer can be relied on.

This is not so in the polio vaccine case. It is true that the overall average polio rate was less among those children who were vaccinated than among those who were not vaccinated. Still some vaccinated children got polio and many unvaccinated children did not get polio. For many reasons, most of which are unknown, people respond quite differently to disease threats.

To demonstrate the efficacy of polio vaccine we need to test it on a large number of children. There are two reasons for this, both a consequence of the varying responses of humans. In the first place, very few people get polio anyway. Thus enough subjects are needed to ensure that some *would* have come down with polio had they not been given the vaccine. To test the efficacy of the vaccine, there has to be a real threat of disease.

In the second place, we only get a "percentage advantage" from the vaccine. Thus we need enough test children so that we can be sure that a difference in the average polio rates is not simply a "chance fluctuation." The fact that human beings vary in their responses to vaccine and disease means that some of the differences we might find between experimental and control groups could be the result of normal variation and not the influence of the vaccine.

To appreciate this second point, consider a coin example. Suppose that we took a fair coin and flipped it 100 times, each time saying, "May the force be with you." Suppose that we then flipped it another 100 times, each time saying nothing. Almost certainly the number of heads in the two collections of 100 flips would differ. The coin might come up heads 54 times when "the force was with it," while coming up heads 48 times with "no force." (Those who are skeptical can try it; while your numbers may differ, it is very likely that there will be a different percentage of heads "with the force" than "without the force.") We should not conclude from this "experiment" that saying "May the force be with you" increases the chances of heads. We would expect at the outset that the number of heads which turn up should be somewhat different in the two sets of flips. This difference is a "chance fluctuation."

If, on the other hand, the coin came up heads 54,000 times out of 100,000 flips when "the force was with it," and 48,000 times out of 100,000 flips when "the force was not with it," we might conclude that there was something to the force. The difference between 54,000 and 48,000 heads out of 100,000 flips is much more "significant" than the difference between 54 and 48 heads out of 100 flips. While the percentages are the same—54/100 = 54,000/100,000 = 54%, and 48/100 = 48,000/100,000 = 48%—the absolute difference between 54,000 and 48,000 is vastly larger than between 54 and 48. As in Chapter 2 (Section 5), it is the absolute difference that matters.

To interpret the results of experimental studies properly we need to know how much difference between the experimental and control groups is enough to rule out the possibility of it arising by chance. There can be no universal answer to this question because the "operation" of chance to produce "chance fluctuations" differs from one context to another. In the case of coins we model chance in terms of binomial probabilities (see Chapter 9). Usually, we model chance variation in crop yields of agricultural experiments with a "normal" bell-shaped probability curve (see Chapter 13). The technical details of either model for chance need not detain us here. The point is that different contexts require different models for chance. Consequently, there is no single answer to how much difference is big enough to rule out chance.

While the particular appropriate chance model differs in different cases, the method of inference used has the same structure. In the briefest outline it is this:

1. We establish a probabilistic model to describe the operation of chance for the given context.
2. We rank the possible experimental outcomes in terms of how well they fit this chance model. For instance, 12 heads in 100 flips fits the chance model that a coin is fair much worse than 48 heads in 100 flips.
3. We compute the probability of a result that fits as badly or more badly than the one found in the experiment in question. This computation is done on the basis of probabilities introduced by the chance model; making this calculation we imagine that the chance model is correct. The lower this probability, the worse the chance model fits.
4. If this probability is low enough, given the context in which the experiment was done, we discard the chance model. We infer that the results could not be accounted for by chance alone, and we look for other accounts for the results.

In a sense, which has to be examined further, the underlying motivation for this kind of inference is this. When the probability of the result that the experiment produced—or a worse result—is very low, we are confronted with a dilemma: Either the chance model is wrong, or a very improbable event has occurred. Depending on the context, it can make sense to opt for the first horn of this dilemma.

This kind of inference is known as a *significance test*, perhaps because we use these tests to determine if the data represent a "significant difference" between experimental and control groups. The probability used to measure the fit between the chance model and the data is called the *level of significance* of the data. If the level of significance is low enough, say it is 0.001, we "reject the chance model at the 0.001 level of significance." Exactly how low is low enough depends on several factors which we examine further in Chapter 13.

Significance tests are another kind of inductive inference. No matter how poorly the data fit the chance model, chance could be the proper account for the data. A fair coin *can* come up heads 12 times in 100 flips. But when the fit judged by a significance test is very bad, it makes more sense to pursue alternative accounts for the data. The guarantee offered by a significance test in place of deductive validity is that the data "allow rejection at a particular, probabilistically measured, level of significance." Just what this guarantee comes to has been the subject of considerable controversy. Chapter 13 focuses on significance tests and their guarantee. For now, we can appreciate significance tests with several examples and the understanding that levels of significance measure the fit of the chance model.

Coins provide the simplest examples. A fair coin "should" come up heads about half the time. The farther the ratio of heads to the number of flips is from 1/2, the worse the fit between the data—which underlies this ratio—and fairness. Here is the ranking of possible outcomes in terms of their fit with chance. We can calculate level of significance probabilities on the basis of the binomial chance model. For instance, were we to test the hypothesis that a coin was fair, and were we to actually get 12 heads in 100 flips, the level of significance would be very low, roughly 0.000000000000000956. We would almost surely discard the hypothesis that the coin was fair, but just happened—by chance—to come up heads 12 times in 100 flips. The rules for computing these probabilities are presented in Chapter 9; we need not worry about them here.

Consider another example more in keeping with the experimental focus of the chapter. One goal of agricultural experimentation is to find soil treatments that increase the yield of a given crop. A researcher might devise a new treatment and test it with the simple experimental design shown in Figure 5.4. Ten plots of land with equal areas are randomly divided into an experimental and a control group of five plots each. Experimental plots get the new soil treatment; control plots get no special treatment. The crop is planted on all the plots and after harvest the yields for the 10 plots are compared to see if the new treatment improved crop yield.

Clearly, to conclude that the new treatment is doing something, the average yield in the experimental plots must differ from the average yield in the control plots. But we need to use a significance test to be confident that the difference we find is not simply due to chance. Usually, we would use normal bell-shaped probabilities to model chance (see Chapter 13, Section 3). Here we compare averages, but we also attend to the amount the crop yield varies whether or not a new treatment is used. Consider two different ways that this experiment might turn out. The *average* yield in the experimental groups is the same in either case, as is the average yield in the control groups. But in one case there is very little variation plot to plot, whereas in the other there is quite a lot of variation plot to plot (Figure 5.5). Outcome **B** provides more compelling evidence than outcome **A** that the soil treatment improves yield. This is because with outcome **A** there is a greater chance that the difference in averages between the experimental and control groups could be a natural fluctuation that has no relationship to the new soil treatment. The reason this is more likely with outcome **A** is because there is greater variation overall.

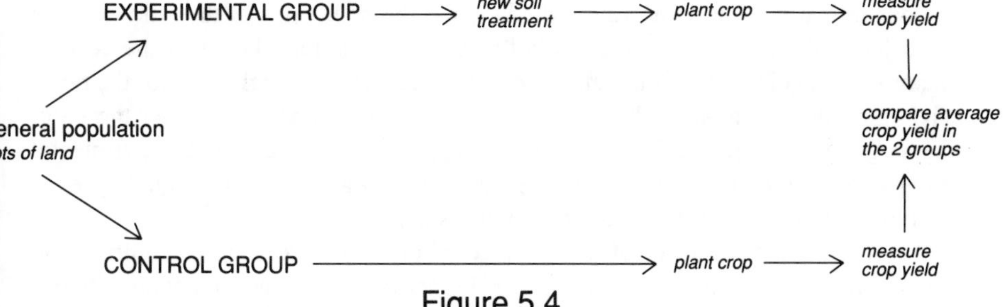

Figure 5.4

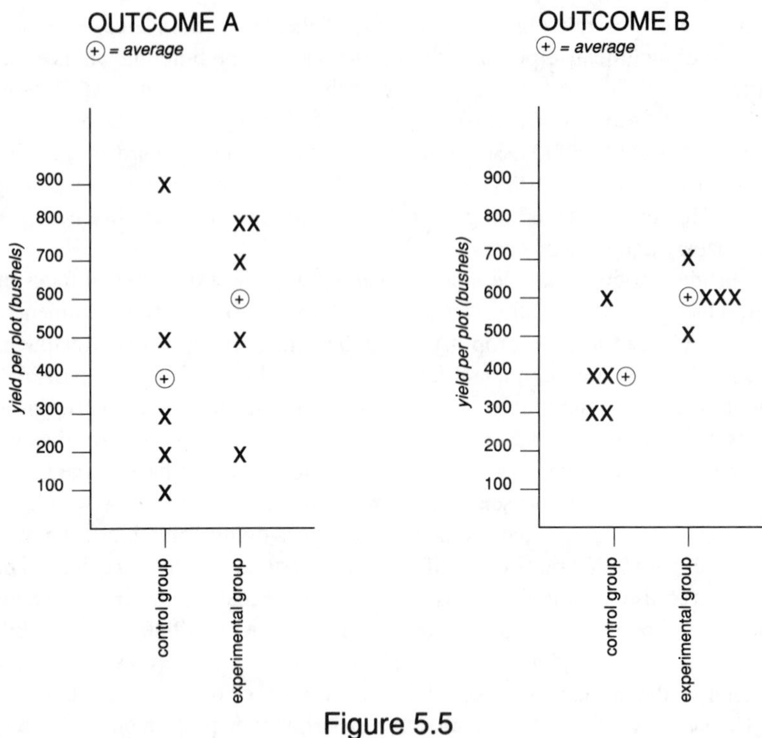

Figure 5.5

To rank the outcomes from this experiment we would compute a ratio of the difference between the averages for the experimental and control groups and the overall variation:

$$\frac{\text{(control group average)} - \text{(experimental group average)}}{\text{variation in the control and experimental groups together}}$$

This ratio combines both bits of information that are necessary to interpret the results of an experiment like this in the right way. The farther the experimental group average is from the control group average, the larger is the numerator, and, holding the denominator at the same value, the larger is the final value of the ratio. On the other hand, the greater the variation in the entire population, the larger the denominator is, and holding the numerator fixed, the smaller is the final value for the ratio. The more overall variation there is, other things being equal, the smaller the ratio; the larger the difference between the averages of the control and experimental groups, the larger the ratio. Thus the larger the ratio, the less adequately does chance alone account for the experimental results.

To compute the level of significance of our data, we need to compute the probability of any value of this ratio that is higher than the value we obtain with our data. The computation would be done with what is known as Student's *t* probability distribution. Student's t provides probabilities of chance in such a case. If this probability was very low, we would reject the hypothesis of chance. In outcome **A** from Figure 5.5, this probability is not very low, roughly 0.25. It is much lower in outcome **B**, roughly 0.02. We would reject the hypothesis of chance if we got outcome **B**. The rules for computing these probabilities are presented in Chapter 13; they need not detain us here.

6. INTERACTING VARIABLES

When experiments focus on one independent variable at a time, they can expose simple cause–effect regularities: taking polio vaccine reduces the chance of having polio. Many, perhaps most, cause–effect relationships are more complicated than this. For example, smokestacks are built to remove fly ash from smoke. One way to do this is to put baffles in the stack and hope the fly ash settles on one of the baffles before leaving the smokestack. Fly ash can also be removed electrically. Fly ash is known to be electrically charged, so by applying the opposite charge to the sides of the smokestack, the fly ash will latch onto the sides of the smokestack instead of leaving with the smoke. It might seem sensible to put charged baffles in the smokestack. It turns out, however, that these two processes *interact* with each other in quite counterintuitive ways. We do not understand what happens when both processes are used, nor is it clear that the combined effect is better than either effect singly.

Variables can *interact* in this way. When experiments are run with only one independent variable, these interactions are not exposed. Consequently, it is important in many contexts to run experiments with more than one independent variable, so that the interactions between independent variables can be uncovered.

Consider an example. Suppose that a philosophy department is considering using a computer to teach introductory logic. Two types of computer teaching programs are available. One works with students on logic problems. This type must be supplemented with some other kind of instruction to present material. The other type of program does not work problems, but presents material, more in the style of an ordinary lecture—except that the student can control the rate at which the material is presented. The philosophy department could install one, the other, or both of these programs. One central concern in determining what to do is the teaching effectiveness of these programs.

We could imagine running two experiments, one comparing the problem-working program against a "normal" method of teaching, the other comparing the material-presenting program against a normal method of teaching. In either case, normal human teaching would supplement and compensate for the particular weakness of each computer program (Figure 5.6). This way of investigating these computer instruction possibilities might teach us something but would certainly not reveal all we want to know. Three variables are explicitly involved in this example. There is the dependent variable of logic ability, and there are two independent variables, computer-*problem*-teaching, and computer-*lecture*-teaching. These two

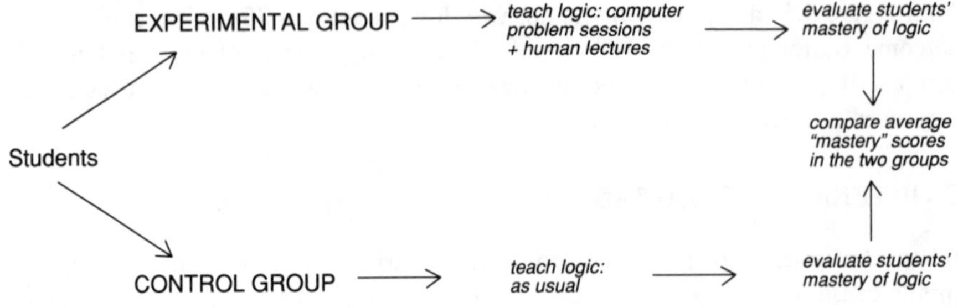

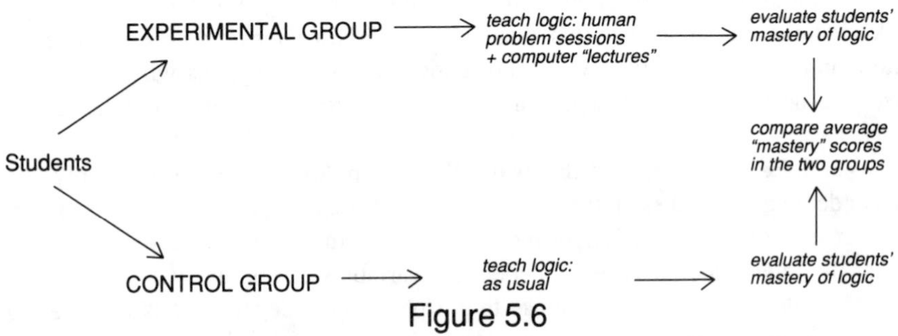

Figure 5.6

independent variables could interact in much the same way that the smokestack variables interact. It may be that computer-problem-teaching does a better job of teaching logic than normal. It may also be that computer-lecture-teaching does a better job of teaching logic than normal. But it may also be that logic instruction done entirely by computer, combining both computer programs, does a worse job than normal. Just the reverse is also possible. It may be that normal teaching is better than either computer program by itself but worse than the combination of the two computer teaching programs.

To run an experiment to determine what relations there are between the independent variables and the dependent variable, four different experimental groups need to be created. We need to have experimental groups like those in the two experiments above (see Figure 5.6). We also need to have a group of students taught by both logic programs and a control group of students taught in the standard way (Figure 5.7). Only in this way do we get a handle on the potential interaction of the two independent variables.

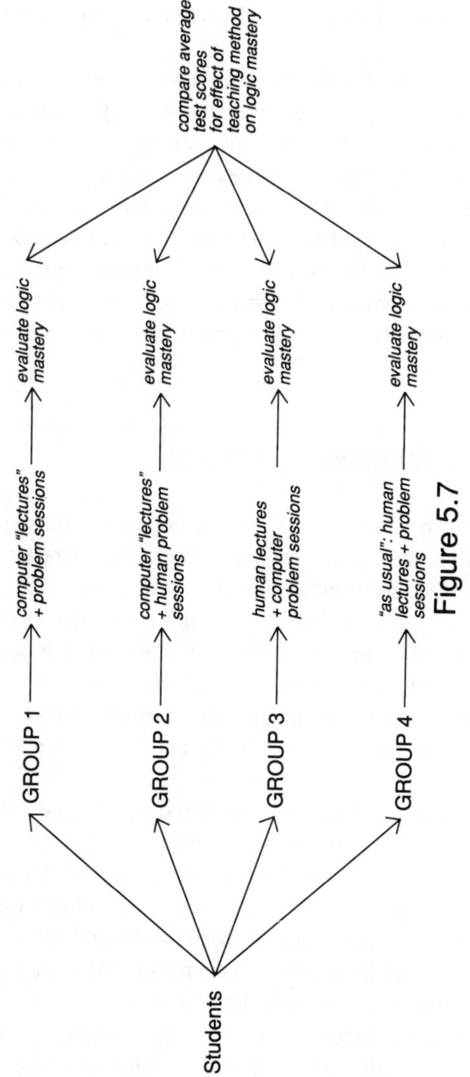
Students
GROUP 1
GROUP 2
GROUP 3
GROUP 4
computer "lectures" + problem sessions
computer "lectures" + human problem sessions
human lectures + computer problem sessions
"as usual": human lectures + problem sessions
evaluate logic mastery
evaluate logic mastery
evaluate logic mastery
evaluate logic mastery
compare average test scores for effect of teaching method on logic mastery

Figure 5.7

We can also use the results of this kind of experiment to find out the effects of the two independent variables alone. We can look at the combined averages of groups 1 and 3 (see Figure 5.7) to see what the effect of computer-*problem*-teaching is. We can look at the combined averages of groups 1 and 2 to see what the effect of computer-*lecture*-teaching is. This design is flexible in this way; it allows information to be discovered about all the relationships that might exist between the variables involved.

As the number of independent variables increases, the number of potential interactions increases quite rapidly, and the number of different experimental groups must be increased commensurately. Not only can each pair of independent variables interact, but triples of independent variables can interact, and so on. This example has two independent variables each with only two values. The same general approach would be used for examples with more than two independent variables, each of which may have two or more values. If three independent variables, each with three values, were involved, 27 ($=3 \times 3 \times 3$) different experimental groups would be needed to examine all of the potential interactions among these variables.

7. VALUE OF EXPERIMENTAL DESIGN

An important aim of experiments is to provide persuasive reason to believe that the variables involved are related in the way they are claimed to relate. Researchers who developed the polio vaccine needed persuasive evidence that taking the vaccine decreases the chance of getting polio. If variables are related as claimed, we can use this understanding to direct our interventions and accomplish desirable ends. Polio is now a rare disease because we have vaccinated much of the population. We whould not have established the vaccination program if there were not good reason to think that such an intervention would bring about its intended end—preventing polio.

One of the most basic and sensible ways to determine how variables are related is by comparing cases. We compare cases where an independent variable has a certain value—a child is vaccinated—with cases where it has another value—another child is not vaccinated. If the two cases are otherwise the same, and if different values of the dependent variable ensue—the child that was not vaccinated got polio and the other child did not—we have reason to believe that the independent variable is causally related to the dependent variable.

In real life several difficulties confront this simple approach. Confounded variables poses one central difficulty. The varying nature of the phenomena studied poses another central difficulty. Experimental design aims to counter these two problems with four strategies:

1. *Comparative design:* Units are divided into groups, each of which is treated differently in terms of the independent variable(s) being studied. The relation-

ship between the independent variable(s) and the dependent variable is established by *comparing* effects on the dependent variable values of units in the different experimental groups.

2. *Averages:* Many units are studied in each of the experimental groups, and the *average* effect on the dependent variable is used as the basis for comparison.
3. *Random assignment:* Units are assigned to groups by a process that makes some use of an objectively *random* source.
4. *Significance tests:* Significance tests are used to check for the possibility that the differences which result from an experiment are merely the result of "chance fluctuations."

In a nutshell, these experiments compare averages of units assigned to experimental groups randomly. Each of these strategies is motivated by the two problems mentioned, confounded variables and varying unit responses.

Rarely can we be sure that the two cases being compared only differ in terms of the independent variable. Virtually always some other variable will distinguish the two cases as well. When the independent variable is confounded with this other variable, one cannot be sure that the independent variable is the source of the difference found in the dependent variable.

There are two basic approaches to avoiding confounded variables. One can attempt to ensure that all of the other variables are the same between the two cases, and one can try to "average out" differences in cases.

Systematically ensuring that the other variables are the same between the two cases is sensible. For a long time, researchers have attempted to determine the degree to which a person's characteristics are a result of genetic inheritance or of upbringing. Identical twins have played a central role in many of these studies. Identical twins provide a case where one of the important variables involved—genetic endowment—is identical for the two cases. This way the effect of the other variable—upbringing—can be studied in isolation.

Unfortunately, it is impossible to ensure that *all* the other variables are the same. For example, researchers have studied the effect of different diets on a rat's weight gain. They discovered that the location of a rat's cage affected the dependent variable of weight gain. Rats in "top-row" cages gained more weight than rats in "bottom-row" cages. If we used only two rats, one receiving the experimental diet and the other receiving the control diet, we could not have them identical in all respects except diet. The two rats have to be kept in two different places. Consequently, there will be some difference, other than diet, in how an experimental and a control rat are treated. Such confounding variables cannot be avoided with just two rats.

The standard approach to this kind of problem is to use more than one unit in experimental and control groups and to attempt to "balance" or "average out" the potential effects of these other variables. Some rats receiving the experimental diet would be in ''top cages'' some would be in ''bottom cages,'' some would be in cages near the door, some would be in cages far from the door, and so on. In this way, when the average is computed for the dependent variable for both the experimental and control rats, it will include values for rats treated in all of these different manners. Thus, while *individual* rats may be different in terms of variables other than the independent variable, the experimental and control *groups* should be the same in terms of averages of these other variables. Whatever effect cage placement has will be ''averaged out.''

Unfortunately, there is lots of evidence that *systematic* approaches to ensuring that the experimental and control units either are identical in terms of relevant variables or that the groups are balanced in terms of relevant variables, can give rise to unexpected and unwanted differences between the two groups. In agricultural trials, for example, researchers once assigned treatments to plots in what appeared to be a systematically balanced way. Suppose that five different treatments, **A**, **B**, **C**, **D**, and **E** were to be compared. A square plot of land, believed to be homogeneous with respect to variables known to be important, would be divided into 25 subplots. Each treatment would be applied to five different subplots picked according to the ''knight's move'' in chess: Any two subplots where the same treatment is applied would be separated by two squares over and one square down or one square over and two squares down:

A B C D E
D E A B C
B C D E A
E A B C D
C D E A B

It was discovered that treatment **B** is to the right of treatment **A** in four out of five cases. Thus, treatment **B** is confounded with being ''downwind'' or ''east'' or ''downslope'' of treatment **A**. The milk study referred to in Section 4 is another example of how systematic approaches can give rise to problems.

For reasons such as these, systematically dividing units into different experimental groups cannot fully serve its purpose. Random assignment provides a very useful alternative. The idea of random assignment is to provide assurance that any differences that are relevant to the dependent variable are balanced, and so can be averaged out, among the different groups in the study. Random allocation cannot ensure that every assignment will be balanced, but it does provide two kinds of guarantee. Random assignments are not biased. Nothing in the method of assignment favors assigning units of one sort to one particular experimental group. Random assignments are precise in ways measurable with significance tests.

Beside the problem of confounded variables, the other obstacle to interpreting the results of experiments is the varying nature of the units studied. Different humans respond differently to the same drug. Different plots of land respond differently to different agricultural treatments. A consequence of this is that many of the relationships between variables are ''probabilistic.'' At best, vaccinating an individual will reduce his or her chance of contracting the disease.

There may be many sources for the varying responses of the units under study. It may be that there are differences between units which we simply do not know about. It may be that there are differences we know about but cannot control in any way. It may be that nature simply is not as regular as we would like to believe.

Fortunately, the experimenter need not determine beforehand the source of this variability. Experiments can be run and we can learn about the probabilistic relationship between variables, all the while being aware that there may be more to learn about the remaining sources of variability.

The varying nature of the units under study does impose certain constraints on the running of experiments. In the first place, because units vary in unpredictable ways, we need to use many units in the different experimental groups to average out these unpredictable sources of variation. Second, we need to measure effects in terms of averages of individual responses, not the individual responses themselves. Finally, we need significance tests to rule out the possibility that the ''normal variation'' of the units under study is all that lies behind an observed difference.

By combining these four strategies—comparative design, averaging results, random assignment, and significance tests—experiments can be interpreted with fair confidence. Unfortunately, as with all inductive methods, experimental design is not a ''sure thing.'' Despite the best effort to avoid confounded variables and the best effort to cope with the varying nature of the units under study, incorrect conclusions can be drawn from well-designed experiments.

8. PROBLEMS WITH EXPERIMENTAL DESIGN

There are several ways that we can be mislead by experimental results:

1. We can overgeneralize the result of our experiment and assume that it applies to some population to which it does not apply.
2. We can mistakenly assume that our assignment of units of experimental groups succeeded in avoiding all important confounding variables.
3. Many experiments are conducted in an explicitly artificial environment. The complex variety of variables that may effect the units under study are controlled—frequently to avoid confounding—but this lack of realism may severely limit the applicability of the results of the experiment.
4. The significance test we use to check against the possibility of natural variation accounting for the results of the experiment may mislead us in a variety of ways.
5. We can carry out the experiment poorly, not attending carefully enough to the physical procedures required by the experimental design, and produce a valueless result.

I will comment briefly on the first four points. The fifth is very important, but there is little appropriate to say about this topic here. Training in the particular field in which one might conduct experiments will be more helpful than general remarks from an introductory text on induction. It is important, however, to keep in mind that an experimental result from a superbly designed experiment may be worthless if the experiment was not carried out carefully.

Regarding 1, overgeneralization. In the narrowest sense, we can only apply the result of an experiment to the population that could have been included in the experimental trial. Analogously, we can only apply the result of a sampling study to the actual *sampling frame* used to get the sample. But in practice we always generalize beyond the population that could have been included in the experiment. We do not want to say that the vaccine is helpful only for the group of children in the polio vaccine study; we want to say this about all (or at least a large proportion) of the children. Similarly, we do not want to conclude that only rats get cancer when injected with red dye number 2. We would not be interested in how red dye number 2 affects rats unless in the process we thought we could learn something about how it affects human beings. We want to apply results of many nonhuman animal studies to all (or most) humans as well.

Here is a worry: To what population can we justly generalize the result of an experiment? To what population does the result apply? There is no general answer to this question. The generalizability of the result of an experiment is a matter to be answered differently in each different experiment. We believe that children are sufficiently alike that they will all (or most will, at any rate) respond similarly to polio vaccine. This conclusion is based on our best understanding of the nature of humans. Thus, the generalizability of the result of an experiment relies on the best available information concerning the populations in question.

Regarding 2, avoiding confounding. It is very difficult to be sure that the experimental and control groups are identical or balanced in terms of every possible relevant variable. There is an indefinitely large number of other variables, most of which we would never think of, and could not systematically balance out for a comparative study. Even if one is careful to assign units to control and experimental groups by a random procedure, it is easy to fail to randomize over certain elements. An agricultural experimenter may always harvest crops from experimental plots in the same order. This order, like the order of the rats' cages discussed in Section 7, may turn out to have an effect on the dependent variable of interest. Thus units may be assigned to groups randomly, but many aspects of the way in which units are treated may not be random.

Regarding 3, lack of realism. The conditions of an experiment differ from "real life." This is not as apparent in the polio study as in other cases. Consider another example. One branch of psychology studies the psychology of understanding language. Some of the experiments in the field involve having a person read words or phrases one at a time from a video screen. The subject can control when the next word or phrase appears on the screen. This kind of reading is not at all like normal reading. Very likely the differences do not bear on the particular issues being addressed by these particular experiments. But in order for the conclusion of the experiment to bear on normal reading—which may be what the researcher ultimately is interested in—we must assume that the differences are unimportant.

Part of the point of running experiments is to isolate the large variety of variables that are mutually involved in the production of the everyday world. This way we seek to isolate and analyze the component causes that help to produce the world in its complexity. But variables interact with each other, and these interactions may be missed when the effects of some of the variables are carefully excluded in the artificial environment of many experiments.

Regarding 4, significance tests. There has been a substantial amount of controversy over the correct interpretation of significance tests. Many of the issues involved concern the mathematical details involved in the construction of these tests. We will consider some of these issues in Chapter 13. Here I briefly mention two common worries about significance tests.

When we use a significance test to guard against the possibility that observed differences are simply chance fluctuations, we construct an explicit model for the operation of chance. If results do not fit the model, we reject it. The question arises, then: If we reject the chance model, do we thereby accept some other account of the differences?

It is very tempting to reply "yes." We are looking to see if the independent variable is causally related to the dependent variable. We look to differences in values of the dependent variable in a comparative experiment for evidence that there is such a relationship. It would seem, then, that by ruling out the possibility that these differences were the result of chance, we are "ruling in" the alternative we are interested in: that the independent variable is causally responsible for the observed differences in the dependent variable.

It should be clear from the previous discussion, however, that we cannot make this inference on the basis of a significance test alone. Our confidence that the observed difference in values of the dependent variable is due to differences in values of the independent variable must also rest on our confidence that we have effectively avoided all other potentially confounding variables. If we have failed to do this, the differences that the significance test tells us are not due to chance may well be attributable to some confounded variable whose existence we do not know of. All we can conclude from a significance test is that the chance model does not measure up to the standards established by a significance test.

Here is another kind of worry about significance tests. Suppose that we flip a fair coin 1,000 times—and then we repeat this 10,000 times. In the end we will have 10,000 results each of the sort 512 heads and 488 tails in 1,000 flips. If the coin really is fair, then *some* of these 10,000 results will be very unusual: 401 heads in 1,000 flips. Something that is unusual is *not* something that never occurs; it is something that *rarely* occurs.

Now suppose, by analogy, that an experimenter conducted 10,000 tests of different substances to see if any of the 10,000 substances increased the risk of heart disease. Suppose that 438 of these 10,000 tests produced a result that was *significant at the 0.05 level*. In one sense, there is nothing more to say; a significant result is a significant result. But from another perspective, we would expect something like 38 *falsely significant* results from 10,000 different tests. The 0.05 level of significance means something like this: The probability of a result as aberrant as the one obtained—given the chance model—is less than 5%. But this implies that in roughly 5% of uses, when the chance model *is right,* an aberrant result should occur. 5% of 10,000 is 500, so the 438 significant results might all be falsely significant. It is just like the coin case: We expect some unusual results in a long sequence of trials.

Some researchers argue that a significant result is not so ''significant'' if it is one of a large population of results. They claim that such ''fishing expeditions'' do not produce persuasive results, because they are virtually guaranteed to produce some ''falsely significant'' results. To compound matters, it is sometimes the policy of journals not to accept research reports unless the results can pass a significance test. Thus, given the large number of researchers attempting to publish their work, we might expect a good proportion of ''falsely significant'' published results.

9. RANDOMIZATION AND FAIRNESS

Randomization is important to experimental design in three distinct ways. First, randomization helps avoid confounding variables. Second, randomizing gives us a way to cope with the variability of the results. Finally, randomization allows us to administer the experiment in a *fair* way. We have discussed the first two advantages above. Here, we focus on the third advantage.

There is much to say about the ethics of experimentation. This is particularly so with experiments on human subjects. Although the issues are not entirely clear, it probably would not have been right to force communities into participating in a fully randomized design experiment to test the efficacy of the polio vaccine. It probably was right to offer the second-grader versus first- and third-grader alternative. Very likely the right of parents to control and be informed about interventions on their children—such as vaccination—outweighs society's right to seek methods that will reduce the incidence of disease overall. But the issue is open to debate.

Most issues involving the ethics of experimentation fall outside the scope of this book. One aspect of the ethics of experimentation, the use of randomization to achieve a fair result, is both of considerable interest and quite closely related to the material we have been explicitly concerned with.

Obviously, when a comparative study is undertaken, subjects are treated differently and exposed to different risks. Some people get the vaccine and some do not. What is a fair way to choose who goes into the different groups—who is exposed to the different risks? By assigning subjects to groups at random, we treat each subject the same insofar as each subject has the same chance of being in any of the experimental groups as each other subject. Thus, randomization allows us both to treat subjects differently—some get the vaccine and some do not—and the same—all the subjects had the same chance of getting the vaccine.

Random methods of allocation are used to achieve "fair results" in contexts other than experiments. The draft of the late 1960s and early 1970s was run by lottery. The order in which men were drafted depended on a ranking of birthdays, and this ranking was produced randomly. Each draft-able person was treated the same in the sense that each had the same chance of having a birthday that was "highly ranked." Yet in the end, some people were drafted and others were not.

Using randomization to ensure fairness is somewhat of a ruse. *Before* we randomize, each person has the *same* chance of getting any of the possible treatments. *After* randomization, people are treated differently. Here we have fairness before the fact only. But perhaps, since people are to be treated differently in any case, randomization ensures the greatest amount of equality of treatment possible.

However, there are situations where such fairness does not seem to be the kind of fairness we are after. One such is the following. Imagine a case where we can do one of two things: either we can save 10 people or we can save one person. These are the only two possibilities; there is no hope for doing both. Furthermore, there are no special reasons to treat any of the 11 people involved differently from the others. What should we do?

Many people incline to saving the greater number of people. Here the single person is treated differently simply because he or she is not a member of a group. In the sense of randomness as fairness, this is not fair. On the other hand, we can give each of the 11 people the same *chance* of being saved. To do this we would flip a fair coin; if it came up heads we would save the group of 10, and if it came up tails we would save the single person. In this way each of the 11 people would have the same chance of being saved, 1/2. Do we want to "be fair" and flip a coin to determine our course of action?

10. SUMMARY

1. Each of the inductive methods we have studied—survey sampling, decision theory, and factor analysis—is fallible, but since each offers a certain kind of guarantee, each is better than guessing.
   (a) The guarantees offered by all of these methods are hypothetical: *If* samples were collected randomly..., *if* utilities and degrees of belief are accurate..., and so on.

(b) Even when these hypothetical requirements are met, the results of applying the method may not be right.

(c) One may argue over the desirability of the guarantee provided by an inductive method, but in the cases we have examined, each has enough *prima facie* plausibility to shift the burden of proof onto the skeptics' shoulders.

2. Experiments are run to determine whether and how two variables are causally related.
   (a) Variables describe properties of the units under study. Each unit has a value of the variables that describe such units.
   (b) In experiments, the experimenter manipulates some of the variables—forces certain units under study to have particular values of the variable—and watches to see if this manipulation has an effect on values of other variables.
   (c) The variable(s) that the experimenter manipulates are called independent variables. The variable(s) on which the effects of the manipulation are monitored are called dependent variables.
   (d) Experiments are done to determine whether changing the value(s) of the independent variable(s) produces a change in the value(s) of the dependent variable(s).

3. Comparative experimental design works by comparing values of the dependent variable in an "experimental" group and a "control" group.
   (a) The experimenter forces all units in the experimental group to have the same particular value of the independent variable, a value that differs from the value of the independent variable which all the units in the control group have.
   (b) If nothing else differs in an important way between the two groups and if the two groups come to have differences in the dependent variable, we are inclined to conclude that the differences in the dependent variable were caused by the differences in the independent variable.

4. Confounded variables are variables other than the independent variable such that all (or most) of the units in one of the experimental groups have similar values for both the independent variable *and* the other variable confounded with it.
   (a) When a variable is confounded with the independent variable in an experiment, one cannot be sure whether differences in the dependent variable were caused by the independent variable or by the confounded variable.
   (b) One can attempt to divide units systematically between experimental and control groups to avoid confounded variables.
   (c) One can also attempt to divide units systematically between experimental and control groups so that values of other variables are "balanced" between the groups involved.
   (d) Unfortunately unconscious and subjective biases tend to undermine these efforts.
   (e) Usually, units are apportioned into experimental and control groups by a process that uses an objectively random source.

5. Even under the most carefully controlled conditions, units that are studied with experimental design will have different values of the variables of interest.
   (a) For example, people just happen to respond differently to disease threats and disease therapies. So, enough units need to be assigned to experimental and control groups so that, irrespective of the independent variable, different values of the dependent variable could occur.

(b) Effects, then, are measured in terms of averages of the values of the dependent variable in the different experimental and control groups.

6. Since units, which are otherwise similar, may have different values of the dependent variable "just by chance," one must use a significance test to ensure that different average values of the dependent variable in the experimental and control groups are not merely the result of chance.
   (a) Significance tests work by establishing a ranking of the possible outcomes in terms of how well "chance alone" can account for these different possibilities.
   (b) With a significance test, one computes the probability of a result as bad as or worse than the result of the experiment, "as bad as..." being measured in terms of the ranking of possible outcomes of the experiment in terms of their fit with the hypothesis of chance. This probability—known as the level of significance—is based on the assumption that chance alone has produced the observed differences.
   (c) If the probability computed with the test of significance is very low, one "rejects the hypothesis that chance alone is responsible for differences observed in the results at the level of significance computed from the data."

7. Variables can interact in counterintuitive ways, and this makes additional demands on experimental design.
   (a) When a single independent variable is examined for its causal relation to the dependent variable, one tries to balance or average out the effects of other variables. But this single independent variable may interact with some of these other variables to produce different effects on the dependent variable.
   (b) When two variables are suspected of interacting, experiments must be designed to expose this interaction. Experimental subjects must be divided into more than two groups. For example, if four independent variables, each with two values, are involved in an experiment, 16 ($= 2 \times 2 \times 2 \times 2$) different experimental groups would be required.

8. While experimental designs provide a good way to discover relationships between variables, they can produce misleading results in several ways.
   (a) The results of an experiment can be overgeneralized and applied to too broad a population.
   (b) Despite the best efforts, an important variable may still be confounded with the independent variable and may be the source of differences found in the dependent variable.
   (c) Many experiments are conducted in carefully arranged and unrealistic settings. Consequently, it may not be appropriate to generalize the results of such experiments to more realistic settings.
   (d) Significance tests may not provide an adequate guard against the effects of chance. For example, when used simultaneously on many experimental results, one would expect "falsely significant" results.

9. Random allocation has three important benefits.
   (a) It provides one useful way to avoid confounding variables.
   (b) It provides one probabilistic foundation for the derivation of probabilities used in significance tests.
   (c) It provides a way to treat subjects of an experiment fairly.

11. REFERENCES

(Fisher, 1935) is the classic introduction to the modern statistical theory of experimental design. (Cox, 1958) is an excellent text on the subject. (Jaeger, 1982) and (Moore, 1985) are good introductory texts with valuable discussions of experimental design and tests of significance. Material on the polio vaccine experiment may be found in (Tanur et al., 1978, Ch. 1). Table 5.1 is adapted from (Meier, 1978), "The Biggest Public Health Experiment Ever," in Tanur et al., eds. (1978), *Statistics: A Guide to the Unknown*. Table 1, p. 12. The smokestack example is taken from (Hacking, 1983). (Taurek, 1977) uses the idea of "fairness as equal chances" to argue against letting the number of people saved help determine what one ought to do.

12. PROBLEMS

1. In each of the following examples, identify the independent and dependent variables. State in a sensible way what values these variables may have.
   (a) Experimenters have found that human subjects in a variety of conditions respond positively to the subliminally presented phrase, "Mommy and I are one." (See Chapter 1 for more details.)
   (b) NASA has conducted tests to see whether adding fins to the back of tractor-trailer trucks can decrease their gas consumption. It seems that a 10% decrease is possible.
   (c) Some studies seem to show that watching violence on television does not promote violent behavior.
   (d) A 1983 study found that the consumption of large quantities of coffee led to an increased chance of getting cancer.
   (e) Experiments are under way to determine whether a new strain of peach tree is more resistant to late spring freezes.

2. Describe five different variables, and the different values they may have, that apply to automobiles.

3. Consider the following alternative method for allocating children to experimental and control groups in a study such as the polio study discussed in Section 2. All children with last names the first letter of which is in the first half of the alphabet, A–M, get vaccinated; all other children are not vaccinated. In what ways might this method of allocation give rise to confounded variables? Is this important? Discuss.

4. Suppose that a person decides to see if there is anything to the rumor that taking vitamin C reduces the chance of contracting colds. He takes a large daily dose of vitamin C all year, and as things turn out, gets four times as many colds as he has had in any previous year. He concludes that there is nothing to these rumors. In what ways might one criticize his conclusion?

5. Use a random number table to assign the following 20 people to an experimental and control group:

Joe	Arnold	Ian	Moe
Doe	Hilary	David	Harry
Larry	Harold	Ignatious	George
Curly	Augustus	Henry	Shirly
Bill	Donald	Moss	Jill

What percentage of the experimental group came from people in the two leftmost columns? Do this assignment four more times and determine the percentages of the experimental group that came from people "on the left." Has your method of random assignment avoided the confounding variable of "left/right?"

6. Describe what it means to say that an experimental result was found to be "significant" by a test of significance at the 0.05 level of significance.

7. Why is it not enough to know that the average value of the dependent variable was different in the experimental and control groups? Why must one know how variable units are in general with respect to the dependent variable?

8. Design experiments to test the following claims regarding relationships between variables. In each case you should determine carefully what units will be experimented on, what variables are involved, and how they will be measured. You should be as specific as you can in your design so as to avoid potentially confounding variables.
   (a) Having a balanced nutritious breakfast improves a child's performance at school.
   (b) The ability of rats to run mazes is genetically influenced.
   (c) House plants grow better when exposed to, (1) classical music, (2) rock and roll, or (3) no music.
   (d) It is easier to read books printed black on white or red on yellow.
   (e) Eating an apple a day keeps the doctor away.

9. French bread bakers say that the quality of the loaf—texture of the heart of the loaf and of the crust, how well it rises, and so on—is determined both by the humidity and the loaf's placement in the oven. Design an experiment to determine whether this is correct. Be aware that these variables may interact.

10. Find the report of an experiment in some popular printed source, such as a newspaper. Attempt to answer the following questions about the experiment.
   (a) What were the independent and dependent variables?
   (b) Was the experiment done by comparative design?
   (c) If there were different groups, how were units in the experiment assigned to different groups?
   (d) What is the general structure of the experiment?
   (e) Are there any confounded variables in the experiment?
   (f) Might any of the variables interact in a way that the experiment would not discover?
   (g) Would it be plausible to suppose that the results of the experiment are due to chance alone?

CHAPTER 6

DESCRIPTIVE STATISTICS

1. OUR TECHNICAL NEEDS

We have seen in the first part of the book four different statistical methods of induction: survey sampling, decision making, factor extraction, and experimental design. You should have some familiarity with what these methods aim to accomplish and how they might succeed in this. You should also have some sense for the various strengths and weaknesses of these methods. To understand these methods in more detail, however, we need some of the technical apparatus of probability and statistics. This is the goal of this part of the book.

In this chapter we see some ways to use statistics to describe portions of the world. Here we discuss the elements of measurement—which provide the numerical descriptions that are the heart of much statistical work. We discuss the ways we can manipulate these numerical descriptions with statistics to give us a useful way to regard whatever bit of the world we are focusing on.

The following three chapters introduce the elements of probability theory. This will provide some more inferential power with which to better understand how each of the statistical methods presented in the first part of the book works. In the third part of the book we reconsider each of these four methods in greater detail with the technical facility provided by this part of the book. This should help to promote a more detailed, fruitful, and critical understanding of these techniques.

2. NUMBERS AND THE WORLD

Measurement plays an important role in all of the methods we have seen. To estimate the average annual income of the population, we might ask each person in a survey sample what their annual income is. This is a simple kind of measurement. To use decision theory, one of the things we need to measure is relatively how desirable the decision maker finds the various available options. This is a more complicated kind of measurement. Factor analysis may help us find properties to measure, such as intelligence or IQ, that are hidden in some sense. When we run experiments, we must measure the units with respect to the variables of interest. All of these methods work by manipulating the results of measurements on units in a population.

Measurement involves assigning numbers to units in a population. We weigh babies when they are born. Scores on SAT tests may help determine whether and where one goes to college. In the first case, babies are the units in our population; the variable we are concerned with is weight. We measure a baby's weight by using a device—a "baby scale"—which provides a number that is the baby's weight. This number is the value of the weight variable for this baby (Figure 6.1). In the case of SAT tests, we look at a population of prospective college students—typically, high-school seniors. We measure a student's "scholastic aptitude" by using a "pencil and paper test," which, as in the case of weight, provides a number which is the value for the scholastic aptitude variable for that student.

Assigning numbers to units is useful for several reasons. In some important respects numbers are more expressive than words; we can make more distinctions

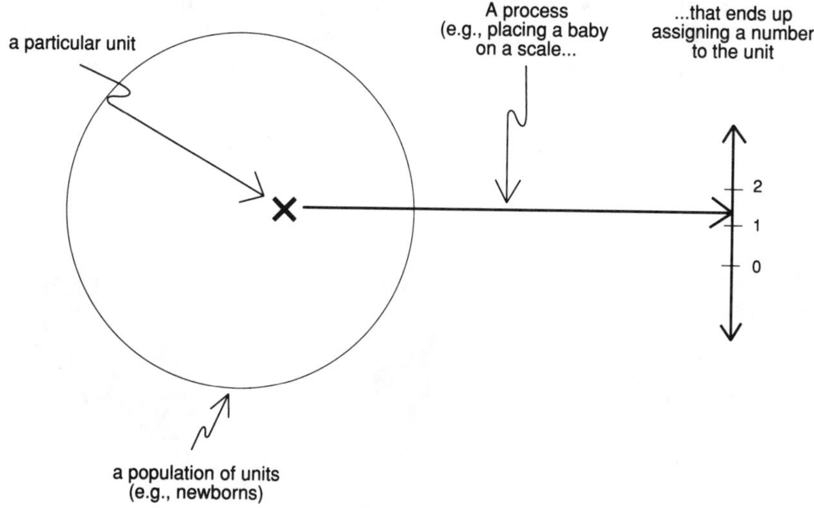

Figure 6.1

about things when we speak of their number than when we describe them in words. For example, we can distinguish between a person whose height is 5 feet 2 inches and one whose height is 5 feet 3 inches. It is hard to make such distinctions with verbal descriptions alone. The fact that we can make such distinctions need not imply that they are interesting or important; although they may be both interesting and important.

Assigning numbers to things also allows us to use mathematical operations and relations to further understand the things we measure. If an IBM personal computer weighs more than an Apple IIC personal computer, and a Zenith Z110 personal computer weights more than an IBM, we can infer that the Zenith is heavier than the Apple as well. The *transitive property* of numbers can be applied to weights:

$$\text{If } \mathbf{A} > \mathbf{B}, \text{ and } \mathbf{B} > \mathbf{C}, \text{ then } \mathbf{A} > \mathbf{C}.$$

Similarly, if Jane is smarter than Joe and Jack is smarter than Jane, then Jack should be smarter than Joe—assuming that we can use this kind of numerical IQ structure to describe intelligence accurately.

Consider another type of example. If an empty car weights 2,000 pounds and John weighs 150 pounds, the car with John in it weighs 2,150 pounds (Figure 6.2). Here the mathematical operation of addition corresponds to the physical operation of "combining" (in this case, "putting inside"). When we measure weights we can describe a physical operation of combination with the mathematical operation of addition. Addition in mathematics allows us to reason about what happens to weights of objects when the objects are put together.

For any particular kind of measurement, however, not every mathematical operation must correspond to some physical operation. When measuring temperatures, the operation of combining does not correspond to addition as it does when measuring weight. We cannot add the temperatures of two objects to find the temperature when we combine them. The temperature of a cup of boiling water com-

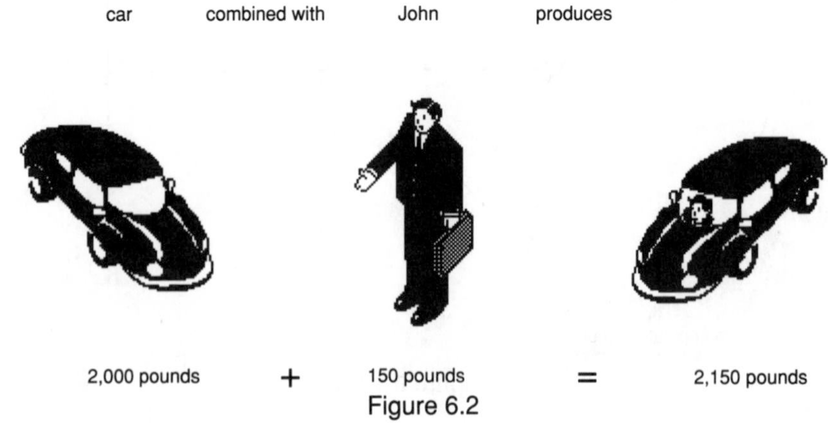

Figure 6.2

bined with a cup of water that has been frozen will not be 212 + 32. In this case the physical operation of combination does not correspond to the numerical operation of addition. For each kind of measurement, we must be clear about which parts of the whole world of mathematical objects, operations, and properties we will use.

To do this, we have to know something about the units we intend to measure. This is why some kinds of measurement seem straightforward, while others seem obscure. Few people question the idea of assigning weights to babies; many people question assigning SAT numbers to college applicants. Some urge that we can "see" weight but we cannot see scholastic aptitude. But people do not walk around with large LED crystal displays of their weight.

Some have argued that the idea of weight is intuitively clear, whereas the idea of scholastic aptitude is rather vague. We can easily check to determine that a newly proposed method for measuring weight is reasonably accurate—make sure that intuitively heavier objects produce bigger numbers than do intuitively lighter objects. We also have a whole series of other methods to measure weight with which to compare a new method. But intuitions regarding scholastic aptitude are not so definite. This sort of vagueness might account for the difference between scholastic aptitude and weight.

A century from now our "intuitions" about scholastic aptitude may not be as vague as they are now. Weight and scholastic aptitude might come to be equally well understood measured properties. On the other hand, 100 years from now our intuitions about scholastic aptitude may be just as vague as they are now. This could be because we have failed to learn enough about scholastic aptitude. It could also be because the underlying reality that the concept of scholastic aptitude is supposed to reflect is less definite than the underlying reality that the concept of weight is supposed to reflect. On the other hand, we may know quite a lot about scholastic aptitude—enough to realize that this property cannot be well modeled with numbers.

Our understanding of a system of measurement is intimately tied up with our understanding of the thing being measured. For a system of measurement to make sense, we must know something about the property we aim to measure. When we measure the property we use the structure provided by numbers to describe it. If this numerical structure does not correspond to the structure of the property we are measuring, our measurements will not be able to tell us about this property.

This observation applies to the most elementary aspect of measurement. When we can make distinctions when we talk about things, the things themselves better also differ. A person who is 5 feet 2 inches better have a different height than a person who is 5 feet 3 inches. In the case of height, this point seems silly. But the same point applies to other measurements as well. A person with IQ 105 better have a different intelligence from a person with IQ 110.

We can put things in a nutshell this way. There is the whole wide world. From all of this we isolate that part which we want to talk about and to measure. All the rest we forget about. We isolate a particular population of units and a particular property—or variable—of these units. We must consider the kinds of operations—such as combining—which we will do with these units. Then there is the whole world of mathematics, full of the usual things we all are familiar with, such as "regular" or counting numbers, fractions, addition, and so on, and stranger things, such as complex numbers, hamiltonians, matrix algebra, and so on. From this world of mathematics, we isolate that part which we want to use to help us measure. The idea of measurement is to associate one kind of number—and some of the operations that we can do with such numbers—with our population of units and the property we wish to measure—and operations we will do with these units. When things work right, the numbers are analogous to the properties of the units.

There are four basic entities that we have going now:

1. There is the whole real world—whatever that means.
2. There is a particular portion of the world that we wish to consider—in particular to measure. Here we isolate an aspect of reality, including only certain objects, certain properties of them, and certain operations with them.
3. There is a particular bit of the world of mathematics we use to *measure* the portion of the world we have isolated. Here we isolate a kind of number and the kinds of relations and operations we wish to consider with these numbers.
4. Finally, there is the whole of mathematics.

We take bits and pieces from the world of mathematics in order to exploit their well-understood *descriptive and deductive* relations. This allows us to better represent the part of the world we are measuring.

We must understand something about the units we aim to measure. We must know what physical operations we want to perform on them and how these operations alter the values of the properties we measure on these units. In short, we need a theory about these units and the property we are measuring on them. Such a theory is called a *relational structure*.

We must also understand what piece of mathematics we intend to use as our scale of measurement. What kind of numbers will be used? What operations and what relationships between these numbers will be used? Answering these questions establishes a *numerical structure*.

The way we assign numbers to units (the numerical structure) must preserve the structure that we believe exists in the piece of the world we are measuring (the relational structure). The relational and numerical structures must share the same descriptive organization. When this is so, we can use the devices of mathematics, descriptive and inferential, to describe the world in a useful way.

For a given scale of measurement, the proof that the structures of the part of the world and of the numbers describing the world are the same is called a *representation theorem*. The representation theorem ensures that the numerical facts we associate with the items we measure actually correspond to some facts about the units being measured.

3. SCALES OF MEASUREMENT

Typically, we can use one of several different scales to measure a given property. We can measure weight, for example, in pounds or kilograms. All of the different scales with which we measure a given property, such as weight, must share a common underlying structure. This is the numerical structure that corresponds to the structure of the property measured.

One way of stating what all of the different scales of the same kind of measurement have in common is to state how one must be able to translate from one scale to another. Consider weight. To convert from pounds to kilograms we multiply by 2.2. A 150-pound man weighs $(2.2 \times 150) = 330$ kilograms. To convert from pounds to ounces, we multiply by 16. A 150-pound man also weighs $(16 \times 150) = 2{,}400$ ounces. To convert from one weight scale to another, one always multiplies by the appropriate "conversion factor." No other kind of conversion will preserve the underlying numerical structure used to measure weight.

Typical temperature scales are different. To convert from Celsius to Fahrenheit, we first multiply by 9/5, *then we add 32*. Thus, 25 degrees Celsius is 77 degrees Fahrenheit:

$$\left(\frac{9}{5} \times 25\right) + 32 = 45 + 32 = 77.$$

Here we both multiply by one conversion factor—9/5—and add a second conversion factor—32. This kind of conversion is used between any two typical temperature scales. The underlying numerical structure used to measure temperature differs from that used to measure weight.

This difference marks a real physical difference between these two kinds of measurement. It is arbitrary what is called zero degrees of temperature. In the Fahrenheit scale, 0 degrees is assigned to the freezing point of salt water. One could just as well invent a different scale where the temperature in deep caves would be 0. Alternatively, one could assign zero to the freezing point of pure (not salt) water as we do with the Celsius scale. Whatever is called 0 degrees does not concern anything intrinsic to the thing measured. This is not so for weight. What is assigned zero weight is *not arbitrary*. 0 weight must be assigned to objects that have no matter as part of them ("nothings," so to speak); we cannot decide that a bar of gold 6 inches × 2 inches × 3 inches counts as 0 weight.

With weight measurement we need to determine a unit of weight: *one* pound, or *one* kilogram, or *one* ounce. Once we have done this, we fix the weight scale to assign a particular set of numbers to the objects we weigh. When we convert from one weight scale to another we multiply by a number that reflects the different size units used by the two scales. The pound unit is 2.2 times as big as the kilogram unit.

With temperature measurement, we must both fix a unit—1 degree Fahrenheit or 1 degree Celsius—and a point that is to count as zero temperature. Once we have fixed both of these values, the temperature scale will assign a particular set of numbers to the objects whose temperatures we take. Here, to convert from one scale to another, we must account for the different size unit—1 degree Celsius is 9/5 times as big as 1 degree Fahrenheit—and the point that counts as zero degrees, 0 degrees Celsius, where pure water freezes, is 32 degrees Fahrenheit.

Establishing the basic means to translate from one scale to another when measuring a particular property is the heart of what is called the *uniqueness theorem* for a system of measurement. It establishes what is common to all the different scales for a given measured property. It establishes the *kind* of scale used to measure a given property.

The kind of scale used to measure something affects the kind of numerical manipulations one can do with measured values. The kind of scale used to measure weight, for example, allows us to take ratios of weight measurements. This is not true for the kind of scale used to measure temperature.

Suppose that the low temperature two days ago was 20 degrees Fahrenheit while the low temperature yesterday was 13.3 degrees Fahrenheit. It would not make sense to say, "The ratio of the low two days ago to that yesterday is 1.5." One might think this makes sense because

$$\frac{\text{low two days ago}}{\text{low yesterday}} = \frac{20 \text{ degrees}}{13.3 \text{ degrees}} = 1.5.$$

But suppose these temperatures were measured on the Celsius scale. To convert from Fahrenheit to Celsius we multiply by 5/9 and subtract 17.77. 20 degrees Fahrenheit is -6.66 degrees Celsius, and 13.3 degrees Fahrenheit is -10.38 degrees Celsius:

$$20° \text{ Fahrenheit} = (5/9 \times 20) - 17.77 = 11.1 - 17.77 = -6.66° \text{ Celsius.}$$
$$13.3° \text{ Fahrenheit} = (5/9 \times 13.3) - 17.77 = 7.39 - 17.77 = -10.38° \text{ Celcius.}$$

The ratio of the low temperature two days ago to that yesterday no longer is 1.5:$-6.66/-10.38 = 0.64$. The statement of the ratio of temperatures is as much a statement about the particular temperature scale used as it is a statement about the weather.

This is not so with the case of weight. Suppose that I weighed 176 pounds 2 months ago and now, after a diet, I weigh 170 pounds. We can say that the ratio of my weight 2 months ago to my current weight is $176/170 = 1.035$. As above, suppose that I measured my weight in terms of kilograms instead of pounds. 176 pounds is $2.2 \times 176 = 387.2$ kilograms; 170 pounds is $2.2 \times 170 = 374$ kilograms. The ratio of weights given in kilograms is the same as that given in pounds: $176/170 = 387.2/374 = 1.035$. Consequently, such a statement about the ratio of two weights does say something about the things weighed and not about the particular scale used to do the weighing.

One lesson from this discussion about ratios of measurements is that we cannot do any arithmetical operation we like to the numbers we find through measurement. This has some important consequences for the kinds of statistical summaries we can make with our measurements.

4. DISTRIBUTIONS

Measurement gives us the raw material for much statistical work. In many cases we start with a series of measurements of one or more variables on a large number of units in a population. These measurements must then be organized to see what lessons they have for us. The first step in organizing a large series of measurements is seeing the set of measurements as a *distribution* of values. The manner in which the values are distributed may provide useful clues about the populations we are concerned with. We start looking at distributions of values from one measured variable. We close the chapter discussing correlation, which concerns two measured variables.

One of the most striking features that we find when we make a lot of measurements is that they vary from unit to unit. There are obvious cases—different people have different heights—and less obvious cases—ball bearings made to very exacting standards still have slightly different diameters. When we measure many units in a population we find a *distribution* of values of the variable measured. One of the first things we do with statistics is organize such distributions so that they tell us more clearly about the units in this population.

In the following example, we can take a set of cumulative scores that students got in a logic course and begin to make sense of what these scores might mean about the effort and understanding each student put into and got from the course. Of course, the numbers alone cannot tell us all that is important about each student's experience in the class. But they can tell us something. The scores represent all the points earned from exams and homework over a one-term course:

164, 43, 84, 76, 163, 115, 124, 129, 117, 0, 153,

153, 130, 119, 96, 157, 163, 134, 76, 124, 160, 110,

159, 99, 150, 174, 148, 138, 113, 85, 0, 116, 160.

Here we have a population of students and a measurement made on each student in the population. The resulting array of numbers—taken from an alphabetical list of students enrolled in the course—is difficult to read.

Some of these scores do not make much sense. Checking the grade sheet reveals that the students with scores of zero never attended class and never did any of the assigned homework or exams. The fact that their name appears on the roll probably represents a mistake in processing their class enrollment. The zeros do not represent a complete failure on the part of the student to understand the course material; they represent no attempt to understand the course material. These students were not *really* enrolled in the course. A similar story lies behind the student with a score of 43. He dropped the course early on—no homework was done after the first 3 weeks. His drop request probably was not processed properly. These students' scores should be dropped from the distribution of scores, for they do not represent anything relevant to the property measured by these scores. Such scores are frequently called *outliers*.

We can learn more from these scores if we simply arrange the scores in ascending (or descending) order. In Table 6.1 the list is more orderly and *ranks* have been assigned. Ranking scores is a simple procedure that gives some useful information about the distribution of scores. The rank tells us where in the distribution the score fell. Thus the 20th score, in ascending order, is 150. The student who received this score scored higher than 19 other students and lower than 10 other students. 76½ is the lowest score—in a tie. With ties, it is common to take the ranks that would be assigned to the tied scores and give the average—or "mean" (but see below)—rank to all tied scores. Thus, the first two scores share ranks 1 and 2 and have the average of these ranks—(1 + 2)/2 = 1½—for their ranks.

We can learn more by looking at a *frequency distribution* for these scores. Here we look at all of the possible scores and determine how frequently they occur in the population of scores.

TABLE 6.1

Score	Rank	Score	Rank	Score	Rank	Score	Rank
76	1½	115	9	134	17	159	24
76	1½	116	10	138	18	160	25½
84	3	117	11	148	19	160	25½
85	4	119	12	150	20	163	27½
96	5	124	13½	153	21½	163	27½
99	6	124	13½	153	21½	164	29
110	7	129	15	157	23	174	30
113	8	130	16				

If we listed all the possible scores, there would be 181 of them (180 was the highest score possible). The vast majority of these scores were not earned by any student; they have frequency zero. There are a few 1s and fewer 2s. Where the 2s fall seems rather an accident than something important about the distribution of scores. The 116 score could well have been 117, and 117 would have had a frequency of 2. By looking at *groups* of scores, instead of single values, we can find a more useful frequency distribution. We might group scores into intervals 10 units wide (see Table 6.2). Here a clearer picture begins to emerge. There are several scores below 100 and then a break. There are several scores between 110 and 120 and then a few scores scattered upward toward 140, and then another break. There are several scores between 150 and 170 and a final high score of 174. The scores roughly fall into three groups: a low group 70–100, a middle group 110–140, and a high group 140–180. I would guess that these differences show significant differences in the degree to which the material in the course was understood.

Grouping scores this way can bring out useful information from data. In this case we can reasonably assume that measuring a student's effort and understanding with logic tests and homework is not perfect. The exact number of points scored is not as important as *roughly* how many were scored. It is like measuring heights with

TABLE 6.2

Score	Frequency
70–79	2
80–89	2
90–99	2
100–109	0
110–119	6
120–129	3
130–139	3
140–149	1
150–159	5
160–169	5
170–179	1

a "rubber ruler" that is only precise to 1/3 of a foot: a person who measures 5 feet 7 inches might be considered in the interval 5 feet 4 inches to 5 feet 8 inches.

Grouping scores throws out some detailed information. If the ruler was in fact more precise than 1/3 of a foot, we could get a misimpression if we only recorded a person's height as in the interval 5 feet 4 inches to 5 feet 8 inches. Consequently, it is important to have an idea of how precise the measuring instrument being used is. When two students have logic scores that differ by 10 points, it is very likely that the students have achieved different levels of understanding and put in different amounts of effort. For two students whose scores differed by a point, one would be less inclined to say this. Of course, this depends on the particular measuring instrument used. Some tests may be better than others.

Sometimes it is useful to present *cumulative* frequency distributions. Table 6.3 presents the frequency of all scores lower than or equal to the given score. From such a table we can easily determine that 80% of all the students scored less than 159 points. 50% scored less than 129 points, and so on.

TABLE 6.3

Score	Frequency	Cumulative Frequency		Cumulative Percent
70–79	2	2	(=0 + 2)	7
80–89	2	4	(=2 + 2)	13
90–99	2	6	(=2 + 4)	20
100–109	0	6	(=0 + 6)	20
110–119	6	12	(=6 + 6)	40
120–129	3	15	(=3 + 12)	50
130–139	3	18	(=3 + 15)	60
140–149	1	19	(=1 + 18)	63
150–159	5	24	(=5 + 19)	80
160–169	5	29	(=5 + 24)	97
170–179	1	30	(=1 + 29)	100

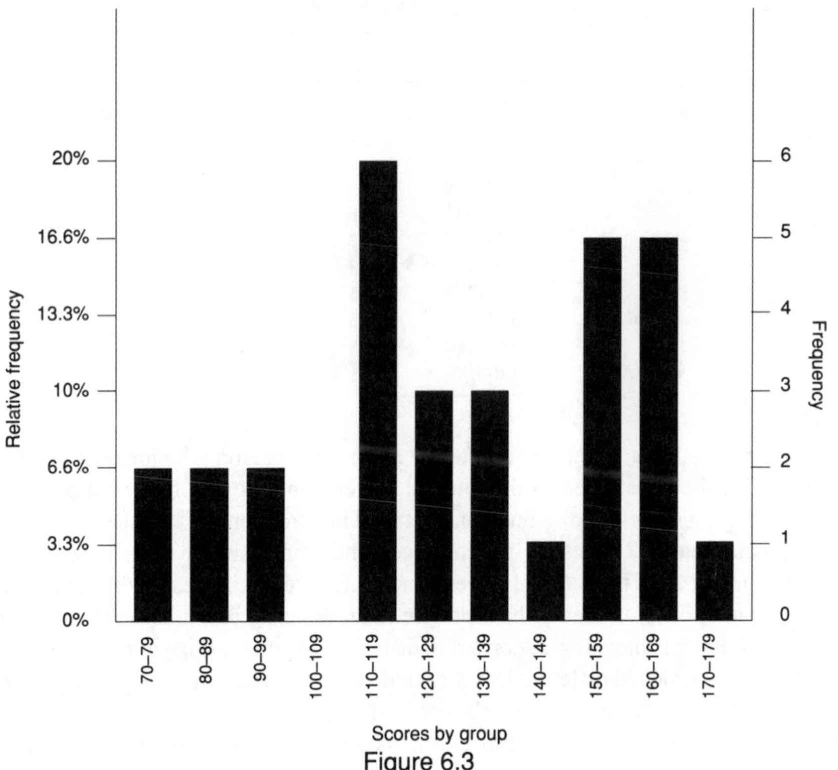

Figure 6.3

Logic–score frequency histogram.

It is also useful to present tabular information like this graphically. We can present the frequency distribution in terms of a *frequency histogram* (Figure 6.3). Here the heights of the bars represent the frequencies of scores by groups over which each bar stands. The vertical axis on the right side provides the *absolute frequency* of scores. Exactly six scores are in the interval 110–119. The vertical axis on the left side provides the relative frequency of the scores. Twenty percent (6/30) of all the scores are in the interval 110–119.

5. AVERAGES

Once we have taken the first step, describing the values of a population with respect to a given variable with a frequency distribution, we can use summary statistics to summarize and bring into the foreground important characteristics of a frequency distribution. *Averages* are one of the most common ways to summarize a frequency distribution. The three most common averages are the mode, the median, and the mean.

Mode. The mode is the simplest of these averages. The mode of a distribution is the value that occurs most frequently in the distribution. Consider an example. Suppose that we measured the shoe size of 1,000 people. We might get the frequency distribution presented in Figure 6.4 in the form of a frequency histogram. The shoe size that occurs most frequently in this distribution is size 8. This is the *mode* of the distribution. It does a reasonable job of showing where the "center" of this distribution lies.

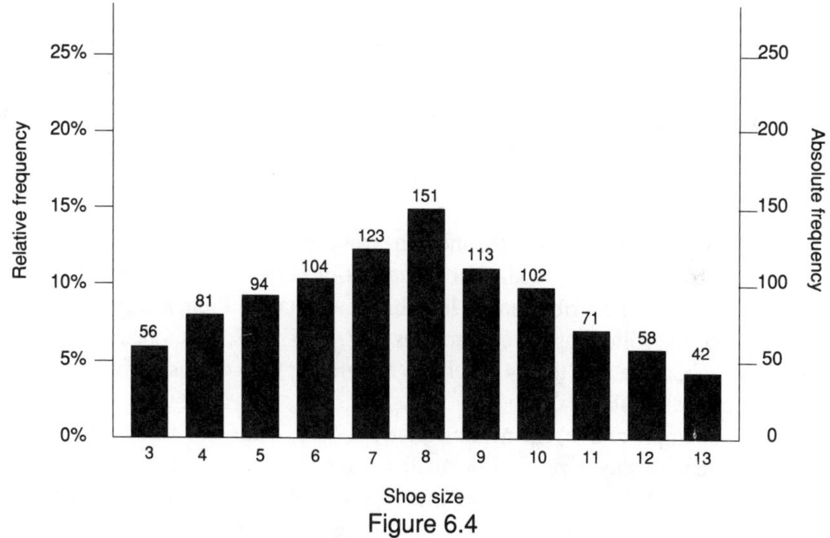

Figure 6.4

Shoe–size frequency histogram.

One thing that is good about the mode is that it does not demand much of the underlying scale of measurement. All that is required is that different measured values represent real differences in the units in the population. We do not have to assume that people with size 8 feet have feet that are twice as large as those of people with size 4 feet. We even do not have to assume that there is a particular *order* to the measured values, although in the case of shoe size there is such an order. When we say that California is the most populous state, we are giving a mode. Here the units are people, and we "measure" them by determining their state of residence. But there is no order to the states; Massachusetts is not "more" than Arkansas. Still we can summarize the resulting frequency distribution with a mode.

Consider another example. Suppose that a company has developed a new kind of battery. Unfortunately, many of the batteries produced do not work very well, stopping after only a few hours. The rest vary in the number of hours they will keep a flashlight bulb illuminated. A sample of 1,000 newly produced batteries results in the frequency distribution shown in Table 6.4. The mode is the first group, 0–50. In some sense, the mode is misleading as a summary of this distribution. In this case, the mode lies in the first category because of the "rejects," the batteries that

TABLE 6.4

Hours Illuminated	Frequency	Cumulative Frequency	Cumulative Percent
0-50	389	389	39
51-100	77	466	47
101-150	142	608	61
151-200	203	811	81
201-250	113	924	92
251-300	76	1,000	100

did not work very long. We get no indication from the mode that many of the batteries work much better. Another type of average, the median, helps in such cases.

Median. In many cases, the median, can provide a better description of the center of a distribution. The median of a distribution is the value such that half of the observed values in the distribution are less than it and half of them are greater than it. The median of the following seven numbers 1, 2, 3, 4, 5, 7, 9 is 4 because three of the seven numbers are less than 4 and three are greater than 4; 4 is halfway between either end of the numbers.

In the example above, the median shoe size is 8. Half of 1,000 is 500. There are 463 people with shoe sizes of 7 or smaller and 614 people with shoe sizes of 8 or smaller. The 500th largest shoe size must be size 8. The median of the battery example distribution is 101–150. This can be read from the cumulative frequency column; 101–150 is the first category where the cumulative frequency is larger than 50%. This median reflects the fact that many batteries—certainly more than half—will power a flashlight for more than 50 hours. In this case, the median is not as misleading as the mode.

When we use a median for an average, the scale must do more than simply categorize values. While California may be the most populous state—the modal state in terms of population—there is no "median state" in terms of population. Similarly, it would not make sense to say that brown is the median hair color. There is no order to hair color; there simply are different categories of hair colors. If brown were the most frequent hair color, we could say that brown was the hair color mode; but no hair color is the median hair color. To use the median, the scale of measurement that underlies the measured values must order the different values.

The median treats each value the same. Relatively large values are not treated differently because they are large, and relatively small values are not treated differently because they are small. This point can be made with another example. We might determine the annual income of 12 people chosen to serve on a jury. Two possible ways this distribution might look are shown in Table 6.5. They only differ in the 11th- and 12th-ranked jurors. In *both* cases the median income lies between \$12,043 and \$12,915. It is common to use the mean—about which, see below—of

TABLE 6.5

Case 1				Case 2			
Income	Rank	Income	Rank	Income	Rank	Income	Rank
$9,642	1	$12,915	7	$9,642	1	$12,915	7
$9,871	2	$14,077	8	$9,871	2	$14,077	8
$9,984	3	$15,448	9	$9,984	3	$15,448	9
$10,185	4	$19,997	10	$10,185	4	$19,997	10
$11,969	5	$28,852	11	$11,969	5	$21,366	11
$12,043	6	$47,842	12	$12,043	6	$24,702	12

the two values the median lies between when there are an even number of observations like this. Here we would fix the median at 12,479 = (12,043 + 12,915)/2. But, the median does not account for the two unusually large incomes in the first case. All the values larger than the median, no matter how much larger, count the same when computing the median. To make this distinction we turn to a third type of average.

Mean. The mean is the average that everybody thinks of as an average. To compute a mean, one adds up all the values obtained and divides by the number of values. The mean of the seven numbers 1, 2, 3, 4, 5, 7, 9 is $(1 + 2 + 3 + 4 + 5 + 7 + 9)/7 = 31/7 \approx 4.43$. In the first juror-income example above, the mean is $16,902.08; while in the second example the mean is less, $14,349.92, reflecting the two lower incomes in the 11th and 12th ranks.

We can also determine the mean number of hours that the batteries described above will illuminate a flashlight (see Table 6.4). Here we need to pick a value in each of the groups to stand for that group's value. The *midpoint* is a good choice. Thus we have 386 batteries in the 0–50 group. Consider each of these as 25. In a sense we imagine that 386 of the batteries illuminated the flashlight for 25 hours. Similarly, we imagine that 77 batteries illuminated the flashlight for 75 hours, 142 for 125 hours, and so on. We could add all these 25s and 75s up one by one, or we could multiply the number in each group by the value for the group and then add all these products:

$$
\begin{aligned}
&(25 \times 389) \\
+\ &(75 \times 77) \\
+\ &(125 \times 142) \\
+\ &(175 + 203) \\
+\ &(225 \times 113) \\
+\ &(275 \times 76) \\
=\ &9{,}725 + 5{,}775 + 17{,}750 + 35{,}525 + 25{,}425 + 20{,}900 = 115{,}100.
\end{aligned}
$$

115,100 divided by the total number of light batteries in the distribution, 1,000, is 115.1. The mean is 115.1—in the 101–150 group.

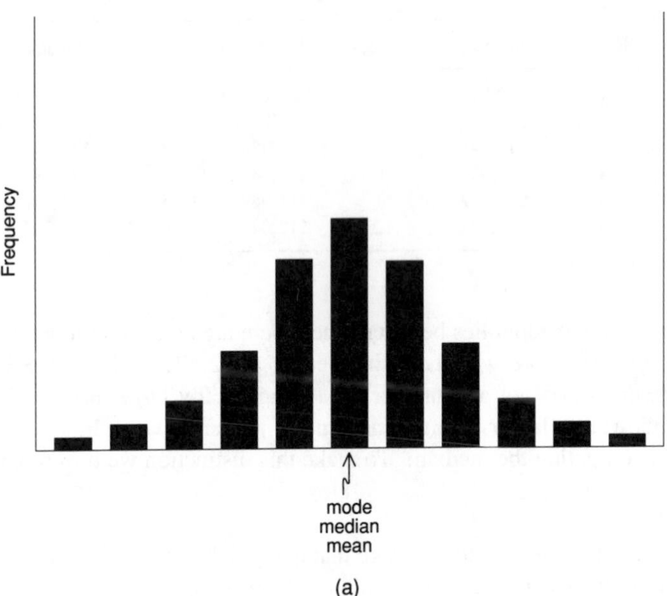

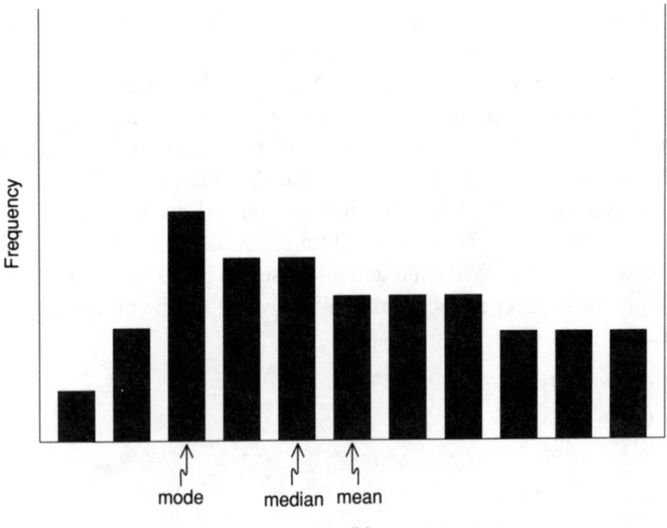

Figure 6.5 (a) Symmetrical and (b) skewed distribution.

Means are strongly affected by extreme results. Suppose, for example, that we measured just one more battery, and we noted that it illuminated a flashlight for 43,000 hours. (This is an extreme example, but you can imagine a result like this when the measurer mistakenly added three 0s after the 43.). In this case the mean would be

$$\frac{115{,}500 + 43{,}000}{1{,}001} = \frac{158{,}100}{1{,}001} \approx 158.$$

This *one* mistake in 1,000 measurements shifts the mean by an entire group. The median, by way of contrast, would hardly budge; only one observation greater than all the rest has been added to the pile. Of course, if we saw the value 43,000 we probably should discard it as an outlier.

To use the mean, the underlying scale of measurement has to provide more structure than simply ordering the elements from small to big. When we measure shoe size, for example, there is no reason to suppose that a size 6 shoe is the same amount bigger than a size 5 shoe as a size 12 shoe is bigger than a size 11 shoe. Here the units do not "stay the same;" there is not that much structure to shoe sizes. Means cannot be used with this little underlying structure. With many scales, however, the intervals do stay the same. A 150–pound man is just as much heavier than a 140–pound man as a 200–pound man is heavier than a 190–pound man. To use the mean, the underlying scale has to provide intervals between different values that are the same throughout the scale.

We can use all of these different averages to describe a distribution more fully. A *symmetrical* distribution is one where the units on either side of the mean are distributed in the same way (Figure 6.5a). One could take the frequency histogram of such a distribution and "fold it in half" down the middle by the mean, and the two sides would coincide. If such a distribution has exactly one mode, then the mean, the median, and the mode will coincide. When a distribution is "skewed" to one side, the mean will be to that side of the median and the median will be to that side of the mode (Figure 6.5b). If you think of the distribution as sitting on a seesaw, it will balance when the pivot is under the mean. There may be fewer observations larger than the mean than there are observations smaller than the mean, but these few are farther from the mean and so "count for more."

6. MEASURES OF DISPERSION

Another important summary statistic measures how spread out the values in a frequency distribution are. The annual incomes of 25–year-olds will have less variation than the annual incomes of 45–year-olds. As with the case of averages, there are several different measures of dispersion. The three most common are the range, quartiles, and the standard deviation.

Range. The range simply measures how far the biggest and the smallest values are from each other. The range of annual incomes in the jury (Table 6.5) is

\$38,200 = 47,842 − 9,642 in the first case, and \$15,060 (24,702 − 9,642) in the second case. While the range tells us something about how spread out the values are, it is completely insensitive to what the distribution is like between the highest and lowest values. A flat distribution, a distribution sharply peaked around the mean, and a distribution with one lone high value can have the same range (Figure 6.6).

Quartiles. Quartiles tell us more about *how* the distribution is spread out. Quartiles extend the idea behind the median. The median is the value where half of the observed values are less and half are greater. Quartiles cut the distribution into quarters. The *first quartile* is the value where one-fourth of the other values are less and three-fourths are greater. The *second quartile* is the median. The *third quartile* is the value where three-fourths of the other values are less and one-fourth are greater.

In either distribution of jury incomes (Table 6.5), for example, the first quartile is between 9,984 and 10,185—call it 10,084.50 = (9,984 + 10,185)/2. The second quartile is the median calculated above, 12,479. And the third quartile is between 15,448 and 19,997—call it 17,722.50 = (15,448 + 19,997)/2. Quartiles can be represented graphically with what is called a "box-and-whisker" plot (Figure 6.7). A rectangular box is drawn with edges at the first and third quartile, and a vertical line is drawn inside the box at the second quartile or median. Whiskers are drawn extending from either end of the box to the largest and smallest values observed. It is pretty easy to get a good idea of how a distribution is spread out from a box-and-whisker plot. The jury incomes in the first case are mostly in the 10,000–17,000 range with, in the first case, a few very large incomes, as high as 47,000.

Standard deviation. While quartiles and box-and-whisker plots do an excellent job of showing how observed values are spread out, they can be somewhat cumbersome to work with. Quartiles use five numbers to summarize a distribution. Sometimes, especially when we know something about the distribution, a single value can serve to summarize the spread of a distribution.

The standard deviation can summarize the spread of a distribution in a single number. The standard deviation can summarize the spread of any distribution, but it is particularly well suited to do so with "normal distributions" or "bell-shaped curves." The normal distribution is a family of frequency distributions that are quite common in statistical work. We encountered them briefly in Chapter 4. They also play an important role in the justification of the polling inferences discussed in Chapter 2. We study them in greater detail in Chapter 9. In fact, it was once thought that the only "natural" frequency distribution was the normal distribution.

Standard deviations also require an underlying scale of measurement with at least as much structure as that used to measure temperature. Standard deviations are not appropriate with measurements, such as shoe sizes, that only provide order.

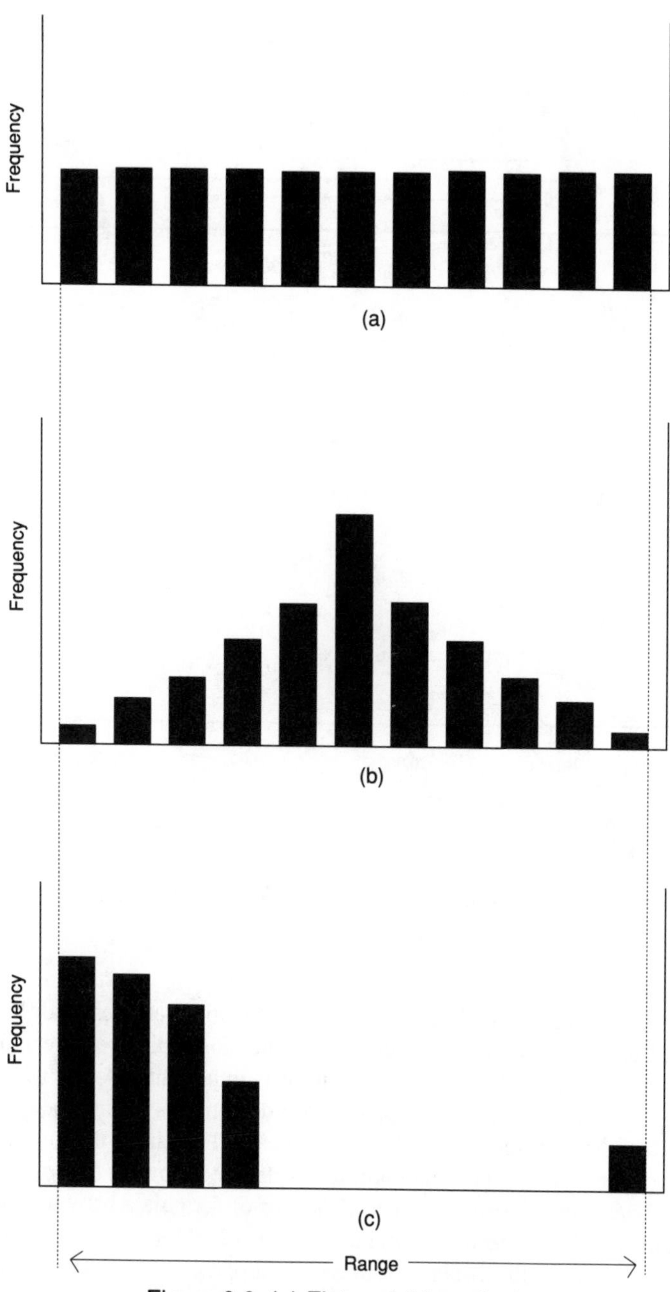

Figure 6.6 (a) Flat and (b) peaked distribution; (c) distribution with an unusual value.

CASE 1

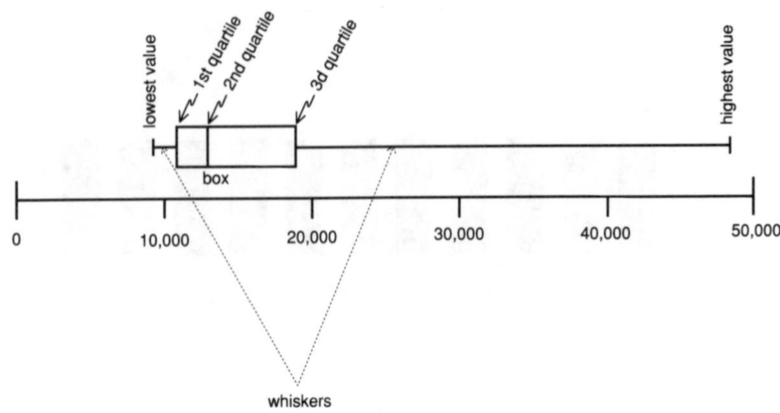

CASE 2

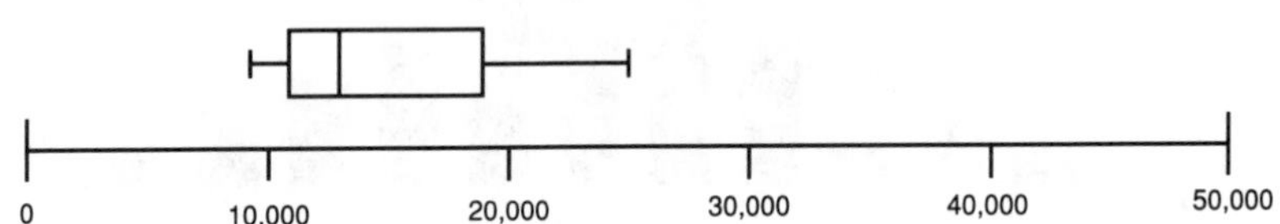

Box-and-whisker plot for jury-income distribution.
Figure 6.7

Computing the standard deviation for a distribution requires a fair bit of arithmetic, and the formula for doing so looks rather forbidding. While most of the computation these days is done by machine, it is important to know *what* is being computed. The basic idea behind the standard deviation is to find the average distance between each observed value and the mean. The larger this number is, the more spread out the observed values are. Consider the following five values: 2, 4, 5, 7, and 7. These might be the number of ounces of formula a baby ate during five daily feedings. We first need to compute the mean $(2 + 4 + 5 + 7 + 7)/5 = 25/5 = 5$. Then we determine the distance from each observation to the mean. The distance between 2 and 5 is 3; the distance between 4 and 5 is 1; and so on. Adding up all these distances results in a dispersion of $3 + 1 + 0 + 2 + 2 = 8$, and an average dispersion of $8/5 = 1.6$.

To implement this idea mathematically and conceptually, several things need to be done. In the first place, finding distances is difficult because "negative distances" must be made positive. The distance between the value 2 and the mean, 5, for example, is, $2 - 5 = -3 \rightarrow +3$. This is unwieldy mathematically. Instead of converting negatives to positives in this way, we square all of the differences: $(2-5)^2 = (-3)^2 = +9$. We have

$$(2-5)^2 + (4-5)^2 + (5-5)^2 + (7-5)^2 + (7-5)^2 =$$

$$(-3)^2 + (-1)^2 + (+0)^2 + (+2)^2 + (+2)^2 =$$

$$9 + 1 + 0 + 4 + 4 = 18.$$

We want the *average* deviation from the mean. If we did not do this, we would get bigger standard deviations, representing greater dispersion, simply by increasing the number of observations, not by these additional observations being dispersed farther from the mean. We have to divide the result we obtain by the number of observations, 5, $18/5 = 3.6$. N is the usual symbol for the total number of observations made; we say that the result is divided by N.

There is one other difficulty. By squaring the differences between the mean and the other values, we squared the units used to measure dispersion. The dispersion of our five measurements of baby formula is 3.6 "*square ounces*" (ounces × ounces) or ounces^2. Sometimes it is useful to take the square root and have our measure of dispersion in the same units as the values measured. When we take the square root, the result is called the *standard deviation*. When we do not take the square root, the summary statistic is called the *variance*, which is useful in some circumstances. The standard deviation of the five measurements 2, 4, 5, 7, and 7 is the square root of 18/5: $\sqrt{18/5} \approx 1.90$.

When we put all of these operations together, the result looks complicated. We need a way to refer briefly to values in the frequency distribution. It is usual to do this by writing $\mathbf{X_i}$, an **X** with a subscript i. We label each of the values with a number, and we refer to individual values by this number, $\mathbf{X_1}$, $\mathbf{X_2}$, $\mathbf{X_3}$, and so on. When we want to refer to the entire series we write $\mathbf{X_i}$, where the subscript i "varies over" all the different "number labels" for the values. It is usual to refer to the mean of all the values by $\overline{\mathbf{X}}$, **X** with a bar on top, called "**X**-bar." With these naming conventions in mind, the formula for the standard deviation is

$$\text{standard deviation} = \sqrt{\frac{\Sigma(\mathbf{X_i} - \overline{\mathbf{X}})^2}{N}}$$

Σ stands for *sum*. We add, or "sum up," each value's squared distance from the mean,

$$(\mathbf{X_1} - \overline{\mathbf{X}})^2 + (\mathbf{X_2} - \overline{\mathbf{X}})^2 + (\mathbf{X_3} - \overline{\mathbf{X}})^2 + \cdots = \Sigma(\mathbf{X_i} - \overline{\mathbf{X}})^2.$$

That is, we compute the squared difference between each value, $\mathbf{X_i}$, and the mean, $(\mathbf{X_i} - \overline{\mathbf{X}})^2$, and we add these squared differences, $\Sigma(\mathbf{X_i} - \overline{\mathbf{X}})^2$. We take the *average* of these, dividing by the total number of observations, N: $\Sigma(\mathbf{X_i} - \mathbf{X})^2/N$, and we restore the units by taking the square root: $\sqrt{\Sigma(\mathbf{X_i} - \overline{\mathbf{X}})^2/N}$.

Table 6.6 gives an idea of how this formula works with the first 12 juror incomes computed similarly. The mean is \$16,902. When there are more than 12 observed values, a table like this becomes rather unwieldy. Many calculators now have a feature that will output the standard deviation of a group of values input to the calculator. None of the tedious arithmetic done above needs to be done "by hand." Still, the idea behind the computation of any standard deviation is nicely captured in this kind of table.

TABLE 6.6

i	X_i	$(X_i - \overline{X})$	$(X_i - \overline{X})^2$
1	9,642	−7,260	52,707,600
2	9,871	−7,031	49,434,961
3	9,984	−6,918	47,858,724
4	10,185	−6,717	45,118,089
5	11,969	−4,933	24,334,489
6	12,043	−4,859	23,609,881
7	12,915	−3,987	15,896,169
8	14,077	−2,825	7,980,625
9	15,448	−1,454	2,114,116
10	19,997	+3,095	9,579,025
11	28,852	+11,950	142,802,500
12	47,842	+30,940	957,283,600
			Total: 1,378,719,779

$$\Sigma(X_i - \overline{X})^2 = 1{,}378{,}719{,}779$$

$$\sqrt{\frac{\Sigma(X_i - \overline{X})^2}{N}} = \sqrt{\frac{1{,}378{,}719{,}779}{12}} = \sqrt{114{,}893{,}315} = \$10{,}719$$

Standard deviations and means can be converted from one scale of measurement to another. For example, suppose that the five baby formula measurements above, 2, 4, 5, 7, and 7, had been measured in milliliters instead of ounces. 1 ounce is 33 milliliters. We would have found the following values: 66, 132, 165, 231,

TABLE 6.7

i	X_i	$(X_i - \overline{X})$	$(X_i - \overline{X})^2$
1	66	−99	9,801
2	132	−33	1,089
3	165	+0	0
4	231	+66	4,356
5	231	+66	4,356
			Total: 19,602

$$\Sigma(X_i - \overline{X})^2 = 19{,}602;$$

$$\sqrt{\frac{\Sigma(X_i - \overline{X})^2}{N}} = \sqrt{\frac{19{,}602}{5}} = \sqrt{3{,}920.4} = 62.61 \text{ milliliters} = 1.9 \text{ ounces}$$

231. We can compute the standard deviation for these measurements. The mean is (66 + 132 + 165 + 231 + 231)/5 = 165 milliliters = 5 ounces—as it should be. The standard deviation is computed in Table 6.7. While the pure numbers are different, 1.9 ≠ 62.61, when we account for the units used, the result is the same, 1.9 ounces = 62.61 milliliters.

7. CORRELATION

We have seen how to talk about variation of the units in a population with respect to *one* measured variable with a frequency distribution. We can use *summary statistics*, like the mean and standard deviation, to describe and emphasize features of a frequency distribution.

Many times, however, we are interested in more than one *variable* of the units in a population. By looking at more than one variable of a population, we can understand *relationships* between different variables of units in the population. It is because SAT scores and freshman GPAs are *related* that SAT scores are frequently used to help determine whether an applicant should be admitted to a college. It is because doctors observed a relationship between the number of cigarettes smoked and the incidence of lung cancer that we began to suspect that smoking causes lung cancer.

Frequently, two variables may be related, but not 100%, so to speak. While, generally speaking, people who are tall are also heavy, it would be wrong to say that someone *must* be heavy because he is tall. It is not uncommon for some people to discount the relationship between smoking and lung cancer because of their "95-year-old relative who has smoked for 80 years." Such cases surely exist, but they do not show that there is no relationship between smoking and lung cancer: proportionally more cases of lung cancer occur among those who smoke than among those who do not. Correlation statistics provide a means to describe relationships between variables such as these, which lie between no connection at all and a 100% connection.

Correlations can show causal tendencies, but can fall short of demonstrating direct causal connections between the variables studied. Generally, people who do well on the SAT have higher freshman GPAs than those of people who do not do well on the SAT. But it would be wrong to give up the idea of doing well in college simply because one did poorly on the SAT. (Of course, this would confirm the relationship between SAT and GPA.) SAT scores allow one to *predict* college GPA; they do not *cause or make certain* the actual GPA a student earns.

When we examined one variable of a population we used a frequency histogram to graphically describe the population with respect to this variable. With two variables, we can use a *scatter plot* to show how the variables are related in the population. Suppose that we measured the height and circumference at the base of each of 100 trees. We could represent each of these measurements with an **X** on graph paper (Figure 6.8). In the figure, the circled **X** is directly above 30 feet on the horizontal scale and directly across from 60 inches on the vertical scale. The tree whose measurements this **X** reflects is 30 feet tall and has a circumference of 60 inches.

The overall shape of this "swarm" of **X**s shows that there is a relationship between tree height and tree circumference. Taller trees have wider trunks—although some tall trees have narrow trunks and some short trees have wide trunks. Intuitively, the closer the relationship is between circumference and height, the more closely grouped together the **X**s would be. The more nearly the **X**s form a line, the more closely two variables are related to each other. When the **X**s form a line we can predict the value of one variable quite accurately from the value of the other variable. When the **X**s are spread out, it is more difficult to predict the value of one variable from the value of the other variable.

The *correlation coefficient* gives us a numerical value that summarizes "how close together" the **X**s are in a scatter plot. Correlation coefficient values vary between -1 and $+1$. When two variables have a correlation coefficient value—or more simply, correlation—near 0, they have very little relationship (Figure 6.9a). When they have a correlation near $+1$ they are closely related in such a way that larger values of one of the variables are usually associated with larger values of the other variable (Figure 6.9b). When they have a correlation near -1 they are closely related such that larger values of one of the variables are associated with smaller values of the other variable (Figure 6.9c).

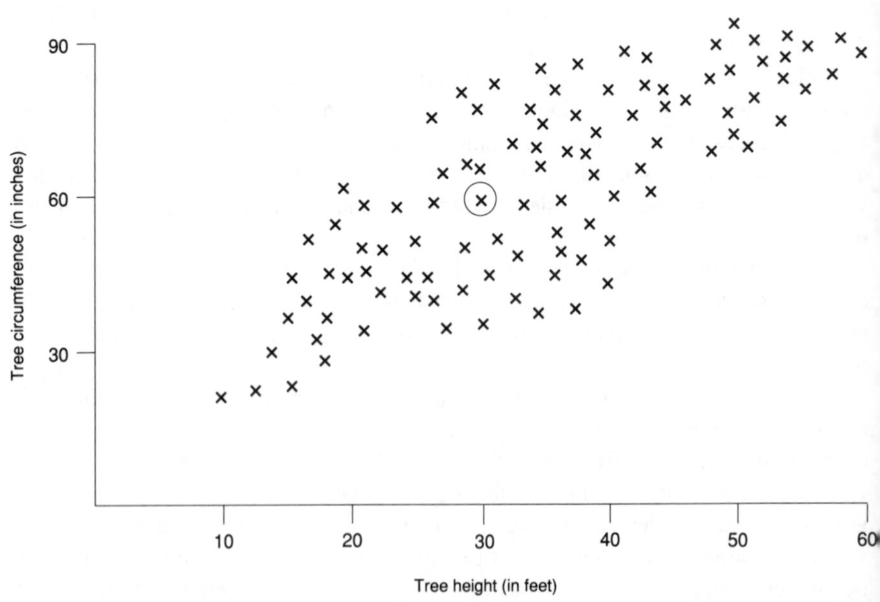

Figure 6.8

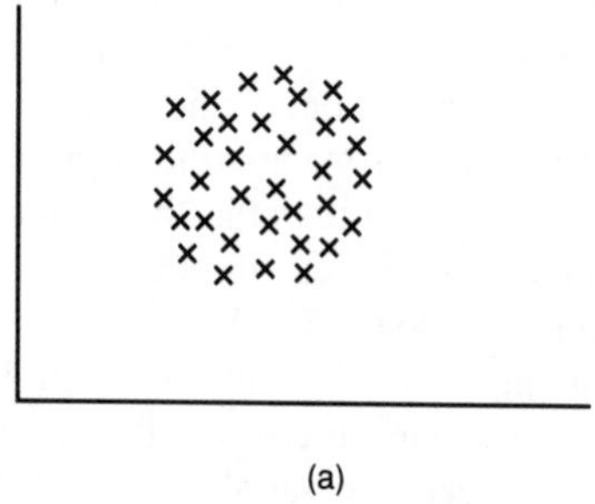

(a)

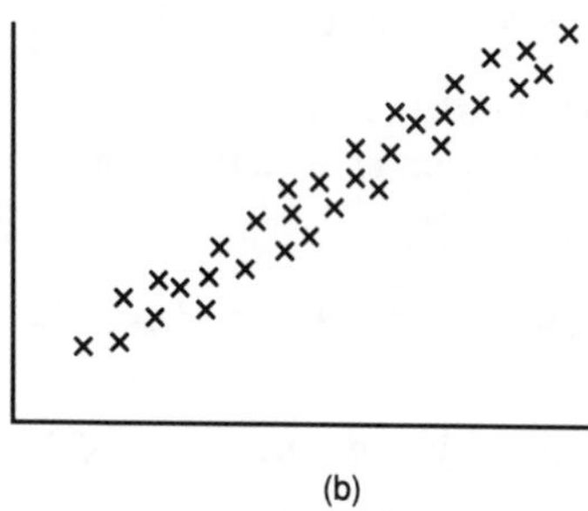

(b)

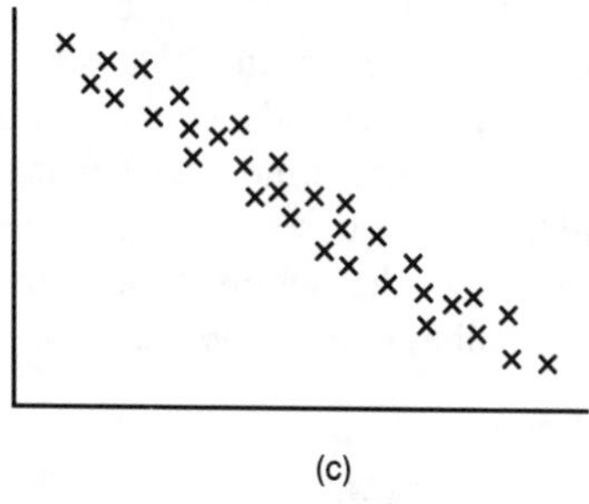

(c)

Scatter plots for two variables:
(a) very little relationship and a correlation near zero;
(b) closely related with a large positive correlation;
(c) closely related with a large negative correlation

Figure 6.9

Consider the population of cars registered in California. The variables of weight and miles per gallon have a negative correlation: the heavier a car, probably, the fewer miles per gallon it will get. The variables of miles per gallon and the year the car was made have a positive correlation: the more recently the car was made—the larger the number of the year it was made—the larger the number of miles per gallon the car will get, on average. On the other hand, the variables of miles per gallon and the number of miles the car was driven on April 12, 1989 have little relationship and a near-zero correlation.

The formula for computing the correlation coefficient looks even more formidable than the formula for the standard deviation. But once taken apart, it can be understood. The correlation between two variables, **X** and **Y**, is usually given the symbol r_{XY}, r for "relationship":

$$r_{XY} = \frac{\Sigma[((\mathbf{X_i} - \overline{\mathbf{X}})(\mathbf{Y_i} - \overline{\mathbf{Y}}))/N]}{\sqrt{\Sigma(\mathbf{X_i} - \overline{\mathbf{X}})^2/N} \times \sqrt{\Sigma(\mathbf{Y_i} - \overline{\mathbf{Y}})^2/N}}$$

We have met the expressions in the denominator; they are the *standard deviations* of the **X** and **Y** variables. The expression in the numerator is the *covariance* of **X** and **Y**, Cov(**X**, **Y**):

$$\text{Cov}(\mathbf{X}, \mathbf{Y}) = \frac{\Sigma(\mathbf{X_i} - \overline{\mathbf{X}})(\mathbf{Y_i} - \overline{\mathbf{Y}})}{N}$$

The correlation between **X** and **Y** is the *covariance of* **X** *and* **Y** divided by the *standard deviation of* **X** times the *standard deviation of* **Y**.

A simple numerical example with a small number of measurements can show how this formula works. Suppose that we put one ice cube in a glass, two ice cubes in a second glass, three in a third, four in a fourth, and five in a fifth glass. We could time how long it took the ice cubes in each of the glasses to melt completely. The results of five such measurements are given in Table 6.8. There is a relationship between the number of ice cubes in a glass and the length of time it takes for them to melt. The more ice cubes in the glass, the more time it takes for them to melt.

Here we have a population of five glasses. We measure two different variables on each of these units—or glasses—the number of ice cubes in a glass, and the length of time it takes for the ice cubes to melt. We can call the number of ice cubes

TABLE 6.8

Individual	Number of Ice Cubes	Time to Melt
Glass 1	1	95
Glass 2	2	120
Glass 3	3	140
Glass 4	4	155
Glass 5	5	160

the **X** variable and the length of time to melt the **Y** variable. When we measure two variables on a single unit we need a convenient way to record which number corresponds to which variable's value. Angle brackets are a common device:

<1, 95>, <2, 120>, <3, 140>, <4, 155>, <5,160>.

The order of the numbers in the brackets tells us which variable is which. The first number tells us how many ice cubes were in the glass—it tells us the value of the **X** variable; the second number tells us how long it took the ice to melt—the value of the **Y** variable. A graph of the data is shown in Figure 6.10.

To calculate the correlation coefficient, r_{XY}, we can construct Table 6.9. We can plug all of these numbers into the correlation coefficient formula:

$$r_{XY} = \frac{\Sigma[((X_i - \overline{X})(Y_i - \overline{Y}))/N]}{\sqrt{\Sigma(X_i - \overline{X})^2/N} \times \sqrt{\Sigma(Y_i - \overline{Y}^2/N}}$$

$$= \frac{165/5}{\sqrt{10/5} \times \sqrt{2{,}870/5}} = \frac{33}{1.414 \times 23.96} = 0.97.$$

So the correlation between the number of ice cubes in a glass and the length of time it takes for the ice to melt is 0.97. This shows that, on average, the larger the number of ice cubes, the longer it takes to melt—not too surprising.

We can better understand this formula by looking at some numerically simpler examples. The numerator of the correlation formula does the main job of summarizing how "line-like" a swarm of Xs in a scatter plot is. The denominator stan-

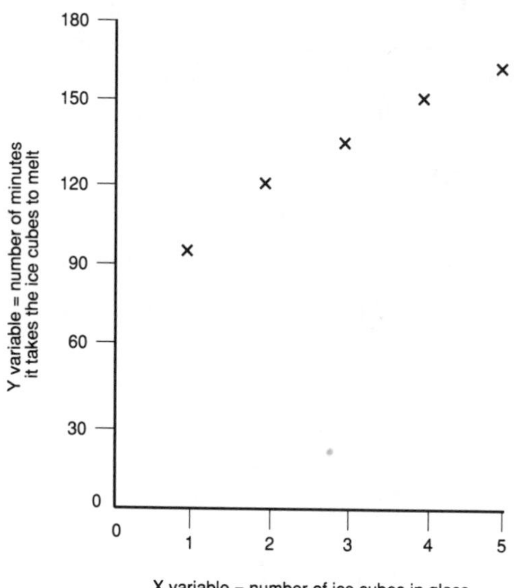

Figure 6.10

TABLE 6.9

i	X_i	Y_i	$(X_i - \overline{X})$	$(Y_i - \overline{Y})$	$(X_i - \overline{X})^2$	$(Y_i - \overline{Y})^2$	$(X_i - \overline{X})(Y_i - \overline{Y})$
1	1	95	−2	−39	4	1,521	+78
2	2	120	−1	−14	1	196	+14
3	3	140	+0	+6	0	36	+0
4	4	155	+1	+21	1	441	+21
5	5	160	+2	+26	4	676	+52
Totals:	15	670	0	0	10	2,870	+165
Totals/*N*:	3	134	0	0	2	574	33

dardizes the units, so correlations can be compared between cases. Here we study the way the numerator works. In Section 9 we study the denominator.

Suppose that we measure four units with respect to two variables, **X** and **Y** (Table 6.10). (Whatever **X** and **Y** might be does not matter to see how the correlation formula works numerically.) We can graph these four pairs, <0, 0>, <4, 0>, <4, 4>, <0, 4> (Figure 6.11). The mean value for the **X** and **Y** variables is the same.

$$\frac{\Sigma(\mathbf{X_i})}{N} = \frac{0 + 4 + 4 + 0}{4} = 2 \qquad \frac{\Sigma(\mathbf{Y_i})}{N} = \frac{0 + 0 + 4 + 4}{4} = 2.$$

The point <2, 2> is the mean point for both distributions. On the graph, it is marked with a star, ✶, and is right in the middle of the four points. We can call ✶ the *center of gravity* of these points.

To calculate the numerator of the correlation coefficient, we multiply the difference between a unit's **X**-variable value and the **X** variable mean, with the difference between that unit's **Y** variable value and the **Y** variable mean. Then we add up these products: In our example, we have the following:

$$(\mathbf{X_1} - \overline{\mathbf{X}})(\mathbf{Y_1} - \overline{\mathbf{Y}}) = -2 \times -2 = +4;$$

$$(\mathbf{X_2} - \overline{\mathbf{X}})(\mathbf{Y_2} - \overline{\mathbf{Y}}) = +2 \times -2 = -4;$$

$$(\mathbf{X_3} - \overline{\mathbf{X}})(\mathbf{Y_3} - \overline{\mathbf{Y}}) = +2 \times +2 = +4;$$

$$(\mathbf{X_4} - \overline{\mathbf{X}})(\mathbf{Y_4} - \overline{\mathbf{Y}}) = -2 \times +2 = -4;$$

$$4 + -4 + 4 + -4 = 0.$$

TABLE 6.10

i	X_i	Y_i
1	0	0
2	4	0
3	4	4
4	0	4

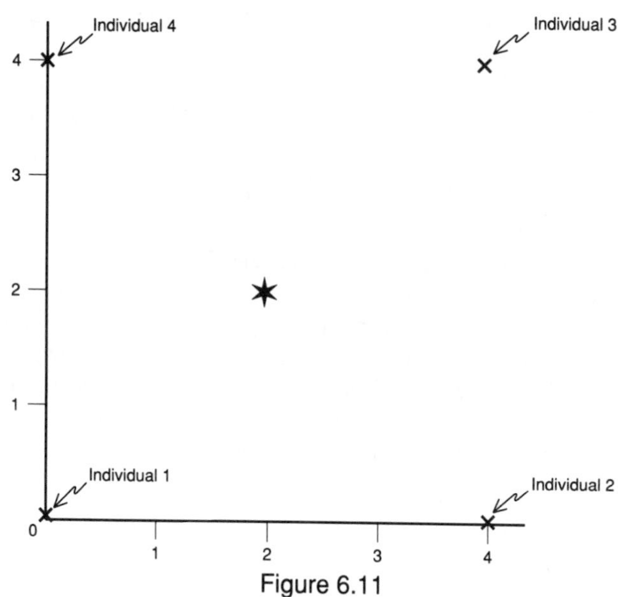

Figure 6.11

A point that is to the *right* of the mean value, ✶, has a *positive* difference between its **X**-variable value and the **X**-variable mean. A point that is to the *left* of ✶ has a *negative* difference between its **X**-variable value and the **X**-variable mean. Similarly, a point *above* ✶ has a *positive* difference between its **Y**-variable value and the **Y**-variable mean. A point *below* ✶ has a *negative* difference between the **Y**-variable value and the **Y**-variable mean. Individuals 2 and 3 are to the right of ✶ and have positive **X**-variable differences. Individuals 1 and 4 are to the left of ✶ and have negative **X**-variable differences. Similar observations can be made about the **Y**-variable. When we multiply these **X**- and **Y**-variable differences, the signs of the numbers make an important difference. Points that are *below and to the left* of ✶ produce a *positive* product of these differences. Points that are *below and to the right* of ✶ yield a negative product. And so on. We make the point graphically in Figure 6.12.

The farther a point is from ✶, the larger the product of its **X**-variable difference and its **Y**-variable difference. In the simple four-point example, all of the points are equally far from ✶, and there is one in each positive/negative "zone." Consequently, we would expect that the contributions to the numerator of the correlation coefficient of these points would sum to 0. The positive contributions cancel the negative contributions. If we make the negative contributions smaller by moving the points for individuals 2 and 4 closer to ✶, we get a positive sum. The value of the numerator of the correlation coefficient for four points <0, 0>, <3, 1>, <4, 4>, <1, 3> is 6:

$$(\mathbf{X_1} - \mathbf{X})(\mathbf{Y_1} - \mathbf{Y}) = (0 - 2)(0 - 2) = -2 \times -2 = +4$$

$$(\mathbf{X_1} - \mathbf{X})(\mathbf{Y_1} - \mathbf{Y}) = (3 - 2)(1 - 2) = +1 \times -1 = -1$$

$$(\mathbf{X_1} - \mathbf{X})(\mathbf{Y_1} - \mathbf{Y}) = (4 - 2)(4 - 2) = +2 \times +2 = +4$$

$$(\mathbf{X_1} - \mathbf{X})(\mathbf{Y_1} - \mathbf{Y}) = (1 - 2)(3 - 2) = -1 \times +1 = -1$$

$$4 + -1 + 4 + -1 = 6.$$

These four points are more "line-like" than the first four points. The larger the **X**-variable value is, the larger the **Y**-variable value is—more or less. On the other hand, if we make the positive contributions smaller by moving the points for individuals 1 and 3 closer to ✶, we get a negative value for the numerator of the correlation coefficient. The numerator of the correlation coefficient measures the average product of the distances of points from the mean for both variables. Doing this gives a measure of how "line-like" the swarm of points is.

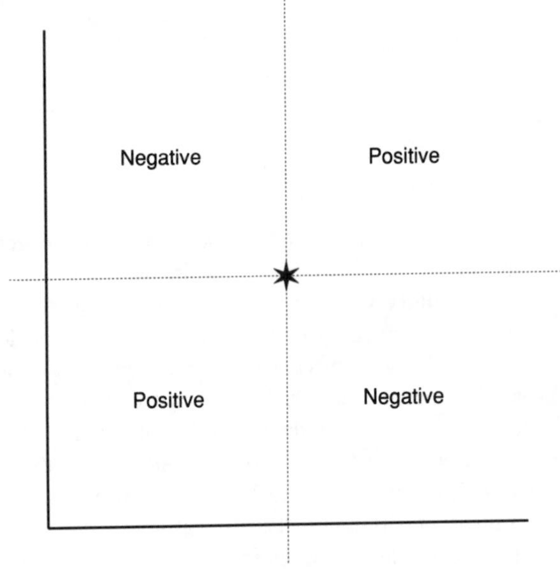

Figure 6.12

The correlation coefficient requires that whatever underlying scales are used to measure the variables of interest have at least as much structure as that used to measure temperature. With temperature scales, numerically equal intervals represent physically identical differences no matter where in the scale the interval occurs. Thirty degrees Celsius is the same amount warmer than 20 degrees Celsius as 47 degrees Celsius is than 37 degrees Celsius. Scales with this kind of structure are called "interval scales." Temperature is measured on an interval scale. Correlation requires measurements made with a scale that has at least as much structure as that provided by an interval scale.

The denominator of the correlation formula serves to standardize the correlation values. It does this by converting the measurements—from whatever scale—to what may be called *standard deviation units*. Standard deviation units are quite useful in certain applications—most especially, for our concerns, factor analysis—and deserve a separate explanation before seeing how they work in the correlation formula.

8. STANDARD DEVIATION UNITS

Recall the baby formula example. A baby drank 2, 4, 5, 7, and 7 ounces of formula during five daily feedings. The mean of these values is 5 ounces. The standard deviation of these values is 1.90 ounces. We can use the mean and standard deviation to construct a new scale with which to express these measurements. We construct the new scale by thinking of each of the values in terms of the number of standard deviations it is from the mean. For instance, 2 ounces is 3 ounces smaller than the mean; but 3 ounces is $(3/1.9) \approx 1.58$ *standard deviations*. We use proportions to compute such a change of unit:

1 standard deviation unit is to 1.9 ounces
as
x standard deviation units is to 3.0 ounces

We solve this equation for x: $1.0/1.9 = x/3.0$: $x = (1.0 \times 3.0)/1.9 = 3.0/1.9 = 1.58$. Instead of expressing the value measured as "2 ounces," we express it as "-1.58 standard deviation units"— minus because it is less than the mean. We can similarly compute the other measured values in terms of standard deviation units (Table 6.11).

Standard deviation units are *insensitive* to the underlying scale of measurement. If we did this conversion for our measurements in milliliters—instead of ounces—we would get the same standard deviation units (see Table 6.7). When we measure in milliliters, the mean is 165 milliliters and the standard deviation is 62.61 milliliters. So the first value, 66 milliliters, is 99 milliliters less than the mean. Use proportions again:

1 standard deviation unit is to 62.61 milliliters
as
x standard deviation units is to 99 milliliters

Solve for x: $1.0/62.61 = x/99.0$: $x = (1.0 \times 99.0)/62.61 = 99.0/62.61 = 1.58$. 99 milliliters is 1.58 standard deviation units. So 66 milliliters is -1.58 standard deviation units, the same number of standard deviation units as when we measure in ounces. Standard deviation units standardize the measurements in this way.

It is important to keep in mind that standard deviation units rely on a fixed population of measured values. When new values are added, the mean and standard deviation can change. When the mean and standard deviation change, all of the

TABLE 6.11

Ounces	Standard Deviation Units
2	−1.58
4	−0.53
5	+0.00
7	+1.05
7	+1.05

standard deviation unit values for the measured values must change as well.

Several items are worth noting about standard deviation units. When we convert to standard deviation units, the mean of the measurements is always zero. Standard deviation units always measure the distance a point is from the mean, and the mean is no distance at all from itself. So the mean must be 0 in standard deviation units. These properties are very useful in the discussion of factor analysis in Chapter 12.

9. THE CORRELATION SCALE

The numerator of the correlation coefficient measures how line-like a bunch of measurements is. The denominator establishes the scale: $-1 \leq r_{XY} \leq +1$. Whatever the underlying scale of measurement for a given collection of measurements, be it pounds, ounces, or kilograms, the correlation coefficient will come out the same. This is one aspect of the objectivity of the correlation coefficient.

Suppose, for example, that we measured separately the weights of a person's left and right arms. We might get 10 pounds for the left arm and 11 pounds for the right arm. We could make such a measurement on the arms of three more people. We could express our results with angle brackets: $<10.0, 11.0>$, $<9.0, 9.8>$, $<10.2, 11.3>$, and $<8.3, 8.9>$. The first value in the brackets tells us the weight of the left arm and the second tells us the weight of the right arm—in pounds. We could also measure these weights in grams, in which case, since 1 pound = 220 grams, we would get different numbers: $<2{,}200, 2{,}420>$, $<1{,}980, 2{,}156>$, $<2{,}244, 2{,}486>$ and $<1{,}826, 1{,}958>$. See Figure 6.13 for the graphs of these two examples. The gram-unit example has a larger numerator for its correlation coefficient than the pound-unit example—143,021.00 as compared to 3.09. If we used only the numerator to measure how line-like a bunch of points are, we would mistakenly conclude that the set with the bigger numbers is more line-like when the examples only differ in the units of measurement used. The denominator of the correlation formula solves this difficulty, and in doing so it establishes the correlation scale.

The algebraic proof that correlations must lie between -1 and $+1$ is somewhat demanding. It requires some care with sums: Σ algebra we can call it. But this kind

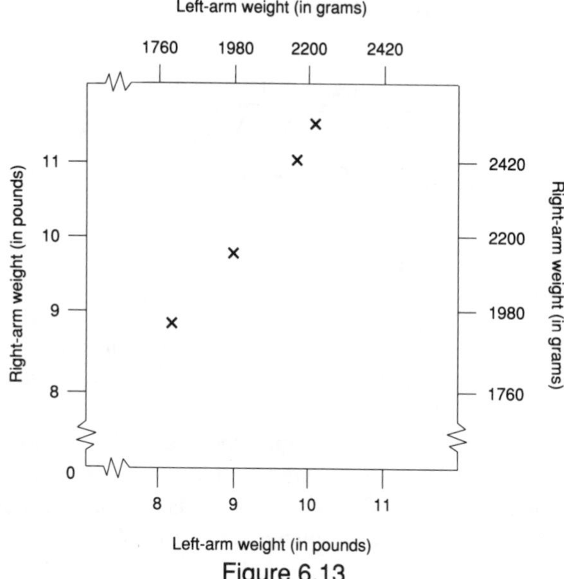

Figure 6.13

of manipulation is central to many statistical operations, and it will be worthwhile to become familiar with it. The most important thing to remember is that a sum expressed with a Σ is still just a sum—a bunch of numbers added up.

We start with the few preliminary observations that follow from using standard deviation units. When we measure two variables, **X** and **Y**, with standard deviation units we ensure that the mean is 0 and the standard deviation is 1:

$$\text{the } \mathbf{X}\text{-variable mean} = \overline{\mathbf{X}} = \frac{\Sigma(\mathbf{X}_i)}{N} = 0;$$

$$\text{the } \mathbf{X}\text{-variable standard deviation} = \sqrt{\frac{\Sigma(\mathbf{X}_i - \overline{\mathbf{X}})^2}{N}} = \sqrt{\frac{\Sigma(\mathbf{X}_i - 0)^2}{N}}$$

$$= \sqrt{\frac{\Sigma(\mathbf{X}_i)^2}{N}} = 1;$$

$$\text{the } \mathbf{Y}\text{-variable mean} = \overline{\mathbf{Y}} = \frac{\Sigma(\mathbf{Y}_i)}{N} = 0;$$

$$\text{the } \mathbf{Y}\text{-variable standard deviation} = \sqrt{\frac{\Sigma(\mathbf{Y}_i - \overline{\mathbf{Y}})^2}{N}} = \sqrt{\frac{\Sigma(\mathbf{Y}_i - 0)^2}{N}}$$

$$= \sqrt{\frac{\Sigma(\mathbf{Y}_i)^2}{N}} = 1.$$

When we use standard deviation units, the correlation formula becomes much simpler:

$$\begin{aligned}
\mathrm{r_{XY}} &= \frac{\Sigma[((\mathbf{X_i} - \overline{\mathbf{X}})(\mathbf{Y_i} - \overline{\mathbf{Y}}))/N]}{\sqrt{\Sigma(\mathbf{X_i} - \overline{\mathbf{X}})^2/N} \times \sqrt{\Sigma(\mathbf{Y_i} - \overline{\mathbf{Y}})^2/N}} \\
&= \frac{\Sigma[((\mathbf{X_i} - 0)(\mathbf{Y_i} - 0))/N]}{1 \times 1} \\
&= \frac{\Sigma(\mathbf{X_i}\mathbf{Y_i})}{N}.
\end{aligned}$$

We see from the second line above that when measurements are expressed in standard deviation units, we only have to use the numerator to calculate the correlation coefficient.

When we use standard deviation units, the standard deviation is simply the square root of the sum of each value squared (divided by N): $\sqrt{\Sigma(\mathbf{X_i})^2/N}$. This must equal 1, since when we use standard deviation units, the standard deviation is 1. Consequently, the sum of the values squared add up to N:

$$\sqrt{\frac{\Sigma(\mathbf{X_i})^2}{N}} = 1 \Rightarrow \frac{\Sigma(\mathbf{X_i})^2}{N} = 1 \Rightarrow \Sigma(\mathbf{X_i})^2 = N.$$

The sum of the **Y**-variable values squared must also add up to N: $\Sigma(\mathbf{Y_i})^2 = N$.

Given this much preparation, we can now show how standard deviation units standardize the correlation scale. We want to show that $-1 \le \Sigma(\mathbf{X_i}\mathbf{Y_i})/N \le +1$. There are two halves to the proof. We must prove (1) that $\Sigma(\mathbf{X_i}\mathbf{Y_i})/N \le +1$, and (2) that $-1 \le \Sigma(\mathbf{X_i}\mathbf{Y_i})N$. Here we prove (1); (2) goes analogously, but is left as an exercise.

Whenever a bunch of positive numbers are added together, the result is always positive, and any number squared is positive. Consequently, the following sum must be positive:

$$0 \le \Sigma(\mathbf{X_i} - \mathbf{Y_i})^2.$$

This sum is just a series like this:

$$(\mathbf{X_1} - \mathbf{Y_1})^2 + (\mathbf{X_2} - \mathbf{Y_2})^2 + (\mathbf{X_3} - \mathbf{Y_3})^2 + \cdots.$$

We can expand each of these terms:

$$(\mathbf{X_1} - \mathbf{Y_1})^2 = \mathbf{X_1^2} - 2\mathbf{X_1}\mathbf{Y_1} + \mathbf{Y_1^2}; \qquad (\mathbf{X_2} - \mathbf{Y_2})^2 = \mathbf{X_2^2} - 2\mathbf{X_2}\mathbf{Y_2} + \mathbf{Y_2^2}; \qquad \text{etc.}$$

which gives us a sum like this:

$$(\mathbf{X_1^2} + -2\mathbf{X_1}\mathbf{Y_1} + \mathbf{Y_1^2}) + (\mathbf{X_2^2} + -2\mathbf{X_2}\mathbf{Y_2} + \mathbf{Y_2^2}) + \cdots.$$

The terms of such a sum can be rearranged, so that each of the $\mathbf{X_i^2}$ terms are together, each of the $\mathbf{Y_i^2}$ terms are together, and each of the $2\mathbf{X_i}\mathbf{Y_i}$ terms are together. Thus, this sum of squares, $(\mathbf{X_i} - \mathbf{Y_i})^2$, is equal to the sum of each of the **X**-variable values squared, $\mathbf{X}_i^2$, plus each of the **Y**-variable values squared, $\mathbf{Y}_i^2$, minus twice each of the products of **X**- and **Y**-variable values, $2\mathbf{X}_i\mathbf{Y}_i$. That is,

$$0 \le \Sigma(\mathbf{X}_i - \mathbf{Y}_i)^2 = \Sigma(\mathbf{X}_i)^2 + \Sigma(\mathbf{Y}_i)^2 - 2\Sigma(\mathbf{X}_i\mathbf{Y}_i).$$

But $\Sigma(\mathbf{X}_i)^2 = \Sigma(\mathbf{Y}_i)^2 = N$, so

$$0 \le \Sigma(\mathbf{X}_i - \mathbf{Y}_i)^2 = \Sigma(\mathbf{X}_i)^2 + \Sigma(\mathbf{Y}_i)^2 - 2\Sigma(\mathbf{X}_i\mathbf{Y}_i) = N + N - 2\Sigma(\mathbf{X}_i\mathbf{Y}_i).$$

So $2\Sigma(\mathbf{X}_i\mathbf{Y}_i) \le 2N$, or $\Sigma(\mathbf{X}_i\mathbf{Y}_i) \le N$, or $\Sigma(\mathbf{X}_i\mathbf{Y}_i)/N \le 1$. Thus, we have proved (1), half of what we need to prove.

Had we started the series of manipulations above with a different sum of squares, $\Sigma(\mathbf{X}_i + \mathbf{Y}_i)^2$, we would have found that $-1 \le \Sigma(\mathbf{X}_i\mathbf{Y}_i)/N$. We can put these two observations together to get what we are after:

$$\frac{-1 \le \Sigma(\mathbf{X}_i\mathbf{Y}_i)}{N \le +1}.$$

In light of this, consider the right arm/left arm example. We can convert our arm weight measurements—<10, 11>, <9, 9.8>, <10.2, 11.3>, and <8.3, 8.9>—to standard deviation units. Here we have four values for the weights of four left-arms—the **X** variable—10.0, 9.0, 10.2, and 8.3. The mean of these values is 9.375—(10.0 + 9.0 + 10.2 + 8.3)/4 = 9.375. The standard deviation of these values is 0.77:

$$\frac{\sqrt{(10.0 - 9.375)^2 + (9.0 - 9.375)^2 + (10.2 - 9.375)^2 + (8.3 - 9.375)^2}}{4}$$

$$= \frac{\sqrt{0.39 + 0.14 + 0.68 + 1.16}}{4} \approx 0.77.$$

The first value, 10.0, is 0.625 larger than the mean; 0.625 is 0.81 of a standard deviation unit (0.77): 0.625/0.77 = 0.81. So we express this measurement as +0.81 instead of 10. We can similarly transform the other **X**-variable values (Table 6.12). We make a similar conversion for the **Y** variable. The mean of the four **Y**-variable values, 11, 9.8, 11.2 and 8.9, is 10.225, and the standard deviation is 0.93. The **Y**-variable values expressed in standard deviation units are listed in Table 6.13. Expressed in pounds, the four points we began with are <10, 11>,

TABLE 6.12 Left-Arm Weights (X Variable)

Pounds	Standard Deviation Units
10.0	+0.81
9.0	−0.49
10.2	+1.07
8.3	−1.40

TABLE 6.13 Right-Arm Weights (Y Variable)

Pounds	Standard Deviation Units
11.0	+0.83
9.8	−0.46
11.2	+1.05
8.8	−1.42

<9, 9.8>, <10.2, 11.3>, and <8.3, 8.9>. We can now express these measurements in terms of the standard deviation units: <+0.81, +0.83>, <−0.49, −0.46>, <+1.07, +1.05>, and <−1.40, −1.42>.

At the beginning of this section we noted that when we measure arm weights in grams the numerator of the correlation coefficient formula is larger than when we measure in pounds. But when we convert the gram measurements to standard deviation units, we get the same standard deviation unit values as we do when we convert the pound measurements to standard deviation units, just as in the baby-formula example above. We can start measurements in pounds—<10, 11>, <9, 9.8>, <10.2, 11.3>, and <8.3, 8.9>—or measurements in grams—<2,200, 2,420>, <1,980, 2,156>, <2,244, 2,486>, and <1,826, 1,958>. In either case we end up with the same measurements in standard deviation units: <+0.81, +0.83>, <−0.49, −0.46>, <+1.07, +1.05>, and <−1.40, −1.42>. Clearly, the correlation for these values is the same whether the values derived originally from pound measurements or gram measurements.

In fact, once expressed in terms of standard deviation units, we can compute the correlation with the numerator alone (Table 6.14). Once we have properly rounded values off, these particular values have the highest possible correlation: +1. This agrees with the graph of the original measurements: Whether in pounds or grams, the points fall almost exactly on a straight line.

TABLE 6.14

i	X_i	Y_i	$(X_i - \overline{X})$	$(Y_i - \overline{Y})$	$(X_i - \overline{X})(Y_i - \overline{Y})$	
1	+0.81	+0.82	+0.81	+0.82	+0.66	
2	−0.49	−0.46	−0.49	−0.46	+0.22	
3	+1.07	+1.05	+1.07	+1.05	+1.12	
4	−1.40	−1.42	−1.40	−1.42	+1.99	
Totals:	0.0	0.0			+3.99	$3.99/4 \approx 1.00$

10. CORRELATION AND CAUSATION

Correlation is a very appealing tool. Clearly, there is some sort of a systematic relationship between the height and weight of people. But equally clearly, it is not a simple one like: People exactly so tall ··· are exactly so heavy ···. Tall people *tend* to be heavier than short people. Correlation is useful for describing this kind of relationship. Since lots of relationships in the social and biological sciences are of this "tendency" sort, correlation is widely used.

From its inception correlation has frequently, and naturally, been interpreted as *partial causation*. When two variables are highly correlated—parental height is correlated with offspring height, for example—we are inclined to suppose that one variable is a cause of the other. But there are many difficulties with this use of correlation. There can be cases where two variables are highly correlated but not directly causally related. There can also be cases where variables are causally related but have a correlation near 0. Here we note a few of these difficulties.

In the first place, correlation measures only the degree of *linear* relationship—the kind of relationship that, when graphed, looks like a straight line. But there are many causal relationships that are not linear. Consider the points that form a parabola—a kind of U-shaped curve. We can describe points lying perfectly on a parabola with the equation

$$y = x^2.$$

These points are very closely related; given the value of one of the variables—x—we can precisely determine the value of the other variable—y. Such relationships are not uncommon; they are used to describe the motion of bodies under the influence of gravity, for example. But the correlation of such points is generally almost 0.

The fact that correlation measures only the degree of linear relationship is important to keep in mind. One should not conclude that two variables have no causal relationship to each other because their correlation is 0. The variables may be related in a nonlinear manner.

This difficulty with correlation can sometimes be accommodated by some mathematical maneuvering. Some relationships that are not linear can be *transformed* into linear relationships by altering the scale of measurement used. For example, in the case of a parabola, if we take the logarithm of both sides of the equation, we convert a parabolic—nonlinear—relationship into a linear relationship:

$$y = x^2 \Rightarrow \log(y) = 2 \times \log(x).$$

So if two variables, **X** and **Y**, related parabolically, are measured on *log scales*, the graph produced will be linear. Log-log graph paper is used to perform this function.

Even in cases where we expect a linear relationship, correlation cannot be identified as partial causation. The correlation coefficient does not specify in which direction the "causal arrow" goes. Consider an example: The age of onset of baldness in a male's maternal grandfather (mother's father), is positively correlated with the age of onset of baldness in the given male. Baldness is transmitted through the mother. So there is a correlation. The age of onset of baldness in a male clearly does not cause (or partially cause) the age of onset of baldness in that male's maternal grandfather. Causes go forward in time. So, at the very least, we have to specify the temporal facts in addition to an observed correlation to make a claim of partial causal relation.

There are other problems. Consider the high correlation between the duration of illumination of two lights in a bank of lights, for instance. The length of time that one of the lights in the set remains on will be very nearly the same as the length of time another light in the set remains on. Both lights are turned on and off by the same switch. Here we have an extremely high correlation between the duration of illumination of one light and that for the other light. But we would be disinclined to say that the causal arrow goes either way—neither light causes the other to remain on. Both are caused by the switch they have in common. This is a case of *common causation*. Some correlations do not reflect any direct causal relationships, but reflect a third *common cause* of both variables.

When the correlation between smoking and cancer was first noted the statistician, R. A. Fisher, suggested that it might be due to a common genetic cause: Individuals who smoke do so because they are genetically predisposed to like smoking, and the same gene also predisposes them to contracting cancer. If Fisher's

Correlation and temporal sequence

A male's baldness is correlated with his maternal grandfather's baldness;

X ≡ Y

but X ⇸ Y,
X ← Y.

Correlation and common causes

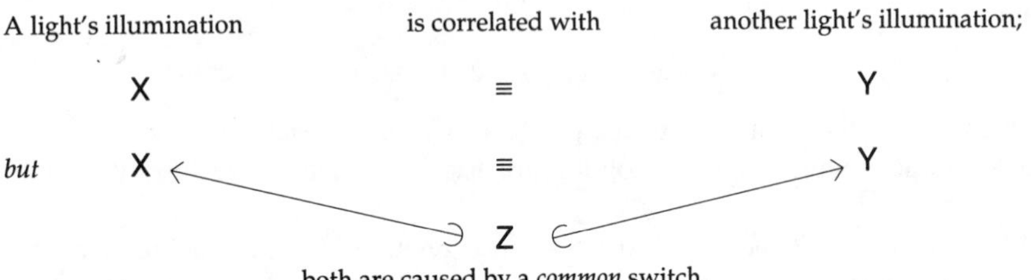

both are caused by a *common* switch.

Spurious correlation

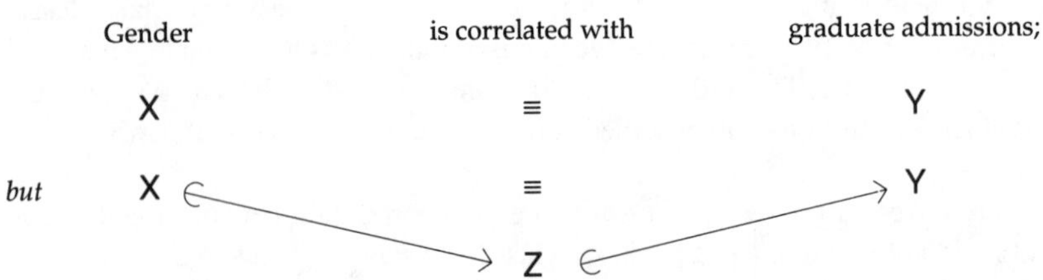

women apply more frequently to departments that are hard to get into.

Figure 6.14

explanation was correct, stopping smoking would not prevent contracting cancer. Subsequent studies, however, have discredited this explanation for the correlation between smoking and cancer.

Third variables can produce *spurious correlations* in other ways. For example, the University of California–Berkeley graduate school was accused of discriminating against women in their admissions. Men were more likely to be admitted than women. However, it turned out that in most departments in the graduate school the chance of being admitted was the same for men and women, and in some it was higher for women. Women happened to apply more frequently to departments that were hard to be admitted to—for either men or women. Thus, the correlations between gender and department-applied-to, and between department-applied-to and admission, provide an analysis closer to the causal explanation in this case. The baseball example in Chapter 8, Section 5, is similar to this one.

Causes and correlations are not identical, but neither do they have nothing to do with each other. When two variables are highly correlated, we are inclined to suppose that there is a causal story to be told. But there are several different kinds of causal stories available. The diagrams for some of these relationships are shown in Figure 6.14.

11. SUMMARY

1. Statistics are used to manipulate the values of measurements.

2. Measurement involves assigning numbers to units in a population.
   (a) Units are measured with respect to a given property, or variable.
   (b) Assigning numbers to units is useful because numerical descriptions can be more expressive than verbal descriptions.
   (c) Assigning numbers to units also allows one to use mathematical operations and implications to reason about the units measured: We associate various mathematical operations with physical operations.
   (d) Different measured properties use different mathematical operations.
   (e) For measurement to be successful, the portion of the mathematical universe used to measure with must be analogous to the portion of the world that is measured. Representation theorems demonstrate that the analogy is accurate.

3. A given property can be measured by many different particular scales: weight in pounds or grams.
   (a) These different scales must share the same numerical structure.
   (b) The methods by which one translates values from one particular scale to another establishes just what all the scales must have in common.
   (c) Some mathematical operations do not make sense with some kinds of measurement scales. For an operation to make sense, it must reflect the units measured and not simply the particular scale used.

4. When many units in a population are measured with respect to the same variable, we get a distribution of values.
   (a) The distribution can be arranged in order by ranks.
   (b) A frequency distribution shows for each possible value how many units have that value.
   (c) A grouped frequency distribution takes the possible values by groups and shows for each group how many units have a value in that group.
   (d) A relative frequency distribution shows for each possible value what proportion of the whole population have that value.

5. There are three important different kinds of averages.
   (a) The *mode* is the value that more units have than any other value. The mode is completely insensitive to any change in the distribution other than what the most common value is.
   (b) The *median* is that value such that half of the observed values are less than it and half are greater. It is more sensitive than the mode to differences in distributions.
   (c) The *mean* is the common "add 'em up and divide by *N*" average. The mean accounts for how much greater or smaller an observed value is from the mean, and not simply, as with the median, whether an observed value is greater or smaller than the median.
   (d) Different averages presuppose different underlying scales of measurement for the values in the distribution. The mode can be used with any scale where different values simply represent some difference. The median requires a scale where there is some order to the values. The mean requires a scale—such as a temperature scale—where the size of an interval on the scale represents the same amount of difference in the property measured, no matter where on the scale the interval falls.

6. There are three common kinds of measures of how spread out or dispersed the values in a distribution are.
   (a) The *range* is the distance between the largest and smallest observed value in the distribution.
   (b) *Quartiles* work like the median: The first quartile is the value such that 1/4 of the observed values are less and 3/4 are greater. The second quartile is the median. The third quartile is the value such that 3/4 of the observed values are less and 1/4 are greater.
   (c) Roughly speaking, the *standard deviation* measures the average distance of all the observed values from the mean. The larger this value is, the more observations are spread out.
   (d) $\sqrt{\Sigma(\mathbf{X_i} - \overline{\mathbf{X}})^2/N}$ is the formula for the standard deviation. The part in the middle, $(\mathbf{X_i} - \overline{\mathbf{X}})$, measures the distance between any observation, $\mathbf{X_i}$, and the mean, $\overline{\mathbf{X}}$. These values are squared. These squared differences are summed up, Σ, and the sum is divided by the number of observations, N, to give the average squared distance of observations from the mean. Finally, taking the square root gives a measure of dispersion with the same units as the units being used to measure with.
   (e) Means and standard deviations can be converted from one scale of measurement to another.

7. Correlation is a useful summary statistic for describing the relationship between values of two variables.
   (a) One begins by measuring each unit in a population with respect to both variables.
   (b) These measurements can be plotted together with a scatter plot. One X can represent the values of both variables for each unit in the population.
   (c) When the plot of Xs is line-like, it is possible to predict the value of one of the variables from the value of the other variable.
   (d) The correlation coefficient measures the degree to which a scatter plot of Xs is line-like.
   (e) The correlation coefficient varies between −1 and +1. Lines can slant up or down. Sometimes two variables are related directly: Small values of one variable are associated with small values of the other and large values with large values. Such variables have a correlation near +1. Other times, two variables relate inversely: Small values of one variable are associated with large values of the other variable, and large with small. Such variables have a correlation near −1. A correlation near 0 occurs when the values of the two variables are not at all line-like.
   (f) The correlation, r_{XY}, between two variables **X** and **Y** is computed from the following formula:

$$\frac{\Sigma[((\mathbf{X_i} - \overline{\mathbf{X}})(\mathbf{Y_i} - \overline{\mathbf{Y}}))/N]}{\sqrt{\Sigma(\mathbf{X_i} - \overline{\mathbf{X}})^2/N} \times \sqrt{\Sigma(\mathbf{Y_i} - \overline{\mathbf{Y}})^2/N}}$$

   (g) The numerator of the correlation formula, $\Sigma[((\mathbf{X_i} - \overline{\mathbf{X}})(\mathbf{Y_i} - \overline{\mathbf{Y}}))/N]$, is the *covariance* of **X** and **Y**; the denominator is the product of the *standard deviation of* **X** and the *standard deviation of* **Y**.
   (h) The numerator measures how line-like the points are. The denominator of the correlation formula standardizes the correlation scale to ± 1.
   (i) Standard deviation units use the mean and standard deviation of a distribution of values to construct a new scale with which to express the values in the distribution. Values are expressed in terms of the number of standard deviations that fall above or below the mean.

8. The correlation between two variables does not demonstrate a causal relation between the variables. It may demonstrate evidence of some causal story involving both variables.
   (a) Correlation provides a measure of *linear* relationship. Only when the observations fall roughly on a line do they have a high (positive or negative) correlation. Consequently, even when one variable is entirely predictable by another variable, if the relation between them is not line-like, they will not be highly correlated necessarily.
   (b) Correlation is independent of time. Two variables, X and Y, may be highly correlated, and it would not be possible to tell whether X was a cause of Y, or vice versa.
   (c) Two variables may be highly correlated even though neither is a cause of the other. Both may be caused by some third variable, and because of this common cause, the two original variables are correlated.

(d) It is also possible for two variables to be correlated because of the casual relations that each has to an intervening third variable.
(e) Generally, however, when two variables are highly correlated, there is some causal story that explains the correlation.

12. REFERENCES

(Stevens, 1951) introduces measurement theory and its relation to summary statistics. (Krantz, et al., 1971) is a thorough and technical treatment of the theory of measurement. (Luce, 1979) is a nice summary of the technical theory of measurement. (Jaeger, 1982) is a completely nontechnical introduction to many statistical concepts, in particular summary statistics and measurement. (Bhattacharyya and Johnson, 1977) is a more technical introduction to statistical methods. (Tukey, 1977) is a superb detailed introduction to data analysis. (Cleveland, 1985) and (Tufte, 1983) are excellent on graphing data. The graduate admissions example is discussed in (Cartwright, 1983).

13. PROBLEMS

1. Take the following population of measurements in inches and find their mean.

   10.0, 11.2, 12.8, 14.4, 17.6, 19.9, 22.5, 25.9, 31.1, 35.0, 38.7

   Call this M. Convert each of these measurements in inches to its equivalent in centimeters. (*Note:* 1 inch = 2.54 centimeters.) Compute the mean of the population expressed in centimeters. Convert M to centimeters. Do you get the same result?
2. Refer to Problem 1. Must one get the same result for any population of measurements in inches? Why or why not?
3. Eggs are frequently sold as small, medium, large, and extra large. We could say that each egg is measured and found to be small, medium, and so on. Would it be appropriate to use a mean to find the average egg size in a population of eggs measured this way? Why or why not?
4. Generate a distribution of values. *Suggestions:* Find 50 leaves from the same tree and measure their length; find 50 acorns and measure their weight (if you have access to a good scale); note the high temperature recorded in the paper for the past month. Arrange the distribution by ranks. Determine the frequency of each possible value—group values, if appropriate. Produce a relative frequency histogram for your distribution. Produce a cumulative relative frequency histogram for your distribution.
5. Refer to Problem 4. Where appropriate, compute the mode, median, and mean of your distribution.
6. Refer to Problem 4. Where appropriate, compute the range, quartiles, and standard deviation for your distribution.
7. Refer to Problem 4. Produce a box-and-whisker plot for your distribution.

8. Produce a box-and-whisker plot for the distribution of inch measurements in Problem 1.
9. Calculate the standard deviation of the following five measurements in feet: 2, 4, 5, 5, 9.
10. Calculate the standard deviation of the distribution of inch measurements in Problem 1.
11. Take a population of 50 books and measure the width and the number of pages of each. Produce a scatter plot from these measurements. What kind of correlation would you say there is between book width and the number of pages?
12. Perform the ice-cube experiment described in Section 7. Calculate the correlation between number of ice cubes in a glass and the length of time it takes for the ice cubes in a glass to melt completely.
13. Consider the population of trees in your home state. Invent three variables: there should be a positive correlation between one pair of variables, a negative correlation between another pair, and a near-zero correlation between a third pair.
14. Take the population of measurements in Problem 1 and convert them to standard deviation units.
15. Prove that $-1 \leq \Sigma(X_i Y_i)/N$; that is, do the other half of the proof whose first half is done in Section 9.
16. Invent two variables that are not directly causally related to each other but which are highly correlated.
17. There is a high correlation between the number of churches and the number of divorces by year. How should we understand this fact?

CHAPTER 7

INTRODUCTION TO PROBABILITY

1. PROBABILITY AND SETS

In addition to the techniques of descriptive statistics, probability mathematics provides the second technical leg on which stand the inductive arguments presented in the first part of the book. To appreciate these arguments more fully, we need some understanding of elementary probability mathematics. This is our project for the next three chapters.

To use probability we first need to know what probability is probability *of*. In terms of the formal techniques of probability mathematics, two approaches to this question are popular. One approach uses the techniques of formal deductive logic and speaks of the probability *of sentences* or propositions. Here one concentrates on the logical form of the sentences and constructs a theory of probability of such beasts. The other approach uses the techniques of set theory and speaks of the probability *of* special kinds of sets called *events*. Here one concentrates on the set-theoretic structure of the events. For our purposes, these different approaches are entirely equivalent. As we see below, we can translate back and forth between the two ways of speaking of probabilities with relative ease.

We develop probabilities in terms of set-theoretic events. This is more natural for many applications; most statistics texts present probability this way. And because the set-theoretic approach is equivalent to the sentence/proposition approach, learning it can provide a better appreciation of the sentence/proposition approach commonly taught in deductive logic.

A *set* is a collection of things. Almost anything can be collected together as a set—coins, presidents, or possible outcomes of some experiment. Sets are nice because the idea of a collection is simple. The operations we perform on sets are intuitive. Yet despite all this simplicity, sets are handy for describing complicated matters.

A set can be described by listing all its members inside curly brackets, { }; $\{a, b, c, d, e\}$ is the set of the first five letters of the alphabet. The order in which these elements occur inside the brackets does not matter. $\{e, c, a, d, b\}$ is the same as the set $\{a, b, c, d, e\}$. All that matters is what is inside the brackets.

Sometimes, instead of listing all the members of a set, we describe the set by stating a property shared by all its members. The set $\{x|x$ is one of the first five letters of the alphabet$\}$ is another way to describe the set $\{a, b, c, d, e\}$. The notation $\{x|x$ ....$\}$ is read, "the set of things x such that x is a ... ." In the context of set theory, "|" is read "such that."

We can also use a capital letter, such as **A**, **B**, or **C**, to name a set. We might understand that

$$\mathbf{A} = \{a, b, c, d, e\}.$$

So whenever **A** occurred in the appropriate context we would understand it to refer to the set containing the first five letters of the alphabet. Sometimes, we use such capital letters to identify some set without concerning ourselves with just what elements are in the set. We speak of the set **A** as an object the members of which we do not care to identify for the moment.

Set talk needs a context. If we are talking about numbers and we speak of a set containing "everything," usually we do not mean to include the house at 2725 Preston Street; we only mean to include numbers, no houses. Even at that, there are many different kinds of numbers—integers, fractions, real numbers, complex numbers, and so on. To speak clearly, we need to have a clear understanding at the outset of what our sets could include: Do we mean to include the complex numbers or only the integers? We accomplish this by specifying a *universe of discourse*. This is the collection of all the "things" that *could* be members of the sets we wish to speak of in the given context.

Once we are clear about our universe of discourse, we can easily distinguish two special sets. They are the universal set and the empty set. The *universal set* is the set containing everything in the universe of discourse. It has a special symbol, **V**. The *empty set*, sometimes called the null set, is the set with no elements; none of the "things" in the universe of discourse are in the empty set. There are several special symbols for the empty set: a pair of brackets containing no elements, { }; a zero with a slash, $\varnothing$; or an upside-down V: $\mathbf{\Lambda}$. I will use $\mathbf{\Lambda}$.

We write $x \in \mathbf{A}$ when x is *an element of* the set **A**: for example, $a \in \{a, b, c, d, e\}$. $2 \in \{x|x$ is an even number$\}$. If something, x, is not an element of a set **A**, we write $x \notin \mathbf{A}$.

Two *sets are equal*, $\mathbf{A} = \mathbf{B}$, when every element of one is also an element of the other:

$$\mathbf{A} = \mathbf{B} \text{ if and only if } x \in \mathbf{A} \text{ if and only if } x \in \mathbf{B}.$$

We say that one set, **A**, is *a subset of* another set, **B**, when every element of **A** is also an element of **B**. We write $\mathbf{A} \subseteq \mathbf{B}$.

$$\mathbf{A} \subseteq \mathbf{B} \text{ if and only if, if } x \in \mathbf{A}, \text{ then } x \in \mathbf{B}.$$

Sometimes we write $\mathbf{B} \supseteq \mathbf{A}$ and say **B** contains **A**. This is just another way to say that **A** is a subset of **B**:

$$\mathbf{B} \supseteq \mathbf{A} \text{ if and only if } \mathbf{A} \subseteq \mathbf{B}.$$

When one set, **A**, is not a subset of another set, **B**, we write $\mathbf{A} \not\subseteq \mathbf{B}$.

Do not confuse the element relationship with the subset relationship. $a \in \{a, b, c, d, e\}$; $a \not\subseteq \{a, b, c, d, e\}$. On the other hand, $\{a\} \subseteq \{a, b, c, d, e\}$, while $\{a\} \notin \{a, b, c, d, e\}$; $\{a\} \in \{a, b, c, d, \{a\}, e\}$. It is important to clearly distinguish the elements of a set from the set they are elements of. The empty set is a set with no elements, every $x \notin \Lambda$. But the set containing the empty set, $\{\Lambda\}$, is a set with one element: $\Lambda \in \{\Lambda\}$. Every set is a subset of itself, $\mathbf{A} \subseteq \mathbf{A}$. (Use the definition of subset carefully to see why this is so.) The empty set is a subset of every set, $\Lambda \subseteq \mathbf{A}$. But there are many sets of which the empty set is not an element; $\Lambda \notin \{a, b, c, d, e\}$.

There are three operations that we will do with sets: union, intersection, and complementation. Each operation produces a set by "doing something" to a given set or pair of sets.

The *union* of a pair of sets, **A** and **B**, is the set containing both the elements of **A** and the elements of **B** (all duplications removed). Suppose that $\mathbf{A} = \{a, b, c\}$ and $\mathbf{B} = \{c, d, e\}$; the union of these two sets is $\mathbf{A} \cup \mathbf{B} = \{a, b, c, d, e\}$. "$\cup$" is the standard notation for the union of two sets.

The *intersection* of a pair of sets, **A** and **B**, is the set that contains all the elements in both **A** and **B**. For example, since c is the only member of both the sets **A** and **B** from above, the intersection of **A** and **B** is $\{c\}$. We use the symbol "$\cap$" for intersection:

$$\mathbf{A} \cap \mathbf{B} = \{a, b, c\} \cap \{c, d, e\} = \{c\}.$$

The *complement* of a set, **A**, is the set that contains everything *not* in **A**. For example, suppose that the universe of discourse consists of just the first five letters of the alphabet; $\mathbf{V} = \{a, b, c, d, e\}$. Let **A** be $\{a, b, c\}$, as above. In this case, the complement of **A** is $\{d, e\}$. I will use the symbol $\neg$ for complement: $\neg\mathbf{A} = \{d, e\}$. This is because d and e are the only elements of **V** that are not in **A**. Of course, if **V** included all the letters in the alphabet,

$$\mathbf{V} = \{a, b, c, d, e, f, g, h, i, j, k, l, m, n, o, p, q, r, s, t, u, v, w, x, y, z\},$$

then the complement of **A** would be a larger set:

$$\neg\mathbf{A} = \{d, e, f, g, h, i, j, k, l, m, n, o, p, q, r, s, t, u, v, w, x, y, z\}.$$

This is why we need a list of all the possible members of the sets we are speaking of before we operate with sets. Without such a list we would not know what to include in the complement of a set.

We can compound set operations with each other in very much the same way that we compound arithmetic operations with each other (and truth functional connectives with each other). Consider, for example, arithmetic operations.

$$(2 + 3) \times 6 = (5) \times 6 = 30.$$

By following the rule "go from the inside out," we first perform the operation inside the parentheses $(2 + 3)$ and get the result 5; then we perform the operation outside the parentheses, $(5) \times 6$, with this partial result to get the final result, 30.

It is the same with sets. Suppose (again) that $\mathbf{V} = \{a, b, c, d, e\}$, that $\mathbf{A} = \{a, b, c\}$, and that $\mathbf{B} = \{c, d, e\}$:

$$\mathbf{A} \cup (\mathbf{B} \cap \mathbf{\Lambda}) = \mathbf{A} \cup \text{the intersection of } \mathbf{B} \text{ and } \mathbf{\Lambda}.$$

But the intersection of **B** and the empty set, **Λ**, is the empty set. So

$$\mathbf{A} \cup (\mathbf{B} \cap \mathbf{\Lambda}) = \mathbf{A} \cup (\mathbf{\Lambda}) = \mathbf{A}.$$

Consider another example.

$$\neg(\mathbf{A} \cup \mathbf{B}) = \neg[\{a, b, c\} \cup \{c, d, e\}] = \neg\{a, b, c, d, e\} = \mathbf{\Lambda}.$$

Or another,

$$\neg\mathbf{A} \cup \neg\mathbf{B} = \neg\{a, b, c\} \cup \neg\{c, d, e\} = \{d, e\} \cup \{a, b\} = \{a, b, d, e\}.$$

Two sets are equal if they contain the same elements. It is usually easiest to show this by showing that each set is a subset of the other.

$$\mathbf{A} = \mathbf{B} \text{ if and only if } \mathbf{A} \subseteq \mathbf{B} \text{ and } \mathbf{B} \subseteq \mathbf{A}.$$

Usually, we show that $\mathbf{A} \subseteq \mathbf{B}$ by considering "an arbitrary element" of **A**, call it "x," and showing that x must also be an element of **B**. In this way we can show, for example, that

$$\mathbf{A} \cap \mathbf{B} = \mathbf{A} \text{ if and only if } \mathbf{A} \subseteq \mathbf{B}.$$

Go from left to right first. We must show that every element of **A** is also an element of **B**—$\mathbf{A} \subseteq \mathbf{B}$—assuming that $\mathbf{A} = \mathbf{A} \cap \mathbf{B}$. Suppose that x is an element of **A**; since $\mathbf{A} \cap \mathbf{B} = \mathbf{A}$, x also must be an element of $\mathbf{A} \cap \mathbf{B}$. But this set is the intersection of **A** and **B**, so x must be an element of both **A** and **B**. In particular, x is an element of **B**.

Now go from right to left. Here we must show both that any element of $\mathbf{A} \cap \mathbf{B}$ is also an element of **A**, and vice versa, that any element of **A** is also an element of $\mathbf{A} \cap \mathbf{B}$, that is, $\mathbf{A} \cap \mathbf{B} = \mathbf{A}$. We assume in this case that $\mathbf{A} \subseteq \mathbf{B}$. Suppose, first, that $x \in \mathbf{A} \cap \mathbf{B}$. Then x is an element of both **A** and **B**; in particular, $x \in \mathbf{A}$. So $\mathbf{A} \cap \mathbf{B} \subseteq \mathbf{A}$. Now suppose that $x \in \mathbf{A}$. Since we can assume here that $\mathbf{A} \subseteq \mathbf{B}$, x must also be an element of **B**. So x is an element of both **A** and **B**: $x \in \mathbf{A} \cap \mathbf{B}$. Thus, $\mathbf{A} \subseteq \mathbf{A} \cap \mathbf{B}$. Put these two conclusions togther and we are done. $\mathbf{A} \cap \mathbf{B} \subseteq \mathbf{A}$ and $\mathbf{A} \subseteq \mathbf{A} \cap \mathbf{B}$; so $\mathbf{A} \cap \mathbf{B} = \mathbf{A}$.

2. SETS AND SENTENCES

For our purposes, set talk and sentence talk are entirely equivalent. We could just as well stick to one kind of talk alone. However, for whatever reason, both kinds of language evolved and it is important to be able to use both and to see that they come to the same thing.

Consider a simple experiment. This experiment is designed to test whether or not a particular person, the "subject," can distinguish Coke from Pepsi. Without the subject's knowledge, one or the other of Coke and Pepsi was poured into a cup; the subject then gets to drink and guess whether it was Coke or Pepsi. If we did this only once, the subject could get the answer right 50% of the time simply by guessing. So we will certainly want to repeat the test several times. For the sake of simplicity, suppose that we perform the test twice.

What are the possible outcomes of two repetitions of the experiment? The subject could get the right answer both times; we will abbreviate this $R_1 \wedge R_2$. The subject could get the wrong answer both times—$W_1 \wedge W_2$. Or the subject could get it right the first time and wrong the second time, or wrong first and right second—$R_1 \wedge W_2$; $W_1 \wedge R_2$. All in all, there are four possible outcomes to this experiment:

1. $R_1 \wedge R_2$
2. $R_1 \wedge W_2$
3. $W_1 \wedge R_2$
4. $W_1 \wedge W_2$

Here I use one standard notation for truth-functional logic; " $\wedge$ " is the truth-functional connective for "and." I use " $\vee$ " for "or."

We have described the possible outcomes of the experiment in terms of four sentences—each a conjunction—and—of two simpler sentences. But we could just as well talk about the set of four possible outcomes as:

$$\{<R, R>, <R, W>, <W, R>, <W, W>\}.$$

Angle brackets, $<$ and $>$, are used to show order. The first outcome, R_1 *or* W_1, is always shown in the first place inside the brackets; the second outcome is shown in the second place inside the brackets: $<\cdot_1, \cdot_2>$.

Consider the sentence "The subject got exactly one trial of the experiment right." In terms of truth-functional connectives, we would write $((R_1 \wedge W_2) \vee (W_1 \wedge R_2))$. Alternatively, we could describe the set of possible outcomes corresponding to the sentence

$$\{<R, W>, <W, R>\}.$$

It is this set because these are the only two possible outcomes where exactly one trial was answered correctly by the subject.

Consider another sentence: "The subject got the first trial correct." In terms of truth-functional connectives we have $((R_1 \wedge R_2) \vee (R_1 \wedge W_2))$. The set corresponding to this sentence is $\{<R, R>, <R, W>\}$. The elements in this set are the only possible outcomes where the first trial was answered correctly.

Now consider the conjunction of these two sentences: "The subject got exactly one trial of the experiment right, *and*, the subject got the first trial correct." Truth functionally, we would write:

$$(((R_1 \wedge W_2) \vee (W_1 \wedge R_2) \wedge ((R_1 \wedge R_2) \vee (R_1 \wedge W_2))).$$

To find the *set* corresponding to this sentence—a conjunction of two sentences—take the *intersection* of the two sets corresponding to each of the conjuncts:

$$\{<R, W>, <W, R>\} \cap \{<R, R>, <R, W>\} = \{<R, W>\}.$$

$<R, W>$ is the only element of both sets; consequently, it is the only possible outcome in the set intersection. This should make sense. The only way for the subject to get one trial of the experiment right and get the first trial correct is for the subject to get the first trial right and the second wrong: $<R, W>$.

Consider the disjunction of these two sentences: "The subject either got exactly one trial of the experiment right, *or* the subject got the first trial of the experiment right." Truth functionally,

$$(((R_1 \wedge W_2) \vee (W_1 \wedge R_2)) \vee ((R_1 \wedge R_2) \vee (R_1 \wedge W_2))).$$

To find the set corresponding to the disjunction of the first two sentences, take the *union* of the two sets corresponding to each of the disjuncts:

$$\{<R, W>, <W, R>\} \cup \{<R, R>, <R, W>\} = \{<R, W>, <W, R>, <R, R>\}.$$

Each of these possibilities, $<R, W>$, $<W, R>$ and $<R, R>$ is in one of the two sets. So they all are in the union of the two sets. Consider negation: "The subject did not get exactly one right." I will use "~" for truth-functional negation:

$$\sim((R_1 \wedge W_2) \vee (W_1 \wedge R_2)).$$

The set corresponding to this sentence is the complement of the set corresponding to the sentence with no negation sign:

$$\neg\{<R, W>, <W, R>\} = \{<R, R>, <W, W>\}.$$

If the subject did not get exactly one right, the subject got either both right or both wrong.

To convert from sentence talk to set talk, we first establish the domain of possibilities. The set corresponding to a given sentence is the set of all possibilities that would "make" the sentence true. The possibility $<R, W>$ "makes" the sentence "The subject got exactly one trial right" true, in the sense that if this possibility happened to be the way the world actually was, the sentence would be true. In general, disjunctions correspond to unions; conjunctions correspond to intersections. Negations correspond to complements.

3. POSSIBLE OUTCOMES AND EVENTS

Probability theory speaks of the probability of an event. "P(**A**)" is read "the probability of event **A**." Events are special kinds of sets, sets of possible outcomes. For example, consider the event of a coin turning up heads two times in three flips. There are three different ways this could happen: <*H*, *H*, *T*>, <*H*, *T*, *H*>, <*T*, *H*, *H*>. Keep in mind that angle brackets are used to show the order. When we speak of the probability of getting two heads in three flips of a coin, we are speaking of the probability of this event: {<*H*, *H*, *T*>, <*H*, *T*, *H*>, <*T*, *H*, *H*>}.

It takes three steps to construct the set of all the events that probabilities are probabilities of in a given context. We construct a list of the *possible outcomes*; we build up *simple events* from the possible outcomes; we construct *compound events* from the simple events.

For the first step, we make a list of all the *possible outcomes*. Suppose that we flip a coin once. What are the possible outcomes? The coin might land heads, *H*, and it might land tails, *T*. If these are the only possible outcomes, we have completed this part of the task. But matters can be more complicated. The coin *could* land on edge, *E*. If we considered this a "real possibility," we would have to include it in our list of possible outcomes. Most of the time, the possibility of the coin landing on edge is not taken seriously and is not included as a "possible" outcome. It is "possible," but as far as most of our probability calculations are concerned, we do not count it as "really possible." Perhaps we want to distinguish between the coin landing heads on the table and heads on the floor; we might now have four possible outcomes: *H–table, H–floor, T–table, T–floor*. On the other hand, perhaps we are not concerned with making this distinction. Most of the time we speak of the two normal possibilities, heads, *H*, and tails, *T*. Thus, there is an element of convention in specifying what is possible and what is not; we make just those distinctions we think are important.

There are two aspects to listing possible outcomes: (1) including everything we consider a "real possibility," and (2) distinguishing different outcomes at the appropriate level of detail. For many of the problems we will run across in this book, listing the possible outcomes will not cause much trouble; coins and dice come with their possible outcomes plain to see. In other cases, matters are murkier. Consider survival rates for different cancers. The survival rate for cancer is defined by the proportion of people diagnosed with a cancer who live 5 more years after diagnosis. There seems to be two possible outcomes: survived 5 years after diagnosis, or did not survive 5 years after diagnosis. But how should we consider a person who appears to have been cured of cancer but who is killed in an auto accident 4 days before the

5-year diagnosis anniversary? Which possible outcome best describes this? There is a tricky problem of describing the possible outcomes in such situations. But in the simple cases we consider at the outset we need not worry about these difficulties.

Once we have an understanding of the possible outcomes, we can construct the *simple events*. The simple events are those sets with only one possible outcome for a member. For each possible outcome there is one simple event. In the coin case, usually we proceed with two possible outcomes from one flip: *H* and *T*. In this case there are two simple events: {*H*} and {*T*}. On the other hand, if we rolled a die once, usually we consider six possible outcomes, one for each of the six faces of the die landing uppermost: *1, 2, 3, 4, 5,* and *6*. The simple events in this case are {*1*}, {*2*}, {*3*}, {*4*}, {*5*}, and {*6*}. Shortly, we will see just why we need the distinction between possible outcomes and simple events.

From the simple events we construct the *compound events*. Any collection of possible outcomes—any set of them—is a compound event. In terms of the operations of set theory, the compound events are all the sets that can be obtained from the simple events by the operations of union, intersection, and complementation.

For example, there are two *possible outcomes*, *H* and *T*, when we flip a coin once. So the *simple events* are {*H*} and {*T*}. The *compound events* include these simple events and two other sets, the set including both *H* and *T*: {*H, T*} ({*H, T*} = {*H*} ∪ {*T*}), and the set including neither: **Λ** (**Λ** = {*H*} ∩ {*T*}). These four sets, **Λ**, {*H*}, {*T*}, {*H, T*}, are all the different collections of possible outcomes; these are the compound events.

It is important to understand what each of these sets refers to. {*H*} and {*T*} are straightforward: {*H*} refers to the coin landing heads; similarly for {*T*}. {*H, T*} refers to the possibility of the coin landing *either* heads or tails. Since these are the only two possibilities, we can be certain at the outset that {*H, T*} will occur; **V** is sometimes called the *certain event*. Similarly, the empty set, **Λ**, refers to the "possibility" of neither heads nor tails occurring. Since we know at the outset that either heads or tails *will* occur, we can be sure that **Λ** will *not* occur; it is sometimes called the *impossible event*. An event is a set of possibilities; we interpret the set as saying that one or the other of the possibilities it contains is the way the world actually is.

Suppose that we toss a six-sided die once. There are six possible outcomes, one for each of the six sides that could land face up. So there are six simple events: {*1*}, {*2*}, {*3*}, {*4*}, {*5*}, {*6*}. There are many compound events. Each of the six simple events is one of the compound events. So are all of the sets containing pairs of possible outcomes (e.g., {*1, 2*} or {*2, 6*}). Sets with triples (e.g., {*1, 2, 3*}) or quadruples (e.g., {*1, 4, 5, 6*}) or quintuples (e.g., {*1, 2, 3, 4, 6*}), also are compound events—as is the certain event, the one sextuple, {*1, 2, 3, 4, 5, 6*} = **V**. There are many compound events ($2^6 = 64$, in fact). Although there are many compound events, the principle behind constructing them should not be difficult to grasp.

The need to distinguish possible outcomes from events should be clearer now. We need to be able to talk about different kinds of events. We might be interested in the event of a die coming up six, {*6*}, but we also might be interested in the die coming up an even number. The event I am interested in in such a case is the *compound event* that includes all of these possible outcomes: two, four, and six, {*2, 4, 6*}. So that we can talk both about events with one possible outcome, and events with more than one possible outcome, we distinguish between possible outcomes and events—sets of any number of possible outcomes.

4. ASSIGNING PROBABILITIES

Now we have all the raw materials for probabilities. But we do not have any probabilities yet. There are two sides to assigning probabilities. There is a very substantial question of how to assign probabilities so that they correctly describe the events in the world. This question is difficult to answer entirely satisfactorily. We canvass some answers in the third part of the book.

But we need not start with this difficult question. Certain kinds of cases, those involving dice, coins, and the like, seem to pose little problem for assigning probabilities. Consider a six-sided die. If we erased all the dots so that the sides were no longer labeled, we could not distinguish one side from another. As far as one can tell by inspection, they are all the same. Consequently, it would seem, each face should have the same probability of landing uppermost. What distinguishing feature favors one side as opposed to another? We can start investigating probability by assuming that each face of the die has the same chance as each other face of landing uppermost. We assign the same probability to each simple event {*1*}, {*2*}, {*3*}, {*4*}, {*5*}, {*6*}.

We can begin our discussion of probability with these *nice cases*. For a time we will focus attention on those "games of chance," coin tossing, dice, cards, roulette, and so on., where we can assign the same probability to each simple event. Eventually, however, we will return to the much more difficult questions of (1) justifying our assignment of equal probabilities to each simple event in nice cases, and (2) finding a way to assign probabilities to events in not-so-nice cases.

But there are still many different ways to assign the same probability to each simple event. Suppose that we toss a six-sided die once. We could assign each simple event probability 1, or we could assign each probability 7. How are we to choose? We choose by making a convention: The sum of all the probabilities assigned to the simple events must total 1. In the case of the six-sided die, since we must assign six equal numbers, one for each simple event, which together sum to 1, each simple event is assigned probability 1/6.

The sum-to-1 convention could be different; but it is a very intuitive way to do things. There is also a nice relationship with frequencies that motivates this convention. Suppose that we toss the die many times, say 1,000,000 times. Given a "fair die" we would expect it to fall with each side uppermost about 1/6 of the time. That is, the relative frequency of the number of times it falls *one* uppermost to the total number of flips should be about 1/6. So if we think of probabilities in terms of these relative frequencies, we are led to the sum-to-1 convention. Not all probabilities can be linked so nicely with frequencies, but when they can, this relationship is suggestive.

5. ADDITION RULE AND COMPLEMENT RULE

Once probabilities are assigned to the simple events, it is a matter of *computation* to find the probabilities for the rest of the compound events. This computation can be rather tricky, and consequently the mathematical rules of probability can be very useful. Probability rules do not create probabilities; they allow us to compute unknown probabilities from those we know.

The first rule might be called "the simplest addition rule" for probabilities. It works only when we assign equal probabilities to all the simple events, something we do with the nice cases. Suppose that we take a regular six-sided die and mark it as follows. On the sides that usually are marked with one dot or six dots, we write the word *one*. On the sides that usually are marked with two or five dots, we write the word *two*. On the sides that usually are marked with three or four dots, we write the word *three*. Suppose that we toss this re-marked die once. How many possible outcomes are there? I say there are three: *one*, *two,* and *three*, for we cannot distinguish between the outcome *one* that used to be "one-dot" and the outcome *one* that used to be "six-dot." If we then assign equal probabilities to the simple events, we assign to each simple event {*one*}, {*two*} and {*three*}, the probability 1/3. But the simple event of {*one*} is just the same, as far as the die is concerned, as the compound event {*1*, *6*} in the regularly marked die; consequently, this compound event should be assigned probability 1/3 = 2/6. So we now know what the probability of this compound event should be.

As a rule of thumb for computing probabilities in nice cases, the probability of any event, **A**, is the ratio of the number of possible outcomes in **A** to the total number of possible outcomes:

$$\mathrm{P}(\mathbf{A}) = \frac{\text{number of possible outcomes in } \mathbf{A}}{\text{total number of possible outcomes}}.$$

This rule is consistent with the relative frequency notion mentioned above. The proportion of outcomes that are either one-dot or six-dots among all the 1,000,000 repetitions of tossing the die should be very nearly equal to the value given by the rule above. Approximately one-sixth of the outcomes will be *1*s and another one-sixth will be *6*s; so one-third will be *1*s or *6*s.

There are two immediate consequences of this simple rule: The probability of the impossible event, **Λ**, is 0. The probability of the certain event, **V**, is 1. Here is our scale of probabilities, $0 \leq \mathrm{P}(\mathbf{A}) \leq 1$.

This rule for finding probabilities is a simple version of a more general addition rule. When two events, **A** and **B**, have no possible outcomes in common—they do not "overlap"—when their intersection is the empty set, the probability of their union is the sum of the probabilities of them separately.

$$\text{If } \mathbf{A} \cap \mathbf{B} = \mathbf{\Lambda}, \text{ then } \mathrm{P}(\mathbf{A} \cup \mathbf{B}) = \mathrm{P}(\mathbf{A}) + \mathrm{P}(\mathbf{B}).$$

This rule is true generally, not just for nice cases.

Simple events never overlap with each other. Suppose that we toss a six-sided die once. Consider two simple events, {*1*} and {*2*}. The probability of each is 1/6 (the number of possible outcomes in {*1*}—or {*2*}—divided by the total number of possible outcomes). The compound event, $\{1\} \cup \{2\} = \{1, 2\}$, has probability 2/6 since it contains two possible outcomes. But note that $P(\{1, 2\}) = P(\{1\}) + P(\{2\}) = 1/6 + 1/6 = 2/6$. Suppose that we add a new simple event {*3*}. Clearly, by the rule of addition,

$$P(\{1, 2, 3\}) = P(\{1, 2\} \cup \{3\}) = \frac{2}{6} + \frac{1}{6} = \frac{3}{6}.$$

What happens if the events **A** and **B** overlap? For example, suppose that we toss a six-sided die once and that $\mathbf{A} = \{1, 2, 3\}$ and $\mathbf{B} = \{3, 4\}$. $P(\mathbf{A}) = 3/6$, one-sixth for each possible outcome in **A**; $P(\mathbf{B}) = 2/6$. But the union of **A** and **B** has only four possible outcomes: $\mathbf{A} \cup \mathbf{B} = \{1, 2, 3\} \cup \{3, 4\} = \{1, 2, 3, 4\}$. So, $P(\mathbf{A} \cup \mathbf{B}) = 4/6 = 2/3$. If we used the addition rule above we would get the wrong answer:

$$\frac{4}{6} = P(\{1, 2, 3\} \cup \{3, 4\}) \neq P(\{1, 2, 3\}) + P(\{3, 4\}) = \frac{3}{6} + \frac{2}{6} = \frac{5}{6}.$$

Using the rule in this case, we get the wrong answer, because we count *3* twice: once for **A** and a second time for **B**. So when events overlap—when their intersection is not empty—we must subtract the outcomes counted twice.

To subtract the outcomes counted twice, we subtract the probability of the intersection of **A** and of **B**. The general rule of addition is

$$P(\mathbf{A} \cup \mathbf{B}) = P(\mathbf{A}) + P(\mathbf{B}) - P(\mathbf{A} \cap \mathbf{B}).$$

Notice that when $\mathbf{A} \cap \mathbf{B} = \Lambda$, $P(\mathbf{A} \cap \mathbf{B}) = P(\Lambda) = 0$. So when the sets do not overlap, we get the simpler rule of addition.

Next consider the *complement rule*. Suppose that we toss a six-sided die once and want to know the probability of *the complement of* {*1*}. The complement of {*1*} is {*2, 3, 4, 5, 6*}. So its probability is 5/6. The following chain of equalities suggests a general rule:

$$\frac{5}{6} = P(\{2, 3, 4, 5, 6\}) = P(\neg\{1\}) = 1 - P(\{1\}) = 1 - \frac{1}{6}.$$

The only new step that used a probability rule is the move from $P(\neg\{1\})$ to $1 - P(\{1\})$. Here is the complement rule:

$$P(\neg\mathbf{A}) = 1 - P(\mathbf{A}).$$

A and $\neg$**A** together include all of the possible outcomes, and $\mathbf{A} \cap \neg\mathbf{A} = \Lambda$. So by the simple rule of addition,

$$\begin{aligned} P(\mathbf{A} \cup \neg\mathbf{A}) &= P(\mathbf{A}) + P(\neg\mathbf{A}) \\ &= \frac{\text{number of possible outcomes in } \mathbf{A}}{\text{total number of possible outcomes}} \\ &+ \frac{\text{number of possible outcomes in } \neg\mathbf{A}}{\text{total number of possible outcomes}}. \end{aligned}$$

Since **A** and ¬**A** include all the possible outcomes, the two numerators above add up to their common denominator, so

$$P(\mathbf{A}) + P(\neg\mathbf{A}) = 1.$$

The complement rule follows by subtracting P(**A**) from both sides:

$$P(\neg\mathbf{A}) = 1 - P(\mathbf{A}).$$

6. EXAMPLES

These are the simple rules for probability. They are only as good as their ability to help us compute probabilities. We need to try them with some examples.

Suppose that we tossed once both a yellow and a red six-sided die. What are the possible outcomes? To answer this, ignore for a moment what happens to the red die; the toss is like our toss of one die: The yellow die can land in one of six possible ways. Now consider the red die. For each of the six possible ways that the yellow die might turn up, the red die can also turn up in six different ways. Thus, there are six red die outcomes for each of the six yellow die outcomes. We display this graphically in Table 7.1. Each of the possible outcomes is listed in angle brackets, < >. Order is important. The first number tells us what the yellow die did; the second number tells us what the red die did. The outcome of the red die coming up three and the yellow die five is not the same as the outcome of the yellow die coming

TABLE 7.1

		Red die outcome:					
		1	2	3	4	5	6
Yellow die outcome:	1	*<1, 1>*	*<1, 2>*	*<1, 3>*	*<1, 4>*	*<1, 5>*	*<1, 6>*
	2	*<2, 1>*	*<2, 2>*	*<2, 3>*	—	—	*<2, 6>*
	3	*<3, 1>*	*<3, 1>*	—	—	—	*<3, 6>*
	4	—	—	—	—	—	—
	5	—	—	—	—	—	—
	6	*<6, 1>*	*<6, 2>*	—	—	—	*<6, 6>*

up three and the red one five. So we use angle brackets and say that <*5, 3*> ≠ <*3, 5*>. Do not be confused by this; order is not important for *sets*: {*3, 5*} = {*5, 3*}.

If we then assign equal probabilities to each simple event, we can compute probabilities of other events. Be sure that you know which are the simple events; they all look like, {<*x, y*>}, for example, *double-six,* is {<*6, 6*>}. What is the probability of the simple event {<*1, 3*>}? It must be 1/36, because there is one possible outcome in the event and there are 36 = 6 × 6 total possible outcomes.

Consider some more interesting events. What is the probability of the event of the two dice summing to seven? The possible outcomes where this happens are along the diagonal from the lower left-hand corner to the upper right-hand corner (Table 7.2). Here they are marked "*sum−7.*" There are six such possible outcomes. So the probability of the *sum−7* event is 6/36 = 1/6. What other events have probability 1/6? *Sum−8* includes five possible outcomes, {<*6, 2*>, <*5, 3*>, <*4, 4*>, <*3, 5*>, <*2, 6*>}; its probability is 5/36.

Look how the addition rule works. What is the probability of tossing a *sum−7* *or* a *sum−8*; that is, what is the probability of the event that is the union: *sum−7* ∪ *sum−8*? Since they do not overlap, by the addition rule it must be

$$\mathrm{P}(\mathit{sum}{-}7 \cup \mathit{sum}{-}8) = \mathrm{P}(\mathit{sum}{-}7) + \mathrm{P}(\mathit{sum}{-}8) = \frac{6}{36} + \frac{5}{36} = \frac{11}{36}.$$

We can show this nicely with the 6 × 6 grid (Table 7.3).

Virtually any question that one can ask about probabilities for one toss of a pair of dice can be answered quickly by reference to this 6 × 6 grid of possible outcomes. Rolling a *double* is more probable than rolling a *sum−8*; 6/36 > 5/36. The probability of getting a sum greater than nine is 6/36. The probability of the event *sum−4* ∪ *double* is 8/36—be careful not to count overlaps twice.

Suppose that we roll our pair of dice twice. How many possible outcomes are there? Reason in the same way as above: For each possible outcome of the first roll there are 36 possible outcomes for the second roll; and there are 36 different first roll possible outcomes. So there are 36 × 36 = 1,296 possible outcomes from two tosses of a pair of dice.

TABLE 7.2

		Red die outcome:					
		1	2	3	4	5	6
Yellow die	1	<*1, 1*>	<*1, 2*>	<*1, 3*>	<*1, 4*>	<*1, 5*>	*sum-7*
outcome:	2	<*2, 1*>	<*2, 2*>	<*2, 3*>	—	*sum-7*	<*2, 6*>
	3	<*3, 1*>	<*3, 2*>	—	*sum-7*	—	<*3, 6*>
	4	—	—	*sum-7*	—	—	—
	5	—	*sum-7*	—	—	—	—
	6	*sum-7*	<*6, 2*>	—	—	—	<*6, 6*>

TABLE 7.3

		Red die outcome:					
		1	2	3	4	5	6
Yellow die	1	*<1, 1>*	*<1, 2>*	*<1, 3>*	*<1, 4>*	*<1, 5>*	*sum-7*
outcome:	2	*<2, 1>*	*<2, 2>*	*<2, 3>*	—	*sum-7*	*sum-8*
	3	*<3, 1>*	*<3, 2>*	—	*sum-7*	*sum-8*	*<3, 6>*
	4	—	—	*sum-7*	*sum-8*	—	—
	5	—	*sum-7*	*sum-8*	—	—	—
	6	*sum-7*	*sum-8*	—	—	—	*<6, 6>*

How ought we list them? We can list them in a big 36 × 36 grid just like the 6 × 6 grid above. What goes down the side of the grid? The 36 possible outcomes of the first toss of a pair of dice. Then we have the 36 possible outcomes of the second toss of the pair running across the top (Table 7.4). What do the entries in the grid look like? They are ordered pairs of ordered pairs: *<<1, 1>, <1, 1>>* is the entry that goes in the upper left-hand corner of the grid. The first element of the first pair is the outcome of the yellow die on the first toss; the second element of the first pair is the outcome of the red die on the first toss. Similarly, the first element of the second pair is the outcome of the yellow die on the second toss; the second element of the second pair is the outcome of the red die on the second toss. So the possible outcome <<4, 4>, <6, 1>> represents the outcome of tossing a pair of fours on the first toss and a "six-one" on the second toss (with the six on the yellow die and the one on the red die). The simple events are one-membered sets of these outcomes: {*<<4, 4>, <6, 1>>*}

There are 1,296 = 36 × 36 entries in this table. So there are 1,296 possible outcomes from tossing a pair of six-sided dice twice. How many possible outcomes do you imagine there are in the experiment of tossing a pair of six-sided dice three times? What about four times? No wonder there are so many different ways a game of backgammon can turn out.

TABLE 7.4

		Second-roll outcome:					
		<1, 1>	<1, 2>	—	—	<6, 5>	<6, 6>
First-roll	*<1, 1>*	—	—	—	—	—	—
outcome:	*<1, 2>*	—	—	—	—	—	—
	.	—	—	—	—	—	—
	.	—	—	—	—	—	—
	.	—	—	—	—	—	—
	<6, 5>	—	—	—	—	—	—
	<6, 6>	—	—	—	—	—	*<<6, 6>,<6, 6>>*

We can start calculating probabilities. Assuming that the dice are fair, we would assign each of the 1,296 simple events in this example the same probability, 1/1,296. To find the probability of an event, determine how many possible outcomes are in that event; divide this number by 1,296. The event of getting a double six twice is {*<<6, 6>, <6, 6>>*}. There is one possible outcome in this event, so its probability is 1/1,296: P({*<<6, 6>, <6, 6>>*}) = 1/1,296.

What is the probability of the event of getting a *double-five* and a *double-six* on the two tosses? First determine what the event looks like:

{*<<5, 5>, <6, 6>>, <<6, 6>, <5, 5>>*}.

The probability of this event is 2/1,296, since it contain two possible outcomes.

Sometimes it is tedious to list all the possible outcomes of an event. But to find the probability of the event, one needs some way of counting the possible outcomes in the event. Consider an example. What is the probability of tossing two doubles in two tosses of two dice? Some of the possible outcomes of this event are:

<<1, 1>, <4, 4>>, <<3, 3>, <6, 6>>, <<2, 2>, <2, 2>>, etc.

But how many are there? How can you sensibly count them?

One way to count is as follows: Suppose that you tossed a *double−1* on the first toss. What could then happen that would result in a *"double-double"*? You could then toss another *double−1*, or you could toss a *double−2*, or a *double−3* or . . . or a *double−6*. How many of these are there? Six. Do the same computation assuming that you tossed a *double−2* first. Again you will find that there are six second-toss outcomes that result in a *double-double*. Thus, there are 36 different ways to get a *double-double*. Each entry on Table 7.5 is a possible outcome *<<x, x>, <y, y>>*. Obviously, there are 36 possible outcomes of a double-double; so the probability of this event is 36/1,296 = 1/36.

Consider a more difficult counting problem. What is the probability of getting *no doubles* in two rolls of two dice? Our problem is to count the number of possible outcomes that do not include any doubles. Keep the 36 × 36 grid (Table 7.4) in mind to organize your thinking.

TABLE 7.5

		Second-toss double number:					
		1	2	3	4	5	6
First-toss	1	—	—	—	—	—	—
double	2	—	—	—	—	—	—
number:	3	—	—	—	—	—	—
	4	—	—	—	—	—	—
	5	—	—	—	—	—	—
	6	—	—	—	—	—	—

How many outcomes in the first row have no doubles in them? They all have a first-roll *double−1*, <*1, 1*>, so, none of the first row entries have *no* doubles.

What about the next row? Here the first roll is a <*1, 2*>, not a double; to have a double in them, they would have to get it from the second roll. How many second-roll elements are doubles? Six. To see this, recall that there are six outcomes which are doubles when a pair of dice is tossed once; so on the second toss of a pair of dice, six possible outcomes are doubles. Conversely, in the second row of this big 36×36 grid there are 30 ($= 6 - 6$) outcomes with no double.

What about the third row? The same result as in the second row. In fact, this result will be the same for any row where the first roll is not a double. How many such rows are there? For the same reason that there are 30 entries in the second row with no doubles, there are 30 rows where the first entry is not a double. So for each of these 30 rows there are 30 possible outcomes that contain no doubles.

What about the other rows? They are like the first row. Each of these is a row where the first roll is a double. So no entry in any of these six rows has no doubles; they contribute no possible outcomes to the calculation.

So there are $30 \times 30 = 900$ possible outcomes that include no doubles. The probability of getting no doubles in two tosses of a pair of dice is 900/1,296. This tedious bit of counting can be done much more easily. But we need more rules to do so.

7. SUMMARY

1. One can speak of the probability of sentences or of events.
   - **(a)** These approaches are equivalent.
   - **(b)** We will speak of the probability of events.
2. Sets are collections of things. Almost anything can be collected as part of a set. There are three important ways for describing sets.
   - **(a)** The elements of a set may be listed inside curly brackets: { }. The order in which items occur does not matter, and duplications are not important: $\{a, b\} = \{b, a\}$ and $\{b, b\} = \{b\}$.
   - **(b)** The elements of a set may be described by noting a property they share. We write $\{x|x...\}$, "the set of things, x, such that x ... ." The dots specify some property that must be true of every member of the set. The set $\{x|x$ is an even integer$\} = \{2, 4, 6, ...\}$.
   - **(c)** A set can be labeled with a capital letter, **A**, **B**, **C**, ...
   - **(d)** Two sets are special. The universal set, **V**, contains every element in the universe of discourse: everything in the current context of discussion. The empty set, **Λ** contains no elements.
3. Three are three important relations we speak of when we speak about sets.
   - **(a)** a is an element of **S**, $a \in$ **S**, is true when the element, a, is a member of the set **S**.
   - **(b)** **A** is a subset of **B**, **A** $\subseteq$ **B**, when every element of **A** is also an element of **B**. Note

that on this definition every set is a subset of itself, **A** ⊆ **A**, and the empty set is a subset of every set, **Λ** ⊆ **A**.

(c) Two sets are equal, **A** = **B**, when they contain exactly the same elements. Note that **A** = **B** just in case both **A** ⊆ **B** and **B** ⊆ **A**.

4. Three important operations can be performed on sets.
   (a) The union of two sets, **A** ∪ **B**, is the set that contains every element which is either in **A** or in **B** or both.
   (b) The intersection of two sets, **A** ∩ **B**, is the set that contains every element which is in both **A** and **B**.
   (c) The complement of a set, ¬**A**, is the set that contains every element in the universe of discourse which is not in **A**.
   (d) These operations compound with each other much as do arithmetical operations.

5. Set talk and sentence talk are equivalent.
   (a) We can think of a sentence as picking out the set of possible worlds where the sentence is true.
   (b) The disjunction of two sentences is the union of the two sets picked out by the two sentences.
   (c) The conjunction of two sentences is the intersection of the two sets picked out by the two sentences.
   (d) The negation of a sentence picks out the set of all possible worlds not in the set picked out by the sentence.

6. Probabilities are of events, which are sets of possible outcomes. Events are constructed in three stages.
   (a) A list of the possible outcomes of some experiment is established.
   (b) The simple events are the sets that contain exactly one possible outcome. There is one such simple event for each possible outcome.
   (c) The compound events are sets of any number of possible outcomes. To construct them from the simple events, one includes every set that can be built from the simple events by taking unions, intersections, and complements.
   (d) There are two special events. The universal or certain event, **V**, which contains all the possible outcomes—and, for this reason, which must occur—and the impossible event, **Λ**, which contains no possible outcomes—and, for this reason, which cannot occur.

7. Probability assigns a number between zero and 1 to each event, **A**: 0 ≤ P(**A**) ≤ 1.
   (a) P(**V**) = 1; P(**Λ**) = 0
   (b) In "nice cases," which include the so-called games of chance, each simple event is assigned the same probability as each other simple event. The sum of all these probabilities is 1

8. Three versions of the addition rule may be stated, in order of increasing generality.
   (a) If the same probability is assigned to each simple event, in nice cases, the probability of any event is the ratio of the number of possible outcomes in the event to the total number of possible outcomes.
   (b) If two events do not overlap, that is, if **A** ∩ **B** = **Λ**, then P(**A** ∪ **B**) = P(**A**) + P(**B**).
   (c) For any two events, P(**A** ∪ **B**) = P(**A**) + P(**B**) − P(**A** ∩ **B**).

9. The complement rule states that the probability of the complement of any event is 1 minus the probability of the event.
   (a) In symbols: $P(\neg \mathbf{A}) = 1 - P(\mathbf{A})$.
   (b) The complement rule can be proven from the addition rule.

8. REFERENCES

There are many good introductions to set theory. (Halmos, 1970) and (Krivine, 1971) are concise and go into much greater depth than here. There are also a variety of good introductions to probability theory. A nice, concise introduction is (Gnedenko and Khinchin, 1962). I have also profitted from (Chung, 1975) and (Woodroofe, 1975).

9. PROBLEMS

1. Consider the following sets:

$$\mathbf{V} = \{x|x \text{ is a date in March 1992}\};$$
$$\mathbf{A} = \{x|x \text{ is a Saturday date in March 1992}\};$$
$$\mathbf{B} = \{x|x \text{ is a weekend date in March 1992}\};$$
$$\mathbf{C} = \{x|x \text{ is a weekday date in March 1992}\}.$$

   What dates do the following sets include as members?
   (a) $(\mathbf{V} \cap \mathbf{\Lambda})$
   (b) $(\mathbf{A} \cup \mathbf{B})$
   (c) $(\mathbf{B} \cup \mathbf{C})$
   (d) $(\mathbf{A} \cap \mathbf{B})$
   (e) $((\mathbf{B} \cup \mathbf{C}) \cap \mathbf{A})$
   (f) $(\mathbf{B} \cup (\mathbf{C} \cap \mathbf{A}))$

2. True or False:
   (a) $a \in \{a, e, i, o, u\}$.
   (b) $a \subseteq \{a, e, i, o, u\}$.
   (c) $\{a\} \subseteq \{a, e, i, o, u\}$.
   (d) $\{a\} \cap \{a, e, i, o, u\} = \{a, e, i, o, u\}$.
   (e) $\{a\} \cap \{a, e, i, o, u\} = \{a\}$.
   (f) $\{a\} \cup \{a, e, i, o, u\} = \{a\}$.
   (g) If $\mathbf{V} = \{a, e, i, o, u\}$, then $\neg\{a\} = \{a, e, i, o, u\}$.
   (h) If $\mathbf{V} = \{a, e, i, o, u\}$, then $\neg\{a, e, i, o, u\} = \mathbf{\Lambda}$.

3. Show that for any three sets **A**, **B**, and **C**:
   (1) If $((\mathbf{A} \cap \mathbf{B}) \cup \mathbf{C}) = (\mathbf{A} \cap (\mathbf{B} \cup \mathbf{C}))$ then $\mathbf{C} \subseteq \mathbf{A}$.
   (2) If $\mathbf{C} \subseteq \mathbf{A}$ then $((\mathbf{A} \cap \mathbf{B}) \cup \mathbf{C}) = (\mathbf{A} \cap (\mathbf{B} \cup \mathbf{C})$.

4. The "power set" of a set is the set containing all the subsets of the given set. Write the power set of the set $\{x\}$. Write the power set of this set, that is, the power set of the set you found for the first part of the problem (this is the power set of the power set of $\{x\}$). It is usual to use the following notation for the power set of a given set, $\mathbf{A}$:$\wp(\mathbf{A})$. Are there more than 100 elements in $\wp(\wp(\wp(\wp(\{x\}))))$? Why or why not? Do not forget that a set is always a subset of itself, and that the null set is a subset of any set.

5. Suppose that we discard all the cards in the deck but the aces and draw one card at random from this "deck" consisting only of aces. What event (set of possible outcomes) does the following sentence describe: "We do not draw a spade from this 'deck'."? What event does the following sentence describe: "We draw either a spade or a heart from this 'deck'."? If each simple event is assigned the same probability, what is the probability of not drawing a spade from this "deck"?
6. Suppose that we toss a loaded six-sided die. This die is loaded such that the probability of each face turning up is proportional to the number of the face. Thus *2* is twice as likely as *1; 3* is three times as likely as *1; 5* is five times as likely; and so on. What are the probabilities of each of the simple events?
7. Prove the complement rule from the addition rule and our rules governing sets.
8. Suppose that you toss a four-sided die once. What are the possible outcomes? What are the simple events? What are the compound events? (List them.)
9. You are to draw one card randomly from a normal deck of playing cards.
   - **(a)** How many possible outcomes are there in this experiment?
   - **(b)** In some sensible manner identify what these possible outcomes are.
   - **(c)** How many simple events are there in this experiment?
   - **(d)** Are there more than 100 total events (simple and otherwise) in this experiment? If so, say why. If not, say why.
10. Suppose that we toss one four-sided and one eight-sided die once.
   - **(a)** Assuming that everything is normal, how many possible outcomes are there to this "experiment?"
   - **(b)** Enumerate all the elements in the event of getting a double.
   - **(c)** Suppose that this is a "nice case." What is the probability of getting a double?

   Let **A** be the event of getting a double. Let **B** be the event of getting a sum of 5. Let **C** be the event of getting a 3 on the four-sided die regardless of what the eight-sided die does.
   - **(d)** What is P(**A**)?
   - **(e)** What is P(**C**)?
   - **(f)** What is P(**A** ∪ **C**)?
   - **(g)** What is P(**B** ∩ **C**)?
   - **(h)** What is P(¬(**B** ∩ **C**))?
   - **(i)** What is P(**A** ∪ (**B** ∩ **C**))?
   - **(j)** What is P((**A** ∪ **B**) ∩ **C**)?

CHAPTER

8

CONDITIONAL PROBABILITY

1. INTRODUCTION TO CONDITIONAL PROBABILITY

Suppose that we toss two dice (a yellow one and a blue one) once. What is the probability that the sum of the spots showing is *eight* or greater? 15/36. Now suppose we knew that the yellow die came up *six*. Given this new information, what is the probability of a sum of *eight* or greater? It is not 15/36. Knowing that the yellow die showed a high number, such as *six*, should make the odds better that the sum of the two dice is high. To get a sum of *eight* or greater, given that the yellow die shows *six*, the blue die must show *two* or greater; the only case where the sum would be less than *eight* is when the blue die comes up *one*. The probability of getting a *two* or greater on the blue die is 5/6. Thus, *given* that the yellow die came up *six*, the probability that the sum is *eight* or greater is 5/6 = 30/36.

This is the central idea behind *conditional probability*. We use a slash, "|", to show conditional probabilities. "P(**A**|**B**)" is read "the probability of event **A** *given* that event **B** occurred"; or, more simply, "the probability of **A** given **B**." In the example above we found that

$$\mathrm{P}(sum-8\ or\ greater|yellow-6) = \frac{5}{6}.$$

B is called the event being "conditioned on." Do not confuse the slash of conditional probability with the slash of division.

Conditional probability works by changing the set of possible outcomes. When the conditioning event is **B**, only those possible outcomes contained in **B** are included as possible outcomes. By conditioning on **B**, one is saying that everything that is not **B**—all the possible outcomes not in **B**—are no longer possible.

Calculating conditional probabilities is not hard. First consider the nice cases where each simple outcome has the same probability. P(**A**) is the unconditional probability of **A**; we calculate it by dividing the number of possible outcomes in **A** by the total number of possible outcomes. Things go similarly for conditional probabilities. To find P(**A**|**B**), find the proportion of **A** outcomes among **B** outcomes; **B** becomes the new "universal set." That is,

$$\mathrm{P}(\mathbf{A}|\mathbf{B}) = \frac{\text{number of outcomes in both } \mathbf{A} \text{ and } \mathbf{B}}{\text{number of possible outcomes in } \mathbf{B}}.$$

This is very similar to the unconditional case:

$$\mathrm{P}(\mathbf{A}) = \frac{\text{number of outcomes in } \mathbf{A} \text{ (and } \mathbf{V})}{\text{number of outcomes in } \mathbf{V}}.$$

Putting (and **V**) in the numerator is not necessary; every possible outcome is in **V** by definition, but including (and **V**) makes clear the relation between conditional and unconditional probability. We might have written P(**A**|**V**): the probability of **A** given that one of the possible outcomes occurs.

This definition of conditional probability can be extended to cases where simple events do not all have the same probability. Conditional probabilities are defined

$$\mathrm{P}(\mathbf{A}|\mathbf{B}) = \frac{\mathrm{P}(\mathbf{A} \cap \mathbf{B})}{\mathrm{P}(\mathbf{B})}.$$

Observe that this definition maintains the relationship above. The conditional probability of **A** given **B** is the proportion of **A**s that are **B** among all the **B**s.

An example: Suppose that we toss one fair die once. What is the probability that a five came up given that an odd number came up, P(*five*|*odd*)? List the possible outcomes:

1 2 3 4 5 6.

Eliminate all the possible outcomes that do not satisfy the event being conditioned on—that an odd number came up:

1 — *3* — *5* —.

Of the remaining possibilities, which are in the event whose probability we want? Just one: *5*.

$$\mathrm{P}(\{5\}|\{1, 3, 5\}) = \frac{\mathrm{P}(\{5\} \cap \{1, 3, 5\})}{\mathrm{P}(\{1, 3, 5\})} = \frac{\mathrm{P}(\{5\})}{\mathrm{P}(\{1, 3, 5\})} = \frac{1/6}{1/2} = \frac{1}{3}.$$

It is different from the unconditional probability, P({*5*}), which is 1/6.

Another example: Suppose that we toss a yellow and a blue die together once. *Given* that we threw a *sum−7*, what is the probability that the blue die came up *six*? To calculate this probability, recall the grid of possible outcomes for one toss of two dice (Table 8.1). To find this conditional probability, the first thing to do is to eliminate all the possibilities that are not in the conditioning event—*sum−7* (Table 8.2). Of the remaining possibilities, which ones satisfy the event whose probability we want? Just the upper right-hand corner, *<1, 6>*. So one of the remaining six possible outcomes is in the event whose probability we want—that the blue die came up six. So P(*blue−6*|*sum−7*) = 1/6.

Conditional probabilities can be counterintuitive. Consider the following problem. Suppose that we toss two fair six-sided dice. What is the probability of throwing a *double-six given* that one of the two dice came up *six*?

One is tempted to respond 1/6. Suppose that one of the dice was blue and the other was yellow. The probability of getting a *double-six* given that the blue die came up *six* is 1/6; similarly, the probability of getting a *double-six* given that the yellow die came up *six* is 1/6. P(*double-six*|*blue−6*) = 1/6 and P(*double-six*|*yellow−6*) = 1/6. Use a 6 × 6 grid like those in the tables to see why this is so. Here we are asked for the probability of a *double-six* given that *either* the blue or the yellow die came up *six*. Taking either the blue or the yellow die individually, the probability is 1/6. So it would seem that the "combined case" should have the same probability.

TABLE 8.1

		Blue die outcome:					
		1	2	3	4	5	6
Yellow die outcome:	1	*<1, 1>*	*<1, 2>*	*<1, 3>*	*<1, 4>*	*<1, 5>*	*<1, 6>*
	2	*<2, 1>*	*<2, 2>*	*<2, 3>*	—	—	*<2, 6>*
	3	*<3, 1>*	*<3, 2>*	—	—	—	*<3, 6>*
	4	—	—	—	—	—	—
	5	—	—	—	—	—	—
	6	*<6, 1>*	*<6, 2>*	—	—	—	*<6, 6>*

TABLE 8.2

		Blue die outcome:					
		1	2	3	4	5	6
Yellow die outcome:	1	—	—	—	—	—	*sum-7*
	2	—	—	—	—	*sum-7*	—
	3	—	—	—	*sum-7*	—	—
	4	—	—	*sum-7*	—	—	—
	5	—	*sum-7*	—	—	—	—
	6	*sum-7*	—	—	—	—	—

TABLE 8.3

		Blue die outcome:					
		1	2	3	4	5	6
Yellow die	1	—	—	—	—	—	<*1*, *6*>
outcome:	2	—	—	—	—	—	<*2*, *6*>
	3	—	—	—	—	—	<*3*, *6*>
	4	—	—	—	—	—	<*4*, *6*>
	5	—	—	—	—	—	<*5*, *6*>
	6	<*6*, *1*>	<*6*, *2*>	<*6*, *3*>	<*6*, *4*>	<*6*, *5*>	<*6*, *6*>

But this is the wrong answer. Start with the 6 × 6 grid of outcomes and eliminate all those that are not in the event being conditioned on—either die comes up six (Table 8.3). There are 11 possible outcomes in the event of either die coming up *six*. One of these is the event of a *double-six*. So the probability of getting a *double-six* given that some *six* came up is 1/11, not 1/6.

Keep in mind that this way of finding conditional probabilities works only for nice cases, when each simple event is assigned the same probability. When they are assigned different probabilities, you have to find the other probabilities, P(**A** ∩ **B**) and P(**B**), and divide: P(**A**|**B**) = P(**A** ∩ **B**)/P(**B**).

2. INDEPENDENT EVENTS AND THE MULTIPLICATION RULE

There is a striking feature of one of the examples above. The conditional probability that the blue die shows *six* given that a *sum*−*7* turns up is the same as the unconditional probability:

$$\frac{1}{6} = \mathrm{P}(\textit{blue}-\textit{6}\,|\,\textit{sum}-\textit{7}) = \mathrm{P}(\textit{blue}-\textit{6}) = \frac{30}{36} = \frac{1}{6}.$$

When this happens the events involved are *probabilistically independent*. In this case the event of the blue die coming up *six* is *independent* of the event of the sum of the dice being *seven*. Knowledge of the conditioning event does not alter the probability of the event in question. The general definition for independent events is this:

A and **B** are independent if and only if P(**A**|**B**) = P(**A**).

The occurrence of **B** does not "affect" the probability of **A**.

There is a peculiar aspect to this definition. One might think that if two events, **A** and **B**, were independent, the events **B** and **A** would also be independent. "Independence" does not sound like a word where it matters which event is stated first. Yet the definition of independence above gives **A** and **B** different roles; in particular, event **A** occurs twice in the definition, whereas **B** occurs once. This raises the question: If **A** is independent of **B**, is **B** also independent of **A**? In terms of the definition of independence with probabilities: If P(**A**|**B**) = P(**A**), does P(**B**|**A**) = P(**B**)? This turns out to be so, and the proof is revealing:

1. First, we suppose that P(**A**|**B**) = P(**A**).
2. By the definition of conditional probability:
$$P(\mathbf{A}|\mathbf{B}) = \frac{P(\mathbf{A} \cap \mathbf{B})}{P(\mathbf{B})}.$$
3. So, multiplying both sides of this equation by P(**B**), we get
$$P(\mathbf{B})P(\mathbf{A}|\mathbf{B}) = P(\mathbf{A} \cap \mathbf{B}).$$
4. Substituting P(**A**) for P(**A**|**B**) from (1) above gives us
$$P(\mathbf{B})P(\mathbf{A}) = P(\mathbf{A} \cap \mathbf{B}).$$
5. Dividing both sides of this equation by P(**A**) gives us
$$P(\mathbf{B}) = \frac{P(\mathbf{A} \cap \mathbf{B})}{P(\mathbf{A})}.$$
6. Since intersections do not care about order, that is, (**A** ∩ **B**) = (**B** ∩ **A**), we have
$$P(\mathbf{B}) = \frac{P(\mathbf{B} \cap \mathbf{A})}{P(\mathbf{A})}.$$
7. Finally, by the definition of conditional probability once again,
$$P(\mathbf{B}) = P(\mathbf{B}|\mathbf{A}).$$
8. So P(**A**|**B**) = P(**A**) if and only if P(**B**|**A**) = P(**B**).

If **A** and **B** are independent, both P(**A**|**B**) = P(**A**) and P(**B**|**A**) = P(**B**).

But we can learn more from this proof. Notice line 4. Here we have a new rule, the *multiplication rule*:

If **A** and **B** are independent, then P(**A** ∩ **B**) = P(**A**) × P(**B**).

Many computations can be simplified by using the multiplication rule.

Consider some examples. The outcome of the first toss of a die does not alter the probabilities for the outcomes of the second toss: different tosses of dice are independent of each other—at least for most dice. Consequently, we can use the multiplication rule. Suppose that we toss one die *twice*. What is the probability of getting a six two times in a row? Observe that the event of throwing two sixes in a row is the intersection of the two events, getting a six on the first throw *and* getting a six on the second throw, P(*six on both*) = P[(*six on 1st*) ∩ (*six on 2nd*)]. These events are independent, so we can use the multiplication rule. What is the probability of getting a six on the first toss of the die? P(*six on 1st*) = 1/6. What is the probability of getting a six on the second toss of the die? P(*six on 2nd*) = 1/6 (see Chapter 7, Section 6). We can put this together to get the answer for the probability we want:

$$\frac{1}{36} = \text{P}(\textit{six on both}) = \text{P}(\textit{six on 1st} \cap \textit{six on 2nd})$$

$$= \text{P}(\textit{six on 1st}) \times \text{P}(\textit{six on 2nd}) = \frac{1}{6} \times \frac{1}{6}.$$

It is easy to check this use of the multiplication rule by directly computing P(*six on both*).

Consider a slightly more complicated example. What is the probability of getting no *sum−7* rolls in two tosses of a pair of dice? The event of *not* getting any *sum−7*s is the event of not getting a *sum−7* on the first toss *and* not getting a *sum−7* on the second toss. It is the intersection of these two events:

$$\text{P}(\textit{no sum}-\textit{7 rolls in two tosses}) = \text{P}(\textit{no sum}-\textit{7 on 1st toss} \cap \textit{no sum}-\textit{7 on 2nd toss}).$$

Apply the multiplication rule. What is the probability of not getting a *sum−7* on the 1st toss? 30/36 (= 5/6). Similarly, the probability of not getting a *sum−7* on the 2nd toss is 5/6. So the probability of not getting a *sum−7* on both tosses is $5/6 \times 5/6 = 25/36$.

What is the probability of getting at least one *sum−7* in two tosses? This is the complement of not getting any *sum−7*s in two tosses. We just found that probability to be 25/36. So

$$\text{P}(\textit{at least one sum}-\textit{7 in 2 tosses}) = 1 - \frac{25}{36} = \frac{11}{36}.$$

The multiplication rule is very useful when the applications we are interested in have two properties. They are repetitious, and the repetitions are independent of each other—outcomes on one repetition do not alter the probabilities for outcomes on other repetitions. Dice tossing is like this. We can repeat the tossing of a pair of dice many times; and whatever happens on one toss of the dice does not influence the probabilities of outcomes on other tosses of the dice.

Consider another example. What is the probability of *not* tossing a *double* with 10 tosses of a pair of dice? Listing all the possible outcomes and counting would be a chore. But with the multiplication rule this problem is relatively simple. The event of not getting a *double* on 10 tosses is the intersection of 10 events:

$$[\textit{no doubles in 10 tosses}] = [(\textit{no double on the 1st toss})$$

$$\cap\ (\textit{no double on the 2nd}) \cap \cdots \cap (\textit{no double on the 10th})].$$

So we can use the multiplication rule:

$$\begin{aligned}
&\text{P}(\textit{no double in 10 tosses}) \\
&\quad = \text{P}(\textit{no double on 1} \cap \textit{no double on 2} \cap \cdots \cap \textit{no double on 10}) \\
&\quad = \text{P}(\textit{no double on 1}) \times \text{P}(\textit{no double on 2}) \times \cdots \times \text{P}(\textit{no double on 10}).
\end{aligned}$$

But the probability of not getting a *double* on the first toss is 5/6. Similarly, the probability of not getting a *double* on the second toss is 5/6. Indeed, this is true for all 10 tosses. So

$$\text{P}(\textit{no double in 10 tosses}) = \frac{5}{6} \times \frac{5}{6} \times \cdots \times \frac{5}{6} \left(\text{for 10 } \frac{5}{6}\text{s}\right).$$

So P(*no double in 10 tosses*) = $(5/6)^{10}$, about 0.16. From this we can infer (using the complement rule) that the probability of tossing at least one *double* in 10 tosses of a pair of dice is $1 - 0.16 = 0.84$.

The multiplication rule does not work when the events involved are not independent. Suppose that we toss one die once. Consider the two events

$$\mathbf{A} = \{3\} \quad \text{and} \quad \mathbf{B} = \{1, 3, 5\}.$$

What are P(**A**) and P(**B**)? P(**A**) = 1/6 and P(**B**) = 1/2. What is P(**A** ∩ **B**)? (**A** ∩ **B**) = {3} ∩ {1, 3, 5} = {3} = **A**. So, P(**A** ∩ **B**) = P(**A**) = 1/6. If we used the multiplication rule here, we would get the wrong answer:

$$\frac{1}{6} = \text{P}(\mathbf{A} \cap \mathbf{B}) \neq \text{P}(\mathbf{A}) \times \text{P}(\mathbf{B}) = \frac{1}{6} \times \frac{1}{2} = \frac{1}{12}.$$

This is as it should be, for **A** and **B** are not independent:

$$\frac{1}{6} = \text{P}(\{3\}) = \text{P}(\mathbf{A}) \neq \text{P}(\mathbf{A}|\mathbf{B}) = \text{P}(\{3\}|\{1, 3, 5\}) = \frac{1}{3}.$$

The multiplication rule can be used only with independent events.

3. DEPENDENT EVENTS AND TREES

When events are not independent we cannot use the multiplication rule. All is not lost, however. In such cases we frequently can use a related rule, the *intersection rule*. It is a consequence of the definition of conditional probability. Recall that

$$\text{P}(\mathbf{A}|\mathbf{B}) = \frac{\text{P}(\mathbf{A} \cap \mathbf{B})}{\text{P}(\mathbf{B})}.$$

So by multiplying both sides of this equation by P(**B**), we get a general rule for the probability of the intersection of two events:

$$\text{P}(\mathbf{A} \cap \mathbf{B}) = \text{P}(\mathbf{B}) \times \text{P}(\mathbf{A}|\mathbf{B}).$$

The *intersection rule* comes in particularly handy when we can use a *probability tree* to represent a sequence of events.

Consider, for example, the following construction of a *probability tree*. Suppose that we are to draw three cards from a normal (52 card) deck of cards—taking the first three cards off the top, one by one, after the deck has been well shuffled. Suppose we are interested in drawing a pair. What are the possible routes we might follow toward this goal? This is a complicated question to answer in full detail. But if we focus exclusively on getting (or failing to get) a pair—we neglect what kind of pair (e.g., sevens or kings) and the suits involved—it is fairly easy to describe the progress we might make in a probability tree.

What could happen? We start by drawing one card. On our second draw, we might draw the same-number card as our first draw or we might not; we might or might not draw a pair on the second draw. If we succeeded and got a pair, we can quit, otherwise, we can draw again. On our third draw, again, there are two possibilities: We could draw a card that matches one of the two cards we hold (thereby giving us a pair) or we could draw something else. We can represent this sequence of possibilities with the tree shown in Figure 8.1. Read this tree from top to bottom. To get a pair, we would have to "turn right" on either the second draw or the third draw. By extending this tree two more draws and adding the appropriate probabilities, we will be able to use it to compute the probability of getting a pair in five draws.

Probability trees are constructed with some goal in mind. The example above has the goal of getting a pair of cards, but other kinds of goals work just as well. Trees are normally read from top to bottom or from left to right. We start with a *node*. The probability trees we will be working with in this chapter use round nodes: ●. From this node we add "branches." Each branch represents one of the different

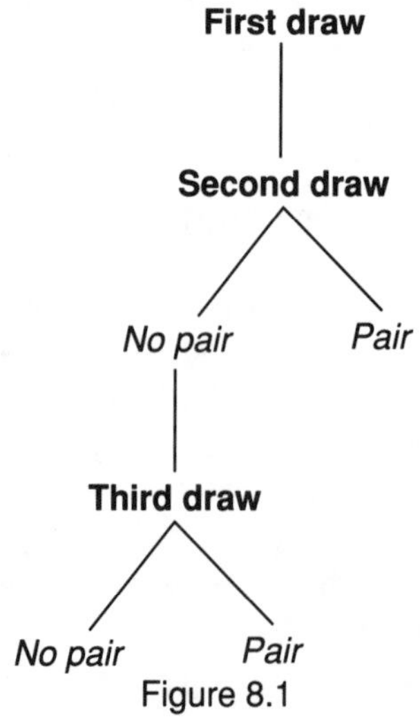

Figure 8.1

things that could happen from a given node. If there are only two things that could happen, we add two branches from the node; if there are more, we add appropriately more branches. Each branch ends in one of two ways. It can end at a new node—from which new branches "sprout," or it can end in a "leaf." The leaves contain descriptions of where we stand regarding our goal (see Chapter 3, Section 4).

Trees represent the order in which we learn about a situation. Consider the following example. Suppose that we are using chalk. We know that our school provides two different brands, Crayola and Academic. At the top node of our tree we do not know what kind of chalk we will be using, nor do we know whether the chalk will break. At the next level of nodes, we have learned something: we know whether it is Crayola or Academic chalk. At the bottom of the tree, we learn whether or not the chalk broke (Figure 8.2). Different nodes of a tree correspond to different states of knowledge about things. The farther down we are, the more we know. For example, suppose that I took a piece of chalk and after using it for awhile, it broke. Only then did I discover that it was Academic chalk. This different way that we might get information can be represented by a modified tree (Figure 8.3). The branches of probability trees are assigned *conditional probabilities*. Think of these as the probability of "going down" a branch *given* "one has arrived" at the node

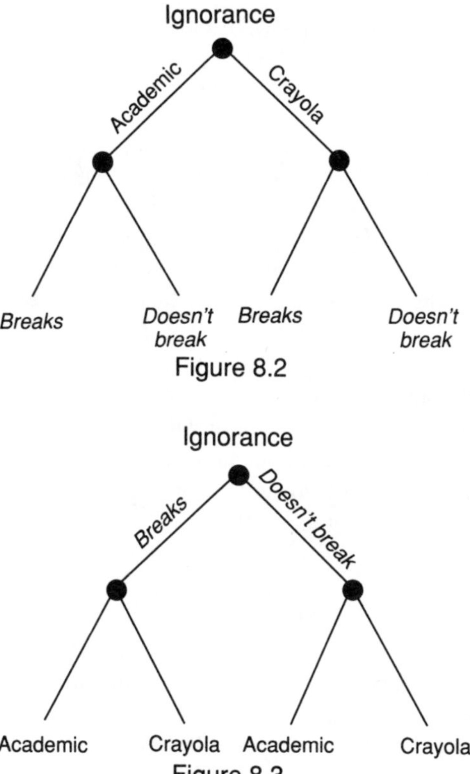

Figure 8.2

Figure 8.3

from which the branch sprouts. In the chalk example, we might suppose that Crayola chalk breaks only 1% of the time (under normal use). This is a conditional probability: the probability of a piece of chalk breaking *given* that it is Crayola chalk. Adopting a natural symbolism, we have that P(**B**|**C**) = 1/100. We might further suppose that the probability of Academic chalk breaking is higher, say 5/100. P(**B**|**A**) = 5/100. We could also suppose that 70% of the school's chalk is Academic and 30% is Crayola. We can insert this kind of information into the tree (Figure 8.4). Frequently we get information of this "conditional" sort—*given* "so and so," the probability of "such and such" is a certain number. Trees give us a natural way to represent such information.

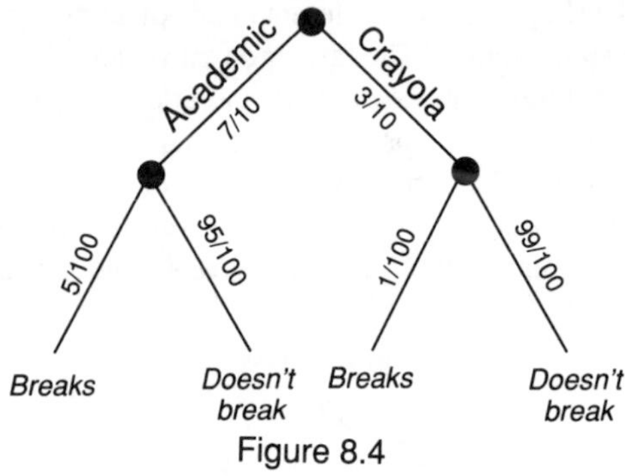

Figure 8.4

Notice that the probabilities of all branches leaving a single node must total 1. Once you are "at" a given node, you must "leave" along one of the branches sprouting from the node. This group of branches represents all of the possible courses nature might take given that one is at the node. If this is not so, the tree is not complete; more branches must be added. For a complete tree, then, the sum of all the branch probabilities leaving a given node must be 1.

We can construct a tree with just a minimal idea about the goal of interest. For example, we could construct a tree representing all the possible outcomes of two tosses of the die (Figure 8.5). We can simplify this tree by focusing on a more clearly defined goal. We should only include different branches for differences that make a difference in our progress toward this goal. Suppose we are playing a board game and we need to advance at least 10 paces to get to some desirable point in the game. Unless we roll a four, five, or six on the first roll, we cannot reach this goal. So we should lump together all the branches for rolling one, two, and three, and all the subsequent branches "below" these branches. All of these parts of the tree lead to failure to achieve 10 paces. Similar observations can simplify the other parts of the tree. A modified tree which includes only that information which is directly relevant to the goal of advancing 10 paces is shown in Figure 8.6. This revised tree is simpler, and it shows more clearly the possible ways of achieving the goal of moving 10 or more paces in two rolls.

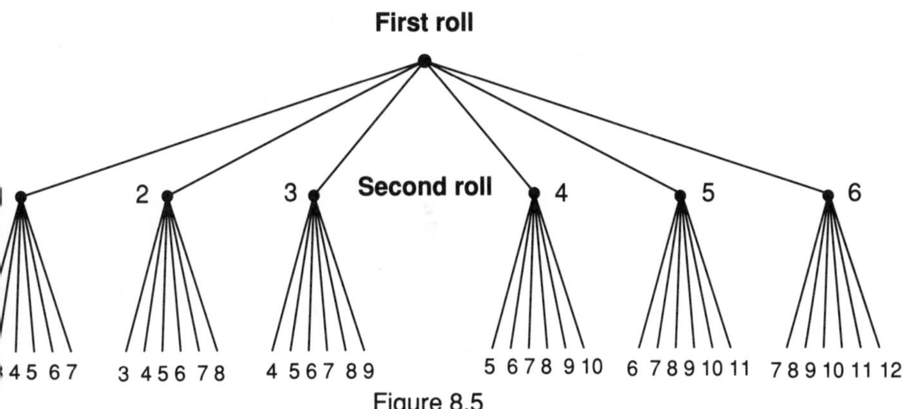

Figure 8.5

Now let's use a tree, its branch probabilities, and the intersection rule to solve a problem. Recall the example above of drawing cards to get a pair. We constructed a tree to describe how things might go as we attempt to get a pair (see Figure 8.1). But what probabilities should we add to the branches? Suppose that we drew the ace of spades on the first draw. What is the probability of getting a pair on the second draw? It is 3/51, because there are three other aces among the 51 cards left in the deck. So the probability of not getting a pair after the second draw is 48/51. If we get a second ace, we are done, for we have achieved our goal of drawing a pair.

But, suppose we did not get another ace; perhaps we got a 6 of clubs. What is the probability of drawing a pair on the third draw? In this situation we hold two unpaired cards. To put it another way, we have two different cards (e.g., ace of spades and six of clubs) to pair up with our third draw. There are six cards in the deck that could pair with either of the cards we hold (three aces and three sixes). The deck has 50 cards left, so the probability of pairing on the third draw is 6/50. The probability of not pairing on the third draw is 44/50. We can put all this information in the tree (Figure 8.7). The event of not getting any pairs in three draws is the intersection of not getting a pair on the second draw and not getting a pair on the third draw:

$$\mathrm{P}(\neg \textit{pair in 3 draws}) = \mathrm{P}(\neg \textit{pair on 2} \cap \neg \textit{pair on 3}).$$

$(\neg \textit{pair on 2})$ and $(\neg \textit{pair on 3})$ are not independent, but we can use the intersection rule to find the probability we want. We can take the values for these probabilities from the tree we have just constructed.

$$\mathrm{P}(\neg \textit{pair on 2} \cap \neg \textit{pair on 3}) = \mathrm{P}(\neg \textit{pair on 2}) \times \mathrm{P}(\neg \textit{pair on 3} | \neg \textit{pair on 2})$$

$$= \frac{48}{51} \times \frac{44}{50} = \frac{2{,}112}{2{,}550} \approx 0.83.$$

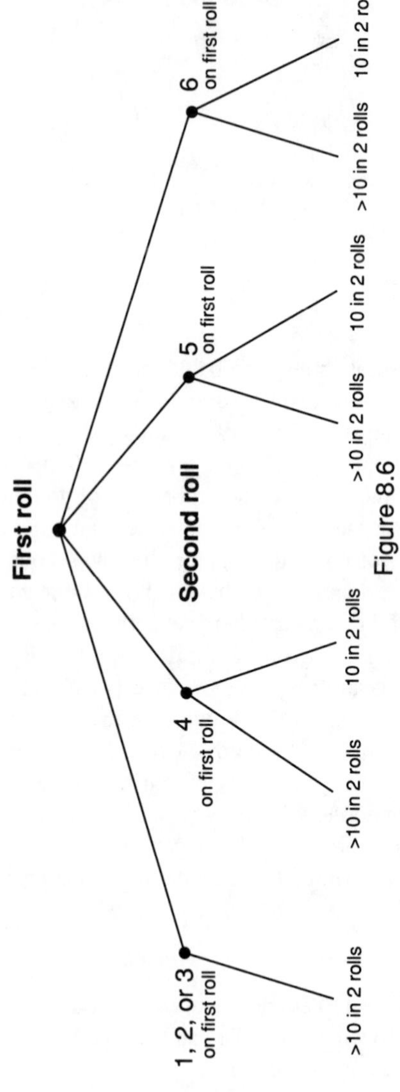

First roll
Second roll
1, 2, or 3
on first roll
4
on first roll
5
on first roll
6
on first roll
>10 in 2 rolls
>10 in 2 rolls
10 in 2 rolls
>10 in 2 rolls
10 in 2 rolls
>10 in 2 rolls
10 in 2 rolls

Figure 8.6

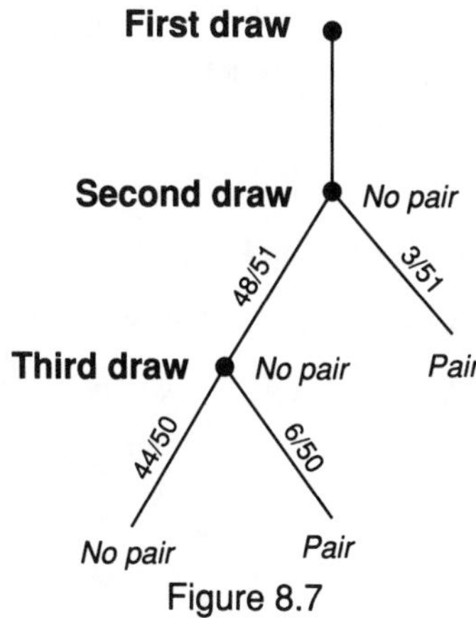

Figure 8.7

P($\neg$*pair on 2*) is just the probability of not pairing our first card with our second draw. P[($\neg$*pair on 3*)|($\neg$*pair on 2*)] is the probability of not pairing either of the first two cards we drew on our third draw—*given* that we did not get a pair on the second draw.

We can extend this tree to find the probability of getting a pair with five draws (Figure 8.8). The probabilities in this tree are determined in the same way as in the

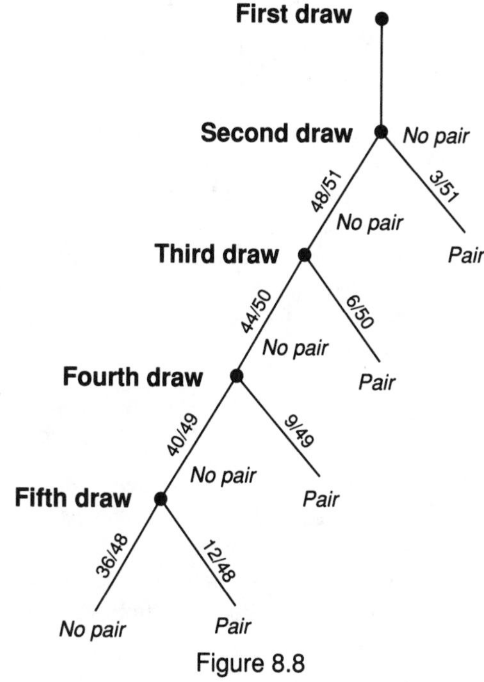

Figure 8.8

smaller tree. After each draw, the number of cards in the deck drops by one, and the number of cards that pair with the cards held increases by three. We now use the intersection rule:

$$\begin{aligned} \text{P}(\neg \textit{pair in 5 draws}) &= \text{P}(\neg \textit{pair on 5} \cap \neg \textit{pair in 1–4}) \\ &= \text{P}(\neg \textit{pair in 1–4}) \times \text{P}(\neg \textit{pair on 5} | \neg \textit{pair in 1–4}). \end{aligned}$$

We can use the intersection rule in the same way to calculate P(¬*pair in 1–4*):

$$\begin{aligned} \text{P}(\neg \textit{pair in 1–4}) &= \text{P}(\neg \textit{pair on 4} \cap \neg \textit{pair in 1–3}) \\ &= \text{P}(\neg \textit{pair in 1–3}) \times \text{P}(\neg \textit{pair on 4} | \neg \textit{pair in 1–3}). \end{aligned}$$

But we know P(¬*pair in 1–3*); we just calculated it to be 2,112/2,550, about 0.83. And we can read off the conditional probability, P(¬*pair on 4*|¬*pair in 1–3*), from the tree, 40/49. So

$$\begin{aligned} &\text{P}(\neg \textit{pair in 1–4}) \\ &= (2{,}112/2{,}550) \times (40/49) = \frac{84{,}480}{124{,}950} \approx 0.68. \end{aligned}$$

Now we can calculate P(¬*pair in 5 draws*)—using the probability we have just calculated for P(¬*pair in 1–4*) and the probability from the tree for P(¬*pair on 5*|¬*pair in 1–4*):

$$\begin{aligned} \text{P}(\neg \textit{pair in 5 draws}) &= \text{P}(\neg \textit{pair in 1–4}) \times \text{P}(\neg \textit{pair on 5} | \neg \textit{pair in 1–4}) \\ &= \frac{84{,}480}{124{,}950} \times \frac{36}{48} = \frac{3{,}041{,}280}{5{,}997{,}600} \approx 0.5. \end{aligned}$$

What is the probability of getting a pair in five draws? Use the complement rule. Not getting a pair in five draws is the complementary event to getting a pair in five draws. So the probability of getting a pair in five draws must be 1 minus 3,041,280/5,997,600, also about 0.5.

This looks like a lot of work. But in fact it is fairly simple. To find the probability of getting to one particular node in a tree, multiply together all of the branch probabilities from the top of the tree to that node. Thus, the probability of getting no pairs in 5 draws equals:

$$\frac{48}{51} \times \frac{44}{50} \times \frac{40}{49} \times \frac{36}{48} = \frac{3{,}041{,}280}{5{,}997{,}600} \approx 0.5.$$

These are just the branch probabilities one "encounters" going from the top of the tree to the end node, which corresponds to getting no pairs in five draws. The calculation above looks awful because we were being careful to apply the intersection rule properly. The wonderful thing about the intersection rule is that we do not need to do any of this; all we need to do is multiply together branch probabilities.

4. THE THEOREM ON TOTAL PROBABILITY

The probability of drawing a pair shows us one way to do probability calculations with trees. We can find the probability of drawing a pair in five draws from a deck of cards because there is only one way *not* to get a pair in five draws—the node at the end of all the "left branchings" in Figure 8.8. We use the intersection rule to calculate the probability of going all the way down the tree to this node. Then we use the complement rule to find the probability of *not* going to this node.

But in many cases we cannot use this trick. Recall the chalk tree (see Figure 8.4). Two different end nodes correspond to chalk breaking. So we cannot use the intersection rule and the complement rule to find the probability that *any* piece of chalk will break. This is where the theorem on total probability is handy.

The theorem on total probability can be stated in a simple form as follows:

$$\mathrm{P}(\mathbf{A}) = \mathrm{P}(\mathbf{B})\mathrm{P}(\mathbf{A}|\mathbf{B}) + \mathrm{P}(\neg\mathbf{B})\mathrm{P}(\mathbf{A}|\neg\mathbf{B}).$$

The probability of an event **A** can be broken into two parts: the probability of **A** that is also **B** and the probability of **A** that is ¬**B**.

There is an important similarity between the theorem on total probability and the intersection rule. The theorem on total probability tells us to calculate two products. Each product is just what we calculate once when we use the intersection rule. Finding "total probabilities" works as nicely as finding "intersection probabilities." All we have to do is multiply the branch probabilities from the top of the tree to the end nodes of interest. Calculate such a product for each of the end nodes of interest and add these products.

We can calculate, for example, the probability of a piece of chalk breaking (see Figure 8.4). The theorem on total probability has us calculate as follows:

$$\mathrm{P}(\mathit{break}) = \mathrm{P}(\mathit{Crayola})\mathrm{P}(\mathit{break}|\mathit{Crayola}) + \mathrm{P}(\mathit{Academic})\mathrm{P}(\mathit{break}|\mathit{Academic})$$

These probabilities are given in the tree:

$$\mathrm{P}(\mathit{break}) = \left(\frac{3}{10}\right)\left(\frac{1}{100}\right) + \left(\frac{7}{10}\right)\left(\frac{5}{100}\right) = \frac{3}{1{,}000} + \frac{35}{1{,}000} = \frac{38}{1{,}000}$$
$$= 0.038.$$

We compute a product for each of the two routes from the top of the tree to the two "breaking leaves:" [(3/10)(1/100)] and [(7/10)(5/100)] Then we add these products.

We can prove the theorem on total probability quite easily. A Venn diagram can help (Figure 8.9). The outside circle contains all the possible outcomes. It is divided into two parts. The top part contains those possible outcomes that are in **B**; the bottom part contains those possible outcomes that are not in **B**. The shaded circle in the middle contains all the possible outcomes that are in **A**.

Consider the following event, ((**B** ∩ **A**) ∪ (¬**B** ∩ **A**)). This is **A**. **A** is made up of two parts, the bottom part, (**B** ∩ **A**), and the top part, (¬**B** ∩ **A**). **A** is the

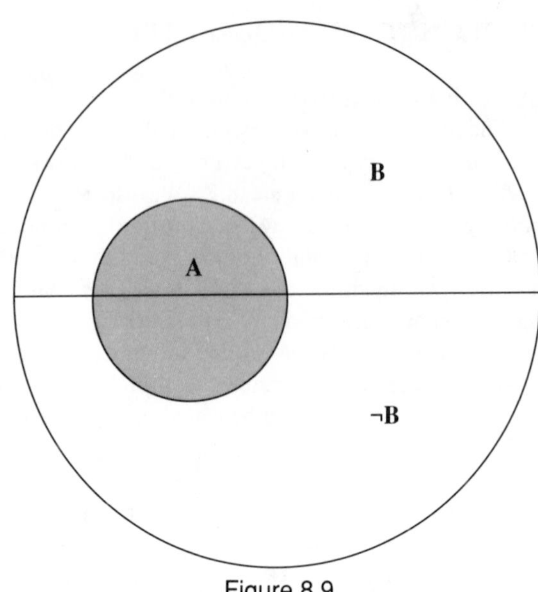

Figure 8.9

union of these two parts: $((\mathbf{B} \cap \mathbf{A}) \cup (\neg\mathbf{B} \cap \mathbf{A}))$. Since the events are the same, the probabilities must also be the same:

$$P(\mathbf{A}) = P[(\mathbf{B} \cap \mathbf{A}) \cup (\neg\mathbf{B} \cap \mathbf{A})].$$

But since these events do not overlap, $[(\mathbf{B} \cap \mathbf{A}) \cap (\neg\mathbf{B} \cap \mathbf{A})] = \mathbf{\Lambda}$, we can use the addition rule:

$$P(\mathbf{A}) = P((\mathbf{B} \cap \mathbf{A}) \cup (\neg\mathbf{B} \cap \mathbf{A})) = P(\mathbf{B} \cap \mathbf{A}) + P(\neg\mathbf{B} \cap \mathbf{A}).$$

Now we can use the intersection rule twice, once with $P(\mathbf{B} \cap \mathbf{A})$ and once with $P(\neg\mathbf{B} \cap \mathbf{A})$:

$$P(\mathbf{A}) = P(\mathbf{B})P(\mathbf{A}|\mathbf{B}) + P(\neg\mathbf{B})P(\mathbf{A}|\neg\mathbf{B}),$$

and we have proved the theorem on total probability.

We can learn from this proof. What did we have to assume to prove the theorem on total probability? We cut up all the possible outcomes into those that were in event **B** and those that were not. By doing this we could use the addition rule and the intersection rule to get the theorem on total probability. But our set of possible outcomes might be chopped up into three parts (Figure 8.10). The shaded circle in the middle remains event **A**. But now there are three other events, **B**, **C**, and **D**, which together make up all of the possible outcomes and which do not overlap each other. We can pick three events like the two events we picked out in our proof above:

$$(\mathbf{B} \cap \mathbf{A}), \quad (\mathbf{C} \cap \mathbf{A}), \quad \text{and} \quad (\mathbf{D} \cap \mathbf{A}).$$

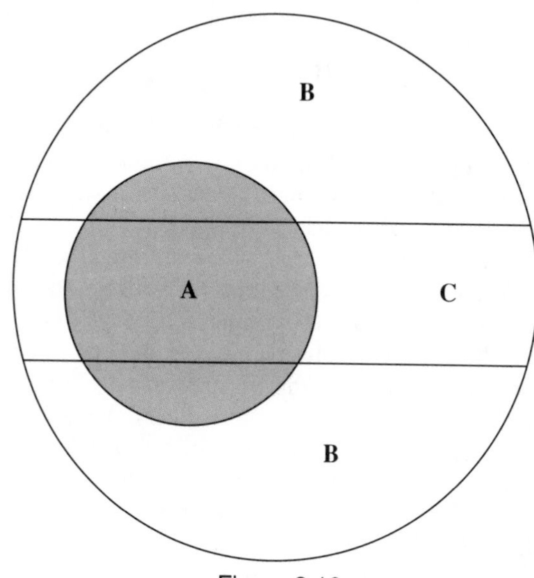

Figure 8.10

As in the proof above, we have

$$\mathbf{A} = (\mathbf{B} \cap \mathbf{A}) \cup (\mathbf{C} \cap \mathbf{A}) \cup (\mathbf{D} \cap \mathbf{A}), \text{ and}$$

$$(\mathbf{B} \cap \mathbf{A}) \cap (\mathbf{C} \cap \mathbf{A}) = \mathbf{\Lambda},$$

$$(\mathbf{C} \cap \mathbf{A}) \cap (\mathbf{D} \cap \mathbf{A}) = \mathbf{\Lambda}, \text{ and}$$

$$(\mathbf{B} \cap \mathbf{A}) \cap (\mathbf{D} \cap \mathbf{A}) = \mathbf{\Lambda}.$$

so we can use the additional rule,

$$\begin{aligned} \mathrm{P}(\mathbf{A}) &= \mathrm{P}[(\mathbf{B} \cap \mathbf{A}) \cup (\mathbf{C} \cap \mathbf{A}) \cup (\mathbf{D} \cap \mathbf{A})] \\ &= \mathrm{P}(\mathbf{B} \cap \mathbf{A}) + \mathrm{P}(\mathbf{C} \cap \mathbf{A}) + \mathrm{P}(\mathbf{D} \cap \mathbf{A}), \end{aligned}$$

and then the intersection rule three times,

$$\mathrm{P}(\mathbf{A}) = \mathrm{P}(\mathbf{B})\mathrm{P}(\mathbf{A}|\mathbf{B}) + \mathrm{P}(\mathbf{C})\mathrm{P}(\mathbf{A}|\mathbf{C}) + \mathrm{P}(\mathbf{D})\mathrm{P}(\mathbf{A}|\mathbf{D}),$$

and we get a more general form of the theorem on total probability.

This trick will work no matter how many parts we cut the set of possible outcomes up into. We can cut **V** into n parts for any number n. Call these parts $\mathbf{P}_1$, $\mathbf{P}_2, \ldots, \mathbf{P}_n$. Suppose that none of these parts overlap ($\mathbf{P}_i \cap \mathbf{P}_j = \Lambda$, for any i and j), and together they include all of the possible outcomes ($\mathbf{P}_1 \cup \mathbf{P}_2 \cup \cdots \cup \mathbf{P}_n = \mathbf{V}$). Such a group of events, $\mathbf{P}_1, \mathbf{P}_2, \ldots, \mathbf{P}_n$, is called a *partition* of **V**. We can use this new concept to state a general form of the theorem on total probability:

For any events $\mathbf{P}_1, \mathbf{P}_2, \ldots, \mathbf{P}_n$ that form a partition of $\mathbf{V}$,

$$P(\mathbf{A}) = P(\mathbf{P}_1)P(\mathbf{A}|\mathbf{P}_1) + P(\mathbf{P}_2)P(\mathbf{A}|\mathbf{P}_2) + \cdots + P(\mathbf{P}_n)P(\mathbf{A}|\mathbf{P}_n).$$

This is the general form for the theorem on total probability.

The concept of a partition is quite useful. A homely analogy with which to think about partitions is a sliced loaf of bread. Each slice may be seen as one element of the partition. Slices of bread are distinct, so no two slices "overlap" each other. Taken together all the slices make up the whole loaf. We have seen several examples of partitions. The simplest partition consists of an event **A** and its complement, $\neg\mathbf{A}$. **A** and $\neg\mathbf{A}$ do not overlap, and taken together they make up the entire space of possible outcomes, **V**. The two events of a piece of chalk breaking or not breaking form a partition of this sort. Suppose that we draw one card from a deck of cards. We could partition the possible outcomes into whether or not the card comes from a "major suit," spades or hearts, or a "minor suit," diamonds or clubs. We could also partition the possible outcomes into whether or not the card was a spade, a heart, a diamond, or a club. Here is a partition of four elements.

Consider the following application of the theorem on total probability. It involves a hybrid lottery game. In this game one first tosses a fair die; the outcome of this toss is some number, *1, 2, 3, 4, 5,* or *6*. Then one spins a standard roulette wheel. (For a description of a standard roulette wheel, see Problem 4 at the end of this chapter.) If the number that comes up on the roulette wheel can be divided evenly by the number that came face up on the die, one wins; otherwise, one loses. What is the probability of winning?

The tree for this game starts with six branches, one for each of the possible outcomes of the die. Each of the nodes at the end of these six branches sprouts two branches—one for winning the lottery and one for losing the lottery. Since the die is fair, the probability for each of the original six branches is 1/6. The probabilities for winning and losing after the die has been tossed vary with the outcome of the die. If the die came up *1*, the probability of winning is quite high—36/38; if the die came up *6* the probability of winning is lower—6/36. The total probability of winning can be calculated with the general form of the theorem on total probability:

$$\begin{aligned} P(W) &= P(\mathit{1})P(W|\mathit{1}) + P(\mathit{2})P(W|\mathit{2}) + P(\mathit{3})P(W|\mathit{3}) \\ &\quad + P(\mathit{4})P(W|\mathit{4}) + P(\mathit{5})P(W|\mathit{5}) + P(\mathit{6})P(W|\mathit{6}) \\ &= \left(\frac{1}{6}\right)\left(\frac{36}{38}\right) + \left(\frac{1}{6}\right)\left(\frac{18}{38}\right) + \left(\frac{1}{6}\right)\left(\frac{12}{38}\right) \\ &\quad + \left(\frac{1}{6}\right)\left(\frac{9}{38}\right) + \left(\frac{1}{6}\right)\left(\frac{7}{38}\right) + \left(\frac{1}{6}\right)\left(\frac{6}{38}\right) \approx 0.39. \end{aligned}$$

Consider another example. What is the probability of drawing *two* pair in five draws from a standard deck of cards? The first chore to solving this problem is to construct a tree that represents how we might wind up with two pair after five draws.

This is a matter of thinking carefully about what can happen after each draw as we attempt to get two pair. Then we can use this tree to find the probability we seek.

After the first draw all that can happen is that we will have a card in our hand. But after the second draw we might have paired our original card or we might have gotten a second unpaired card (Figure 8.11). The same kind of process goes into thinking out what might happen after the third draw. Only this time we must consider *separately* two different situations: first, where we hold a pair, and second, where we hold two unpaired cards. *Given* that we hold a pair, two things might happen: We might draw a third card of the same number as our pair (and have three of a kind), or we might draw some other card (and have a pair and another card). On the other hand, *given* that we hold two unpaired cards, two other things might happen: We might pair one of these cards (and have a pair and another card), or we might draw a third unmatched card (and have three unmatched cards). When we consider what might happen on the fourth draw we must consider separately four situations, one for each of the four branches sprouting from either of the third-draw nodes. And so we go down the tree.

The next chore is to add probabilities to the different branches of the tree. For example, the probability of pairing our first card with our second draw is 3/51; the probability of *not* pairing on the second draw is 48/51. (Note that 3/51 + 48/51 = 51/51 = 1. The probabilities of all the branches sprouting from a node must sum to 1.) Consider the probabilities for the next draw. *Given* that we hold a pair, the probability of drawing to three of a kind is 2/50 (two of the 50 cards remaining in the deck match the pair we hold), and the probability of drawing a third unmatched card is 48/50. *Given* that we hold two unpaired cards, the probability that we pair one of them is 6/50 (there are three cards that match one of the cards we hold and three that match the other), and the probability that we draw a third unmatched card is 44/50.

Trees help organize complicated problems. We imagine we "are at" a given node, and determine the conditional probabilities for all of the branches sprouting from this node. We do this for each node in the tree down to the bottom. It is easier to determine these conditional "branch" probabilities one node at a time than it is to determine the final probability we seek. With these branch probabilities in hand, we

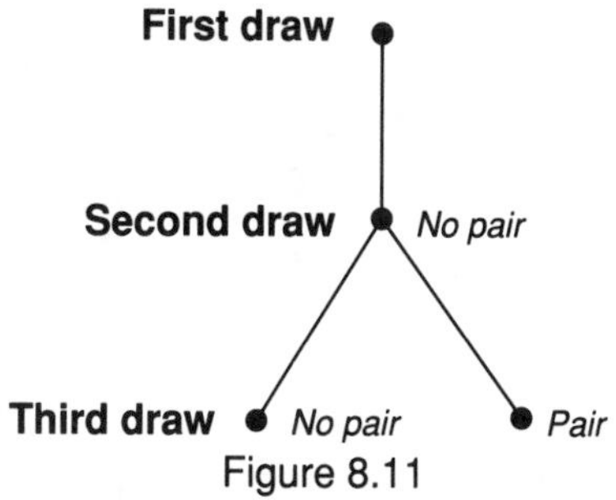

Figure 8.11

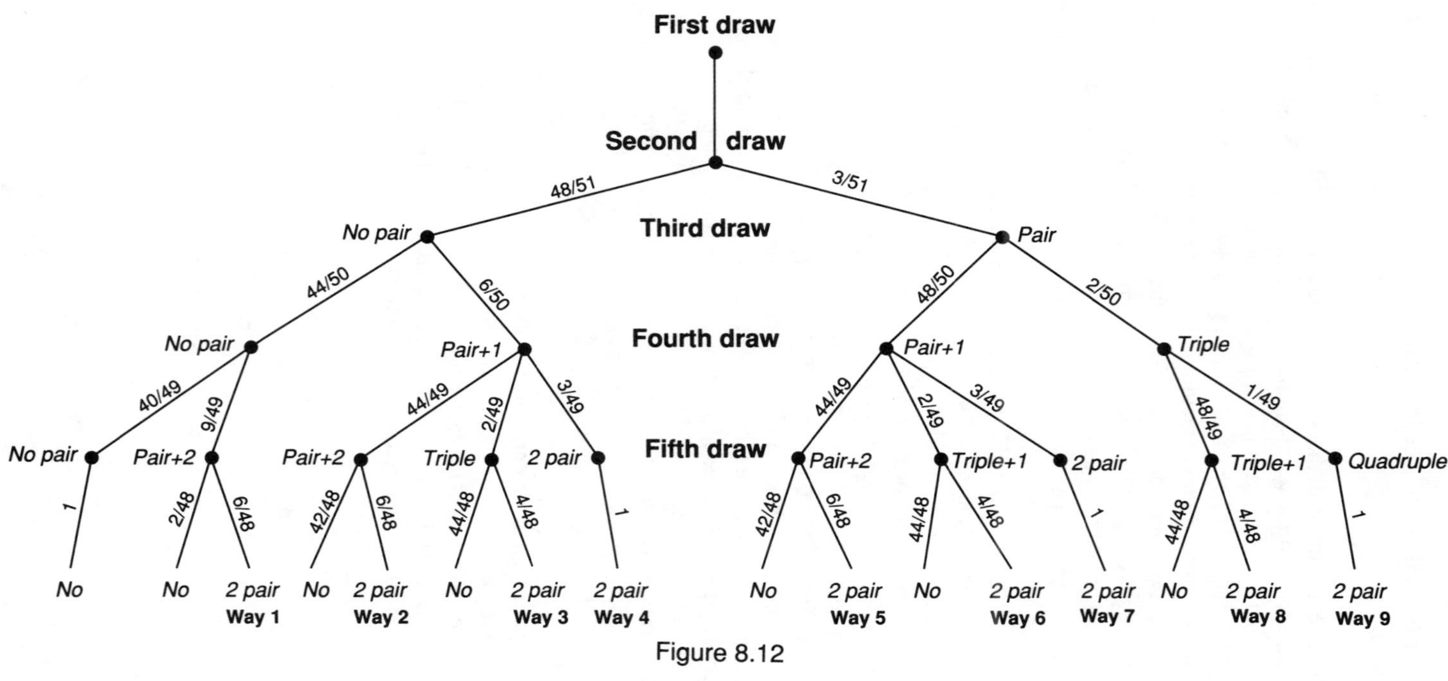

First draw
Second draw
48/51
3/51
No pair
Third draw
Pair
44/50
6/50
48/50
2/50
No pair
Pair+1
Fourth draw
Pair+1
Triple
40/49
9/49
44/49
2/49
3/49
44/49
2/49
3/49
48/49
1/49
No pair
Pair+2
Pair+2
Triple
2 pair
Fifth draw
Pair+2
Triple+1
2 pair
Triple+1
Quadruple
1
2/48
6/48
42/48
6/48
44/48
4/48
1
42/48
6/48
44/48
4/48
1
44/48
4/48
1
No
No
2 pair
Way 1
No
2 pair
Way 2
No
2 pair
Way 3
2 pair
Way 4
No
2 pair
Way 5
No
2 pair
Way 6
2 pair
Way 7
No
2 pair
Way 8
2 pair
Way 9

Figure 8.12

can use the theorem on total probability to determine the probability we seek. A completed tree for drawing two pair is shown in Figure 8.12.

Our last chore is to multiply together branch probabilities for each branch leading to the result of interest—two pair. We then add up these products to find the "total probability." There are nine different ways to get two pair as shown in Figure 8.12. Take each in turn. The product we get for *way 1* (as labeled in Figure 8.12) is (48/51)(44/50)(9/49)(6/48) ≈ 0.019. The product we get for *way 2* is (48/51)(6/50)(44/49)(6/48) ≈ 0.013. We must compute the product for each way to get two pair. Then we add all of these products together (Table 8.4).

TABLE 8.4

Way 1	(48/51)(44/50)(9/49)(6/48)	≈	0.01902
Way 2	(48/51)(6/50)(44/49)(6/48)	≈	0.01268
Way 3	(48/51)(6/50)(2/49)(4/48)	≈	0.00038
Way 4	(48/51)(6/50)(3/49)(48/48)	≈	0.00691
Way 5	(3/51)(48/50)(44/49)(6/48)	≈	0.00634
Way 6	(3/51)(48/50)(2/49)(4/48)	≈	0.00019
Way 7	(3/51)(48/50)(3/49)(48/48)	≈	0.00346
Way 8	(3/51)(2/50)(48/49)(4/48)	≈	0.00019
Way 9	(3/51)(2/50)(1/49)(48/48)	≈	0.00005
		Total:	0.04922

Applying the theorem on total probability is simple. All we have to calculate are products of branch probabilities (the nine rows above) and sum of these products (the total of the right hand column). The situation is exactly analogous to finding products of branch probabilities when using the intersection rule. The only difference is that using the intersection rule allowed us to find the probability of only one node at the bottom of a tree. Now we can find the probability of any number of nodes at the bottom of the tree.

5. EXPECTATION

Expectations are weighted averages. The theorem on total probability can be thought of as telling us how to take *weighted averages of probabilities*. We can better understand expectations by connecting them with the theorem on total probability, and vice versa, we can better understand the theorem on total probability by connecting it with the concept of expectation or of weighted averages.

The mechanics of taking an average are straightforward (see Chapter 6, Section 5). A drama group might perform three shows of "Half a Sixpence" over a weekend and wish to know the average attendance per show. 376 people attended the first show, 408 the second, and 397 the third. The average attendance per show was (376 + 408 + 397)/3 = 1,181/3 = 393 2/3. Suppose three kinds of tickets were sold to the show. Center section tickets cost $5.00, side section tickets cost $3.50, and standing room tickets cost $1.00. Of the 1,181 tickets sold, 582 were center section, 431 were side section and 168 were standing room tickets. What was the average amount of money received per ticket? This could be done directly by adding 582 \$5.00s to 431 \$3.50s to 168 \$1.00s. A tedious addition. Then we would divide the sum by 1,181. We can simplify this computation by multiplying \$5.00 by 582, adding this to the product of \$3.50 and 431, and adding this to the product of \$1.00 and 168:

$$\frac{(582 \times \$5.00) + (431 \times \$3.50) + (168 \times \$1.00)}{1{,}181}$$

$$= \frac{\$2{,}910.00 + \$1{,}508.50 + \$168.00}{1{,}181}$$

$$= \frac{\$4{,}586.5}{1{,}181} = \$3.88.$$

The average receipt per ticket was \$3.88.

We could do the same computation by doing the division first:

$$\left(\frac{582}{1{,}181} \times \$5.00\right) + \left(\frac{431}{1{,}181} \times \$3.50\right) + \left(\frac{168}{1{,}181} \times \$1.00\right)$$

$$= (0.49280 \times \$5.00) + (0.36494 \times \$3.50) + (0.14225 \times \$1.00)$$

$$= \$2.46400 + \$1.27731 + \$0.14225 \approx \$3.88.$$

While the computation is more cumbersome, there are several useful points to notice about this approach. The three numbers we multiply by the three ticket prices, 0.49280, 0.36494, and 0.14225, add up to 1. They must, for they are the *proportions* of all 1,181 tickets sold of each of the three kinds of tickets sold. Each ticket sold had to be of one of these three kinds, so the sum of the three proportions must be 1,181/1,181 = 1. We could put this information in a small probability tree (Figure 8.13). We find the average ticket price by multiplying the ''probability of each ticket price'' by the ticket price and adding up the products:

$$(0.49280 \times \$5.00) + (0.36494 \times \$3.50) + (0.14225 \times \$1.00) \approx \$3.88.$$

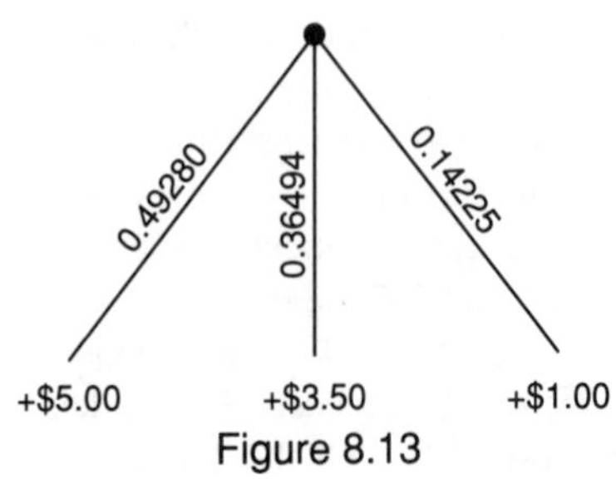

Figure 8.13

The operation is similar to the operation we perform to find "total probabilities." The difference is that in the case of total probabilities, we were multiplying probabilities by other probabilities instead of by ticket prices. In either case, what we are doing in computing a *weighted average*. But we are not giving each of the three different prices equal "weight" in the average. A "simple average" of ticket prices, $(\$5.00 + \$3.50 + \$1.00)/3 \approx \$3.17$, would be misleading because there were more center-section tickets sold than either of the other two kinds. Indeed, almost half of all the tickets sold were center-section tickets. Thus, to find a more accurate average we *weight* the ticket prices in our computation of the average according to each ticket price's proportional representation: 0.49280 of the tickets sold were \$5.00 tickets, 0.36494 were \$3.50 tickets, and 0.14225 were \$1.00 tickets. Think of a simple average as a weighted average where all the weights are equal.

\$3.88 is the *expected* ticket price. We are not using the word "expected" with its usual sense of something to anticipate for the future, although this sense is not as far off as one might think. If we could anticipate these proportions of sales—0.49280, 0.36494, and 0.14225 of \$5.00, \$3.50, and \$1.00 tickets, respectively—for future shows, \$3.88 is how much we should *anticipate* to collect per ticket sold once all the tickets have been sold; it is the average ticket receipt. In general, however, the word "expect" refers to a weighted average, like those computed above.

We can now better understand such facts as the following, reported in the 1986 *Statistical Abstract of the United States*. A 29-year-old white male has a life expectation of 44.1 years. What this number represents is a weighted average. We consider all of the possibilities: A 29-year-old male could die at the age of 29, he could live for just one more year, he could live for 2 years, and so on. We have data that give us a good idea of what percentage of 29-year-old males die at age 29, live for one more year, for 2 more years, and so on. We use these percentages as probabilities and the number of years lived as values, and we compute a weighted average: We multiply each value 0 (for zero more years lived), 1 (for one more year lived), and so on, with the associated probability. We then add these products. The result is the life expectation of a 29-year-old male—44.1 years.

6. SIMPSON'S PARADOX

With the theorem on total probability we are interested in weighted averages of probabilities—*averages of averages*. This can lead to counterintuitive results. Consider two baseball players, George and Larry. Their batting records split into games played at home and games played on the road are listed in Table 8.5. Their combined or total hitting average is a weighted average of each of their home and away averages: *a weighted average of hitting averages*. Most of George's at-bats were done during home games—100 out of 110. His "overall" average is weighted to reflect this fact:

TABLE 8.5

	Home		Away	
	George	Larry	George	Larry
Hits	40	5	3	35
Misses	60	5	7	65
At-bats	100	10	10	100
Average	0.400	0.500	0.300	0.350

$$\left(\frac{100}{110} \times 0.400\right) + \left(\frac{10}{110} \times 0.300\right) = 0.391.$$

The weights, 100/110 and 10/110 (which sum to 1, as they should), reflect the relative proportion of at-bats George had at home—100/110—and away—10/110. Larry's weights are just the reverse of George's, as most of Larry's at-bats came during away games:

$$\left(\frac{10}{110} \times 0.500\right) + \left(\frac{100}{110} \times 0.350\right) = 0.364$$

(see Figure 8.14). These computations are just the theorem on total probability in action.

There is a paradoxical aspect to these weighted averages. George's and Larry's combined or total hitting averages can be summed up as in Table 8.6. George has a hitting average of 0.391; Larry's average is 0.364. Evidently George is a better hitter than Larry (other things—extra-base hits, clutch hitting, and so on, being equal). But recall their averages for home and away games (Table 8.5). Larry is a better hitter playing home games *and* playing away games. This is so despite the fact that George has a better "overall" average. The result is known as *Simpson's paradox*.

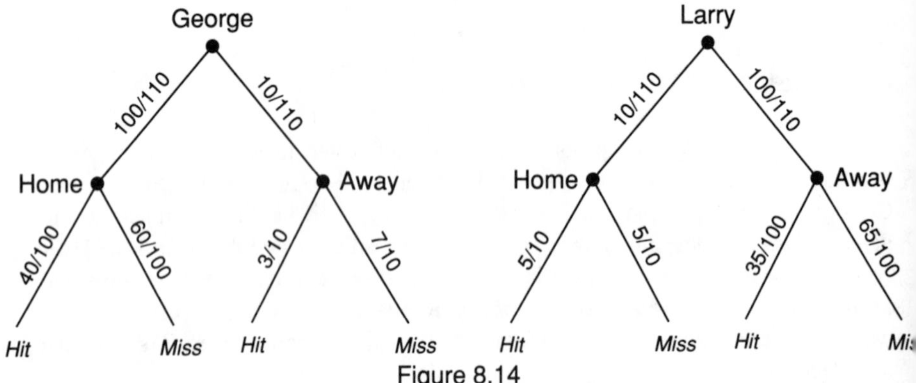

Figure 8.14

TABLE 8.6

	George	Larry
Hits	43	40
Misses	67	70
At-bats	110	110
Average	0.391	0.364

We can understand how this paradoxical result came about when we look at how the combined averages relate to the home and away averages. George's combined average, 0.391, is a weighted average of his home average, 0.400, and his away average, 0.300; but because most of George's at-bats came during home games, we weight his home average 100/110 and his away average 10/110. We use just the reverse weights for Larry. Here is the key point to notice: Both players had lower averages on their away games. George's combined average is weighted for home games—when hits were easier for both players; Larry's combined average is weighted for away games—when hits were harder for both players. George has a better overall average because of his good fortune to be at bat more during home games, when hits came relatively easily.

In general, we need to be aware that the way we partition the population can have a potentially misleading impact on the weighted averages we compute. This occurs when the variable we partition with is relevant to the variable we are interested in. At-bats being home or away—the variable we partitioned with in the example above—is relevant to hitting averages—the variable we are interested in. This is because it is easier to get hits during home games. In such cases the relative proportions of trials—the weights used in computing the overall average—can have a significant impact on the combined average.

Unfortunately, we may not always know the relevant components and their weights in a combined average. Perhaps no one ever kept track of George's and Larry's separate home and away averages. All we would know is that George's average was 0.391 and Larry's was 0.364. We would reasonably (although incorrectly perhaps) conclude that George is the better hitter. It is important to check for how the averages are weighted in partitions we know are relevant—home versus away games. It is also important to recognize that we still may have overlooked or been unaware of some relevant partition; the conclusions we draw from such information can be wrong.

The numbers describing George's and Larry's hitting averages might describe experimental data on the efficacy of a new cure for a disease. We simply may not know, for instance, that this disease is more virulent for people who regularly drink fluoridated water, and that most of those people who were tested with the new cure did not drink fluoridated water. From the combined data (Table 8.7) the new cure looks promising. But when considered in the two subpopulations, this promise vanishes. The problem is that we may not know to look at these subpopulations.

TABLE 8.7

	Combined Data		Not Fluoridated		Fluoridated	
	New Cure	Old Cure	New Cure	Old Cure	New Cure	Old Cure
Disease cured	43	40	40	5	3	35
Not cured	67	70	60	5	7	65
Cases	110	110	100	10	10	100
Average	0.391	0.364	0.400	0.500	0.300	0.350

Conclusions from comparisons of averages can mislead because we are unaware of some relevant third variable and we have unwittingly used unequal proportions of trials with respect to this third variable.

7. BAYES' RULE

Recall the chalk tree (see Figure 8.4). Suppose that the piece of chalk I am using breaks and crumbles beyond recognition. I might be interested in knowing the probability that it was a piece of Crayola chalk. That is, I might be interested in P(*Crayola*|*break*). We use Bayes' rule:

$$\mathrm{P}(\mathit{Crayola}|\mathit{break}) = \frac{\mathrm{P}(\mathit{Crayola})\mathrm{P}(\mathit{break}|\mathit{Crayola})}{\mathrm{P}(\mathit{break})}.$$

Thus, we can quickly calculate P(*Crayola*|*break*) = (0.3)(0.01)/(0.038) = 0.079.

The proof of Bayes' rule is straightforward. While we will use Bayes' rule on a variety of occasions to help solve many problems of inductive inference, it is important to keep in mind just how simple it is. Bayes' rule follows quickly from our definition of conditional probability:

$$\mathrm{P}(\mathbf{A}|\mathbf{B}) = \frac{\mathrm{P}(\mathbf{A} \cap \mathbf{B})}{\mathrm{P}(\mathbf{B})}.$$

We can multiply the right-hand side of this equation by 1 in the particular form of P(**A**)/P(**A**):

$$\mathrm{P}(\mathbf{A}|\mathbf{B}) = \frac{\mathrm{P}(\mathbf{A} \cap \mathbf{B}) \times \mathrm{P}(\mathbf{A})}{\mathrm{P}(\mathbf{B}) \times \mathrm{P}(\mathbf{A})}.$$

We can rewrite the right-hand side, exchanging the P(**A**) and P(**A** ∩ **B**) in the numerator:

$$\mathrm{P}(\mathbf{A}|\mathbf{B}) = \frac{\mathrm{P}(\mathbf{A}) \times \mathrm{P}(\mathbf{A} \cap \mathbf{B})}{\mathrm{P}(\mathbf{B}) \times \mathrm{P}(\mathbf{A})}.$$

Recall that by definition, $P(\mathbf{B} \cap \mathbf{A})/P(\mathbf{A}) = P(\mathbf{B}|\mathbf{A})$. So

$$P(\mathbf{A}|\mathbf{B}) = \frac{P(\mathbf{A}) \times P(\mathbf{B}|\mathbf{A})}{P(\mathbf{B})}.$$

This relationship, Bayes' rule, holds for any pair of events **A** and **B**.

In many cases where we will use Bayes' rule, we will need to calculate P(**B**) using the theorem on total probability. So it is useful to build this right into the rule:

$$P(\mathbf{A}|\mathbf{B}) = \frac{P(\mathbf{A})P(\mathbf{B}|\mathbf{A})}{P(\mathbf{A})P(\mathbf{B}|\mathbf{A}) + P(\neg\mathbf{A})P(\mathbf{B}|\neg\mathbf{A})}.$$

If we have a more complicated partition of the possible outcomes, we can use the more complicated version of the theorem on total probability in the denominator. This gives us a more complicated form of Bayes' rule: For any events, $\mathbf{P}_1$, $\mathbf{P}_2$, ..., $\mathbf{P}_n$, which form a partition of **V**,

$$P(\mathbf{A}|\mathbf{B}) = \frac{P(\mathbf{A})P(\mathbf{B}|\mathbf{A})}{P(\mathbf{P}_1)P(\mathbf{B}|\mathbf{P}_1) + \cdots + P(\mathbf{P}_n)P(\mathbf{B}|\mathbf{P}_n)} = \frac{P(\mathbf{A})P(\mathbf{B}|\mathbf{A})}{P(\mathbf{B})}.$$

This is the general version of Bayes' rule. Typically, **A** will be one of the elements of the partition. For example, if **A** was $\mathbf{P}_1$, Bayes' rule would read as follows:

$$P(\mathbf{P}_1|\mathbf{B}) = \frac{P(\mathbf{P}_1)P(\mathbf{B}|\mathbf{P}_1)}{P(\mathbf{P}_1)P(\mathbf{B}|\mathbf{P}_1) + \cdots + P(\mathbf{P}_n)P(\mathbf{B}|\mathbf{P}_n)}.$$

We use Bayes' rule to calculate a conditional probability, P(**A**|**B**). The rule tells us to calculate a particular quotient. The numerator in Bayes' rule has two parts multiplied together. The first is the unconditional probability of the event to the left of the slash, |, P(**A**). This is called the *prior probability of* **A**, because it is the probability of **A** prior to knowing **B**. For this reason, P(**A**|**B**)—the conditional probability we are calculating—is called the *posterior probability of* **A**, because it is the probability of **A** posterior to, or after, learning **B**. The second part of the numerator is the "reversed" conditional probability, P(**B**|**A**). This is called the *likelihood* of **B** *given* **A**. Finally, the denominator contains some version of P(**B**) either in its simplest form, P(**B**), or in some more complicated form found by using the theorem on total probability:

$$P(\mathbf{A}|\mathbf{B}) = \frac{\text{(prior probability of } \mathbf{A}) \times \text{(likelihood of } \mathbf{B} \text{ given } \mathbf{A})}{\text{some form of the probability of } \mathbf{B}}.$$

Consider the following artificial example. The PROB Company makes and sells widgets in Columbia, South Carolina. Unfortunately, some person who buys widgets from the PROB has stolen 13 widgets. As it happens, PROB only sells widgets to people from Columbia, South Carolina, Boston, Massachusetts, and Singapore. Approximately 70% of PROB's customers come from Columbia, 20% from

Boston, and 10% from Singapore. Initially, we have reason to suspect that the culprit comes from Columbia. Let **C**, **B**, and **S** stand for the event that the culprit comes from Columbia, Boston, and Singapore, respectively. We have the following *prior probabilities:*

$$P(\mathbf{C}) = \frac{7}{10}, \quad P(\mathbf{B}) = \frac{2}{10}, \quad \text{and} \quad P(\mathbf{S}) = \frac{1}{10}.$$

But the robber has left evidence. The robber made some calculations on a pad of paper on the desk in PROB's office. We notice that the robber crosses his or her sevens like so: $\not{7}$. Most people raised in the United States do not cross their sevens. How can we use this evidence?

We call the local crime statistics lab and discover that only 10% of people who live in Columbia cross their sevens, 20% of people who live in Boston cross their sevens, and 90% of people who live in Singapore cross their sevens. That is, we know the following:

$$P(\not{7}|\mathbf{C}) = \frac{1}{10}, \quad P(\not{7}|\mathbf{B}) = \frac{2}{10}, \quad \text{and} \quad P(\not{7}|\mathbf{S}) = \frac{9}{10}.$$

This seems somewhat incriminating evidence for PROB's Singapore customers.

How incriminating is it? We want to know the relative chances that the crime was committed by a Columbian, a Bostonian, and a Singaporean, *given* our evidence of a crossed seven. That is, we want to know these probabilities: $P(\mathbf{C}|\not{7})$, $P(\mathbf{B}|\not{7})$, and $P(\mathbf{S}|\not{7})$. We can use Bayes' rule:

$$P(\mathbf{S}|\not{7}) = \frac{P(\mathbf{S})P(\not{7}|\mathbf{S})}{P(\mathbf{S})P(\not{7}|\mathbf{S}) + P(\mathbf{B})P(\not{7}|\mathbf{B}) + P(\mathbf{C})P(\not{7}|\mathbf{C})}.$$

We then calculate

$$P(\mathbf{S}|\not{7}) = \frac{(1/10)(9/10)}{(1/10)(9/10) + (2/10)(2/10) + (7/10)(1/10)} = \frac{9}{20}.$$

By a similar calculation we can find that $P(\mathbf{B}|\not{7}) = 4/20$ and $P(\mathbf{C}\not{7}) = 7/20$. (Notice that $9/20 + 4/20 + 7/20 = 1$.) **C**, **B**, and **S** are still the only possibilities, so their probabilities must sum to 1—even conditional on the evidence.

These *posterior probabilities* reflect our evidence. The evidence does point to a Singaporean, although the chances are still less than 1/2 that the crime was committed by a Singaporean. What is more, future evidence could change these probabilities—perhaps the criminal inadvertently left an old Boston Red Sox baseball game ticket stub behind.

This is how Bayes' rule provides a plausible kind of inductive argument. We started thinking that it was most likely that the crime was committed by a Columbian. After incorporating the evidence we saw that the probability that the crime was committed by a Columbian dropped from 7/10 to 7/20, while the probability that the crime was committed by a Singaporean soared from 1/10 to 9/20. Our premises set forth our information about initial or *prior probabilities* concerning the Columbian, Bostonian, and Singaporean customers. They also include information about the frequencies with which Columbians, Bostonians, and Singaporeans cross their sevens. Our conclusion is a probability assessment revised according to Bayes' rule. Of course we had to assume many things to make the argument work. We had to know about the initial frequencies of Columbian, Bostonian, and Singaporean customers, and we had to have the various crime statistics available. Such information is not always available. Also, for a conclusion we only get a probability that the crime was committed by the Singaporean; we cannot be certain. Still the argument presents a persuasive example of one kind of inductive argument. We used similar types of arguments in Chapter 3, Section 7, when we examined fallible information. In Chapter 11 we explore the Bayesian approach to induction, which as the name implies, makes much of Bayes' rule.

8. SUMMARY

1. Conditional probability P(**A**|**B**) is the probability of one event, **A**, on the assumption that another event, **B**, occurred.
   (a) P(**A**|**B**)is read, "the probability of **A** *given* **B**." The event being conditioned on is to the right of the slash, |. This slash is read, "given"; it is not the slash of division.
   (b) Conditioning on **B** changes the set of possible outcomes to include only those in event **B**.
   (c) When all the simple events have the same probability, P(**A**|**B**) is the proportion of **B**s that are also **A**.
   (d) In general, P(**A**|**B**) = P(**A** ∩ **B**)/P(**B**).
2. Independent events are those where knowing that one event occurred does not alter the probability of the other event: P(**A**|**B**) = P(**A**).
   (a) If **A** and **B** are independent, so are **B** and **A**. That is, P(**A**|**B**) = P(**A**) if and only if P(**B**|**A**) = P(**B**).
   (b) The multiplication rule states that when **A** and **B** are independent, P(**A** ∩ **B**) = P(**A**) × P(**B**). The multiplication rule is very useful for computing probabilities when (i) a probability experiment is repetitious, and (ii) repetitions are independent of each other.
3. Probability trees can be used to represent many probability problems.
   (a) Trees are like flow charts. They represent the order in which information about what is going on becomes available.
   (b) Trees consist of nodes (●), branches, and leaves; they are read top to bottom or left to right. The branches that "sprout" from a node represent all of the possible things that could happen given that one arrives at that node. The leaves are the final outcomes at the ends of the final branches on the tree.
   (c) Branch probabilities are conditional probabilities of going down a particular branch given that one arrives at the node from which the branch sprouts. Thus, the sum of branch probabilities for all the branches leaving a particular node must be 1.

(d) Trees are best built with a fairly particular goal in mind. This goal can help determine what distinctions must be built into the tree—by using different branches—and what distinctions can be lumped together in a single branch. Only those differences that make a difference as far as achieving the goal need be distinguished with different branches.

(e) Trees also help simplify conceptualizing complicated problems. One builds a tree node by node. At each node one need only consider those possibilities that make a difference, given arrival at that particular node. In this way, both the group of possible outcomes can be kept small—for each node—and the branch probabilities can be determined more easily.

4. The intersection rule states: $P(\mathbf{A} \cap \mathbf{B}) = P(\mathbf{B}) \times P(\mathbf{A}|\mathbf{B})$.
   (a) This rule is particularly useful when events are not independent.
   (b) Because of the intersection rule, doing probability computations with probability trees is simple. One follows the path from the beginning of the tree to the leaf of interest, multiplying all of the branch probabilities one encounters on the path. This product is the probability of arriving at that leaf.

5. A partition of events is a set of events, $\mathbf{P}_1, \mathbf{P}_2, \ldots, \mathbf{P}_n$, with two important characteristics.
   (a) Any two elements of the partition, $\mathbf{P}_i$ and $\mathbf{P}_j$, have no common elements: $\mathbf{P}_i \cap \mathbf{P}_j = \mathbf{\Lambda}$.
   (b) The union of all the elements of a partition includes everything: $\mathbf{P}_1 \cup \mathbf{P}_2 \cup \cdots \cup \mathbf{P}_n = \mathbf{V}$.

6. The theorem on total probability allows us to compute the probability of some event, **A**, by dividing it up into exclusive components that together constitute the whole event.
   (a) In the simplest case, we compute the probability of an event, **A**, by considering two components—the part of **A** that is **B** (for some other event **B**), and the part of **A** that is $\neg\mathbf{B}$. In this case the theorem states that

$$P(\mathbf{A}) = P(\mathbf{B})P(\mathbf{A}|\mathbf{B}) + P(\neg\mathbf{B})P(\mathbf{A}|\neg\mathbf{B}).$$

   (b) In general we use a partition, $\mathbf{P}_1, \mathbf{P}_2, \ldots, \mathbf{P}_n$, to cut the event we want to know, the probability of **A**, into exclusive and exhaustive parts:

$$P(\mathbf{A}) = P(\mathbf{P}_1)\ P(\mathbf{A}|\mathbf{P}_1) + P(\mathbf{P}_2)P(\mathbf{A}|\mathbf{P}_2) + \cdots + P(\mathbf{P}_n)P(\mathbf{A}|\mathbf{P}_n).$$

   (c) The theorem on total probability can help computing the probability of finishing a probability tree any one of several leaves. First, one travels from the top of the tree to each leaf of interest, multiplying the branch probabilities passed on route. Then one adds these products together. The result is the "total probability" one seeks.

7. Expectations are weighted averages.
   (a) To find an expectation, one multiplies the probability of each possible event by the "value" of the event and then adds these products together. The probabilities are the weights used in computing the average.
   (b) Taking expectations is thus the same process as that conceptualized in the theorem on total probability, which really is a weighted average of probabilities.
   (c) Sometimes, taking expected probabilities can produce unexpected and paradoxical results. This occurs when there is a relationship between the variable used to divide

possibilities into kinds—to which the weights apply—and the variable determining the final probabilities being weighted.

8. Bayes' rule states another useful relationship for computing conditional probabilities:

$$\mathrm{P}(\mathbf{A}|\mathbf{B}) = \frac{\mathrm{P}(\mathbf{A})\mathrm{P}(\mathbf{B}|\mathbf{A})}{\mathrm{P}(\mathbf{B})}.$$

(a) In typical applications we think of event **A** as some hypothesis whose truth we want to know; **B** is some evidence we have collected to ascertain the truth of **A**.

(b) P(**A**|**B**), then, is the posterior probability of **A**—the probability of **A** after knowing **B**. P(**A**) is the prior probability of **A**—prior to knowing **B**. P(**B**|**A**) is the probability of finding the evidence if **A** were true, called the likelihood of **B** given **A**. P(**B**) is the "total" probability of the evidence, usually found through an application of the theorem on total probability.

9. REFERENCES

The probability references for Chapter 7 are also relevant here. (Raiffa, 1970) does a nice job of presenting probability trees. Simpson's paradox has received extensive discussion in the philosophical literature on probabilistic causality [e.g., (Cartwright, 1983) and (Otte, 1985)]. There is a wonderful discussion of it in G. U. Yule's old text (Yule, 1911).

10. PROBLEMS

1. Suppose that we toss two fair 12-sided dice, a green one and a yellow one. Calculate the following probabilities.

(a) P(*sum−23*|*yellow−9*).
(b) P(*yellow−9*|*sum−23*).
(c) P(*double*|*yellow−9*).
(d) P(*yellow−9*|*double*).
(e) P(*sum−20 or greater*|*double*).
(f) P(*double−1*|*sum−10 or greater*).
(g) P(*sum−13*|*double*).
(h) P(*sum−13*|*sum−10 or greater*).

2. Suppose that we toss two fair six-sided dice. What is the probability of throwing a *double-one* given that a die came up *one*?

3. What is the probability of getting eight heads in a row when a fair coin is tossed? Assume that different tosses of the coin are independent.

4. Assign the same probability to each simple event in one turn of a standard roulette wheel. A standard roulette wheel has 38 buckets in which the ball can finally come to rest; 36 of these are numbered 1 through 36, of which half are red and half are black. The two remaining buckets are green and are numbered "0" and "00." Suppose that we spin the wheel once.

(a) What is the probability of a red number coming up?
(b) What is the probability of not getting either a red number or a black number?

(c) If we now add a second turn of the roulette wheel, what are the possible outcomes from both turns? You should not list them; describe them intelligently.

(d) Assume that each turn of the wheel is independent of each other turn. What is the probability of not getting any red numbers in two turns?

(e) Return to one turn of the wheel. Is the event of getting an odd number independent of the event of getting a 14? Why or why not?

5. Two events, **A** and **B**, are independent if and only if P(**A**) = P(**A**|**B**). Independence is a symmetric relationship. That is, if **A** and **B** are independent, **B** and **A** are independent; independence does not depend on order. Is independence reflexive? That is, is **A** independent of **A**, for all events **A**? If so, prove it; if not, present a counterexample. Is independence transitive? That is, if **A** is independent of **B**, and **B** is independent of **C**, is **A** independent of **C**? If so, prove it; if not, present a counterexample.

6. Prove that P(**A**|**B**) = P(**A**) if and only if P(**A**|**B**) = P(**A**|¬**B**). Here is another criterion for probabilistic independence.

7. Suppose that you are to draw five times without replacing the cards from a well-shuffled deck of cards. What is the probability of *not* drawing a flush—all five cards in the same suit?

8. Suppose that you hold a pair of aces (clubs and diamonds, say). You begin drawing cards at random from a normal deck of cards, so your first draw will give you a third card to hold. You do not replace cards after you draw them.
   (a) What is the probability of drawing a third ace on your first draw?
   (b) What is the probability of drawing a third ace in two draws?
   (c) What is the probability of drawing a third ace in three draws?
   (d) What is the probability of drawing a third ace in four draws?
   (e) What is the probability of drawing a third ace in five draws?
   (f) What is the minimum number of draws to take so that the probability of drawing a third ace in that number of draws is greater than 1/4?

9. Assume that the probability of any given person having any given birthday is the same for each birthday (1/365 for each). What is the probability of two people in a group of 25 sharing a birthday?

10. Consider another version of the hybrid lottery described in Section 4. In this case, the die used is loaded. The probability of each face turning up is proportional to the number on the face. Thus, rolling a *2* is twice as likely as rolling a *1;* rolling a *3* is three times as likely as rolling a *1;* and so on. Write out a tree, including branch probabilities, to describe this lottery. Calculate the probability of winning.

11. What is the probability of drawing five cards from a normal deck of cards and getting a full house—that is, three of a kind and two of a kind (e.g., three kings and two eights)?

12. What is the expected value of the following gamble? You are to roll a pair of dice. If the dice come up a 7 or 11, you win 100 dollars. If the dice come up 2 or 12, you lose 200 dollars. Otherwise, the bet is off.

13. What is the expected value of the following gamble? You are to flip a fair coin. If it comes up heads, you win one dollar, and the wager is over. If it comes up tails, you lose your dollar, but you flip again for double stakes—two dollars. If the coin comes up heads this time, you win two dollars. If it comes up tails, you lose two dollars, but flip

again for four dollars. If it comes up heads, you win four dollars. If it comes up tails, you lose four dollars. But in either case the wager is over.

14. Suppose that you live in a town with two taxi companies—yellow cab and red cab, whose taxis are yellow and red, respectively. Of the total taxis, 75% are yellow and 25% are red. A hit-and-run automobile accident has occurred. Observers are certain that a taxi was involved, and an eyewitness claims that it was a red cab. But careful testing reveals that the eyewitness will correctly identify a taxi's color only 80% of the time (under the conditions present at the time of the accident). For the sake of convenience, let "*R*" mean that the witness says it was a red cab and *R* mean it was a red cab; use a similar convention for "*Y*" and *Y*. Tests reveal, then, that $P(``R"|R) = P(``Y"|Y) = 80\%$. What is the probability that the taxi involved was red given the witness's testimony?

15. Doe and her husband have been married only a short time and do not yet want a baby; they have been careful to use a method of contraception that claims to be 95% effective. Despite this, Doe worried that she was pregnant. She tested herself with a home pregnancy test kit which claims to detect 90% of all pregnancies it is used on. It produces a false positive report that the woman testing herself is pregnant on only 5% of uses. Doe's test was positive for pregnancy. Given this positive report, what is the probability that Doe is pregnant?

CHAPTER

9

BINOMIAL PROBABILITIES

1. INTRODUCTION TO BINOMIAL PROBABILITIES

The experiment of flipping a coin once has two possible outcomes, *HEADS* and *TAILS*. There are two simple events and four compound events: $\mathbf{\Lambda}$, {*HEADS*}, {*TAILS*}, and {*HEADS, TAILS*}. If we assign each simple event the same probability, 1/2, we can very quickly determine all of the probabilities associated with this experiment:

$$P(\mathbf{\Lambda}) = 0, \quad P(\{HEADS\}) = \frac{1}{2}, \quad P(\{TAILS\}) = \frac{1}{2}, \quad \text{and} \quad P(\mathbf{V}) = 1.$$

This is perhaps the simplest of all probability models; it is not very interesting. However, many phenomena in nature are binomial. We can easily liken the birth of a girl with heads and that of a boy with tails. Surviving a potentially fatal illness can be likened to heads and succumbing to tails. Since binomial events are so common, it will do us some good to have a closer look at them.

We can extend the simple coin-flipping model above in two ways. (1) We can consider a case of many independent trials with the simple model; thus, instead of flipping the coin once we flip it many times, *assuming* that the outcomes of different flips are probabilistically independent of each other. (2) We can consider cases where the probabilities are not the same for each of the simple events; thus, instead of flipping a "fair" coin, we flip a "loaded" coin. We can combine these two kinds of extensions by imagining flipping a loaded coin many times.

For example, it may be known that there is a 50–50 chance of a boy or a girl being born. If a couple hopes to have five children, what are the chances of them having no more than one boy among the five? Here is an example extending the simple coin-flipping model in the first way, where we repeat the binomial trial five times.

Another kind of example: It was calculated during World War II that the chance of a bomber crew not getting shot down on any individual mission was 0.96; this does not sound like bad odds for the bomber crews. By analogy, it is very likely a coin will land heads when it is heavily loaded for heads. But bomber crew members frequently signed on for a tour of duty consisting of 60 missions. Assuming that the chances of survival on each mission are 0.96, the chance of a crew member not being shot down on all 60 missions is a rather more discouraging 1/11.

We can conceptualize these examples in the following way. We imagine a large urn. The urn contains many balls that are either red or yellow. Our "experiment" consists of shaking up the urn so that each ball has the same chance of being drawn, drawing one ball out, noting its color, and replacing it. We can then repeat this procedure as many times as we wish.

The probability that the ball we draw out will be a red ball is equal to the proportion of red balls in the urn. This is because each ball has the same chance of being drawn. The probability of drawing out a red ball is the compound event of drawing out any one of the individual red balls—each of which has the same probability of being drawn as each other red ball. Use the addition rule. Similarly, the probability of drawing out a yellow ball is equal to the proportion of yellow balls in the urn.

We can think of getting a boy as drawing a red ball, and getting a girl as drawing a yellow ball. We model the assumption that there is the same chance for either sex to be born by assuming that the urn has the same number of red and yellow balls in it. We can imagine drawing from the urn five times. We can think of a bomber plane being shot down as drawing from an urn with 4% red balls and 96% yellow balls. We imagine drawing from this urn 60 times and we ask what the chance is that we get no red balls—1/11.

We can best learn to calculate these binomial probabilities by taking a very specific example. Imagine an urn filled with 2/3 yellow balls and 1/3 red balls. We will draw from the urn five times, being careful to replace balls after noting their color. What is the probability of getting three yellow and two red balls in the five draws, P(*3–yellow and 2–red*)?

There are two parts to figuring out this problem. First, we have to count how many possible ways one can get three yellow and two red balls in five draws. Second, we have to determine the probability of each different way. We can then put both bits of information together with the addition rule and get the probability we want.

2. COUNTING

How many ways are there of getting three yellow and two red balls? Here is one: <*y*, *y*, *y*, *r*, *r*>; that is, we draw a yellow ball on the first three draws and a red ball on the fourth and fifth draws. We might also draw yellow and red balls alternately: <*y*, *r*, *y*, *r*, *y*>. But there are more. How many more? We can ask for the same information by asking in how many different color sequences three yellow and two red balls can be put into an egg carton. Importantly, we need not worry about which yellow ball is which and which red ball is which.

The last sentence is our first clue: without worrying which yellow ball is which and which red ball is which. If we give our three yellow balls the names *Joe*, *Moe*, and *Doe*, and we give our two red balls the names *Harry* and *Larry*, then when we say that we are not going to worry which ball is which, we are saying that the arrangement

y–Joe, y–Moe, y–Doe, r–Larry, r–Harry,

does not differ, as far as we are concerned, from the arrangement

y–Moe, y–Doe, y–Joe, r–Harry, r–Larry.

Both are instances of the sequence <*y*, *y*, *y*, *r*, *r*>.

Paradoxically, we can best find out how many color sequences there are by first asking how many different arrangements there are when we *do* worry about which ball is which. The argument goes as follows: We can show that the number of different ways there are to arrange five *named* balls, A, is equal to the product of the number of different color sequences, B, and the number of ways to arrange five named and colored balls in a specified color sequence, C. That is,

the number of different color sequences [B]
× the number of ways to arrange five named and colored balls
in a specified color sequence [C]

---

the number of different ways there are to arrange
five *named* balls [A].

B × C = A. But the number we want to determine is B, so we divide, B = A/C. As it happens, we can determine A and C relatively easily.

Consider an example with only two yellow balls and one red ball: *y–Doe, y–Moe, r–Harry*. There are six different ways for *Doe, Moe, and Harry* to stand in a line:

(1) *y–Doe, y–Moe, r–Harry*
(2) *y–Moe, y–Doe, r–Harry*
(3) *y–Doe, r–Harry, y–Moe*
(4) *y–Moe, r–Harry, y–Doe*
(5) *r–Harry, y–Doe, y–Moe*
(6) *r–Harry, y–Moe, y–Doe.*

Notice the groups of two. If we could only see a ball's color and not its name, two different arrangements in the same group would not be distinguishable from each other:

	y y r		**y r y**
(1)	*y–???, y–???, r–?????*	(3)	*y–???, r–?????, y–???*
(2)	*y–???, y–???, r–?????*	(4)	*y–???, r–?????, y–???*

	r y y
(5)	*r–?????, y–???, y–???*
(6)	*r–?????, y–???, y–???.*

There are only three different color sequences: <*y, y, r*>, <*y, r, y*>, <*r, y, y*>. For each of these three color sequences, there are two different ways to arrange the balls:

	y y r		**y r y**
(1)	*y–Doe, y–Moe, r–Harry*	(3)	*y–Doe, r–Harry, y–Moe*
(2)	*y–Moe, y–Doe, r–Harry*	(4)	*y–Moe, r–Harry, y–Doe*

	r y y
(5)	*r–Harry, y–Doe, y–Moe*
(6)	*r–Harry, y–Moe, y–Doe.*

So the total number of ways to arrange three named balls, A, is six. The number of color sequences, B, is three. The number of ways to arrange three named and colored balls in a specified color arrangement, C, is two. $\mathsf{A} = 6 = 3 \times 2 = \mathsf{B} \times \mathsf{C}$; $\mathsf{A} = \mathsf{B} \times \mathsf{C}$.

Now take the case with five different balls. Suppose that each ball had a name. How many different ways are there to arrange these five named balls? What is A? We could imagine taking them one by one and placing them in an egg carton. We have five choices for the first slot of the egg carton. Once the first ball is placed we have four choices for the second slot, since we used up one ball in the first slot. We have three choices for the third slot, two choices for the fourth slot, and only one choice for the last, fifth, slot. We could imagine displaying these choices in a big tree (Figure 9.1). For each of the first five branches we reach a node with four branches. Then for each of these nodes reached from one of the four branch nodes, we will reach a node with three branches. Then for each of these three branch nodes we will reach a node with two branches. Finally, each of these branches reach a node with only one branch. So there are $5 \times 4 \times 3 \times 2 \times 1 = 120$ paths from the top to the bottom of the tree.

The number of different ways we could arrange these five named balls is called the *permutations* of five things (balls in this case) taken five at a time (we do not leave any balls out). Because of this tree, we can see that the number of different permutations of five things taken five at a time is $5 \times 4 \times 3 \times 2 \times 1 = 120$. Put

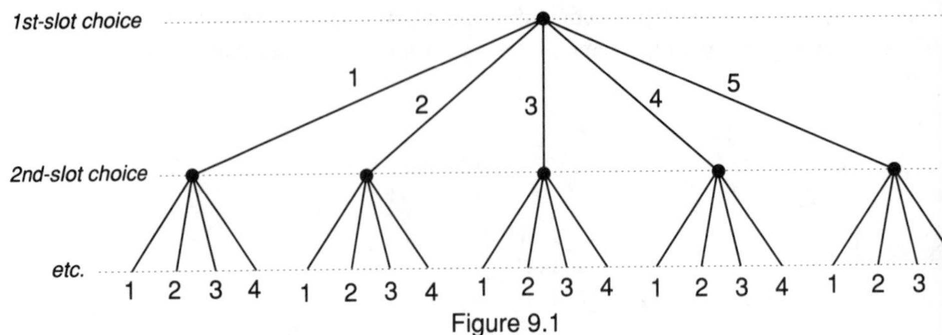

Figure 9.1

briefly, the number of permutations of five things taken five at a time is five *factorial*, $5! = 5 \times 4 \times 3 \times 2 \times 1 = 120$. In general, F factorial is written $F!$ and is equal to $F \times (F-1) \times (F-2) \times \cdots \times 2 \times 1$. By definition, $0!$ equals 1.

How many ways are there to arrange five named and colored balls in a previously specified color sequence, say, $<y, y, y, r, r>$? How many different ways are there to arrange *y–Joe, y–Moe, y–Doe, r–Harry,* and *r–Larry* to get just this sequence of yellows and reds?

Take the red balls first. We have two red balls to place in the last two slots. We could put *Harry* first and *Larry* second or we could put *Larry* first and *Harry* second. For the first red placement we have two choices, *Harry* or *Larry*; for the second red placement we have no choice, we must put either *Harry* or *Larry*, whichever remains after the first choice. There are just two ways to arrange the red balls.

Now consider the yellow balls. For the first yellow slot we have three choices: *Joe, Doe,* and *Moe*; for the second slot we have two choices—the two left after we have filled the first slot. We must put the remaining yellow ball in the last slot. There are six ways to arrange the three yellow balls. See the tree in Figure 9.2. Each of the different routes from the top of this tree to the bottom represents a different way to arrange the five balls. The first three slots concern the choices of the three yellow balls. There are three branches after the top node, representing the fact that we have three choices of yellow balls for the first slot. Each of these branches results in a node with two branches, representing the fact that we now have only two yellow balls to choose from for the second slot. Each of these branches results in a node with only one branch, representing the fact that we have no choice for the third slot; we must put the remaining yellow ball in it. These branches result in nodes with two branches, representing the fact that we have two red balls to choose from for the fourth slot. Finally, these branches result in nodes with only one branch, representing the fact that we must place the remaining red ball in the last slot. There are $3 \times 2 \times 1 \times 2 \times 1 = 3! \times 2! = 6 \times 2 = 12$ routes to the bottom of the tree.

We have just calculated the number of different ways to arrange five named and colored balls in the color sequence $<y, y, y, r, r>$. There is nothing intrinsically important about this color sequence, $<y, y, y, r, r>$. It could have been any

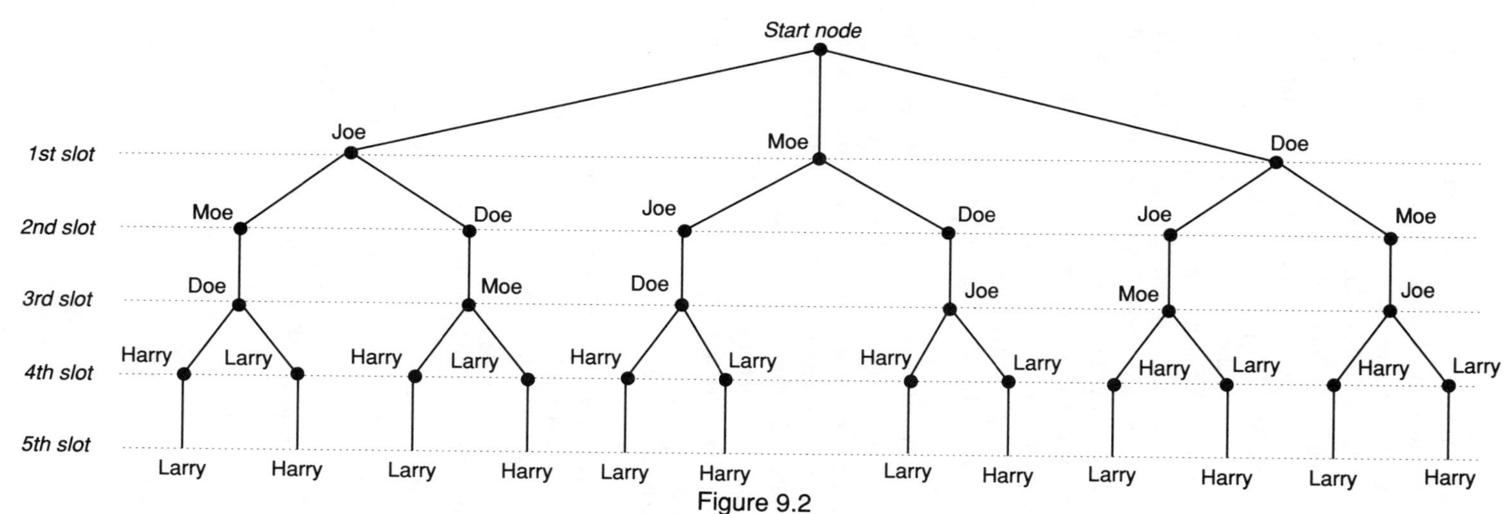
Start node
1st slot
2nd slot
3rd slot
4th slot
5th slot
Joe
Moe
Doe
Moe
Doe
Joe
Doe
Joe
Moe
Doe
Moe
Doe
Joe
Moe
Joe
Harry
Larry
Harry
Larry
Harry
Larry
Harry
Larry
Harry
Larry
Harry
Larry
Larry
Harry
Larry
Harry
Larry
Harry
Larry
Harry
Larry
Harry
Larry
Harry

Figure 9.2

arrangement of the three yellows and two reds. For example, suppose that we had to arrange the five named balls in the alternating color arrangement, <*y*, *r*, *y*, *r*, *y*>. There would be three choices for the first *yellow* ball (*Joe*, *Doe*, or *Moe*), two choices for the second *yellow* ball—skipping the red ball for the moment—and no choice for the remaining *yellow* ball. Finally, we would have to fill in the two red ball slots; there would be two choices for the first *red* slot (*Harry* and *Larry*) and no choice for the other red slot. The particular order in which the colors occur in the color sequence does not affect the number of ways to arrange the five named and colored balls in the given color sequence.

Put another way, the problem of arranging three *named* yellow and two *named* red balls in a specified color sequence is just two permutation problems side by side. We have to put three *named* yellow balls in some order and two *named* red balls in some order. The number of ways to arrange the yellow balls is 3!; the number of ways to arrange the red balls is 2!. No matter what color sequence is specified, there are $(3! \times 2!)$ ways to arrange the five balls in that color sequence. In general, we can arrange Y named yellow balls and R named red balls in a given color sequence in $Y! \times R!$ ways.

We can count the number of ways to arrange N *named* things—$N!$. We can also count the number of ways to arrange Y yellow and R red *named and colored* things in a specified color sequence—$Y! \times R!$. Now we can divide and conquer. We know that the number of ways to arrange N named balls regardless of color is the product of the number of different color sequences and the number of ways to arrange the named and colored balls in a given color sequence. Thus, the number of different color sequences—the number we want to determine—is the quotient of the number of ways to arrange N named objects, regardless of color—$N!$—and the number of ways to arrange Y yellow and R red balls in a specified color sequence—$Y! \times R!$, $B = N!/(Y! \times R!)$.

This quotient is called the number of *combinations* of Y plus R things. We have just shown that it is equal to the number of permutations of N $(= Y + R)$ things—$(Y + R)!$—divided by the number of permutations of Y things, $Y!$, times the number of permutations of R things $R!$. In the particular case at hand, the number of different color sequences with three yellow and two red balls is

$$\frac{(3+2)!}{(3! + 2!)} = \frac{5 \times 4 \times 3 \times 2 \times 1}{3 \times 2 \times 1 \times 2 \times 1} = \frac{5 \times 4 \times \cancel{3} \times \cancel{2} \times \cancel{1}}{\cancel{3} \times \cancel{2} \times \cancel{1} \times 2 \times 1} = 10.$$

And generally, the number of different color sequences with Y yellow balls and R red balls, the number of *combinations* of Y plus R balls is

$$\frac{(Y + R)!}{(Y! \times R!)}.$$

This finishes the counting part of the problem.

3. PROBABILITY

To find the probability of drawing three yellow and two red balls from an urn containing 2/3 yellow and 1/3 red balls, we need to find the probability of each of the yellow and red sequences. We need, for example, to determine the probability of getting three yellow balls followed by two red balls <*y, y, y, r, r*>. We must determine such a probability for each of the 10 different color sequences we counted in the preceding section. Happily, each of these 10 probabilities is the same. In the end we need only determine one of these probabilities; we can then multiply this probability by the number of different color sequences and we will have the result we seek: P(*3–yellow and 2–red*).

First we must determine the probability of a single color sequence, <*y, y, y, r, r*> for example. To figure out this probability, we proceed draw by draw.

What is the probability of drawing one yellow ball from the urn—forgetting the other draws? Since there are 2/3 yellow balls in the urn, the probability of drawing one yellow must be 2/3. Now we put that ball back in the urn and draw again; so the probability of drawing a yellow ball on the second draw must also be 2/3. Draws are independent; so the probability of getting two yellow balls in a row is, by the multiplication rule, 2/3 × 2/3 = 4/9. Adding a third draw and a third yellow ball adds another 2/3 to this product: 2/3 × 2/3 × 2/3 = 8/27. So the probability of drawing three yellow balls in a row is 8/27.

The fourth draw in our sequence, <*y, y, y, r, r*>, is red. Since draws are independent, the probability of getting a red ball on the fourth draw is not affected by the three previous yellow draws. What is the probability of drawing a red ball from the urn? By reasoning similar to above, it must be 1/3; 1/3 of the balls in the urn are red. The probability of drawing two red balls in a row, on the fourth and fifth draws, is 1/3 × 1/3 = 1/9.

Putting these calculations together: The probability of drawing three yellow balls followed by two red balls is

$$\underset{\substack{\text{first-draw}\\ \text{probability}}}{\frac{2}{3}} \times \underset{\substack{\text{second-draw}\\ \text{probability}}}{\frac{2}{3}} \times \underset{\substack{\text{third-draw}\\ \text{probability}}}{\frac{2}{3}} \times \underset{\substack{\text{fourth-draw}\\ \text{probability}}}{\frac{1}{3}} \times \underset{\substack{\text{fifth-draw}\\ \text{probability}}}{\frac{1}{3}}$$

$$= \left(\frac{2}{3}\right)^3 \times \left(\frac{1}{3}\right)^2 = \frac{8}{243}.$$

Since draws are independent of each other, this probability, 8/243, is not affected by the order in which the different colors are drawn. Consider the probability of drawing three yellow and two red balls in the sequence <*y, r, y, r, y*>. The probability of drawing the first yellow ball is 2/3; the probability of then drawing a red ball is 1/3. The probability of drawing a yellow followed by a red ball is 2/3 × 1/3 = 2/9, since draws are independent. Extending this line of reasoning, the probability of drawing this particular alternating sequence of yellow and red balls is

$$\underset{\substack{\text{first-draw}\\ \text{probability}}}{\frac{2}{3}} \times \underset{\substack{\text{second-draw}\\ \text{probability}}}{\frac{1}{3}} \times \underset{\substack{\text{third-draw}\\ \text{probability}}}{\frac{2}{3}} \times \underset{\substack{\text{fourth-draw}\\ \text{probability}}}{\frac{1}{3}} \times \underset{\substack{\text{fifth-draw}\\ \text{probability}}}{\frac{2}{3}}$$

$$= \left(\frac{2}{3}\right)^3 \times \left(\frac{1}{3}\right)^2 = \frac{8}{243}.$$

All of the orders in which we might draw three yellow and two red balls have the same probability, $(2/3)^3 \times (1/3)^2 = 8/243$. Generally, the probability of drawing balls in any of the possible specific color sequences with Y yellow and R red balls is $(2/3)^Y \times (1/3)^R$.

Now we know the probability of drawing any specific sequence of Y yellow and R red balls. We also know how many different sequences there are with given numbers, Y and R, of yellow and red balls. Since these sequences are all mutually exclusive—we cannot get more than one in a given "experiment"—we can use the addition rule to find the probability of the union of them:

$$\text{P}(\textit{3-yellow and 2-red}) = \text{P}(\langle y, y, y, r, r\rangle) + \text{P}(\langle y, r, y, r, y\rangle) + \cdots + \text{P}(\langle r, r, y, y, y\rangle).$$

The probabilities that go into the "..." above are the other seven sequences of three yellow and two red balls. By our counting argument above we know that there are 10 different sequences. But the probability of each of these is the same, 8/243. Since there are 10, the sum of all of them is 10 × 8/243 = 80/243. That is,

$$\text{P}(\textit{3-yellow and 2-red}) = \frac{8}{243} + \frac{8}{243} + \cdots + \frac{8}{243} = 10 \times \frac{8}{243} = \frac{80}{243}.$$

What if we had been drawing from an urn with a different proportion of yellow and red balls—say, 1/4 yellow and 3/4 red? The argument here is essentially the same. The only difference is that the probability of drawing a yellow ball is 1/4, not 2/3; the probability of drawing a red ball is 3/4, not 1/3.

This change does not affect the counting argument. The number of ways to get three yellow and two red balls is still 5!/(3! × 2!) = 10.

The probabilities change. The probability of drawing a yellow ball is 1/4 instead of 2/3; the probability of drawing a red ball is 3/4, not 1/3. Draws are still independent. Consider one of the sequences, $\langle y, y, y, r, r\rangle$. The probability of drawing this particular sequence is

$$\frac{1}{4} \times \frac{1}{4} \times \frac{1}{4} \times \frac{3}{4} \times \frac{3}{4} = \left(\frac{3}{4}\right)^2 \times \left(\frac{1}{4}\right)^3 = \frac{9}{1{,}024}.$$

The reasoning is just the same as above. The probability of getting one of any of the 10 different sequences of three yellow and two red balls is 9/1,024, and there are 10 of these sequences. So P(*3–yellow and 2–red*) = 10 × 9/1,024 = 90/1,024 ≈ 0.088.

Summarizing: The number of different sequences of *Y* yellow and *R* red balls is

$$\frac{(Y+R)!}{(Y! \times R!)}.$$

This is the number of *combinations* of *Y* plus *R* things. Each of these sequences has the same probability as each other. If we suppose that the probability of drawing a yellow ball on a single draw is p and that the probability of drawing a red ball on a single draw is $(1 - p)$, the probability of getting any specific *Y* yellow and *R* red balls is

$$p^Y \times (1-p)^R.$$

The probability, then, of drawing *Y* yellow and *R* red balls is:

$$\frac{(Y+R)!}{Y! \times R!} \times p^Y \times (1-p)^R.$$

This is the formula for computing binomial probabilities. It puts together all the information we have labored over for the past pages. Be careful to notice where all the *p*s, $(1 - p)$s, *Y*s, and *R*s come from, and what they mean.

4. AN EXAMPLE: BINOMIAL PROBABILITIES AND BAYES' RULE

To get some experience using the binomial formula, we can use it with Bayes' rule. Suppose that the "next room" contains 1,000 urns. Of these urns, 500 contain 66 yellow balls and 33 red balls—*A-urns*. The other 500 urns contain 25 yellow balls and 75 red balls—*B-urns*. One of these urns is selected at random and brought into our room. It is not labeled; our problem is to find out what kind of urn it is. We cannot look inside the urn, but we can draw balls out of the urn, replacing each one after it is drawn. Suppose that we draw five balls out of the urn and get one red and four yellow balls. Given this evidence, which kind of urn is most likely in front of us?

It stands to reason that we have an *A-urn* because *A-urns* have more yellow balls in them than do *B-urns*. Since we got more yellow balls in our sample, it seems reasonable to suppose that we have an *A-urn*. But can we be more specific?

To be more specific, we use Bayes' rule. Let **E** stand for our evidence of one red and four yellow balls. Let **A** stand for the event of there being a *A-urn* in front of us, and **B** stand for the event of there being a *B-urn* in front of us. According to Bayes' rule,

$$P(\mathbf{A}|\mathbf{E}) = \frac{P(\mathbf{A})P(\mathbf{E}|\mathbf{A})}{P(\mathbf{A})P(\mathbf{E}|\mathbf{A}) + P(\mathbf{B})P(\mathbf{E}|\mathbf{B})}.$$

Thus, to find the probability that there is an *A-urn* in front of us, given this evidence, P(**A**|**E**), we need to know four other probabilities: P(**A**), P(**B**), P(**E**|**A**), and P(**E**|**B**).

Of these four probabilities, two are easy. P(**A**) = P(**B**) = 1/2. This reflects the fact that we chose our urn randomly from a room half filled with *A-urn*s and half with *B-urn*s. So, before we have done any withdrawing of balls, we have a 50–50 chance of having either type of urn.

The other two probabilities, P(**E**|**A**) and P(**E**|**B**), are straightforward binomial probabilities. P(**E**|**A**) is the probability of getting four yellow balls and one red ball given that drawing from an urn with 2/3 yellow and 1/3 red balls in it.

$$\begin{aligned} P(\mathbf{E}|\mathbf{A}) &= P(\textit{4–yellow and 1–red}|\textit{A-urn}) \\ &= \frac{(4+1)!}{4! \times 1!} \times \left(\frac{2}{3}\right)^4 \times \left(\frac{1}{3}\right)^1 = 5 \times \left(\frac{16}{243}\right) = \frac{80}{243}. \end{aligned}$$

P(**E**|**B**) is similar except we assume that we draw from an urn with 1/4 yellow and 3/4 red balls.

$$\begin{aligned} P(\mathbf{E}|\mathbf{B}) &= P(\textit{4–yellow and 1–red}|\textit{B-urn}) \\ &= \frac{(4+1)!}{4! \times 1!} \times \left(\frac{1}{4}\right)^4 \times \left(\frac{3}{4}\right)^1 = 5 \times \left(\frac{3}{1{,}024}\right) = \frac{15}{1{,}024}. \end{aligned}$$

We can plug all of this information into our formula for Bayes' rule:

$$\begin{aligned} P(\mathbf{A}|\mathbf{E}) &= \frac{P(\mathbf{A})P(\mathbf{E}|\mathbf{A})}{P(\mathbf{A})P(\mathbf{E}|\mathbf{A}) + P(\mathbf{B})P(\mathbf{E}|\mathbf{B})} \\ &= \frac{(1/2)(80/243)}{(1/2)(80/243) + (1/2)(15/1{,}024)} = \frac{(81{,}920/248{,}832)}{((81{,}920 + 3{,}645)/248{,}832)} \\ &= \frac{81{,}920}{85{,}565} \approx 0.96. \end{aligned}$$

By a similar calculation we can see that P(**B**|**E**) is 3,645/248,832 ≈ 0.04. Of course, we could have calculated P(**B**|**E**) by subtracting P(**A**|**E**) from 1. The urn is either an *A-urn* or a *B-urn*. So the probability of it being a *B-urn* must be 1 − P(**A**|**E**).

5. THE BINOMIAL DISTRIBUTION

Baby births can also be modeled as binomial trials with a constant probability, p, of a male baby being born and $(1 - p)$ of a female baby being born. For the purposes of illustration, we can assume that births are independent of each other, and that there are equal chances for male and female births. We imagine, then, that baby births are like drawing balls out of an urn. Half of the balls in the urn are yellow (for female babies) and half are red (for male babies).

Consider a hospital where 10 babies are born during a particular day. We "draw out of this urn 10 times." We can ask 11 questions:

1. What is the probability of drawing 10 yellow balls and zero red balls?
2. What is the probability of drawing nine yellow balls and one red ball?
3. What is the probability of drawing eight yellow balls and two red balls?
4. What is the probability of drawing seven yellow balls and three red balls?
5. What is the probability of drawing six yellow balls and four red balls?
6. What is the probability of drawing five yellow balls and five red balls?
7. What is the probability of drawing four yellow balls and six red balls?
8. What is the probability of drawing three yellow balls and seven red balls?
9. What is the probability of drawing two yellow balls and eight red balls?
10. What is the probability of drawing one yellow ball and nine red balls?
11. What is the probability of drawing zero yellow balls and 10 red balls?

The questions are repetitious. But each of them can be answered using the binomial law. Take question 1. The probability of drawing 10 yellow and zero red balls is

$$\frac{(10+0)!}{10! \times 0!} \times \left(\frac{1}{2}\right)^{10} \times \left(\frac{1}{2}\right)^{0} = 1 \times \left(\frac{1}{2}\right)^{10} \times 1 \approx 0.00097.$$

(Recall that any number to the power zero is one, $a^0 = 1$, and that $0! = 1$ as well.) Take question 2. The probability of drawing nine yellow balls and one red ball is 10 times larger:

$$\frac{(9+1)!}{9! \times 1!} \times \left(\frac{1}{2}\right)^{9} \times \left(\frac{1}{2}\right)^{1} = 10 \times \left(\frac{1}{2}\right)^{10} \approx 0.0097.$$

We do a similar computation for question 3:

$$\frac{(8+2)!}{8! \times 2!} \times \left(\frac{1}{2}\right)^{8} \times \left(\frac{1}{2}\right)^{2} = 45 \times \left(\frac{1}{2}\right)^{10} \approx 0.0439.$$

And so it goes.

Working out answers to all 11 questions gives the probabilities that are listed in Table 9.1, (approximated to the nearest 1/1,000). Notice that these answers are symmetrical around number 5. Why is this so? The probability of four boys and six girls being born is the same as the probability of six boys and four girls being born. This is just what you would expect when each has the same probability of 1/2 on a single trial.

TABLE 9.1

	Event	Probability
1.	10 yellow and 0 red	1/1,000
2.	9 yellow and 1 red	10/1,000
3.	8 yellow and 2 red	44/1,000
4.	7 yellow and 3 red	117/1,000
5.	6 yellow and 4 red	205/1,000
6.	5 yellow and 5 red	246/1,000
7.	4 yellow and 6 red	205/1,000
8.	3 yellow and 7 red	117/1,000
9.	2 yellow and 8 red	44/1,000
10.	1 yellow and 9 red	10/1,100
11.	0 yellow and 10 red	1/1,000

Also notice that the probability of some intermediate number of both boys and girls being born is larger than an overabundance of either. In particular note that the probability of four, five, or six boys being born (and the corresponding number of girls) is 656/1,000, slightly larger than 1/2. The probability of three, four, five, six, or seven boys being born (and the corresponding number of girls) is 890/1,000. The "odds" favor nearly equal numbers of male and female babies. We represent this graphically in Figure 9.3. Such a graph shows clearly that the chances of getting a result "near the middle" far outweigh the chances of getting a result near either end of the graph—at the "tails."

This is called a *binomial distribution*. By graphing the distribution of binomial probabilities (with N trials and equal chances) we represent all of the possible out-

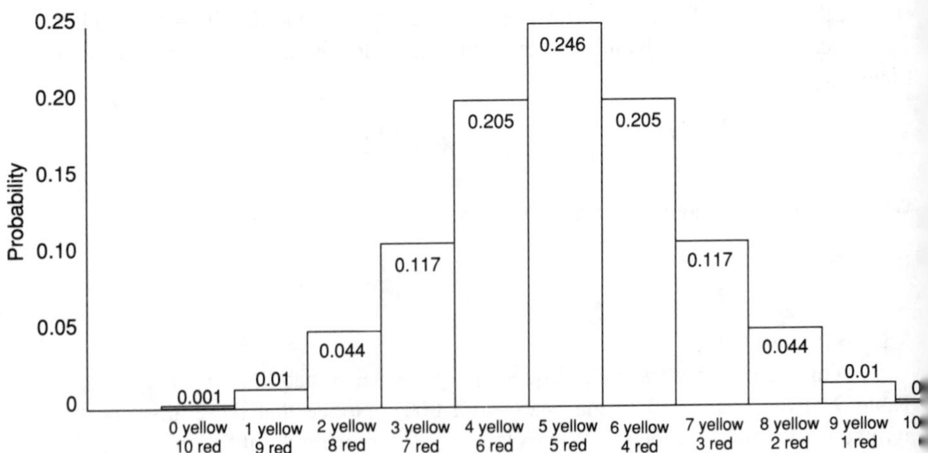

Figure 9.3

comes, neglecting the order of colors drawn. Here we have graphed the binomial distribution for 10 trials. By a similar process we could graph the binomial distribution for 100 or 100,000 trials. The calculations would get increasingly tedious, but in principle such a graph could be drawn, and with the aid of computers, it is not such a chore.

This distribution of probabilities covers all of the possible binomial outcomes. We can calculate other probabilities from this distribution—P(*4, 5, or 6 yellow in 10 trials*) = 656/1,000. In an important sense the probabilities in the binomial distribution function like the probabilities we assign to simple events. We can use them to calculate other probabilities and they cover all of the (binomial) possibilities.

We calculated these binomial probabilities on the basis of "more primitive" probabilities: Each ball in the urn has the same chance of being drawn on any trial and the trials are independent. But we could, in some contexts, just begin with binomial probabilities. We may trust these binomial probabilities for reasons other than a derivation from equal chances assigned to each ball being drawn. Perhaps data from many births show a binomial distribution of male and female births. Perhaps we have a biological model of birthrates that has the binomial distribution as a consequence—but makes no claim about probabilities for individual trials. We may also have reason to trust the assignment of equal probabilities to each ball being drawn. Different contexts can call for different underlying rationales for probability assignments. The important thing to notice is that a *distribution* of probabilities, such as the binomial distribution, is an assignment of probabilities to every possible (binomial) outcome.

Probabilistic computations typically begin from a *distributional assumption*—we might model births with a binomial distribution. This distributional assumption serves the purpose of assigning probabilities to every outcome. Here we focus on a coarser description of the possible outcomes—the order of colors is ignored—and assign probabilities directly to these (binomial) events. We start with a binomial distribution.

6. BERNOULLI'S THEOREM

Instead of considering a small hospital where 10 babies are born during a given day, we could consider all the babies born during a given day in the United States. There would be many more calculations to do, but the result would be overwhelmingly in favor of getting about equal numbers of either sex. In a sense, it is because of the binomial law that the number of male children born is just about the same as the number of female children born.

We can say more than this. Around the year 1700, Jacob Bernoulli proved one of the first profound theorems of probability. Bernoulli considered a case very much like those we have been considering; but he asked what would happen if the number of trials got arbitrarily large. Thus, suppose that we are drawing balls from an urn, noting the color of the balls and replacing them. Suppose further that the urn has only two different colors of balls inside, red and yellow, and that the proportion of yellow balls is p. Suppose that we draw N times from the urn, where N is a large number. Bernoulli asked: What is the probability that the ratio of the number of yellow balls, Y, drawn to the total number drawn, N, will differ from p by more than some small fraction ε; that is, $P[(p - \varepsilon) \leq Y/N \leq (p + \varepsilon)] = ?$

Consider the example above; $p = 1/2$. Suppose that we count 1/10 "near"; $\varepsilon = 1/10$. Consider the case when we draw 10 times from the urn; $N = 10$. We have already discovered that

$$P\left[\left(\frac{1}{2} - \frac{1}{10}\right) \leq \frac{Y}{10} \leq \left(\frac{1}{2} + \frac{1}{10}\right)\right] = P\left(\frac{4}{10} \leq \frac{Y}{10} \leq \frac{6}{10}\right)$$

$$= P(4 \leq Y \leq 6) = P(Y = 4 \cup Y = 5 \cup Y = 6)$$

$$= \frac{205}{1{,}000} + \frac{246}{1{,}000} + \frac{205}{1{,}000} = \frac{656}{1{,}000} = 0.656.$$

Suppose we let N grow modestly to 20. We need to calculate $P[(1/2 - 1/10) \leq Y/20 < (1/2 + 1/10)] = P(8 \leq Y \leq 12)$. One might guess that this probability will be the same as the case with 10 draws, 0.656. In fact, it is larger.

$$P(Y = 8) = \frac{20!}{12! \times 8!} \times \left(\frac{1}{2}\right)^8 \times \left(\frac{1}{2}\right)^{12} \approx 0.12;$$

$$P(Y = 9) = \frac{20!}{11! \times 9!} \times \left(\frac{1}{2}\right)^9 \times \left(\frac{1}{2}\right)^{11} \approx 0.16;$$

$$P(Y = 10) = \frac{20!}{10! \times 10!} \times \left(\frac{1}{2}\right)^{10} \times \left(\frac{1}{2}\right)^{10} \approx 0.18;$$

$$P(Y = 11) = \frac{20!}{9! \times 11!} \times \left(\frac{1}{2}\right)^{11} \times \left(\frac{1}{2}\right)^9 \approx 0.16;$$

$$P(Y = 12) = \frac{20!}{8! \times 12!} \times \left(\frac{1}{2}\right)^{12} \times \left(\frac{1}{2}\right)^8 \approx 0.12.$$

So $P(8 \leq Y \leq 12) \approx 0.12 + 0.16 + 0.18 + 0.16 + 0.12 = 0.74$. When the number of trials is doubled from 10 to 20, the probability that the proportion of yellow balls observed to the total number of balls observed is within 1/10 of 1/2 increases from 0.656 to 0.74. If we double N again from 20 to 40, the probability gets larger still:

$$P\left[\left(\frac{1}{2} - \frac{1}{10}\right) \leq \frac{Y}{40} \leq \left(\frac{1}{2} + \frac{1}{10}\right)\right] = P(16 \leq Y \leq 24) \approx 0.85.$$

As N gets larger, the probability of getting a result within 1/10 of p also gets larger.

We display this graphically in Figure 9.4. In the graph, I have superimposed the binomial distribution for $N = 20$ on top of the binomial distribution for $N = 10$.

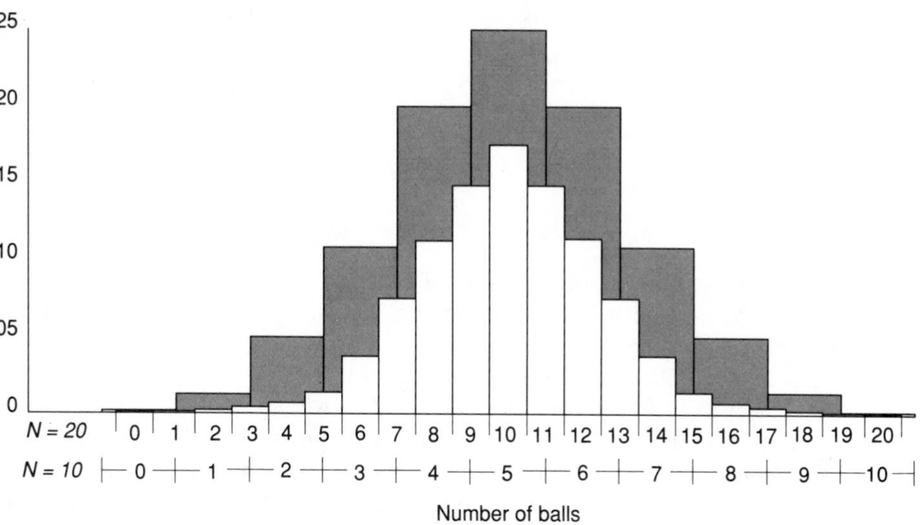

Figure 9.4

The white bars, superimposed on the shaded bars, are for $N = 20$; the shaded bars are for $N = 10$. All of the probabilities for $N = 20$ are smaller than their counterparts with $N = 10$. The probability of five out of 10 balls drawn being yellow is about 250/1,000 (0.24609); the probability of 10 out of 20 balls drawn being yellow is about 175/1,000 (0.17620). Indeed, as the number of trials gets larger, the probability of getting *exactly* 1/2 yellow balls gets smaller. But, more important, notice that the probabilities for $N = 20$ are more closely clumped together, near 1/2, than are the probabilities for $N = 10$. The probability of a proportion of yellow balls "far" from 1/2 is smaller when $N = 20$ than when $N = 10$.

Bernoulli proved that as N is allowed to grow arbitrarily large, this probability approaches 1:

$$\mathrm{P}[(p - \varepsilon) \leq \frac{Y}{N} \leq (p + \varepsilon)] \rightarrow 1 \text{ as } N \rightarrow \text{infinity}.$$

Bernoulli showed that for any small fixed deviation, ε, eventually, the number of trials N will get large enough that the probability that the proportion of yellow balls observed to the total number of trials, Y/N, is closer to p than ε is as close to 1 as we please. In the example we considered above we set ε to 1/10. We found that with 40 trials the probability of observing a proportion, Y/N, within 1/10 of the true proportion, 1/2, was 0.85. If we considered cases with larger numbers of trials this probability would have gotten closer to 1—as close as we like for some N. Of course, we need not have chosen 1/10; it is a convenient small fraction to use. Bernoulli's theorem hold for any ε we care to consider, no matter how small.

We can actually say something stronger. We can find limits such that for some fixed small deviation, ε, and some fixed large probability, P, there is some large number of trials, N, such that the probability of being within ε of p is P or greater:

For any ε and any P, there is a T such that

$$P[(p - \varepsilon)) \leq \frac{Y}{N} \leq (p + \varepsilon)] \geq P$$

for any number of trials, N, larger than T.

There is one important feature to realize about Bernoulli's theorem. The probability of observations being within some small fraction of the true proportion does get large as N gets large. But it only reaches the limit of one when the number of trials is infinite. Thus, for any finite number of trials there is always some probability, however small, that the observed proportion will not be ''near'' (within ε of) the true proportion, p. Bernoulli's theorem shows that the probability of this happening is very small for large values of N; but the improbable can happen.

The conclusion of the theorem is rather as one might expect. The proportion of the number of yellow balls should get closer to the actual proportion of yellow balls in the urn. Bernoulli's theorem shows that the probability of this happening gets very large as the number of trials gets large. So just what we might expect to happen has a large probability of happening.

Consider male and female births. Since the number of trials in this case is very large, there is almost zero probability that the number of male births should differ significantly from the number of female births—assuming that the probability of a male being born is 1/2. This result, of course, applies to any case of binomial trials; when the number of trials is very large, there is only a small probability that the proportions observed will differ appreciably from the true probabilities.

7. THE NORMAL CURVE AND PROBABILITY DENSITY FUNCTIONS

There is another important feature of the binomial distribution. When the number of trials is fairly large the shape of the binomial distribution can be well approximated by a *normal,* or bell-shaped, curve. If you focus on the peaks of the bars in the two superimposed graphs in Figure 9.4, you will see two such bell-shaped curves. To explain this result, we need to take a small diversion to explain the normal curve.

There are many normal curves. ''Normal'' refers to a family of curves. Each curve in the family is bell-shaped. Each has a single peak or hump in the middle. Each curve falls off from its peak symmetrically on either side. Normal curves can differ from each other in two respects. One normal curve can peak at a different place than another normal curve. Normal curves also can differ by how ''steep'' they are. Some normal curves are relatively flat, others are relatively steep. Two superimposed normal curves are shown in Figure 9.5; one is relatively flat and has a peak to the right of the other, steeper normal curve.

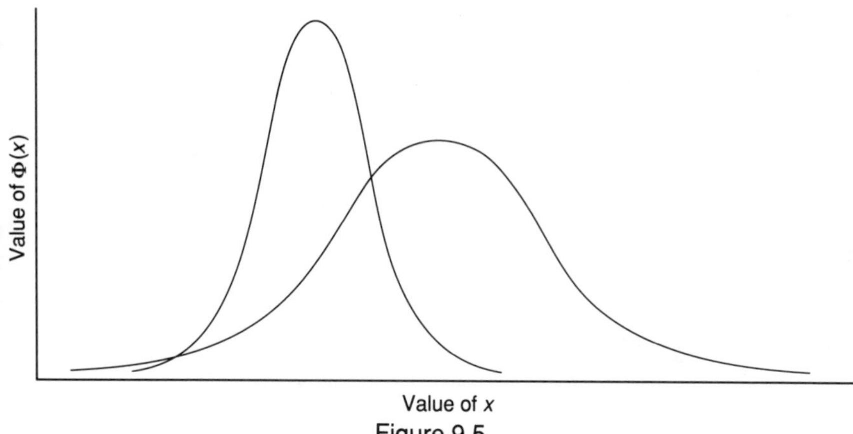

Figure 9.5

We can pick the specific normal curve we are interested in by specifying *where* its peak is and how *sharply peaked* it is. Two values, the *parameters* of the curve, are used to do this. The first, μ, called the *mean*, marks the peak of the curve. The second, σ, called the *standard deviation*, describes the curve's steepness. The smaller σ is, the steeper the curve is. Put another way, the smaller σ is, the more the curve is near the mean, μ.

We met these parameters, the mean and standard deviation, in Chapter 6. The mean is the average value. While the normal curve represents infinitely many values (see below), in quite a natural sense the average of these values is the mean—center—of the curve. The standard deviation is the average spread of values around the mean. The larger the standard deviation, the more spread out the values are—the flatter or less "clumped together" the curve.

Many times we will think of a given group of measurements as a sample taken from an infinite population with values spread out like a normal curve. The mean of our sample, $\overline{\mathbf{X}}$, is a good estimate for the mean of the normal curve, μ. The standard deviation of our sample, $\sqrt{\Sigma(\mathbf{X}_i - \overline{\mathbf{X}})^2/N}$, is a good estimate for the standard deviation of the normal curve, σ. [For technical reasons, one usually divides by $N - 1$ instead of by N when estimating the standard deviation of a normal curve. $\sqrt{\Sigma(\mathbf{X}_i - \overline{\mathbf{X}})^2/(N-1)}$ is an unbiased estimator of σ, while $\sqrt{\Sigma(\mathbf{X}_i - \overline{\mathbf{X}})^2/N}$ is not (see Chapters 10 and 13). Of course, when N is large the difference between $(N - 1)$ and N is negligible.]

Both of these parameters also have a geometric interpretation in terms of the graph of the normal curve they describe (Figure 9.6). The mean, μ, marks the location of the curve's peak. The standard deviation, σ, is a bit more complicated to describe. Each normal curve has three parts. The left-hand "tail" is that part of the curve which is cupped *up* like a "∪." The right-hand tail is similarly cupped up. The middle portion of the curve is cupped down like a "∩." The distance from the center of the curve, from the mean, μ, to the point where the curvature changes, is

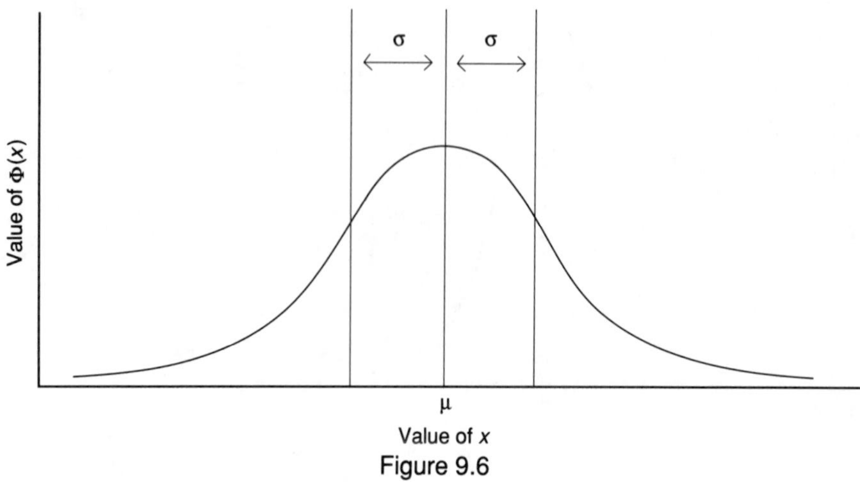

Figure 9.6

the standard deviation, σ. Thus, the larger the standard deviation, the greater the distance from the mean to the point where each tail begins.

These graphs are described by the following messy-looking equation:

$$\Phi(x) = \frac{1}{\sqrt{2\pi\sigma^2}} e^{[(x - \mu)/2\sigma]^2}$$

The equation is stated in terms of the mean, μ, the standard deviation, σ, and a bunch of other numerical constants with fixed values such as 2, $\pi(\approx 3.14159)$ and e (≈ 2.71828). Thus, once values for μ and σ are fixed, the equation states a single relationship between values of x and values of the function, $\Phi(x)$.

The detailed mathematics of this function are not important for us. One conceptual point is important: This function is a *probability density function*. So far, all of the probabilities we have considered arise in cases where there are only a finite number of possible outcomes. There are cases that can produce infinitely many possible outcomes. For example, if we measure a length with a perfectly precise and accurate ruler, there are an infinite number of possible measurements that could result. Of course, we never have perfectly precise rulers, but we can consider the possibility of such an *ideal* case. When there are an infinite number of possible outcomes, we use a *probability density function* to describe probabilities.

Consider an example. Suppose that we measured the heights of human beings with a perfectly precise ruler. As a matter of fact, human heights are distributed in a way that very closely resembles the normal probability density function. The probability that a randomly selected person has a height between 5 feet 8 inches and 6 feet 8 inches is expressed as the *area* under the density function between 5 feet 8 inches and 6 feet 8 inches (Figure 9.7). The idea of determining probability as the *area*

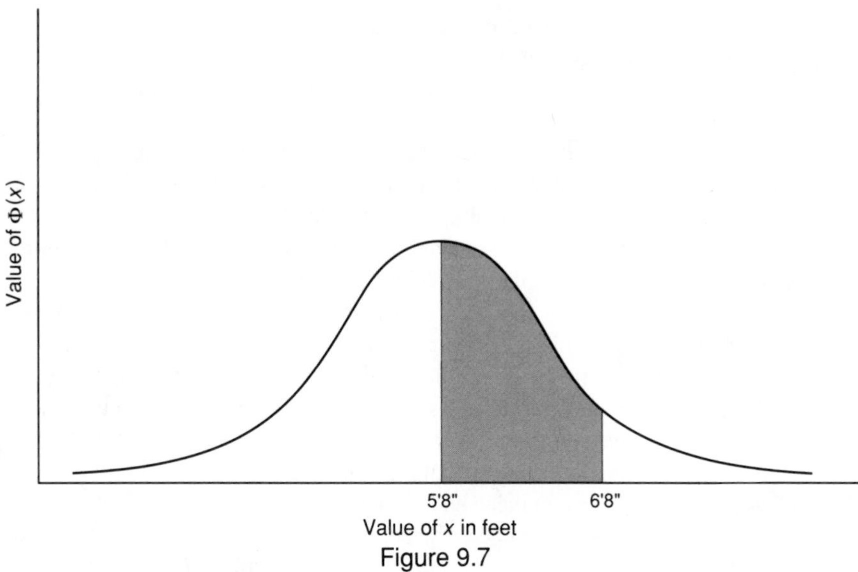

Figure 9.7

under a probability density function is a generalization of the way we have been determining probabilities all along. Earlier we calculated the probability of getting four, five, or six yellow balls when we drew five times from an urn with 1/2 yellow balls inside. We added the probabilities for these three outcomes:

$$\underset{\text{P(4 yellow)}}{0.20508} + \underset{\text{P(5 yellow)}}{0.24609} + \underset{\text{P(6 yellow)}}{0.20508} = 0.65625.$$

This is just as if we added the lengths of the bars in a bar graph of the binomial distribution (Figure 9.8). If we assume that the widths of each of these bars is 1,

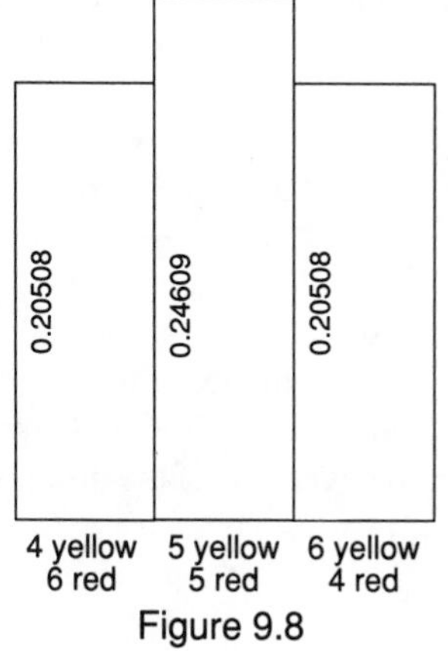

Figure 9.8

adding these lengths is equivalent to finding the area the bars take up. This is just what we do with probability density functions.

With the binomial distribution we have probabilities for each of the possible binomial events. With the normal probability density function we have probability density values for each possible value. When we calculate probabilities based on a binomial distribution, we add up the relevant binomial probabilities. When we calculate probabilities based on a normal probability density function we compute the areas under the normal curve. If we added together all the probabilities from all possible binomial events, we would get one; this is the certain event. If we found the area under the entire spread of the normal probability density function, we would similarly find one—again, this is the certain event.

In the same way that the binomial distribution can function like assignments of probabilities to simple events—it provides probabilities for all possible outcomes—the normal probability density function similarly works like an assignment of probabilities to simple events. We can say that a certain variable has a *normal distribution*. We might specify an exact mean and standard deviation or leave these as "free parameters" whose values will be determined by the data. We imagine a variable, such as height, which has different values for different members of the population. This variable is imagined as taking any of an infinite spread of values (e.g., from 0 to infinity). Saying that it has a normal probability density function—a normal distribution—describes how probabilities are spread among these values. In the same way that we calculate further probabilities from an assignment of probabilities to simple events, we can calculate further probabilities from the understanding that a certain variable has a certain probability density function. Thus, sometimes we can make a distributional assumption of a probability density function—like the normal distribution—for infinitely many outcomes, instead of a probability distribution—like the binomial distribution—for finitely many outcomes.

In general, one must use integral calculus to find areas under curves like this. Happily, those areas under the normal density function which will concern us have already been determined. We need not do any calculus to make use of the idea of a probability density function. Three probabilities that we will have occasion to use are

$$P[(\mu - \sigma) \leq x \leq (\mu + \sigma)] \approx 0.67;$$
$$P[(\mu - 2\sigma) \leq x \leq (\mu + 2\sigma)] \approx 0.95;$$
$$P[(\mu - 3\sigma) \leq x \leq (\mu + 3\sigma)] \approx 0.99;$$

That is, the probability of an observation, x, occurring *within* one standard deviation of the mean is about 0.67. The probability of an observation occurring within two standard deviations of the mean is about 0.95. The probability of an observation occurring within three standard deviations of the mean is about 0.99. This is shown graphically in Figure 9.9.

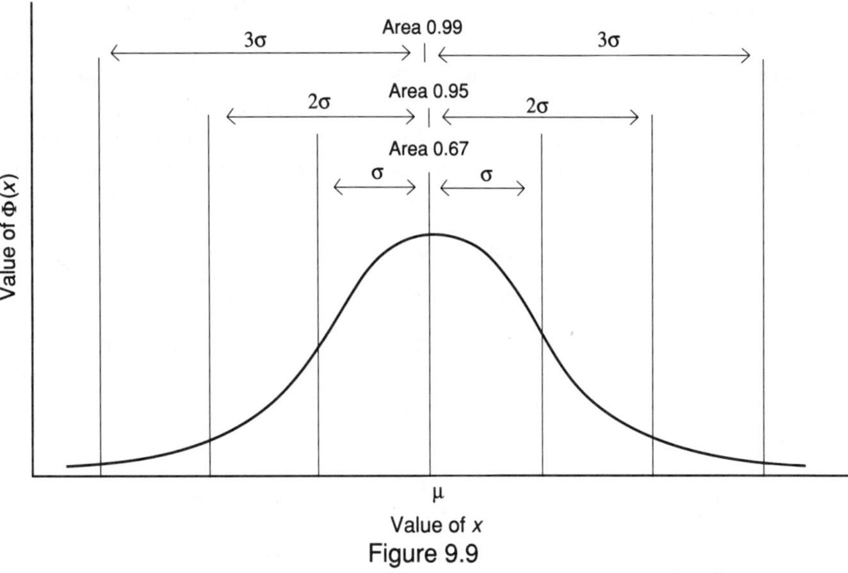

Figure 9.9

8. THE BINOMIAL DISTRIBUTION AND THE NORMAL DISTRIBUTION

With this background we can now understand an important result known as the central limit theorem. The shape of the binomial distribution—with proportion p of "red balls"—can be well approximated by a normal distribution. The number of observations needs to be fairly large—30 is plenty. This is plausible from a visual inspection of the binomial distribution and the normal distribution.

We do not go into the proof of the central limit theorem. But we do make use of its consequences, particularly in our discussion of polling inferences in Chapter 10. It is for this reason that we need to know something of what this theorem proves.

The binomial distribution is a collection of probabilities that covers all the possible binomial outcomes. We can use the normal distribution to provide approximate probabilities for any collection of binomial events. For example, if we draw 100 times from an urn with red and yellow balls, there are exactly 101 different binomial events; each has an exact binomial probability. We can approximate these 101 binomial probabilities with probabilities based on a normal distribution. If we wanted to know the probability of drawing between 25 and 37 red balls, we can use a probability for $P(25 \leq R \leq 37)$ taken from the appropriate normal distribution. We will not get the exact value, but we will get a very close value. Since normal distribution probabilities are easy to find—from widely available tables—we are saved the work of many binomial computations. Since many things are binomial in nature, the central limit theorem—and the normal distribution—have turned out to be very important in statistical work.

The particular normal distribution appropriate to approximate a particular binomial distribution is picked from the family of normal distributions, by specifying its mean, μ, and standard deviation, σ. When we draw N times from an urn with proportion p of red balls, we use the normal distribution with the following mean and standard deviation:

$$\text{Mean:} \quad \mu = N \times p.$$

$$\text{Standard deviation:} \quad \sigma = \sqrt{N \times p \times (1 - p)}.$$

Consider an example. Suppose that we draw 1,000 times from an urn with 1/2 red balls in it. What is the probability that we get a result of at least 468 red balls and at most 532 red balls? To calculate this probability we can use the normal approximation with:

$$\text{Mean:} \quad \mu = 1{,}000 \times \frac{1}{2} = 500.$$

$$\begin{aligned} \text{Standard deviation:} \quad \sigma &= \sqrt{N \times p \times (1 - p)}. \\ &= \sqrt{1{,}000 \times \frac{1}{2} \times \left(1 - \frac{1}{2}\right)} = \sqrt{250} \\ &\approx 15.81. \end{aligned}$$

Notice several numerical conveniences: We are looking for the probability of a result within 32 of the mean of 500. 32 is roughly twice the standard deviation of the normal curve approximation: $32 \approx 2 \times 15.81$ $(=\sigma)$. The mean plus 32 is 532, and the mean minus 32 is 468. Thus, the probability of getting between 468 and 532 red balls is approximately equal to the probability of getting an observation within two standard deviations of the mean of this particular normal distribution. This fact about normal distributions has been determined. The probability is 0.95:

$$\begin{aligned} &P[(\mu - 2\sigma) \le x \le (\mu + 2\sigma)] \\ &\qquad \approx P[(\text{Np} - 2\sqrt{Np(1-p)}) \le R \le (\text{Np} + 2\sqrt{Np(1-p)})] \\ &\qquad = P[(500 - 2 \times 15.81) \le R \le (500 + 2 \times 15.81)] \\ &\qquad = P[468.38 \le R \le 531.62] \approx P[468 \le R \le 532] = 0.95. \end{aligned}$$

It is much easier to find this probability with the normal approximation than it would be to calculate all of the 64 binomial probabilities for each of the different numbers of outcomes of red balls between 468 and 532.

Consider another example. Suppose that we draw 1,200 times from an urn with 33 red balls and 66 yellow balls. We can approximate the binomial distribution of probabilities for such an example with a normal curve with the following mean and standard deviation:

$$\text{Mean:} \quad \mu = N \times p$$

$$= 1{,}200 \times \frac{1}{3} = 400.$$

$$\text{Standard deviation:} \quad \sigma = \sqrt{N \times p \times (1 - p)}.$$

$$= \sqrt{1{,}200 \times \frac{1}{3} \times \left(1 - \frac{1}{3}\right)} = \sqrt{266.66}$$

$$\approx 16.33.$$

Given what we know about normal distributions, we can quickly calculate several different binomial probabilities. For instance:

$$P(383 \leq R \leq 417) \approx P[(\mu - \sigma) \leq x \leq (\mu + \sigma)] \approx 0.67;$$

$$P(367 \leq R \leq 433) \approx P[(\mu - 2\sigma) \leq x \leq (\mu + 2\sigma)] \approx 0.95;$$

$$P(351 \leq R \leq 449) \approx P[(\mu - 3\sigma) \leq x \leq (\mu + 3\sigma)] \approx 0.99;$$

The last of these probabilities is quite remarkable. There is a 99% probability that we will get more than 351 and less than 449 red balls in our sample. On the face of things, it would seem quite possible that we might get 313 red balls in our sample, and indeed, we might, but the odds are strongly against this.

Indeed, if we did get a result of 313 red balls we might begin to suspect that the urn had fewer than 33 red balls inside. Exactly how we might turn this suspicion into an inference is what polling studies are all about. We discuss the details of such logic in Chapters 2 and 10. For now, it is worth pondering the shape of the normal curve as it approximates binomial probabilities (Figure 9.10). Virtually all of the

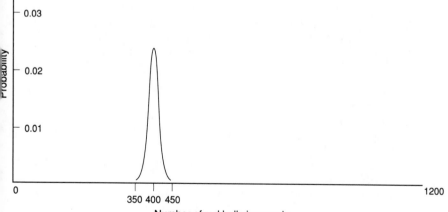

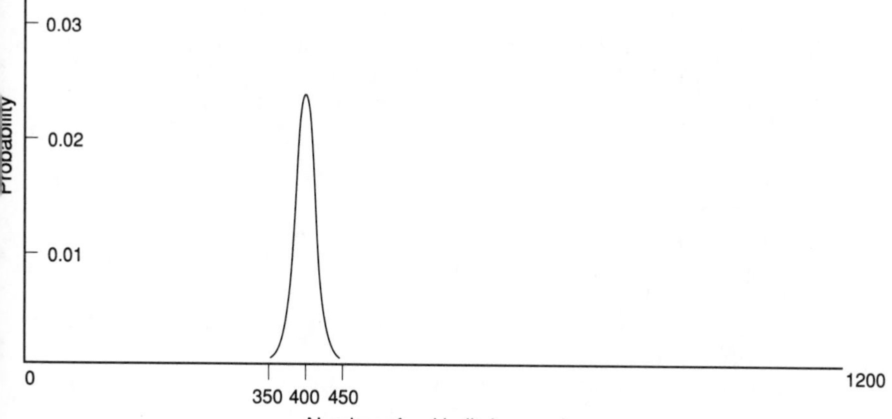

Figure 9.10

probability is in a little hump between 350 and 450. In relative terms, virtually all of the probability is within $50/1200 = 4.5\%$ of the mean. It is because binomial probabilities clump together in this way, when N is large, that we can make useful inferences about the contents of an urn from a sample taken from it. Binomial probabilities simply do not (probabilistically) allow very aberrant results.

9. SUMMARY

1. The formula for computing binomial probabilities was derived.
   - **(a)** One asks for the probability of getting Y yellow and R red balls from an urn with proportion p of yellow balls and $(1 - p)$ of red balls.
   - **(b)** There are two parts to this problem. One must *count* the number of different ways to get Y yellow and R red balls, and one must calculate the probability of each of these ways. Answers to these questions can be combined with the addition rule to answer the question.
   - **(c)** There are N factorial, $N!$, ways to arrange N different objects. This is called the number of *permutations* of N objects.
   - **(d)** There are $Y! \times R!$ ways to arrange Y different yellow objects (balls) and R red balls in a previously specified color arrangement.
   - **(e)** The total number of ways to arrange N objects ($N!$) is equal to the product of the number of different color sequences and the number of different arrangements for each color sequence ($Y! \times R!$).
   - **(f)** Thus, the number of different color sequences is the quotient of the total number of different arrangements and the number of different arrangements for each color sequence. This is called the number of *combinations* of N things taken Y at a time. This is the number of different ways to draw Y yellow and R red balls from an urn: $N!/(Y! \times R!) = (Y + R)!/(Y! \times R!)$.
   - **(g)** Assuming that p is the probability of drawing a yellow ball on a single draw, and $(1 - p)$ is the probability of drawing a red ball on a single draw, the probability of each particular way of drawing Y yellow and R red balls is: $p^Y \times (1 - p)^R$.
   - **(h)** Thus, if one draws N times from an urn containing a proportion, p, of yellow balls and $(1 - p)$ of red balls, and balls are replaced after their color is noted, then the probability of getting R red and Y yellow balls is $(Y + R)!/(Y! \times R!) \times p^Y \times (1 - p)^R$.

2. The *binomial distribution* describes a set of related probabilities calculated with the binomial formula.
   - **(a)** If one draws from an urn—with only yellow and red balls—N times, there are $N + 1$ binomial events: getting zero yellow balls (and N red balls), getting one yellow ball (and $N - 1$ red balls), and so on.
   - **(b)** The binomial distribution is the set of probabilities for each of these $N + 1$ binomial events.
   - **(c)** The most probable binomial event is that event with the same proportion of yellow balls in the sample as there are yellow balls in the urn.
   - **(d)** The binomial distribution functions like an assignment of probabilities to simple events.

3. Bernoulli's theorem was presented without proof.
   (a) Bernoulli considers the probability of getting a proportion of yellow balls in one's sample "near" the proportion of yellow balls in the urn.
   (b) Bernoulli asks for the probability of getting a proportion of yellow balls in the sample (Y/N) near (ε) the actual proportion of yellow balls in the urn (p): $P[(p - \varepsilon) \leq Y/N \leq (p + \varepsilon)]$.
   (c) The probability of getting a result "near" the proportion of yellow balls in the urn increases as the number of draws from the urn increases.
   (d) Bernoulli's theorem shows that this probability increases to 1 as the number of balls drawn, N, increases indefinitely.
   (e) It can also be shown that for any ε and any P, there is a T such that for any number of trials, N, larger than T: $P[(p - \varepsilon) \leq Y/N \leq (p + \varepsilon)] \geq P$.

4. Probability density functions and, in particular, the normal curve were introduced.
   (a) Each normal curve is bell shaped and symmetric around the single center peak (mean) of the curve.
   (b) Normal curves can differ from each other in two respects: They can be centered in different places, and they can be more or less steep.
   (c) Two parameters are used to pick a unique normal curve from the family of normal curves. The *mean*, μ, specifies where the peak of the normal curve lies. The *standard deviation*, σ, specifies how steep the curve is.
   (d) Each normal curve is a *probability density function*. These are functions used to describe probabilities when there are an infinite number of possible outcomes.
   (e) To use probability density functions to calculate probabilities, one calculates the area under the density function where the outcomes of interest lie.

5. The central limit theorem was presented without proof.
   (a) Suppose that one draws N times from an urn with proportion p of yellow balls. The normal curve can be used to approximate the binomial distribution associated with these N draws from the urn.
   (b) In particular, one uses the normal curve with the following mean, $\mu = N \times p$, and standard deviation, $\sigma = \sqrt{N \times p \times (1 - p)}$. This approximation is good for $N = 30$ and gets better as N gets larger.

10. REFERENCES

Material covered in this chapter is part of most good introductions to probability theory; see the references for Chapters 6 and 7.

11. PROBLEMS

1. How many different ways are there to arrange nine different objects in a row?
2. Suppose that three of the nine objects from Problem 1 are red and six are black. How many different red–black color sequences can one make with these nine objects?
3. How many different ways are there to arrange 25 different objects in a row?

4. Suppose that 14 of the objects from Problem 3 are yellow and 11 are red. How many different ways are there to arrange them in the following color order:

<*y*, *r*, *y*, *r*, *y*, *r*, *y*, *r*, *y*, *r*, *y*, *r*, *y*, *r*, *y*, *r*, *y*, *r*, *y*, *r*, *y*, *r*, *y*, *y*, *y*>?

5. How many different color sequences are there with 14 yellow and 11 red colors in the row?

6. Suppose that the probability of a baby being a boy is 1/2 and that different births are probabilistically independent of each other.
   (a) What is the probability that no more than one out of five children in a family will be a girl?
   (b) What is the probability that all 10 children in one family will be girls?
   (c) What is the probability that half of the 10 children in one family will be girls?
   (d) What is the probability that four, five, or six of the children in one family will be girls?

7. Suppose that you draw 20 balls from an urn with 40 yellow balls and 80 red balls. Each ball has the same chance of being drawn and balls are replaced after each draw.
   (a) What is the probability of drawing 10 balls of each color?
   (b) What is the most probable of the 21 different binomial events that could result from these 20 draws?

8. Suppose that the "next room" contains 1,200 urns; 800 of them contain 75 orange balls and 25 green balls; 400 of them contain 90 orange balls and 10 green balls. One of these urns is brought to you; it was picked at random from all the urns in the room.
   (a) What is the probability that the urn has 75 orange balls in it?
   (b) Suppose that you draw one ball and it turns out to be green. Given this evidence, what is the probability that the urn has 75 orange balls in it?
   (c) Suppose that you draw 49 more balls from the urn, replacing them after noting their color. In total you see 43 orange balls and 7 green balls. Given all of this evidence, what is the probability that the urn has 75 orange balls in it?
   (d) Given all of the evidence in part (c), what is the probability that the urn has 90 orange balls in it?

9. Suppose that you draw six balls from an urn with 40 yellow balls and 80 red balls. Each ball has the same chance of being drawn and balls are replaced after each draw.
   (a) How many different binomial events could result from these six draws?
   (b) What are they?
   (c) Calculate the probability for each one.
   (d) Graph the probabilities from part (c).
   (e) What is the most probable binomial event in this experiment?

10. Suppose that you draw 50 times from an urn with 40 yellow balls and 80 red balls.
    (a) What normal distribution approximates the binomial distribution for this case?
    (b) What number of yellow balls drawn occurs at the mean of this distribution?
    (c) Determine which binomial events fall within two standard deviations of the mean.

11. Suppose that you draw some number of times, N, from an urn with 40 yellow balls and 80 red balls; let Y be the number of yellow balls drawn. If $\varepsilon = 1/10$ and $P = 0.95$, how big must N be before

$$P\left[\left(\frac{1}{3} - \varepsilon\right) \leq \frac{Y}{N} \leq \left(\frac{1}{3} + \varepsilon\right)\right] \geq P?$$

12. Suppose that you draw 2,000 times (replacing balls after each draw) from an urn with 4/10 yellow balls in it.

(a) What is the most likely number of yellow balls to be in your sample?

(b) What is the mean and standard deviation of the appropriate normal curve for approximating this binomial distribution?

(c) What are the limits, three standard deviations to either side of the mean, outside of which it would be very unlikely to get a result?

(d) Within what percentage of the sample size of 2,000 "ought" one—in the sense of part (c)—get a result?

CHAPTER
10

CONFIDENCE INTERVALS AND INFERENCE

1. POLLS AND URNS

In Chapter 2 we saw that we can get accurate information about a large population by looking at a small sample of units from the population. We defined two properties, bias and precision, which together gave us our definition of accuracy: An accurate method of sampling is unbiased and precise. We saw that randomly selecting units from our population can be accurate, and furthermore, the precision of the method depends on the absolute number of units sampled, not on the relative proportion of the population sampled. Random sampling introduces probability. With the help of some probability mathematics, we can justify precise versions of these claims.

The overall idea behind the theoretical justification for polling arguments can be put nicely in the aphorism: "The world is an urn filled with balls of various different colors." We have seen several uses of urns already. And much of the justification for polling arguments is a particular application of the urn problems we have already run across.

The basic problem is this: We want to know the relative proportions of the different colors of balls inside a particular urn. The sure-fire way to find out is to look at each ball and note its color. But in many cases we cannot do this; we can only look at a small sample of balls. Given the balls we observe, we hope to estimate the true proportions of colors in the urn.

This urn problem is the central metaphor for survey sampling. The balls in the urn constitute the *population*. The individual balls represent *units*. Ball colors represent different values of the *variable* of interest. Those balls that we look at correspond to our *sample*. The problem for the pollster is to make a good inference about all the balls in the urn—the population—on the basis of information from a small number of balls that have been withdrawn and examined—the sample. If we want to know what proportion of the labor force is employed, for example, we imagine an urn filled with balls that can be one of two different colors—"yellow" for those who are employed and "blue" for those who are not. Our question, then, is what proportion of all the balls in the urn are yellow? If the variable has more than two values, we imagine an urn filled with balls of as many different colors as values of the variable. Here, for simplicity, we will deal with balls that might be one of two colors.

The problem is to estimate the proportions of the different colors of balls by looking at a small sample of balls. The urn might contain 100,000,000 balls; each ball in the urn might be either yellow or blue. Some proportion, call it p, of these balls is yellow. We want to look at some number of balls in the urn, call it N (2,000 perhaps), and estimate the value of p. The N balls we withdraw constitute our *sample*. Suppose that Y balls (1,232 perhaps) in the sample are yellow. The proportion of yellow balls in our sample, Y/N, is the *sample statistic* with which we hope to estimate the *population parameter*, p. If Y was 1,232, then $Y/N = 1{,}232/2{,}000 = 61.6\%$ of our sample was yellow. We want to estimate that p is approximately 61.6%. Two problems with this inference present themselves: How approximate is our estimate, and how good is this approximation?

The advantage of thinking about polling in terms of urns is that it is easy to understand random sampling. Each ball in the urn is given a predetermined chance of being in the sample. In the simplest case, each ball has the same chance of being in the sample. We can use probability mathematics to help us, first, show that random sampling is not *biased*, and second, measure how *precise* random sampling can be.

2. BIAS

If our method of sampling is *unbiased*, sample statistic values should not systematically tend to be larger or systematically tend to be smaller than the population parameter. We can use the *expected value* (Chapter 8, Section 5) of the sample statistic to render this idea precisely. The expected value of the sample statistic is the sum of the products of the value of the sample statistic and the probability of that value occurring—for every possible sample statistic value. We take this weighted average of all the possible statistic values as our measure of bias. If the average is equal to the true population parameter, the method is not biased: on average, it does not systematically favor values larger than the true value or systematically favor values smaller than the true value.

Consider an example. Suppose that we randomly select three balls from an urn with blue and yellow balls. Our sample statistic, the proportion of yellow balls in the sample, $Y/3$, can have only four different values 0/3, 1/3, 2/3, and 3/3. Suppose that 1/4 of the balls in the urn are yellow. The expected value of our sample statistic is the sum of four products:

$$\underbrace{\frac{0}{3}}_{} \times \left[\frac{3!}{0! \times 3!} \times \left(\frac{1}{4}\right)^0 \times \left(\frac{3}{4}\right)^3\right]$$
$$+ \frac{1}{3} \times \left[\frac{3!}{1! \times 2!} \times \left(\frac{1}{4}\right)^1 \times \left(\frac{3}{4}\right)^2\right]$$
$$+ \frac{2}{3} \times \left[\frac{3!}{2! \times 1!} \times \left(\frac{1}{4}\right)^2 \times \left(\frac{3}{4}\right)^1\right]$$
$$+ \frac{3}{3} \times \left[\frac{3!}{3! \times 0!} \times \left(\frac{1}{4}\right)^3 \times \left(\frac{3}{4}\right)^0\right]$$

⇑ sample statistic value ⇑ sample statistic probability

The first term in each of these products is the value of the statistic, $Y/3$. The second term is the probability of getting this value. By taking the product of all of these pairs and summing all of the products we compute the expected value of the statistic. Doing all of the arithmetic, we find that the expected statistic value is equal to the true population parameter, 1/4: $0 + 9/64 + 6/64 + 1/64 = 16/64 = 1/4$.

It is common to write "$E[(Y/3)|(p = 1/4)] = 1/4$" for such statements about expectations. The form of this expectation notation is similar to the form of probability notation except that we find expectation values instead of probability values. The statement is read: "the expected value of the statistic $Y/3$, given the true population parameter is 1/4, is 1/4."

Here we assumed that we knew the value of the population parameter, $p = 1/4$. With survey sampling we cannot make this assumption. But we still can show that *whatever the value of p,* the expected value of $Y/3$ is equal to p. This requires a bit of algebra, as shown in Table 10.1. When we draw three balls from the urn, $N = 3$, for any value of the population parameter, p, the expected value of $Y/3$ is equal to p. We have shown that Y/N is an unbiased statistic in the special case where $N = 3$.

TABLE 10.1

Y/3	P[(Y/3)]	Y/3 × P[(Y/3)]
0	$3!/(0! \times 3!) \times p^0 \times (1-p)^3$	0
1/3	$3!/(1! \times 2!) \times p^1 \times (1-p)^2$	$p - 2p^2 + p^3$
2/3	$3!/(2! \times 1!) \times p^2 \times (1-p)^1$	$2p^2 - 2p^3$
1	$3!/(3! \times 0!) \times p^3 \times (1-p)^0$	p^3
	Total:	p

This is true for any value of N. The expected value of Y/N *for any* value of N is equal to p, whatever the value of p. We can skip the detailed proof of this, but it should be clear what the proof establishes:

$$\text{For all values of } p \text{ and all values of } N,\ \text{E}[(Y/N)] = p.$$

An *unbiased* method of sampling is one where the expected value of the sampling statistic is equal to the true population parameter no matter what value p has. When we randomly sample a population, we are assured that the expected value of Y/N is equal to the true population parameter, p. Using the sample proportion, Y/N, from a random sample is an unbiased method to estimate p.

3. PRECISION: CALCULATING CONFIDENCE INTERVALS

Precision measures the degree to which sample statistic values clump together. Since using the sample proportion from a random sample is unbiased, we can measure precision by the degree to which sample statistic values clump together near p. What counts as *near* is somewhat arbitrary. Suppose, for example, that "near" is within 1/10 of p; then we can measure precision in terms of the probability that all the sample statistic values, Y/N, are within 1/10 of p:

$$\text{P}\left[\left(\frac{Y}{N} - \frac{1}{10}\right) \leq p \leq \left(\frac{Y}{N} + \frac{1}{10}\right)\right].$$

If this probability is high, we know that sample statistic results will tend to be "near"—within 1/10 of—p. We need not count 1/10 as "near." We could pick any small "*margin of error*," and call it ε. We measure precision, then, in terms of the probability—the *level of confidence*—that a given method of sampling will produce results within the specified margin of error:

$$\text{P}\left[\left(\frac{Y}{N} - \varepsilon\right) \leq p \leq \left(\frac{Y}{N} + \varepsilon\right)\right] = \text{level of confidence.}$$

Usually, a set *level of confidence* is sought, and a large enough number of units is sampled to provide a useful margin of error. Random sampling allows us to calculate such probabilities, and this is how random sampling gives us control over the precision of our method of sampling.

We can begin by assuming that we know the value for p. In general, of course, we do not know p, but the mathematics are similar enough to make this simpler case a useful trial run. Furthermore, even in the simpler case where we know p, we demonstrate a striking fact about random sampling: The precision of random sampling depends on the *number* of balls sampled, not on the *percentage* of balls sampled.

Suppose that we draw 16 balls—replacing each after drawing it—from an urn where 1/2 of the balls are yellow and 1/2 are blue. In general, we want to compute probability that the true population parameter, p, is within a margin of error of our sample statistic:

$$\mathrm{P}\left[\left(\frac{Y}{16}-\varepsilon\right)\leq p\leq\left(\frac{Y}{16}+\varepsilon\right)\right].$$

With a little algebra, we can turn these probabilities into relatively straightforward binomial probabilities. Notice that

$$\left(\frac{Y}{16}-\varepsilon\right)\leq p \text{ if and only if } \frac{Y}{16}\leq(p+\varepsilon)$$

Similarly, $p\leq(Y/16+\varepsilon)$ if and only if $(p-\varepsilon)\leq(Y/16)$. Together, we have shown that

$$\left(\frac{Y}{16}-\varepsilon\right)\leq p\leq\left(\frac{Y}{16}+\varepsilon\right) \text{ if and only if } (p-\varepsilon)\leq\frac{Y}{16}\leq(p+\varepsilon).$$

Since the statements are algebraically equivalent, their probabilities must be the same:

$$\mathrm{P}\left[\left(\frac{Y}{16}-\varepsilon\right)\leq p\leq\left(\frac{Y}{16}+\varepsilon\right)\right]=\mathrm{P}\left[(p-\varepsilon)\leq\frac{Y}{16}\leq(p+\varepsilon)\right].$$

If we assume that $p=1/2$ and $\varepsilon=1/8$ (for instance), we have a straightforward computation with binomial probabilities:

$$\mathrm{P}\left[\left(\frac{1}{2}-\frac{1}{8}\right)\leq\frac{Y}{16}\leq\left(\frac{1}{2}+\frac{1}{8}\right)\right]=\mathrm{P}\left(\frac{3}{8}\leq\frac{Y}{16}\leq\frac{5}{8}\right)=\mathrm{P}(6\leq Y\leq 10).$$

To calculate this probability, we must find the probability of getting either 6 yellow (and 10 blue) balls, or 7 yellow (and 9 blue) balls, and so on. We must calculate five different binomial probabilities. The probability of drawing 6 yellow balls from an urn that contains 1/2 yellow balls is

$$\frac{(6+10)!}{6!\times 10!}\times\left(\frac{1}{2}\right)^{6}\times\left(\frac{1}{2}\right)^{10}\approx 0.12.$$

We can similarly compute the probability for the other four events. The five probabilities we calculate are 0.12, 0.17, 0.20, 0.17, and 0.12. Adding these five values up gives a total probability of 0.78.

We can do a similar calculation when we draw 32 balls from the urn. In order to be within 1/8 of 1/2, when drawing 32 balls, we must get 12, 13, 14, 15, 16, 17, 18, 19, or 20 yellow balls. There are 9 binomial calculations to do. When we do them and add up the results we find that the probability of being within 1/8 of 1/2 is 0.89. It is greater than our smaller 16 balls sample. The probability of being within 1/8 of 1/2 when we draw 64 balls is 0.97—larger still.

All of these computations apply to the equivalent statements about the precision of sampling:

$$P\left[\left(\frac{Y}{16}-\frac{1}{8}\right) \leq p\left(=\frac{1}{2}\right) \leq \left(\frac{Y}{16}+\frac{1}{8}\right)\right] = 0.78;$$

$$P\left[\left(\frac{Y}{32}-\frac{1}{8}\right) \leq p\left(=\frac{1}{2}\right) \leq \left(\frac{Y}{32}+\frac{1}{8}\right)\right] = 0.89;$$

$$P\left[\left(\frac{Y}{64}-\frac{1}{8}\right) \leq p\left(=\frac{1}{2}\right) \leq \left(\frac{Y}{64}+\frac{1}{8}\right)\right] = 0.97.$$

If we did not know the value of p, we would have just the kind of probability statements we want to measure the precision of our method of sampling. For a margin of error of 1/8, when 64 balls are sampled, the level of confidence is 0.97. That is, there is a probability of 97% that the population parameter will be within 1/8 of the sample statistic.

Despite the fact that these calculations presuppose that we know the value of the true population parameter, they hold one important moral about survey sampling. At no point did we need to know how many balls were in the urn. We calculated these probabilities in terms of the *number* of balls drawn from the urn, not the *proportion* of the total balls in the urn drawn. The precision of a random sample does not depend on the proportion (of the total population) in the sample; it depends on the absolute number of balls in the sample. This is striking because we can get precise results looking at a tiny fraction of the total population. As far as precision is concerned, a sample with 2,000 units from a population with 200,000,000 units is just as precise as a sample with 2,000 units from a population with 200,000.

We can now turn to the case where we do not know the value of the population parameter, p, and we wish to estimate its value from the sample statistic, Y/N. We wish to determine how precise our estimate is. To do this we exploit the fact that binomial probabilities can be well approximated by the normal distribution.

Recall how to use the normal distribution to approximate binomial probabilities. Each normal curve is specified by two *parameters*, the mean, μ—which tells us where the center of the curve is—and the standard deviation, σ—which tells us how "spread out" the curve is. We use the number of draws, N and the true probability, p, to set values for the mean, μ, and standard deviation, σ:

Mean: $\mu = N \times p.$

Standard deviation: $\sigma = \sqrt{N \times p \times (1-p)}.$

For any normal distribution, the probability of an observation, Y, being within two standard deviations of the mean is 0.95:

$$P[(\mu - 2\sigma) \leq Y \leq (\mu + 2\sigma)] = 0.95.$$

The specific normal distribution involved does not matter.

For example, suppose that $N = 50$ and $p = 1/3$. We use a normal distribution with mean $16\frac{2}{3}$, and standard deviation $3\frac{1}{3}$, to approximate the binomial probabilities.

$$\text{Mean:} \qquad \mu = N \times p = 50 \times \frac{1}{3} = 16\frac{2}{3};$$

$$\text{Standard deviation:} \qquad \sigma = \sqrt{N \times p \times (1-p)} = \sqrt{50 \times \frac{1}{3} \times \frac{2}{3}}$$

$$= 3\frac{1}{3}.$$

We can find, for example, that the probability of drawing between 10 and 23 yellow balls from this urn is 0.95:

$$\begin{aligned} &\mathrm{P}[(\mu - 2\sigma) \leq Y \leq (\mu + 2\sigma)] \\ &\qquad = \mathrm{P}[(Np - 2\sqrt{Np(1-p)}) \leq Y \leq (Np + 2\sqrt{Np(1-p)})] \\ &\qquad = \mathrm{P}\left[\left(16\frac{2}{3} - 6\frac{2}{3}\right) \leq Y \leq \left(16\frac{2}{3} + 6\frac{2}{3}\right)\right] = \mathrm{P}\left(10 \leq Y \leq 23\frac{1}{3}\right) \\ &\qquad = 0.95. \end{aligned}$$

Even if we do not know what the value of p is, survey sampling is like conducting N binomial trials. We can approximate these binomial probabilities with a normal distribution with mean, $\mu = Np$, and standard deviation, $\sigma = \sqrt{Np(1-p)}$. Even when we do not know the value of p, we know that for any value of p:

$$\begin{aligned} &\mathrm{P}[(\mu - 2\sigma) \leq Y \leq (\mu + 2\sigma)] \\ &\qquad = \mathrm{P}[(Np - 2\sqrt{Np(1-p)}) \leq Y \leq (Np + 2\sqrt{Np(1-p)})] = 0.95. \end{aligned}$$

We can use this probability statement to get a 95% confidence level probability statement about the sample survey when we do not know p.

First, we can invert the inequalities just as we did when we supposed we knew the value of p:

$$[(\mu - 2\sigma) \leq Y \leq (\mu + 2\sigma)] \text{ if and only if } [(Y - 2\sigma) \leq \mu \leq (Y + 2\sigma)].$$

Consequently, the probabilities of these inequalities must be the same. We can express μ and σ appropriately in terms of p and N to use the normal distribution to approximate the binomial distribution:

$$\begin{aligned} &\mathrm{P}[(Y - 2\sigma) \leq \mu \leq (Y + 2\sigma)] \\ &\qquad = \mathrm{P}[(Y - 2\sqrt{Np(1-p)}) \leq Np \leq (Y + 2\sqrt{Np(1-p)})]. \end{aligned}$$

Finally, we can divide everything by N to give what is just about the right kind of probability statement about precision:

$$\mathrm{P}\left[\left(\frac{Y}{N} - \frac{2\sqrt{Np(1-p)}}{N}\right) \leq p \leq \left(\frac{Y}{N} + \frac{2\sqrt{Np(1-p)}}{N}\right)\right] = 0.95.$$

Here we have a statement that there is a high probability—95%—that the population parameter—p—will be within a margin of error—$2\sqrt{Np(1-p)}/N$—of the sample statistic.

There is a problem. The size of this margin of error, $2\sqrt{Np(1-p)}/N$, depends on p. It seems that we must know p to estimate p. Although in a certain sense this is true, we can use the largest value that the expression for the margin of error can take as a conservative estimate for the margin of error. Consider Table 10.2. $2\sqrt{Np(1-p)}/N$ is largest when $p = 1/2$. When $p = 1/2$,

$$\frac{2\sqrt{Np(1-p)}}{N} = \frac{2\sqrt{N(1/2)^2}}{N} = \frac{\sqrt{N}}{N}.$$

For moderately larger values of N, $\sqrt{N}/N$ is fairly small. When the sample size is 2,000 we get an interval of $\pm$ 2.2%: $\sqrt{2{,}000}/2{,}000 \approx 2.2\%$. When the sample size is smaller, 500, we get a margin of error of $\pm$ 4.5%: $\sqrt{500}/500 \approx 4.5\%$.

Suppose, for example, that $N = 2{,}000$. We can make the following conservative but useful confidence interval probability statement:

$$\mathrm{P}\left[\left(\left(\frac{Y}{2{,}000} - 0.022\right) \leq p \leq \left(\frac{Y}{2{,}000} + 0.022\right)\right)\right] \geq 0.95.$$

This statement is conservative because we know that the margin of error can be no larger than 0.022; it might be smaller if p is not near 0.5. It is useful because $\pm$ 2.2% is small enough to inform us about the value of p. Such a probability statement is known as a *95% confidence interval* for p.

The level of confidence increases if we increase the margin of error—at a fixed sample size For example, we can increase the level of confidence to 99%, by taking

TABLE 10.2

Value of N	Value of p										
	0.0	**0.1**	**0.2**	**0.3**	**0.4**	**0.5**	**0.6**	**0.7**	**0.8**	**0.9**	**1.0**
100	0.0	0.060	0.080	0.092	0.098	0.100	0.098	0.092	0.080	0.060	0.0
500	0.0	0.027	0.036	0.041	0.044	0.045	0.044	0.041	0.036	0.027	0.0
1,000	0.0	0.019	0.025	0.029	0.031	0.032	0.031	0.029	0.025	0.019	0.0
1,500	0.0	0.015	0.020	0.024	0.025	0.026	0.025	0.024	0.020	0.015	0.0
2,000	0.0	0.013	0.018	0.020	0.022	0.022	0.022	0.020	0.018	0.013	0.0
5,000	0.0	0.008	0.011	0.013	0.014	0.014	0.014	0.013	0.011	0.008	0.0
10,000	0.0	0.006	0.008	0.009	0.009	0.010	0.009	0.009	0.008	0.006	0.0

$$\frac{2\sqrt{Np(1-p)}}{N}$$

a margin of error based on plus or minus three standard deviations:

$$\begin{aligned}P[(\mu - 3\sigma) \leq Y \leq (\mu + 3\sigma)] \\ &= P[(Np - 3\sqrt{Np(1-p)}) \leq Y \leq (Np + 3\sqrt{Np(1-p)})] \\ &= P\left[\left(\frac{Y}{N} - 3\sqrt{Np(1-p)}/N\right) \leq p \leq \left(\frac{Y}{N} + 3\sqrt{Np(1-p)}/N\right)\right] = 0.99.\end{aligned}$$

Again we can get conservative and useful confidence interval statements. When $N = 2{,}000$, the largest $3\sqrt{Np(1-p)}/N$ can be is $0.034 = 3.4\%$:

$$P\left[\left(\left(\frac{Y}{2{,}000} - 0.034\right) \leq p \leq \left(\frac{Y}{2{,}000} + 0.034\right)\right)\right] \geq 0.99.$$

When $N = 500$, we get an interval of $\pm 6.7\%$. Thus 99% of the time when we randomly sample 500 of the nation's 90,000,000 voters, we should get a result, *Y/500*, within 6.7% of the true population parameter, p.

4. STRUCTURE OF THE ARGUMENT

Here is a method to accurately estimate the value of a population parameter from the value of a sample statistic, computed from what can be a relatively small sample. While polling studies are common, this method is used in a much wider variety of cases. Here we examine the basic structure of the argument in order to appreciate the generality of the method, and to direct our critical examination of this method.

We start with a premise that establishes the relationship between survey sampling and mathematical probability.

> *Premise 1:* We can well describe the outcome of polling in terms of binomial urn-type probabilities.

Among other things, this requires that draws from the urn be both random—each ball has the same chance of being drawn—and independent—the outcome of one draw has no effect on the probabilities of subsequent draws. By drawing a certain number, N, of balls from the urn we wish to estimate the proportion, p, of a particular color (yellow, say) of balls in the urn.

Premise 1 tells us that we can use probability theory to discuss survey sampling. In fact, this premise is not met in practice. It is important to determine the manner and degree to which polling studies deviate from a formal binomial model (see Chapter 2, Sections 6–8). In general, there is always a serious issue of whether the statistical/probabilistic model used to describe a particular "real-life" situation is adequate. We do not concern ourselves here with these issues. We do concern ourselves with the specific details of how these statistical/probabilistic models can help us make inductive inferences.

We take information from our sample to learn about the population. But we do not take all the information in the sample. The sample statistic, *Y/N*, contains the information we keep from the sample. This is our second premise:

> *Premise 2:* The ratio, Y/N, of the number of balls, Y, of a specified color (e.g., yellow) to the total number, N, in our sample provides the information with which we can make an inference about the population parameter, p.

We do not worry about the order in which balls are drawn, for example. This premise may not seem important at this stage. It is quite natural to use Y/N to estimate p. p is the proportion in the whole population that we are concerned with, and Y/N is the corresponding proportion in our sample. Natural or not, there is some need to say why it is right to use this statistic. This is particularly evident in cases where several "natural" statistics suggest themselves.

We describe the accuracy of our method of sampling in terms of three central concepts, bias, margin of error, and level of confidence. Our method is accurate in the sense given by the following two premises:

> *Premise 3:* The method is not biased: $E(Y/N) = p$.
>
> *Premise 4:* Random sampling gives us control over the margin of error and level of confidence:
>
> $$P\left[\left(\frac{Y}{N} - \varepsilon\right) \leq p \leq \left(\frac{Y}{N} + \varepsilon\right)\right] = \text{level of confidence.}$$

These two premises establish the concept of accuracy in technical terms. We want an unbiased method—understood in terms of mathematical expectation—which allows control over precision through probability statements such as $P[(Y/N - \varepsilon) \leq p \leq (Y/N + \varepsilon)]$. This way of understanding accuracy emphasizes the "long-run" characteristics of the method. A specific sample may overestimate the truth, but *on average*, "applying the method repeatedly," the method should not overestimate (or underestimate) the truth. A specific sample may produce results that fall outside the margin of error, ε, but this should only occur rarely given a high level of confidence probability.

There is much controversy over the appropriateness of such a concept of accuracy. It has an impact on what specific conclusion this method of inference allows one to draw (see below). Some urge that this "method" concept of accuracy is fully adequate. But others urge that we need a concept of accuracy that applies to specific sample results, and this requires additional specific features of survey sampling. This controversy is discussed below and in Chapter 13. Others reject this approach to inference entirely (see Chapter 11).

There are several mathematical tricks which then put the argument in its final detailed form:

> *Premise 5:* We can approximate a binomial distribution, with N draws and probability p, with a normal distribution with mean, $\mu = Np$, and standard

deviation, $\sigma = \sqrt{Np(1-p)}$. N must be large—30 or greater—and p must be moderate—$0.1 \leq p \leq 0.9$.

Premise 6: For any normal distribution:

$$P[(Np - 2\sqrt{Np(1-p)}) \leq Y \leq (Np + 2\sqrt{Np(1-p)})]$$

$$= P\left[\left(\frac{Y}{N} - \frac{2\sqrt{Np(1-p)}}{N}\right) \leq p \leq \left(\frac{Y}{N} + \frac{2\sqrt{Np(1-p)}}{N}\right)\right]$$

$$= 0.95.$$

Premise 7: No matter what the value of p, for moderate values of N, $2\sqrt{Np(1-p)}/N$ is small enough to allow for useful confidence interval statements.

These premises assert specific mathematical or probabilistic facts. We need not worry about algebra or the theory of probability here. We need to be aware of the constraints these mathematical relationships impose on sampling. Premise 5, for instance, requires a moderate value of p; we cannot use the normal approximation to binomial probabilities when p has an extreme value—near 0 or near 1. Premise 7 requires a moderately large value of N for the margin of error to be small enough to be useful. Bearing these prerequisites in mind, we should focus on the other premises that establish the appropriateness of probabilities in survey sampling in the first place.

It is a little tricky to state the conclusion. We can directly, without any serious misunderstanding, infer the following:

$$P\left[\left(\frac{Y}{N} - \frac{\sqrt{N}}{N}\right) \leq p \leq \left(\frac{Y}{N} + \frac{\sqrt{N}}{N}\right)\right] \geq 0.95.$$

But we want to be able to make inference in particular cases. Suppose, for example, that we found that 311 couples from a random sample of 1,500 couples were childless. We would compute the following confidence interval for the proportion of childless couples in the population—p:

$$\left(\frac{311}{1{,}500} - \frac{\sqrt{1{,}500}}{1{,}500}\right) \leq p \leq \left(\frac{311}{1{,}500} + \frac{\sqrt{1{,}500}}{1{,}500}\right) \equiv (0.18 \leq p \leq 0.23).$$

But what should be made of this interval? p is some *fixed* constant proportion; p is either in the interval or is not in the interval; either $0.18 \leq p \leq 0.23$ or not. Does the evidence from our sample give us *reason* to think that p is in this interval? Some researchers urge that we should infer that there is at least a 95% probability (the level of confidence) that p is in this interval, $P(0.18 \leq p \leq 0.23) \geq 0.95$. Others claim that such probability statements make no sense; either p is in the interval or not and there is no probability about it. This question is one aspect of the question raised above about the appropriateness of the concept of accuracy used to develop this method of inference.

5. ANOTHER URN PROBLEM

To better appreciate the importance of Premises 2, 3, and 4, we can examine another urn problem. Two main facts emerge from this example. First, when different statistics are used, different interval estimates can result. Premise 2 is important; we need a reason to choose the statistic we choose. Second, interval estimate probabilities apply before the sample is drawn. Premises 3 and 4 are important; accuracy is a feature of the *method* of sampling, not of *specific samples*. To make a further claim about a specific sample result, further claims need to be established about the probabilistic context involved.

Suppose that we randomly draw balls (replacing each ball after it is drawn) from an urn containing exactly L different balls, numbered 1 to L. There might be only one ball in the urn ($L = 1$), or there might be more balls in the urn. By noting the numbers on the balls drawn, we wish to estimate how many balls are in the urn, L.

We can use the number of the highest-numbered ball drawn from the urn to construct one kind of confidence interval estimate for L. Suppose that we draw twice from this urn. We calculate the probability that the highest-numbered ball drawn, call it $\mathbf{X}_{\text{max}}$, is numbered higher than some number, R (less than L):

$$P(R \leq \mathbf{X}_{\text{max}} \leq L).$$

The probability of drawing each different pair of balls from the urn is $(1/L^2)$. We can graph these possible outcomes where the $\mathbf{X}_1$-axis represents the result of the first draw, and the $\mathbf{X}_2$-axis represents the result of the second draw (Figure 10.1). The outside corner of the square—points between R and L—contains all of the points

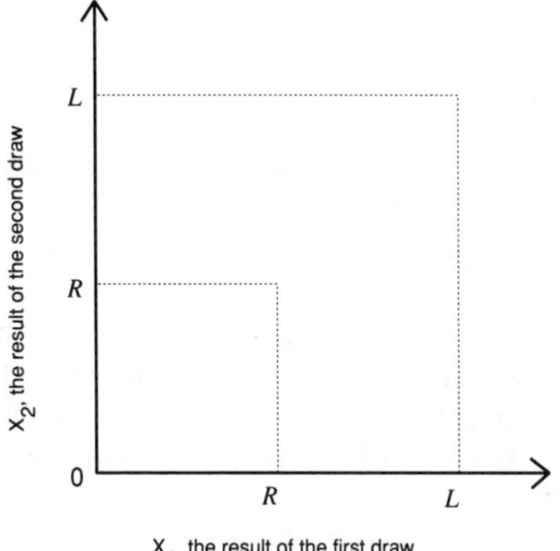

Figure 10.1

where the highest number drawn, $\mathbf{X}_{max}$, is higher than R. Since each pair of outcomes has probability $(1/L^2)$, the probability of the highest number drawn being higher than R is equal to the area of the outside corner of the square, where units are chosen so that the area of the whole square is 1: $(L^2 - R^2)(1/L^2)$.

We can express R in terms of L. There is some positive number less than 1, call it a, such that $R = (a \times L)$. We have just determined that

$$P(R \leq \mathbf{X}_{max} \leq L) = P[(a \times L) \leq \mathbf{X}_{max} \leq L] = (L^2 - R^2)\,\frac{1}{L^2}$$

$$= [L^2 - (a \times L)^2]\,\frac{1}{L^2} = 1 - a^2.$$

Now we can construct a confidence interval probability for L:

$$P[(a \times L) \leq \mathbf{X}_{max} \leq L] = P\left[\mathbf{X}_{max} \leq L \leq \frac{\mathbf{X}_{max}}{a}\right] = 1 - a^2.$$

If we wanted a 95% confidence interval for L, we would pick $(1 - a^2) = 95\%$, or $a \approx 0.22$. We have

$$P[(0.22 \times L) \leq \mathbf{X}_{max} \leq L] = P\left[\mathbf{X}_{max} \leq L \leq \frac{\mathbf{X}_{max}}{0.22}\right] = 1 - a^2 = 0.95.$$

If, for example, the two balls drawn were numbers 73 and 100, $\mathbf{X}_{max} = 100$, and we might infer that L is larger than 100 and smaller than 454 (= 100/0.22).

By similar reasoning, we can produce a confidence interval for L when we draw 16 times from the urn:

$$P[(a \times L) \leq \mathbf{X}_{max} \leq L] = P\left[\mathbf{X}_{max} \leq L \leq \frac{\mathbf{X}_{max}}{a}\right] = 1 - a^{16}.$$

When $(1 - a^{16}) = 95\%$, $a \approx 0.83$. Suppose that we obtained the following 16 observations (arranged in order):

17, 89, 130, 241, 379, 493, 533, 614,
707, 825, 901, 986, 1,071, 1,161, 1,162, 1,411.

$\mathbf{X}_{max}$ is 1,411, so we might infer that $(1{,}411 \leq L \leq 1{,}411/0.83) \equiv (1{,}411 \leq L \leq 1{,}700)$.

This is one way to construct confidence interval probabilities for L. Here is another. Instead of using the number of the highest-numbered ball drawn, $\mathbf{X}_{max}$, to construct a confidence interval, we can use the mean, $\overline{\mathbf{X}}$, of all the numbers on the balls drawn. It can be shown that $\overline{\mathbf{X}}$ has an approximately normal distribution, with mean $L/2$ and a standard deviation $L/\sqrt{12N}$. Consider the example above where $N = 16$. The distribution of $\overline{\mathbf{X}}$ is approximately normal with a mean, $\mu = L/2$, and a standard deviation, $\sigma = L/\sqrt{12N} = L/\sqrt{12 \times 16} = L/13.86$. We can then infer that

$$P\left[\left(\frac{L}{2} - 2\left(\frac{L}{13.86}\right)\right) \le \overline{\mathbf{X}} \le \left(\frac{L}{2} + 2\left(\frac{L}{13.86}\right)\right)\right]$$

$$= P[0.36 \times L \le \overline{\mathbf{X}} \le 0.64 \times L] = P[1.56 \times \overline{\mathbf{X}} \le L \le 2.77 \times \overline{\mathbf{X}}] = 0.95.$$

We have another method for making 95% confidence interval estimates for L. The mean of the 16 observations above is $\overline{\mathbf{X}} = 671.38$. So we might infer that

$$(1.56 \times 671.38 \le L \le 2.77 \times 671.38) \equiv (1{,}047 \le L \le 1{,}860).$$

We have two different confidence interval estimates for L, given the same 16 observations: $(1{,}411 \le L \le 1{,}700)$ and $(1{,}047 \le L \le 1{,}860)$. The intervals are different, yet each was produced by a method that yields intervals which have a probability of 95% of including the true value, L. In this case, the $\mathbf{X}_{max}$-interval is a proper part of the $\overline{\mathbf{X}}$-interval. With other samples, the two intervals can be completely different. Suppose we had drawn, for instance, the following 16 balls:

92, 93, 94, 95, 96, 97, 98, 99,
101, 102, 103, 104, 105, 106, 107, 108,

The $\mathbf{X}_{max}$-interval would be $(108 \le L \le 108/0.83) \equiv (108 \le L \le 130)$. The $\overline{\mathbf{X}}$-interval would be $[(1.56 \times 100) \le L \le (2.77 \times 100)] \equiv (156 \le L \le 277)$. Both estimates are based on methods that guarantee a 95% level of confidence, and they disagree entirely.

One point about confidence intervals to be aware of is that different intervals, with the same level of confidence, can result from different methods of estimation. The statistic chosen is very important to the interval produced. There is another strange feature to be aware of.

Suppose we knew in advance that the largest number of balls the urn could contain is 1,500. This does not alter the computations above, but it does reveal a peculiarity in some of the confidence intervals we compute with the $\mathbf{X}_{max}$ statistic. Suppose that we draw twice and the highest numbered ball was 337. We might infer the following 95% confidence interval: $(337 \le L \le 337/0.22) \equiv (337 \le L \le 1{,}531)$. Now consider: If we drew ball 337, we know that $337 \le L$, and furthermore, we know that $L \le 1{,}500 \le 1{,}531$. Thus, we can be *100% certain* that L is in this *95% confidence interval*. Indeed, any time $\mathbf{X}_{max}$ is higher than 330 (= 1,500 × 0.22), the 95% confidence interval that we would compute would be trivial in this way; we could be certain in advance that L would be in the 95% confidence interval.

Confidence level probabilities are probabilities that a given method *will* produce an interval which includes the true value. Without further constraints, confidence level probabilities are not probabilities that a particular interval *does* include the true value. There is a difference between evaluating probabilities before the trial has been conducted and evaluating them after the trial has been conducted. Before the trial we can say that the probability of the interval (that *will* be produced) covering the true value is 95%. For trivial intervals, such as those above, we can also say—after the trial—that the interval certainly covers the true value.

The disturbing fact is that we do run the trial, and we do have the information provided by the trial; we do know which particular outcomes occurred and what 95% confidence interval can be computed based on these outcomes. It seems we should be able to reach whatever conclusion is warranted about the unknown true value based on *all* the information at our disposal. In short, since we make our inferences after the trial, we should base them on after-trial probabilities, not before-trial probabilities. The example above shows, however, that confidence level probabilities are before-trial probabilities.

There are three steps in the construction of a confidence interval estimate. Consider the example above for concreteness: We want to estimate how many balls, L, are in the urn given two draws from the urn. First, we use a statistic to state a probability whose value is independent of the parameter we wish to estimate, L. Thus, for any value of L, the following probability is $1 - a^2$:

$$P(R \leq \mathbf{X}_{\max} \leq L) = P[(a \times L) \leq \mathbf{X}_{\max} \leq L] = 1 - a^2.$$

Second, we invert the inequalities to produce an equivalent probability statement giving bounds for L instead of bounds for $\mathbf{X}_{\max}$:

$$P[(a \times L) \leq \mathbf{X}_{\max} \leq L] = P\left[\mathbf{X}_{\max} \leq L \leq \frac{\mathbf{X}_{\max}}{a}\right] = 1 - a^2.$$

Third, we add values. To get a 95% confidence interval we pick $a = 0.22$. We use the number on the highest-numbered ball—suppose it is 100, for example—to give a value for $\mathbf{X}_{\max}$. The result is a confidence interval for L:

$$100 \leq L \leq 454\left(= \frac{100}{0.22}\right).$$

Unfortunately, we cannot know for certain whether or not L is in this interval.

We know that there is a 95% probability of this method of inference yielding intervals that contain the true value for L. But we would like more. We would like to say something about the particular interval produced. Some statisticians have urged that under certain conditions, we can make an additional inference to

$$P(100 \leq L \leq 454) \geq 0.95.$$

Here the probability statement concerns the specific interval estimate. This probability includes information supplied by the trial—information used to compute the bounds on the inequalities; it is an after-trial probability statement. Other statisticians, most notably Jerzy Neyman, have denied that such an inference is ever possible.

6. NEYMAN'S GAMBIT

In essence, Neyman claimed that we can never reach any conclusions regarding the intervals produced in particular cases. But that is not a tragedy. We *cannot* make any justified *inference* about the true value based on the information provided by the trial. We can, however, *act* as if the confidence interval we compute after the trial is a reasonable interval estimate for the true value. We can justify acting this way by noting that if we base our actions on methods of estimation that have a 95% level of confidence, 95% of the time—on average—our actions will be based on the truth. There is nothing, however, which can ensure that our actions are based on truth on any particular occasion.

Neyman views the application of probability in science broadly as the sequential application of three activities. First, one distinguishes a sequence of trials that seem to produce stable long-run frequencies. One then guesses a "chance mechanism" or "probability model" to describe these sequences. Finally, one uses the guessed chance model to deduce rules for behaving in response to frequencies observed in the future.

For example, dice tossing produces stable frequencies. We might guess that tosses of a particular pair of dice are independent of each other and have the same probabilities of outcomes as each other. This is the probability model. Neyman sees the problem of statistics, then, to answer the question of how we should *act* given the different possible outcomes of many tosses. We use the probability model to deduce rules of what Neyman calls *inductive behavior*.

In many cases, these rules of behavior are just what the name implies. One might, for example, have a rule that says when to discard a pair of craps dice as not fair, based on the outcomes of many tosses. Or one might have a rule that says when to reject a shipment of ball bearings as out of specifications, based on measurements made on a sample from the shipment.

In other cases, Neyman's rules are more nearly like what we would usually call inferences. One might have a rule to "adopt" a particular "loaded-dice" probability model for a pair of dice based on the outcomes of many tosses. In a similar vein, one might adopt a particular model of gene linkage based on data from breeding experiments. In either case, one is *adopting* a given probability model; one is not *inferring* that the model is true. One is choosing among different ways to act regarding the dice or genetics.

Given this approach, the central problems are to establish criteria for optimal rules of behavior and to show that advocated methods satisfy these criteria. Generally speaking, these criteria may be concerned with the truth of propositions that endorse the behavior, or with the particular values and desires of the "actor." A gambler might agree to play craps with a pair of dice because observations show that it is reasonable to treat the dice as fair; here, it is the truth of the proposition that the dice are fair that endorses the behavior. Alternatively, a gambler might decline to play with a pair of dice because the stakes are too high; here it is the value the gambler attaches to the stakes which endorses or underlies the behavior.

The primary criteria used to justify confidence interval rules concerns the truth of the propositions in question. Neyman would have us imagine an indefinitely long sequence of uses of confidence interval estimation. If the method used had a 95% level of confidence, then 95% of the estimates would contain the true value; 5% of the estimates would not. This is not quite correct, but we can postpone a more accurate version to the next section. For now we say that *on average* 95% of the estimates would contain the truth.

The example in Section 5 shows that there can be more than one way to estimate at a 95% level of confidence. Both the $\overline{\mathbf{X}}$ and the $\mathbf{X}_{\max}$ statistics produce estimates that contain the true value 95% of the time on average. These methods are equivalently good at including the true value in the intervals they produce. They differ, however, in the size of the intervals they produce. The $\overline{\mathbf{X}}$-method typically produces larger intervals than does the $\overline{\mathbf{X}}_{\max}$-method. We might say that the $\mathbf{X}_{\max}$-method includes fewer false estimates than the $\overline{\mathbf{X}}$-method.

Here we appeal to two different kinds of errors. One can erroneously exclude the true value from an interval estimate. Alternatively, one can erroneously include false values in an interval estimate. Of course, any honest interval will include false values; but in a straight-forward sense, consistently narrower intervals include fewer false values.

One wants a method to make estimates that minimizes both kinds of these errors. We can approach this problem by stipulating a confidence level, and so controlling the probability of the first kind of error, and then seeking a statistic that produces the narrowest intervals—the margin of error—minimizing the second kind of error.

Unfortunately, many problems do not allow for a neat, unique solution; no statistic can be found that produces narrower intervals for every possible value of the parameter being estimated. A variety of approaches to this problem have developed. One might advocate the statistic that produces intervals which, on average, are narrowest. Alternatively, one might advocate the statistic with the narrowest widest interval, that is, consider the worst case for each potentially acceptable statistic—the case with the widest interval—and adopt that statistic with the narrowest such interval. Many other considerations can come into play here, considerations that should reflect the particular situation calling for estimation.

Neyman does not describe his approach to confidence interval estimation as a method of inductive inference. On Neyman's view, *inference* requires that we use data—after they have been gathered—along with other bits of background knowledge—the probability model—to conclude that some statement is true. We might "probabilify" the conclusion instead and say that the probability of the conclusion given the premises is 95%. But since Neyman believes that we are never justified in drawing such conclusions—probabilified or not—inductive inference is not possible. We simply cannot know or have reason to believe that a particular interval includes the true value.

Thus, while it *seems* that interval estimates should consider the results of the trial and produce something along the lines of "after-trial" probabilities, Neyman denies that this is possible. But with "before-trial" probabilities, we can evaluate different rules of behavior. We can then adopt those rules of behavior which have optimal long-run characteristics. We can justify "inductive behavior" but not inductive inference.

7. CRITICISMS OF NEYMAN

Neyman urges that his rules of inductive behavior are reasonable rules because of their "long-run operating characteristics." In the long run, using these rules will minimize the number of either kind of error one can make—erroneously excluding the true value from the estimated interval and erroneously including false values in the estimated interval. This approach to interval estimation can be criticized on several distinct grounds; here are two.

As he acknowledges, Neyman cannot claim that a 95% level of confidence method will include the true value on 95% of uses. A fair coin *can* come up heads 3/4 of the time in a long sequence of flips. Similarly, a sequence of estimates from a method with a 95% level of confidence *can* produce intervals which include the true value only 25% of the time. The probability of either happening is small and approaches zero as the number of flips or uses of the method gets indefinitely large. (See Chapter 9, Section 6 on Bernoulli's theorem.) But these improbable possibilities are still possibilities.

In light of this, all that Neyman can claim is that *the probability* that 95% of the estimates containing the true value is nearly 1, and approaches 1 in the limit, as the number of applications of the method involved increases indefinitely. We say that the limiting relative frequency (of containing the true value) *converges in probability* to the true probability (95% for a method of estimation with a 95% level of confidence). The limiting relative frequency does not *converge absolutely*. This is why I adopted the euphemism that a method with a 95% level of confidence will produce intervals that contain the true value 95% of the time *on average*.

The best Neyman can claim for the long-run operating characteristics of his rules is that the probability is very high that the percentage of errors one actually makes will be near the error-rate probabilities of the rules used. This is an important point because it shows us that Neyman cannot avoid probability in justifying his rules.

Neyman claims that we can have *no reason* to think that a particular interval estimate includes the true value. All we can claim for the interval is that the method that produced the interval has a 95% level of confidence, and this should be reason enough to justify our inductive behavior. It seems that we must be happy with being right 95% of the time without knowing when. But we do not even get this much. We cannot know if the *actual sequence of uses* of a 95% level of confidence method of estimation is, in fact, 95% successful. We can know only that there is a high probability that it has a 95% success rate. It is not clear why we should be motivated by a high probability of success for a particular method of inference, if there is no reason to think that the success rate when we actually use the method is high.

Even if we grant that having a high probability of having the success rate be nearly 95% is desirable, it is not clear that this approach to inductive inference is desirable. R. A. Fisher criticizes the very criteria Neyman advocates; science needs a theory of inductive *inference*, not inductive *behavior*. A *rule* of behavior tells us in advance what to do in any of a series of possible situations. We need not consider each situation on its own merits—after the data are in. Fisher likened a researcher adopting a rule of behavior to a cog in a computer: For such and such data, adopt such and such intervals at such and such a level of confidence. But, Fisher complained, scientists should not evaluate data blindly; the merits of experimental outcomes should be considered on a case-by-case basis. Thus, if statistics is to be useful to science, it must provide ways to help evaluate data *after* the data are collected.

Consider the trivial intervals from Section 5. Seen as a *rule* of behavior, we adopt an interval estimate for the number of balls in the urn. Since we are using a rule of behavior, no thought need be given to the interval produced; if questioned, we can correctly claim that it arose from a rule which produces intervals containing the true value in 95% of uses on average. We need not notice that some particular application of the rule produced an interval of which we could be 100% certain that it contained the truth. We would blindly follow a rule and ignore the obvious. Such an approach to data analysis, in many applications any way, is not right.

In some applications, it may make sense to use a Neyman-style approach. It is more economical to use a rule to govern the acceptance and rejection of shipments of ball bearings than to evaluate each shipment on its own merits. Furthermore, in such cases there will clearly be a sequence of uses of the rule. One can justifiably take comfort in the long-run operating characteristics of the rule.

It probably is not right to think of science as the industrial-style acceptance or rejection of hypotheses. The situations that typically arise in science do not have this kind of repetitive nature. Science needs to evaluate the bearing of given specific bits of data on given specific hypotheses. Rules of behavior do not answer this need.

Neyman's reply to such criticism is twofold. In the first place, Neyman observes that we cannot have any reason to believe that a given interval estimate is one of the 95% of estimates which include the true value; we cannot *infer* that a given estimate includes the true value. If science needs such methods of inference, science is in trouble. But, Neyman observes in the second place, use of a 95% level of confidence rule does ensure that one will erroneously exclude the truth from one's estimate in only 5% of cases (on average). Thus, while we cannot infer that a given interval estimate includes the true value, we can at least take solace in the long-run characteristics of the method. Such solace fills the void left by there being no possible method of inference.

8. CONFIDENCE INTERVALS AND INFERENCE

There is something suspicious in Neyman's reply to Fisher. Few would disagree that discarding a shipment of ball bearings is an action; some, however, would disagree that adopting a given probability model is an action. Suppose that we flip a coin 1,000 times and get 639 heads; as Neyman has it, we would "adopt" the opinion that the chance for heads on each flip is roughly 2/3. This seems very much like inferring that the probability for heads is roughly 2/3. One is inclined to accuse Neyman of playing with words here. What is the difference between adopting and inferring?

Perhaps much of the controversy is based on a semantic misunderstanding. Whether one calls it inductive behavior or inductive inference, there is no disagreement about the technical characteristics of Neyman-style confidence interval estimation. The estimates are based on the long-run characteristics of before-trial probabilities. We might as well say that Neyman does provide canons of inference. The question that remains is whether such canons are sensible or not.

A canon of inductive inference should present an argument schema which shows when certain kinds of premises license asserting a certain kind of conclusion. Neyman does present such canons. They look like this:

Statistical model employed: Polling can be described with binomial probabilities.
Data: Y of the N randomly chosen units in the survey are childless couples.
Conclusion: So the proportion of childless couples is $Y/N \pm \varepsilon$.

We need not probabilify the conclusion; we can simply assert it. Probability helps describe the kind of argument employed. Arguments such as these do not guarantee that their conclusions will be true. Instead, they guarantee that given true premises, 95% of the time (on average) the conclusion also will be true.

Fisher criticized such inference schemas on the grounds that they advocate ignoring particular information that may be present in particular cases. But we do use the particular information from a particular trial. We do *infer*, for example, that the coin is biased to come up heads roughly 2/3 of the time when we get 639 heads in 1,000 flips. Such an inference schema can underwrite cases where we would infer trivial intervals. But the fact that additional information is present and useful in such cases need not impugn the schema. A thinking researcher simply would not use it in such cases. Calling something an inference schema does not require, contrary to Fisher, that we apply it blindly and ignore whatever particular information is at hand in a particular case.

The variety of methods of interval estimation might seem a valid criticism of such methods as rules of inference. Different statistics, such as $\mathbf{X}_{max}$ and $\overline{\mathbf{X}}$, can license different and even contradictory interval estimates at the same level of confidence. Since we can deductively infer (A and B) from A and B separately, this multiplicity of methods may result in canons of inference that lead to contradictions. In the case of deductive inference, such a problem looms large, for on pain of irrationality, the conclusion of a deductive argument is forced on those who assent to the premises.

We need not regard inductive arguments this way. The fact that an inference is licensed by a rule of inductive inference does not require that we draw the inference. The use of inductive inferences may depend on the context of use. Neyman's program of establishing different criteria to distinguish the different interval estimates that can be made at a given level of confidence allows us to tailor the rules we use to the particular context in which we use them. Evidence need not bear on hypotheses in some context-free way; we can use the context to motivate the selection of criteria. We can express our caution in drawing an inductive inference in terms of probabilities, such as levels of confidence.

There remains a question about circularity. The premises to these inductive arguments include a premise setting out the statistical model. What justifies the use of this probability model? Two kinds of answer are possible. We might simply say that the model is just a guess; indeed, it is a guess whose adequacy can be compared with other possible models. Ultimately, we might have to abandon it and the inferences based on it in favor of some other model. Alternatively, we might say that the model is justified inductively. The long run of experience leads us to the justified view that, for example, random sampling a population can be described with binomial trials. According to this answer, interval estimation presupposes an "inductive premise." But perhaps this is not too bad, for confidence intervals allow us to produce refined inductions (e.g., the proportion of childless couples is 36% ± 3%) on the basis of very gross inductions (e.g., random sampling produces binomial trials with *some* true parameter, p, of "success"). In either case there remains the task of understanding the extra-statistical reasons for adopting a model.

9. SUMMARY

1. Polling may be thought of as drawing balls out of an urn.
   - **(a)** Balls in the urn correspond to units in the population.
   - **(b)** Different values of the variable of interest correspond to different colors of the balls.
   - **(c)** A survey sample corresponds to drawing balls randomly from the urn.
   - **(d)** There is a fixed proportion of units in the population which have the same value of the variable of interest; analogously, there is a fixed proportion, p, of balls in the urn which are one color.

2. Sample survey outcomes can be described with binomial probabilities.
   - **(a)** We sample N balls from an urn with proportion, p, of "yellow" balls inside. Each ball is taken randomly and replaced after being examined. The probability of getting a proportion of yellow balls in the sample, Y/N, is computed with the binomial formula.
   - **(b)** This proportion, Y/N, is used to estimate the value of p.
   - **(c)** This method of estimating p is not biased in the specific sense that the expectation of Y/N is equal to p for any value of N and any value of p.
   - **(d)** The precision of this method of estimating is understood in terms of the probability—called the level of confidence—of statistic values being within a predetermined margin of error, ε, of p: $P[(Y/N - \varepsilon) \leq p \leq (Y/N + \varepsilon)]$ = the level of confidence.
   - **(e)** If we knew p, these level of confidence probabilities could be computed with several applications of the binomial formula.

(f) Since for any value of p, calculations with the binomial law depend on the number of balls in the sample and *not* on the proportion of the total population in the sample, the accuracy of a survey sample estimate depends on the number of balls in the sample and *not* on the percentage of the population sampled.

3. The normal distribution approximates binomial probabilities when N is largish (30 or more) and p is moderate: $0.1 \leq p \leq 0.9$.

(a) The normal distribution with mean $\mu = N \times p$, and standard deviation, $\sigma = \sqrt{N \times p \times (1 - p)}$, is appropriate for this approximation.

(b) For any normal distribution, and hence for a normal distribution approximating binomial probabilities, we have

$$
\begin{aligned}
&P[(\mu - 2\sigma) \leq Y \leq (\mu + 2\sigma)] \\
&\quad = P[(Np - 2\sqrt{Np(1-p)}) \leq Y \leq (Np + 2\sqrt{Np(1-p)})] \\
&\quad = P\left[\left(\frac{Y}{N} - 2\sqrt{\frac{Np(1-p)}{N}}\right) \leq p \leq \left(\frac{Y}{N} + 2\sqrt{\frac{Np(1-p)}{N}}\right)\right] \\
&\quad = 0.95.
\end{aligned}
$$

(c) $P[((Y/N - 2\sqrt{Np(1-p)}/N) \leq p \leq (Y/N + 2\sqrt{Np(1-p)}/N))] = 0.95$ is in the right form for a confidence interval around p with margin of error $\pm 2\sqrt{Np(1-p)}/N$ and level of confidence 95%.

(d) For a 95% confidence level probability and any value of p, the largest value the margin of error, $2\sqrt{Np(1-p)}/N$, can take is quite small for moderate values of N.

4. Four kinds of premises underlie confidence interval arguments.

(a) One kind of premise states the basic probabilistic model using probabilities to describe the world.

(b) Another kind of premise establishes the sample statistic that is used to estimate the unknown parameter of interest.

(c) Another kind of premise establishes what is an accurate method of sampling.

(d) Specific mathematical and probabilistic relationships are necessary to produce appropriate and useful confidence interval statements.

5. Confidence interval probabilities can be difficult to interpret.

(a) Different—and in some cases contradictory—estimates can be made for the same population parameter, at the same level of confidence with the same data. This can occur when different statistics are used to construct the confidence interval probabilities.

(b) In some cases confidence intervals can be trivial in the sense that one can be 100% certain—after the trial has been run—that the true value of the parameter lies in a 95% level of confidence interval.

(c) Confidence interval probabilities are probabilities that the interval that *will* be produced *will* cover the true value; they are before-trial probabilities.

(d) But one estimates after the trial is run. Thus, there is a question of why before-trial probabilities are appropriate after the trial has been run.

6. Jerzy Neyman advocates understanding methods of confidence interval estimation as rules of inductive behavior.
   (a) Neyman denies that it is possible, except in unusual cases, to draw justified inferences with particular interval estimates.
   (b) Instead, Neyman suggests rules for how to act in response to the different kinds of data we might collect.
   (c) Rules for interval estimation should produce intervals that only rarely exclude the truth, and they should produce narrow intervals—they should include fewer false values.
   (d) Typically, rules cannot be found that produce the best results in terms of both criteria for any possible value of the unknown parameter of interest. Thus, the particular criteria used may reflect features of the context of estimation.

7. Neyman's approach may be criticized.
   (a) The relative frequency of a sequence of trials converges in probability to the true probability. Thus, there is no deductive guarantee that 95% of uses of a method of estimation with a 95% level of confidence will produce intervals that cover the truth.
   (b) It may not be appropriate to evaluate data after the trial has been run through the blind adherence to some rule adopted before the trial. This could result in one ignoring the triviality of a trivial interval estimate, for example. In general, it does seem that we want reason to trust particular estimates in particular cases.

8. Understood differently, however, Neyman's confidence interval approach might indeed establish sensible canons of inductive argument.
   (a) Neyman provides confidence interval argument schemata of the following sort:

      Statistical model employed (e.g., binomial).

      Data (e.g., 332 out of 1,500 chosen units are . . .).

      Conclusion (e.g., so p is in the interval 332/1,500 $\pm$ 2.6%).

   (b) Such arguments do not guarantee the truth of their conclusions given the truth of their premises, but they can have a high level of confidence guarantee; they should produce true conclusions most of the time.
   (c) One need not accept the conclusion of every inductive argument. Whether one does or not may depend on factors extrinsic to the guarantee provided by the argument (e.g., what particular interval was produced).

10. REFERENCES

Most introductory texts cover the development of confidence intervals for binomial parameters—as might be appropriate for survey sampling inferences. Two that I have found useful are (Freedman et al., 1978) and (Mood et al., 1974). Many of the important concepts used in the discussion of interval estimation were first presented in (Fisher, 1922) and (Fisher, 1925). The confidence interval approach to estimation was first developed in (Neyman, 1937). Many texts, including (Neyman, 1950), now present confidence intervals this way. Neyman defends the "inductive behavior'' interpretation of his approach in several places, including (Neyman, 1957) and (Neyman, 1977). The example with two statistics for estimating the number of balls in an urn is adapted from (Neyman, 1977).

Criticisms of Neyman abound in the philosophical literature. The ''trivial'' interval version of this example is developed in (Seidenfeld, 1979). The before-trial/after-trial distinction is discussed in detail in (Hacking, 1965), as is the ''convergence in probability'' criticism. Fisher attacked Neyman in many publications; they are repeated in his final extended work on the topic, (Fisher, 1956). The idea that Neyman might indeed be offering a theory of inductive inference is developed in detail in (Hacking, 1980).

11. PROBLEMS

1. Suppose that you draw five balls, replacing each one after noting its color, from an urn with an unknown proportion, p, of yellow balls. Let Y be the number of yellow balls observed from the five balls drawn. Show that $Y/5$ is an unbiased statistic for estimating the proportion of yellow balls in the urn, p.
2. Suppose that one conducts a poll with a sample size of 500. Assuming that the sampling was random, what margin of error at the 95% level of confidence can be reported for such a poll? What margin of error at the 99% level of confidence can be reported for such a poll?
3. Do Problem 2, but suppose that the sample size was 1,200 instead of 500.
4. Using the $\mathbf{X}_{max}$-method, construct a confidence interval estimate for the number of balls in an urn from which 6 balls have been drawn: numbers 77, 568, 1004, 1093, 1672, and 2011.
5. Do Problem 4, but use the $\overline{\mathbf{X}}$-method instead.
6. Why do the results from Problems 4 and 5 disagree? What lessons does this have for understanding confidence interval estimation? Discuss.
7. Explain the distinction between ''before-trial'' and ''after-trial'' probabilities. Why might one be interested in after-trial probabilities of confidence intervals? Why might one be suspicious of them?
8. In what sense are ''trivial'' interval estimates trivial? Why is it still appropriate to say that they are 95% level of confidence intervals? Does the fact that confidence intervals can be trivial show that nothing can be learned from confidence interval estimation? Why or why not?
9. What is ''inductive behavior?'' Why is it ''inductive?'' How does it differ from ''inductive inference?'' Discuss the merits of this way of coping with the problem of induction.
10. Explain how it is possible for a sequence of tosses of a fair coin to come up heads exactly 1/3 of the time. Is this possible no matter how many trials there are in the sequence?
11. Explain the distinction between absolute convergence and convergence in probability.
12. What should one make of the ''convergence in probability'' problem for Neyman if one accepts the view of Section 8 that Neyman does offer a theory of inductive inference?

CHAPTER

11

BAYESIAN PROBABILITY AND RATIONALITY

1. LEARNING FROM, AND ACTING ON, EXPERIENCE

Only rarely can inductive investigations yield results we can be certain of. This poses a difficulty. We may interested to know what proportion of married couples in the United States have no children. We may do some kind of investigation—perhaps take a random sample—and end up with the conclusion, "There are 36 ± 3% childless married couples in the United States." Such conclusions are worrisome because we know they may be wrong. If the conclusion was the result of an application of confidence intervals, we might qualify our conclusion by saying, "I can infer at a 95% level of confidence that. . . ." But for some people this is still uncomfortable.

Another approach is to use probability to help express the attitude one should have toward the fallible conclusions of inductive arguments. Instead of categorically asserting or denying a conclusion, one expresses a *degree of belief* in it. Probability can be used to provide a scale by which to measure these degrees of belief. This use of probability differs from the use employed in confidence interval inferences. Here probabilities describe states of mind, not sequences of trials, and consequently, this kind of probability is usually called *subjective* or *personalist*.

What a person learns from experience is reflected in changes in his or her degrees of belief. The conceptual framework provided by probabilistic degrees of belief provides a means to express the commonly uncertain results of inductive learning about the world. Induction is a matter of shifting probabilities attached to beliefs.

Simply describing the attitude one should have toward fallible inductive conclusions in terms of degrees of belief is not quite satisfactory. What does it mean to have degree of belief of 0.8 that—to take an example from Chapter 3—one has acute appendicitis? Although this may be deceptive, there is a certain intuitive clarity to being fully certain of the truth of some statement about the world. If one is certainly ill with appendicitis, one's options for dealing with the situation are relatively straightforward in important respects. *That* is just how the world is—or so one believes. But a degree of belief of 0.8, what does that mean?

Both to flesh out what it means to have a degree of belief and to see how such degrees of belief bear on getting on in the world, Bayesian probability is commonly accompanied by Bayesian decision theory. By combining an explicit probabilistic description of a person's degrees of belief with an explicit utility scale description of a person's desires, we can produce both a powerful decision theory and an answer to what degrees of belief mean.

The Bayesian approach to induction provides a conceptually elegant approach to induction. It provides a probabilistic framework for characterizing the state of belief that results from inductive investigations. This same probabilistic framework provides a means to characterize inductive learning from these investigations by means of Bayes' rule. Finally, it provides an integrated decision theory that gives Bayesian inductions a practical significance.

The Bayesian approach buys all of this at the cost of four central assumptions. It must assume that a person's "partial beliefs" can be, or at least ought to be, characterized in terms of probability. It must assume that people can rank outcomes in terms of a numerical utility scale. It must assume that, in response to evidence, the probabilities assigned to a person's beliefs shift according to Bayes' rule. Finally, it must assume that actions with the highest expected utility are preferable to other actions.

2. THE DUTCH BOOK ARGUMENT

In contrast to confidence interval probabilities that attach to sequences of trials, Bayesian degrees of belief probabilities attach to states of mind. Both may be descriptively inaccurate. The relative frequency of heads in tosses of a coin may not converge to the probability supposed to apply. A person may not have degrees of belief that obey the probability rules. When frequency probabilities fail, we must try other models to describe the trials. But when degrees of belief probabilities fail we have another option: We can say that a person's degrees of belief *should* obey the probability rules, even if they do not. A person whose degrees of belief do not obey the probability rules is *irrational* in some important sense. Here is an explicit *normative* aspect to Bayesian degrees of belief. We can characterize degrees of belief in terms of preferred decisions. Some decisions *should*, by their very nature, never be made. Degrees of belief that correspond to such decisions are irrational. We extract the normative component of the Bayesian approach from decisions no one should make.

Decisions to take bets give us a simple way to see this normative aspect of Bayesian probability in action. They also give us one way to understand degrees of belief. When betting, one decides which among several risky options is preferable. A person may consider betting on baseball, for instance, weighing three options, not betting, and betting for or against the Boston Red Sox to win the American League pennant.

In their roughest sense, degrees of belief correspond to the degree one is convinced that something is (or will be) the case. Sometimes the amount one is willing to stake in a bet reflects such conviction. A person willing to bet $1,000 on the Red Sox may be more convinced that the team will win than another person willing to bet only $10. But the stake may only reflect a person's financial state: A wealthy person is more likely to bet $1,000 than a poor person. Instead of the stake one is willing to bet, we can use the *odds* at which one is willing to bet to connect up with degrees of belief. A person convinced that the Red Sox will win should be willing to bet at worse odds—contribute more money for fixed winnings—than a person convinced they will lose.

Consider an example: Suppose that two people, call them Walter and Mary, are going to bet with each other on the fate of the Red Sox. They decide to limit their betting to a pot of $10; their two contributions to the pot must total $10. Whoever wins the bet takes the pot. If Walter was convinced that the Red Sox will win, he should be willing to contribute more than $5 to the pot. He might even be willing to contribute $9, to collect the $10 pot if he wins. He risks losing $9 to win just $1, but he is convinced the Red Sox will win. Of course, he would be willing to put up less than $9, but suppose that $9 is the most he is willing to bet for a $10 pot. The ratio of this amount, $9, to the pot, $10, $9/$10 = 0.9, is his *personal betting rate* for the Red Sox winning.

Like probabilities, personal betting rates are ratios which are greater than zero and less than 1. If Walter's personal betting rate for the Red Sox was higher than 1—1.5 say—he would be willing to contribute more than $10—in this case $15, since $15/$10 = 1.5—to collect a maximum of $10 for winning the bet. No matter whether the Red Sox won or lost, Walter would lose money. This is not a true bet. If Walter's personal betting rate was less than zero then, - 0.5 say, again we would not have a true bet. To participate in this bet, Mary would first have to pay Walter $5 and then contribute the entire $10 to the pot. This is not true betting.

With a somewhat stronger relationship between a person's betting rates and the bets he or she will accept, one can show that *rational* betting rates *must* be probabilities to be rational. A person whose betting rates are not probabilities will accept a collection of bets—a "book" of bets—which will result in a net loss no matter what happens. Such a set of bets is called a *dutch book*. The "dutch book argument" is designed to show that a person's degrees of belief, understood as betting rates, must behave like probabilities to be rational.

We have shown that betting rates should be ratios between zero and 1. To show that they *should be* probabilities, we need to show that they are additive in the way probabilities are, to adopt a sensible notation:

$$\mathrm{BR}(\mathbf{A} \cup \mathbf{B}) = \mathrm{BR}(\mathbf{A}) + \mathrm{BR}(\mathbf{B}) - \mathrm{BR}(\mathbf{A} \cap \mathbf{B}),$$

We argue in two stages. First we show that if a person's betting rates for all the elements of any partition sum to 1, his or her betting rates are additive. Then we show that it would be irrational for a person's betting rates on all the elements of some partition not to sum to 1.

Suppose that a person's betting rates attached to all the elements of any mutually disjoint and exhaustive collection of events—any *partition* (see Chapter 8, Section 4)—sum to 1. If this were the case, these betting rates are additive. Figure 11.1 will help. We can pick out several partitions from this figure. We have, to begin, a 4-element partition; the stuff that is just **A** and not **B**, the stuff that is just **B** and not **A**, the stuff that is both **A** and **B** and the stuff that is neither **A** nor **B**. For simplicity use the following names:

$$\mathbf{S}_1 = \mathbf{A} - \mathbf{B}; \qquad \mathbf{S}_3 = \mathbf{A} \cap \mathbf{B}; \text{ and}$$

$$\mathbf{S}_2 = \mathbf{B} - \mathbf{A}; \qquad \mathbf{S}_4 = \mathbf{V} - (\mathbf{A} \cup \mathbf{B}).$$

These events can be combined to form several other partitions. Here are two 2-element partitions: $[\mathbf{S}_1 \cup \mathbf{S}_2 \cup \mathbf{S}_3]$, $[\mathbf{S}_4]$ and $[\mathbf{S}_1 \cup \mathbf{S}_2]$, $[\mathbf{S}_3 \cup \mathbf{S}_4]$. Here are two 3-element partitions: $[\mathbf{S}_1 \cup \mathbf{S}_2]$, $[\mathbf{S}_3]$, $[\mathbf{S}_4]$, and $[\mathbf{S}_1]$, $[\mathbf{S}_2]$, $[\mathbf{S}_3 \cup \mathbf{S}_4]$. Given our

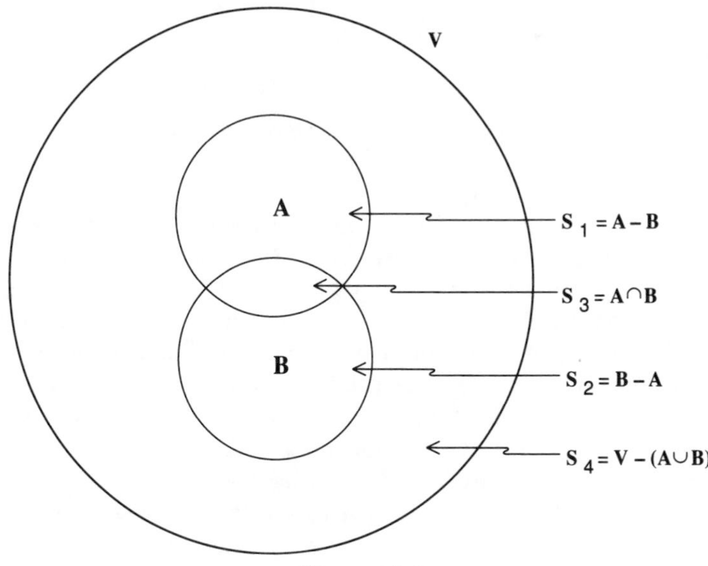

Figure 11.1

assumption that the betting rates for the elements of *any* partition sum to 1, we have the following:

$$\text{BR}(\mathbf{S_1}) + \text{BR}(\mathbf{S_2}) + \text{BR}(\mathbf{S_3}) + \text{BR}(\mathbf{S_4}) = 1,$$

$$\text{BR}(\mathbf{S_1} \cup \mathbf{S_2} \cup \mathbf{S_3}) + \text{BR}(\mathbf{S_4}) = 1,$$

$$\text{BR}(\mathbf{S_1} \cup \mathbf{S_2}) + \text{BR}(\mathbf{S_3} \cup \mathbf{S_4}) = 1,$$

$$\text{BR}(\mathbf{S_1} \cup \mathbf{S_2}) + \text{BR}(\mathbf{S_3}) + \text{BR}(\mathbf{S_4}) = 1, \text{ and}$$

$$\text{BR}(\mathbf{S_1}) + \text{BR}(\mathbf{S_2}) + \text{BR}(\mathbf{S_3} \cup \mathbf{S_4}) = 1.$$

By our naming conventions, we have

$$\mathbf{A} \cup \mathbf{B} = (\mathbf{S_1} \cup \mathbf{S_3}) \cup (\mathbf{S_2} \cup \mathbf{S_3}) = (\mathbf{S_1} \cup \mathbf{S_2} \cup \mathbf{S_3}).$$

So

$$\text{BR}(\mathbf{A} \cup \mathbf{B}) = \text{BR}(\mathbf{S_1} \cup \mathbf{S_2} \cup \mathbf{S_3}).$$

But

$$\text{BR}(\mathbf{S_1} \cup \mathbf{S_2} \cup \mathbf{S_3}) = \text{BR}(\mathbf{S_1} \cup \mathbf{S_2}) + \text{BR}(\mathbf{S_3}),$$

since both are equal to $1 - \text{BR}(\mathbf{S_4})$. We can similarly show that

$$\text{BR}(\mathbf{S_1} \cup \mathbf{S_2}) = \text{BR}(\mathbf{S_1}) + \text{BR}(\mathbf{S_2}) = 1 - \text{BR}(\mathbf{S_3} \cup \mathbf{S_4}).$$

Putting all of this together, we have

$$\begin{aligned}
\text{BR}(\mathbf{A} \cup \mathbf{B}) &= \text{BR}(\mathbf{S_1} \cup \mathbf{S_2} \cup \mathbf{S_3}) \\
&= \text{BR}(\mathbf{S_1}) + \text{BR}(\mathbf{S_2}) + \text{BR}(\mathbf{S_3}) \\
&= [\text{BR}(\mathbf{S_1}) + \text{BR}(\mathbf{S_3})] + [\text{BR}(\mathbf{S_2}) + \text{BR}(\mathbf{S_3})] - [\text{BR}(\mathbf{S_3})] \\
&= \text{BR}(\mathbf{S_1} \cup \mathbf{S_3}) + \text{BR}(\mathbf{S_2} \cup \mathbf{S_3}) - \text{BR}(\mathbf{S_3}) \\
&= \text{BR}(\mathbf{A}) + \text{BR}(\mathbf{B}) - \text{BR}(\mathbf{A} \cap \mathbf{B}).
\end{aligned}$$

We have shown that for any two events, **A** and **B**, if a person's betting rates on all the elements of any partition sum to 1, then $\text{P}(\mathbf{A} \cup \mathbf{B}) = \text{P}(\mathbf{A}) + \text{P}(\mathbf{B}) - \text{P}(\mathbf{A} \cap \mathbf{B})$.

To show that betting rates *should* be probabilities, we must show that the betting rates for the elements of any partition *should* sum to 1. There are two parts to this proof. First, we need to show that if a person's betting rates on all the elements of some partition do not sum to 1, a dutch book can be made against this person. Second, we need to show that if they do sum to 1, no dutch book is possible.

Consider the first part. To see how the proof goes, consider a simple 2-element partition: the Red Sox win the pennant, **W**, and the Red Sox lose the pennant, **L**. Suppose that Walter's betting rate for **W** was 0.9 and his betting rate for **L** was 0.2: $0.9 + 0.2 = 1.1 \neq 1$. As these are his betting rates, Walter would be willing to make the following two bets:

Bet 1: Walter bets on **W**—for the Red Sox.
Walter's stake: \$9;
Mary's stake: \$1.

Bet 2: Walter bets on **L**—against the Red Sox.
Walter's stake: \$2;
Mary's stake: \$8.

Walter is sure to win one of the bets and lose the other. Walter will collect exactly one pot worth \$10. But Walter has to put \$11 into both bets. Thus, no matter what happens, Walter would lose \$1 with these two bets. Indeed, any time Walter's betting rates for **W** and **L** add up to more than 1, he will be subject to such a dutch book of bets. Walter's stake in two bets on **W** and **L** would be \$10 × (his rate for **W** + his rate for **L**). His stake would have to be greater than \$10, since the sum of his rates for **W** and **L** is greater than 1. But the most that he could get back from the bets is \$10—together they are a sure loss. Such betting rates are irrational.

This result generalizes to a partition with more than two elements. Consider a partition with *N* elements, such that a person's betting rates for all these elements sum to greater than 1. Such betting rates mean that this person would be willing to make *N* \$10-pot bets, one on each element of the partition at his or her stated rate. This person will have to stake \$10 × (the sum of his rates), and this will be greater than \$10, since the sum of his rates is greater than 1. But since these elements form a partition, he or she will win exactly one of these *N* bets. One \$10 pot will be collected, for a stake greater than \$10—a sure loss.

On the other hand, if Walter's betting rates add up to less than 1, this kind of argument will not do. Walter, in fact will make money no matter what happens. Betting rates on **W** and **L**, as we have defined them, which add up to less than 1 are not irrational. If, however, we adopt a stronger relationship between a person's betting rates and the bets that he or she is willing to accept, we can show that betting rates on **W** and **L** which sum to less than 1 are just as "irrational" as rates which sum to greater than 1. We define a person's betting rate as the ratio of the amount that he or she is willing to wager, *W*, to the amount in the pot, *P*. Here we allow *W* and *P* to be either positive *or negative*. Suppose that Walter's rates for **W** and **L** were 0.7 and 0.2, respectively. Then Mary would happily make the following two bets with Walter:

Bet 3: Walter bets on **W**—"for" the Red Sox.
Walter's stake: \$−7;
Mary's stake: \$−3.

Bet 4: Walter bets on **L**—"against" the Red Sox.
Walter's stake: \$−2;
Mary's stake: \$−8.

One can think of negative contributions as bills that one owes. In *bet 3*, Walter contributes a bill for \$7. This, with a bill of Mary's for \$3, constitute the pot. If the Red Sox win the pennant, Walter "wins" the bet; he collects both bills and owes \$10. Walter will "win" one of these bets and lose the other. He will end up with \$10 in bills, while wagering \$9 in bills. No matter what happens, he will end up owing \$1 more after the pennant than before it.

This way of defining betting rates does allow us to show that betting rates which do not behave like probabilities allow for the possibility of a dutch book. When betting rates on the elements of a partition sum to less than 1, bets with negative pots are used. When they sum to greater than 1, normal bets are used. But this way of defining betting rates is odd, for in effect, Walter is betting against the Red Sox in *bet 3*, even though it is technically a bet "for" the Red Sox.

So far we have only shown that a dutch book can be made against a person whose betting rates on the elements of some partition do not sum to 1. We must also show that no dutch book is possible when the betting rates on the elements of any partition do sum to 1. Here we only show that no book of *two* bets can result in a sure loss. The general case with any number of bets is mathematically more complicated, but similar in essentials.

Suppose that Walter's betting rates on the elements of any partition sum to 1, and, for concreteness, consider a book of just two bets. Here we cannot assume a fixed size of pot, nor can we assume that **A** and **B** are a partition. We must guard against *any* dutch book. We do assume that Walter's betting rate for **A** is α and that his betting rate for **B** is β. Walter makes two bets, one bet on **A** with a pot of \$**S**, the other bet on **B** with a pot of \$**T**, for two dollar amounts **S** and **T**:

Bet 5: Walter bets on **A**—whatever **A** might be.
Walter's stake: $\$\alpha \times \mathbf{S}$;
Total pot: \$**S**.
Walter collects \$**S** if **A** is true; otherwise, Walter loses his stake, $\$\alpha\mathbf{S}$.

Bet 6: Walter bets on **B**—whatever **B** might be.
Walter's stake: $\$\beta \times \mathbf{T}$;
Total pot: \$**T**.
Walter collects \$**T** if **B** is true; otherwise, Walter loses his stake, $\$\beta\mathbf{T}$.

Walter's betting rates behave as probabilities, by assumption, so $0 \leq \alpha, \beta \leq 1$. Since we make no assumptions about **A** and **B**, we can set these bets so that $\mathbf{S} \geq \mathbf{T} \geq 0$.

There are two cases to consider, (1) $\mathbf{A} \cap \mathbf{B} = \Lambda$ and (2) $\mathbf{A} \cap \mathbf{B} \neq \Lambda$. Consider the first case. At best Walter could win one of these two bets. Thus, to show that no dutch book is possible, we must show that at least one of the pots in these bets is greater than the total amount Walter has staked (i.e., $\alpha\mathbf{S} + \beta\mathbf{T} \leq \mathbf{S}$). We know that $\alpha + \beta \leq 1$, since $\mathbf{A} \cap \mathbf{B} = \Lambda$. We have, by assumption, $\mathbf{S} \geq \mathbf{T} \geq 0$. So

$(\mathbf{S} - \mathbf{T}) \geq 0$. Since $0 \leq \alpha \leq 1$,

$$\alpha(\mathbf{S} - \mathbf{T}) \leq (\mathbf{S} - \mathbf{T}).$$

We can do a little algebraic manipulation on this inequality, to find

$$\alpha\mathbf{S} - \alpha\mathbf{T} + \mathbf{T} \leq \mathbf{S},$$

$$\Rightarrow \alpha\mathbf{S} + (1 - \alpha)\mathbf{T} \leq \mathbf{S}.$$

Since $\alpha + \beta \leq 1$, we know that $\beta \leq (1 - \alpha)$, so

$$\alpha\mathbf{S} + \beta\mathbf{T} \leq \alpha\mathbf{S} + (1 - \alpha)\mathbf{T} \leq \mathbf{S}$$

which is what we needed to prove.

In the second case $\mathbf{A} \cap \mathbf{B} \neq \Lambda$. Here we cannot assume that $\alpha + \beta \leq 1$, but in this case it is possible for Walter to win both bets. So, in this case we simply have to show that the sum of the pots in both bets can exceed his stake: $(\alpha\mathbf{S} + \beta\mathbf{T}) \leq (\mathbf{S} + \mathbf{T})$. But this is obvious since $0 \leq \alpha, \beta \leq 1$.

Part of the point of this discussion of the dutch book argument is to show how degrees of belief can be tied to decisions—via the bets one is prepared to accept—and how certain degrees of belief consequently are irrational. The dutch book argument is attractive because it relies on a simple, concrete, and easily understood kind of decision with which to tie degrees of belief: betting. It shows us why it is not too great a stretch of the imagination to claim that a person's degrees of belief *should* behave like probabilities.

Ultimately, however, the argument is not satisfactory. To make it go, we need to adopt a peculiar notion of betting rate—where betting for something really can be betting against it. Indeed, there may be people who have degrees of belief but whom are disinclined to make bets of this sort. I might have *degrees of belief* about the Red Sox which *do* behave like probabilities, and I might decline *betting* with a "serious baseball fan" for fear that my ignorance about the Red Sox would get me into trouble even if I am not subject to a dutch book of bets. The following two sections do the same kind of work as the dutch book argument, but in both a more general and a more persuasive way.

3. CONSTRUCTING A UTILITY SCALE

One aspect of decision theory that tends to bother people is the assumption of a numerical utility scale. To determine which of two risky ventures is preferable, we must be able to determine relatively how preferable each outcome is in numerical terms. This kind of decision theory must assume that utilities can be measured with a scale of measurement that is as structured as the scale used to measure temperature (see Chapter 6, Sections 2 and 3). We can arbitrarily fix what outcome has zero utility and we can arbitrarily fix the size of the unit. But once these two values have been fixed, every other outcome has a precise numerical utility on this scale. Such scales are known as "interval scales."

Although when thinking about options, numbers usually do not immediately come to mind, we can construct them by doing some thought experiments. Consider a simple example. Suppose that you are considering booking a plane flight a month ahead. The trouble is that while you plan to finish a construction job you have taken on, something may come up and the job may not be finished, in which case you would have to cancel or delay your trip. Two kinds of tickets are available: you can book an inexpensive and nonrefundable ticket, or you can book an expensive but refundable ticket. It would be better to pay less money, but you do not want to lose the price of the ticket if you do not finish the job (Figure 11.2). Clearly, $B \geq C \geq A$, but to decide which ticket to buy, you need to know where, between A and B, C falls.

First we establish a scale. Buying the inexpensive ticket and being able to take the trip as planned is the best outcome; let $B = 100$. But having to lose the price of the inexpensive ticket is the least desirable outcome; let $A = 0$.

The question is, relative to this scale, where is C? Suppose you knew that there was a good chance that you would finish the job. Suppose that in your opinion the chance is greater than 0.9. Ask yourself: ''In this situation, would I gamble on the inexpensive ticket?'' If you would, then you know that $C \leq 90$ (Figure 11.3). The expected utility for buying the inexpensive ticket is $(0.1 \times 0) + (0.9 \times 100) = 90$. If this option is preferable to buying the expensive ticket, you know that its utility is higher than the utility for buying the expensive ticket. Now imagine another case: Suppose the chance that you finish the job is only 0.5. If in this case you would opt for the expensive ticket, you would know that the utility of the expensive ticket is greater than $50 = (0.5 \times 0) + (0.5 \times 100)$. You now have upper and lower bounds for C: $50 \leq C \leq 90$. By running through a series of these hypothetical considerations of this sort, you should be able to narrow these bounds.

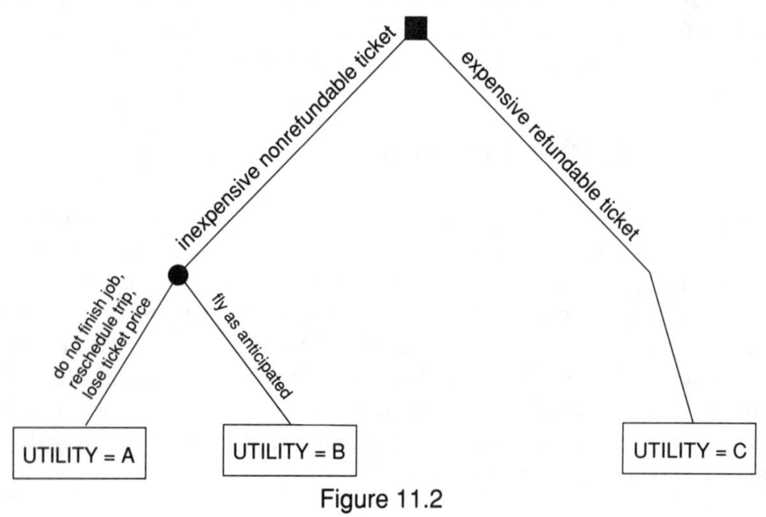

Figure 11.2

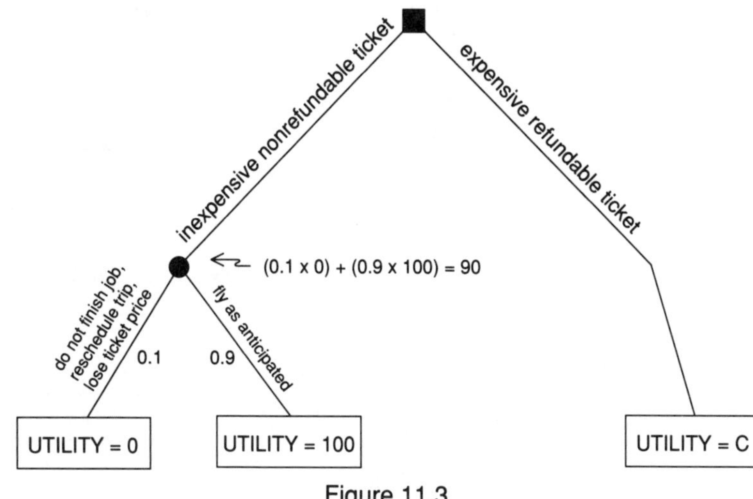

Figure 11.3

Consider another example (see Chapter 3, Problem 7). A 35-year-old women is pregnant and concerned that her fetus not have Down's syndrome. If she was certain that it had Down's syndrome, she would have an abortion. Some of the amniotic fluid that surrounds the fetus can be taken from the womb in a procedure called "amniocentesis." Cells in this fluid shed by the fetus can be examined to determine whether the fetus has Down's syndrome. Unfortunately, there are two problems. The test is not perfect; it can produce the wrong result, either falsely positive (for Down's syndrome) or falsely negative. Also, the test can induce a spontaneous miscarriage. See the decision tree in Figure 11.4. The appropriate decision for this woman depends on the probabilities of the various outcomes. But it also depends on how desirable she finds the different outcomes. This may seem to pose a problem; how can she find sensible numbers for these utilities?

There are six possible outcomes in this simplified tree. We establish an "interval" utility scale by supposing that the best outcome is giving birth to a baby without Down's syndrome—utility 100, and suppose that the worst outcome is giving birth to a baby with Down's syndrome—utility zero. (For some people these two outcomes may not be the best and worst, and an alternative analysis would be necessary.) These values provide utilities for all but two of the possible outcomes, a miscarriage and an abortion. Clearly, the decision of whether or not to have amniocentesis depends on the utilities this woman attaches to these possible outcomes.

To determine these utilities, we can conduct a series of thought experiments similar to those we conducted above. We ask the woman to consider the following hypothetical situation: She knows that there is a 50% chance that the fetus has Down's syndrome. Assuming that no tests are possible, would she opt for an abortion in this case? We have a simple decision tree (Figure 11.5). If the woman would opt for an abortion under these conditions, we know that her utility for an abortion is

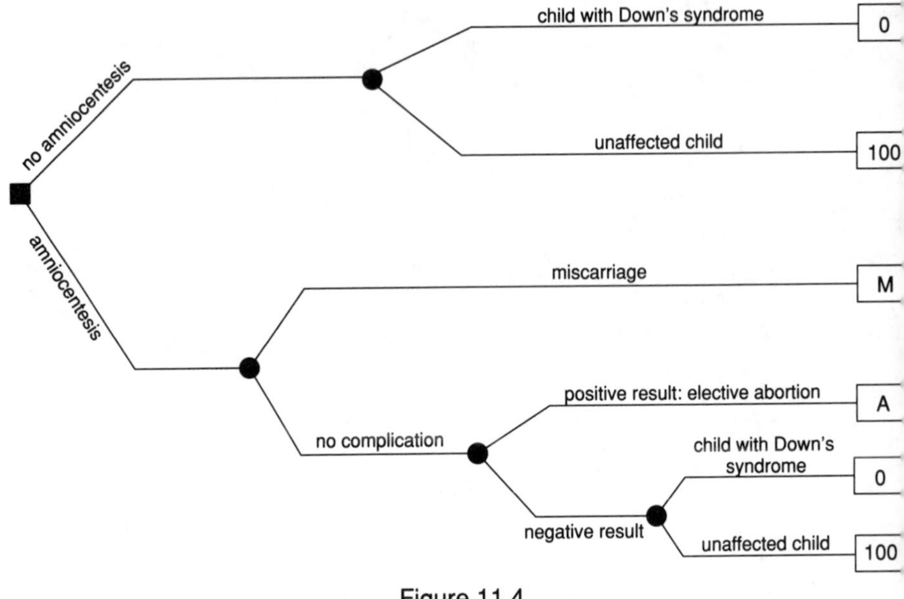

Figure 11.4

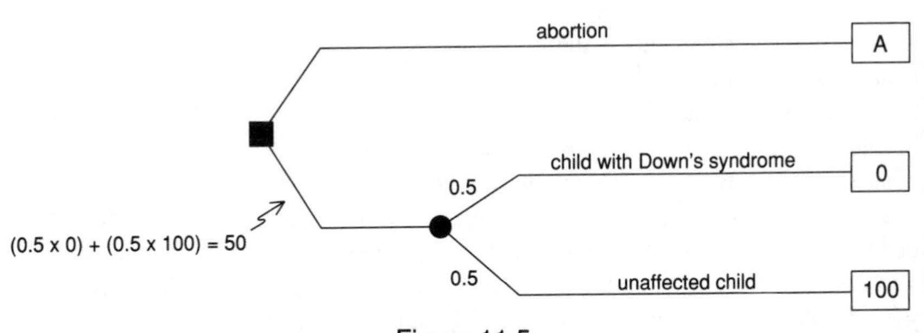

Figure 11.5

greater than 50 = (0.5 × 0) + (0.5 × 100). Suppose, then, that the chance that the fetus has Down's syndrome is 1/10. If she would prefer to carry the fetus to term in this case, we know that the utility she assigns to having an abortion is less than 90 = (0.1 × 0) + (0.9 × 100). By successively altering these hypothetical chances we can get a pretty good fix on the utility that this woman assigns to having an abortion. Similar kinds of experiments can be done to determine the utility she assigns to having a miscarriage.

The basic approach used in constructing interval scaled utilities is to have the decision maker compare pairs of gambles. Here, the normative component is less obvious than with the dutch book argument, but it is there nonetheless. This approach assumes that a person's choices among gambles *should* obey certain rules. For instance, when the utility of two options is the same, the person should be happy to substitute one for the other. Conversely, when a person is indifferent between two options the utility assigned to both *should* be the same. If one option, A, is preferred to another, B, and B is preferred to a third, C, then A *should* also be preferred to C.

4. FINDING PROBABILISTIC DEGREES OF BELIEF

By a series of thought experiments similar to those used to find interval scaled utilities, we can find personal probabilistic degrees of belief. Here it is common to use what might be called calibrating urns. This can be explained by example.

Recall the Red Sox bets. We used Walter's betting rate—the most he would pay for a $10-pot bet on the Red Sox winning the American League pennant—to find his degree of belief that the Red Sox will win. Walter might decline to bet on the grounds that he has no idea whether or not the Red Sox will win. According to the definition of betting rates, Walter has a degree of belief of zero that the Red Sox will win—he is not willing to put up any money to collect a $10 pot if they win. This may not express Walter's views about the Red Sox. He may decline to bet because he fears the knowledge of the person proposing to bet with him. In fact, Walter may think that there is a pretty good chance that the Red Sox will win. His betting rate, however, turns out not to be a good way to ascertain his degree of belief.

Another way to find Walter's degrees of belief is to offer him a series of *hypothetical* options. He could wager $5 at even odds on the Red Sox or he could draw a ball from an urn with 50 red balls and 50 blue balls. If he gets a red ball, he receives $5; if he gets a blue ball, he loses $5 (Figure 11.6). The utilities of the outcomes of these two gambles are the same. Thus, if Walter has a preference for one gamble, it must reflect, at some level, something about his degrees of belief. Suppose that he prefers to draw from the urn. We can infer that his degree of belief that the Red Sox will win is less than 0.5—which is the reasonable value for his degree of belief that he will win with the urn. Walter is not required to bet. We are only interested in his preference between these two gambles. He can also prefer not betting to taking either gamble.

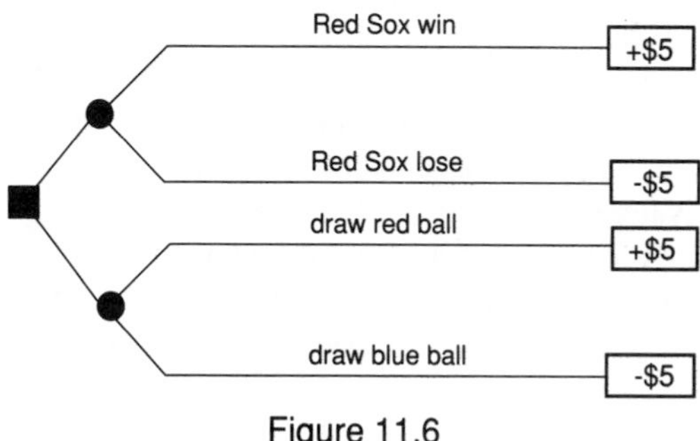

Figure 11.6

We could then offer another pair of options: the same bet on the Red Sox, but instead of drawing from an urn with 50 red and 50 blue balls, he would get to draw from an urn with 25 red and 75 blue balls; again he wins when he draws a red ball. If he still prefers the urn, we could reduce the number of red balls further still, all the way to zero red balls and 100 blue balls if necessary. Eventually, there will be some number of red balls in the urn where he would prefer to gamble on the Red Sox. By using a sufficient number of such comparisons we should be able to find a number which, in comparison with these calibrating urns, represents Walter's subjective degree of belief that the Red Sox will win.

We can put this another way, there is some number, R, of red balls, such that Walter would be indifferent between gambling on the Red Sox and gambling on drawing a red ball from an urn with R out of 100 red balls. Since the utilities for winning and losing in either gamble are the same, we infer that $R/100$ is Walter's personal degree of belief that the Red Sox will win.

This way of finding degrees of belief has the consequence that degrees of belief must be probabilities. Fundamentally, the reason is this: We find gambles with risks that are probabilities—because of the frequencies behind urn drawings. When someone is indifferent between two gambles, he or she is willing to substitute one for the other. Thus a "probabilistic gamble" can be substituted for a gamble with risks that are not obviously probabilistic.

This point can be made in greater detail by continuing with the Red Sox example. If Walter's degrees of belief about the Red Sox were probabilities, they must be additive: $\text{DoB}(\mathbf{W}) + \text{DoB}(\mathbf{L}) = 1$, to use a self-evident notation. Suppose that Walter is indifferent between a gamble on the Red Sox and drawing from an urn with R out of 100 red balls—Walter's degree of belief that the Red Sox will win is $R/100$. For Walter's degrees of belief to be probabilities, he must have degree of belief $(100 - R)/100$ that the Red Sox will not win: $\text{DoB}(\mathbf{W}) + \text{DoB}(\mathbf{L}) = R/100 + (100 - R)/100 = 1$. That is, given the manner we have for determining degrees of belief, he would also be indifferent between gambling against the Red Sox and drawing from an urn with $(100 - R)$ red balls in it. Here is an argument which shows that he should have such preferences.

Consider the following hybrid gamble: A fair coin is flipped, the outcome of which determines how prizes are awarded in the Red Sox bet. In Figure 11.7, the upper subtree, marked A, is the bet on the Red Sox we have considered all along. The lower subtree, B, has the payoffs reversed. We have shown that Walter is indifferent between subgamble A and drawing from an urn with R out of 100 red balls. By a series of hypothetical options like those above we can also find another number, S, such that Walter would be indifferent between subgamble B and drawing from an urn with S red balls. We want to show that $S = 100 - R$.

Since Walter is indifferent between these two urn gambles, with R and S red balls, and bets for and against the Red Sox, respectively, we can substitute these two urn gambles (Figure 11.8). We can compute the expected utility of the urn gamble:

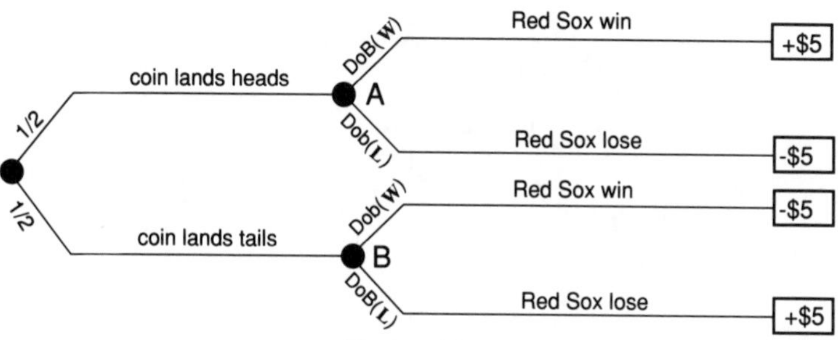

Figure 11.7

$$\left(\frac{1}{2}\right)\left[\left(\frac{R}{100}\times +5\right)+\left(\frac{100-R}{100}\times -5\right)\right]$$
$$+\left(\frac{1}{2}\right)\left[\left(\frac{100-S}{100}\times -5\right)+\left(\frac{S}{100}\times +5\right)\right]$$
$$=\left(\frac{1}{2}\right)\frac{R-50}{10}+\left(\frac{1}{2}\right)\left(\frac{S-50}{10}\right)=\frac{R+S-100}{20}.$$

Now suppose that the coin toss came after the Red Sox had won or lost (Figure 11.9). Since this is the same gamble as the original hybrid coin/Red Sox gamble, it must have the same expected utility. Thus the expected utility of this new way of putting the hybrid coin/Red Sox gamble must be $(R + S - 100)/20$. But we can also compute its utility directly. It is zero:

$$\frac{R}{100}\left[\left(\frac{1}{2}\times +5\right)+\left(\frac{1}{2}\times -5\right)\right]+\frac{S}{100}\left[\left(\frac{1}{2}\times -5\right)+\left(\frac{1}{2}\times +5\right)\right]=0.$$

These results must be the same. They are utilities for the same gamble:

$$\frac{R+S-100}{20}=0;$$
$$\Rightarrow R+S=100;$$
$$\Rightarrow S=100-R.$$

This is what we wanted to show. As with the dutch book argument, with more than two bets, the proof gets algebraically more complicated, but the underlying ideas are the same.

Here we use the force of substitutivity and transitivity of choices among gambles to show that degrees of belief should be probabilities. A person whose degrees of belief were not probabilities would violate these principles somewhere in his or her choices of gambles. Since these principles are plausible regulative cannons for choices among risky alternatives, it is plausible that a person's degrees of belief should be probabilities.

1/2
1/2
coin lands heads
coin lands tails
DoB(W)
DoB(L)
DoB(W)
DoB(L)
Red Sox win
Red Sox lose
Red Sox win
Red Sox lose
+$5
-$5
-$5
+$5
is equivalent to
1/2
1/2
coin lands heads
coin lands tails
R /100
(100 - R)/100
(100 - S)/100
S /100
draw red
draw blue
draw blue
draw red
+$5
-$5
-$5
+$5

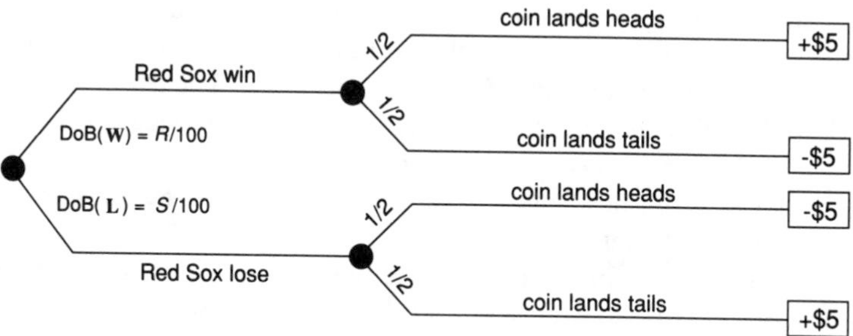

5. TWO OTHER SOURCES FOR DEGREES OF BELIEF

The arguments in the previous sections show why it is plausible to demand that a person's degrees of belief obey the probability laws and that his or her utilities be measurable with an interval scale. In one sense, as far as what might be called the "logic of consistency" is concerned, that is the end of matters. We have a theory which says "if you have such and such preferences among gambles . . . , then you should also have these other preferences. . . ." This is rather like the cannons of deductive logic. If, for example, you believe that all dogs have fleas, and Socrates is a dog, then deductive logic requires that you also believe that Socrates has fleas. To do otherwise is inconsistent. But, depending on just who or what "Socrates" refers to, you probably should not believe that Socrates, the philosopher, is a dog. A logic of consistency does not require one to have sensible beliefs, it only requires beliefs that are mutually consistent.

When we use Bayesian theory to help make medical decisions, for example, we want something more than risk-taking consistency. In the pulmonary embolism example (see Chapter 3, Section 5) we noted that 5% of patients treated with anti-coagulants had a serious undesirable side effect. This 5% is not simply the patient's degree of belief about this—although in the example we have treated it as her degree of belief. This 5% is taken from the frequencies of such events recorded in medical experience. Thus, we require her degrees of belief to be particular probabilities—5% in this instance.

This is a dangerous requirement, for there may be something about this woman which makes her more prone than average to a serious side effect. If there were and if she knew about it, of course, she should take this additional information into account; her degree of belief that she will have a serious side effect, sensibly, might be higher than 5%. But if she knew of no reason to distinguish herself from other people in the population—as far as such side effects are concerned—she ought to take the frequency probability for her degree of belief. This is sometimes known as the "frequency principle."

The frequency principle has tremendous initial appeal. We made extensive use of it developing the decision trees in Chapter 3. The choices among hypothetical gambles used to extract probabilities in Section 4 were substantially influenced by frequency information. This 30-year-old woman may have no strong convictions about her chances for a serious side effect. She may know of no reason she would be more or less likely than the "average person" to have a serious side effect. In such a situation, knowing the frequency may largely determine her convictions. In many medical contexts, given how much patients typically know, frequencies sensibly determine degrees of belief.

The frequency principle need not be interpreted in an overly strong sense. It is possible that the 30-year-old woman might believe that she always bleeds easily from cuts. This might be little more than a hunch—"It seems that I bleed almost immediately when I scratch an insect bite, much more quickly than any of my friends." Such hunches can undermine use of the frequency principle. The principle operates only when one knows of *no reason* to distinguish oneself from others in the population in relevant respects.

The frequency principle gives us one other source for finding degrees of belief; Bayes' rule gives us another. In the preceding section we argued that a person's degrees of belief should obey the probability laws. This does not tell us what to do when we learn something new. In the pulmonary embolism example we considered running tests to determine whether the chest pain was caused by a pulmonary embolism (see Chapter 3, Section 7). If a lung scan is done and it is positive for pulmonary embolism, the patient's degrees of belief should change to reflect this new information. Bayes' rule tells us how such changes should go.

In Chapter 3 we used little "helping trees" to see how information from tests such as a lung scan should modify degrees of belief (see Figures 3.11 and 3.12). Bayes' rule wraps such reflections up into a simple formula. One starts with a prior (to the evidence) assignment of probabilities to one's beliefs, **A**, **B**, **C**, and so on—$P_{prior}(\mathbf{A})$, $P_{prior}(\mathbf{B})$, $P_{prior}(\mathbf{C})$, and so on. One gets some evidence, **E**, which now is assigned probability 1. One shifts the probabilities assigned to **A**, **B**, and so on, to posterior (to the evidence) probabilities according to Bayes' rule for conditional probabilities:

$$P_{posterior}(\mathbf{E}) = 1;$$

$$P_{posterior}(\mathbf{A}) = P_{prior}(\mathbf{A}|\mathbf{E}) = \frac{P_{prior}(\mathbf{A}) \times P_{prior}(\mathbf{E}|\mathbf{A})}{P_{prior}(\mathbf{E})}; \text{ and}$$

$$P_{posterior}(\mathbf{B}) = P_{prior}(\mathbf{B}|\mathbf{E}) = \frac{P_{prior}(\mathbf{B}) \times P_{prior}(\mathbf{E}|\mathbf{B})}{P_{prior}(\mathbf{E})}; \text{ etc.}$$

We require posterior probabilities to equal prior probabilities conditional on the new evidence: $P_{posterior}(\mathbf{A}) = P_{prior}(\mathbf{A}|\mathbf{E})$.

Reconsider the lung scan example. We want the posterior probability—degree of belief—that the woman had a pulmonary embolism given a positive lung scan: $P_{posterior}(\mathbf{PE})$. According to Bayes' rule we should compute the following:

$$P_{prior}(\mathbf{PE}|+) = \frac{P_{prior}(\mathbf{PE}) \times P_{prior}(+|\mathbf{PE})}{P_{prior}(+)}.$$

We know all of the prior probabilities on the right-hand side of this equation. $P_{prior}(\mathbf{PE})$ is just the initial estimate that she had a pulmonary embolism; in this example it was 0.5. $P_{prior}(+|\mathbf{PE})$ is the sensitivity of the test: The test will correctly detect 90 out of 100 pulmonary embolisms. (Notice the use of the frequency principle here.) $P_{prior}(+)$ can be found with the theorem on total probability:

$$P_{prior}(+) = [P_{prior}(\mathbf{PE}) \times P_{prior}(+|\mathbf{PE})] + [P_{prior}(\neg\mathbf{PE}) \times P_{prior}(+|\neg\mathbf{PE})].$$

Here we already know $P_{prior}(\mathbf{PE})$ and $P_{prior}(+|\mathbf{PE})$. Consistency of degrees of belief requires that $P_{prior}(\neg\mathbf{PE}) = 1 - P_{prior}(\mathbf{PE})$. $P_{prior}(+|\neg\mathbf{PE})$ is the false positive rate of the test—which, in this example, was 0.3. We can plug all of this information into Bayes' rule:

$$P_{posterior}(\mathbf{PE}) = \frac{P_{prior}(\mathbf{PE}) \times P_{prior}(+|\mathbf{PE})}{[P_{prior}(\mathbf{PE}) \times P_{prior}(+|\mathbf{PE})] + [P_{prior}(\neg\mathbf{PE}) \times P_{prior}(+|\neg\mathbf{PE})]}$$

$$= \frac{0.5 \times 0.9}{(0.5 \times 0.9) + (0.5 \times 0.3)} = 0.75.$$

This result, 0.75, is the same as the result we found using the helping trees (see Figure 3.12).

Bayes' rule determines the proportion of positive results, $P_{prior}(+)$, among those which are truly positive, $[P_{prior}(\mathbf{PE}) \times P_{prior}(+|\mathbf{PE})]$. This is just what we did with the "helping trees" in Chapter 3. Bayes' rule expresses this more concisely. By requiring that posterior probabilities equal appropriate prior probabilities—found using Bayes' rule—we have a persuasive way to determine how degrees of belief should respond to new information.

6. SENSITIVITY ANALYSIS

Doubts about precise utilities and degrees of belief may remain. It is very difficult to have much confidence that we know what a person's degrees of belief or utilities are with any exactitude. Hypothetical choices among gambles, such as those above, may not elicit precise values for degrees of belief and utilities.

Thus it is useful to see how precise we have to be, to be confident of our decision-theoretic recommendations. This is called *sensitivity analysis*. Here one typically examines a decision tree after it has been constructed in full detail to see if the decision-theoretic recommendations change when different values for degrees of belief or utilities are used. There is no formula for doing this, as each analysis depends on the specific features of the decision tree at hand. But the general approach and goals are the same.

Here is a sensitivity analysis of the pulmonary embolism example from Chapter 3, Section 5. There we looked at a case of a woman who had just been through a period of severe chest pains. There is, according to the doctor's best informed judgment, a 50% chance that these pains were caused by a blood clot lodged in the woman's lungs. If this were the case, the usual treatment is to administer anticoagulants to thin the blood, and thereby diminish the chance of future clots. If such treatment is not administered, there is a 50% chance of future clots occurring, and if they do occur, another 50% chance that the woman would die from this disease. The treatment reduces the chance of future clots from 50% to 15%. Unfortunately, such a treatment can have a serious side effect of a bleeding episode requiring hospitalization. We wish to determine whether anticoagulant treatment is appropriate in this situation.

We can begin looking at the utilities used in the pulmonary embolism example. Recall Figure 3.5. We assigned utilities to the outcomes by assuming that the disutility of a second pulmonary embolism was the same as the disutility of a serious hemorrhage. If either was a component of the outcome—death aside—we subtracted 10. Similarly, we subtracted 3 for any outcome—death aside—where anticoagulant treatment was used (see Table 3.1). This manipulation of utilities assumes that there is a natural, nonarbitrary, zero for the utility scale—death.

Suppose that the disutility of a serious side effect is the same as the disutility of a second embolism. In Chapter 3 we supposed that both had a disutility of 10. Imagine that it is some fixed but unknown value, represented by the variable **X**. Similarly, suppose that the disutility of having the treatment is another fixed but unknown value, represented by the variable **Y**. We can produce a revised decision tree with these variable utility values in place of -10 and -3 (Figure 11.10). We can take expectations in terms of the variables **X** and **Y**. Doing so, we can find that the utility of not having anticoagulant treatment is $87.5 - 0.125\mathbf{X}$. The utility for having the treatment is $96.25 - 0.085625\mathbf{X} - 0.9625\mathbf{Y}$.

When these expected utilities are equal the patient would be indifferent between having and not having anticoagulant treatment. Thus, if these two equations are equal to each other we get an "indifference equation"—a line of pairs of utility values, each pair corresponding to a case of indifference. The indifference line is found by algebraically manipulating the following equality:

$$87.5 - 0.125\mathbf{X} = 96.25 - 0.085625\mathbf{X} - 0.9625\mathbf{Y}$$

$$\Rightarrow 0.9625\mathbf{Y} = 0.039375\mathbf{X} + 8.75$$

$$\Rightarrow \mathbf{Y} = 0.040909\mathbf{X} + 9.0909.$$

A graph of this equation is shown in Figure 11.11. Pairs of utility values that fall above this line correspond to cases where no treatment is preferred to treatment. Pairs of utility values that fall below this line correspond to cases where treatment is preferred.

If we assume that the disutility of the treatment is fairly small—in Chapter 3 we took it to be 3, but anything less than 9 will suffice—then treatment would be

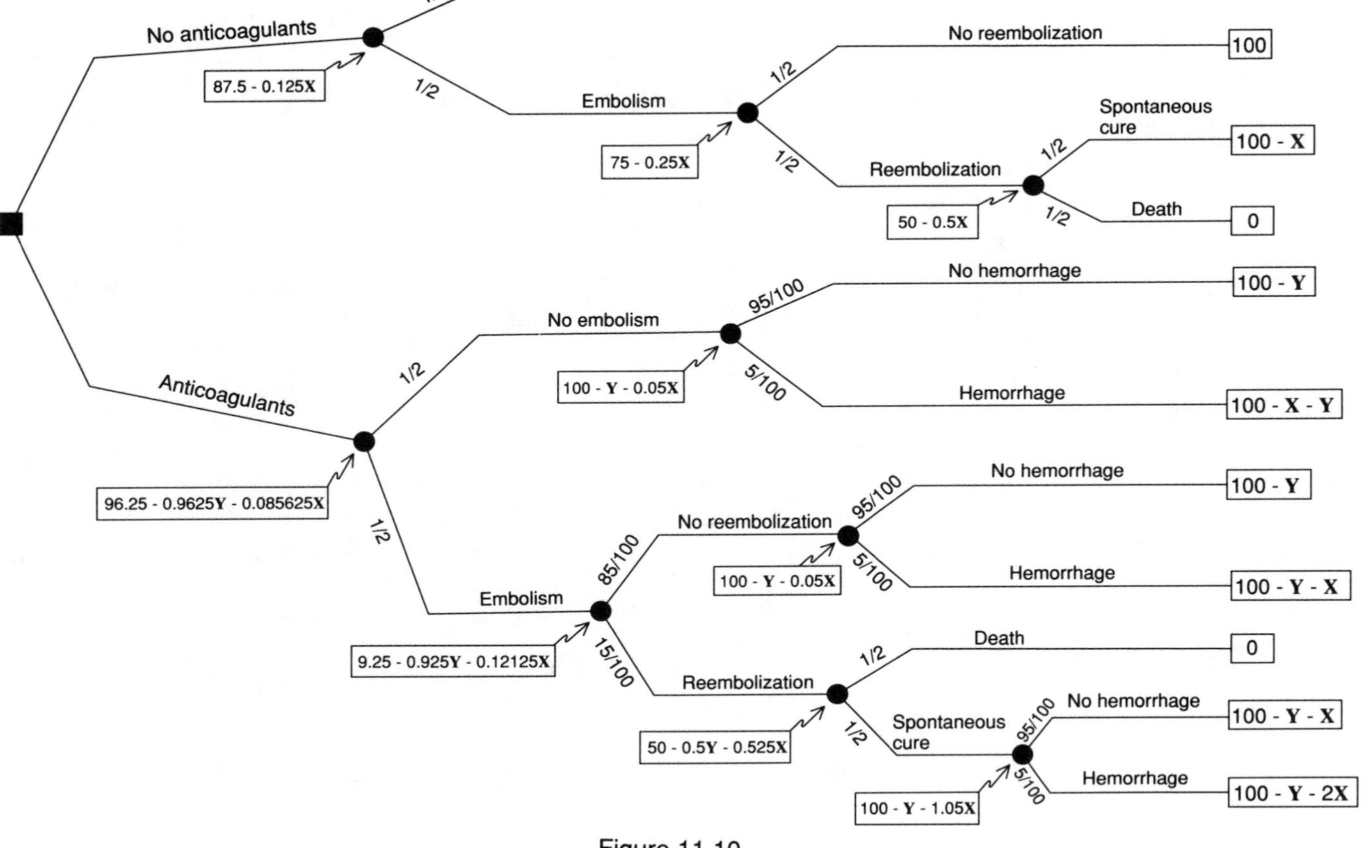
No anticoagulants
1/2
87.5 - 0.125X
1/2
Embolism
75 - 0.25X
1/2
No reembolization
100
1/2
Reembolization
50 - 0.5X
1/2
Spontaneous cure
100 - X
1/2
Death
0
Anticoagulants
96.25 - 0.9625Y - 0.085625X
1/2
No embolism
100 - Y - 0.05X
95/100
No hemorrhage
100 - Y
5/100
Hemorrhage
100 - X - Y
1/2
Embolism
9.25 - 0.925Y - 0.12125X
85/100
No reembolization
100 - Y - 0.05X
95/100
No hemorrhage
100 - Y
5/100
Hemorrhage
100 - Y - X
15/100
Reembolization
50 - 0.5Y - 0.525X
1/2
Death
0
1/2
Spontaneous cure
100 - Y - 1.05X
95/100
No hemorrhage
100 - Y - X
5/100
Hemorrhage
100 - Y - 2X

Figure 11.10

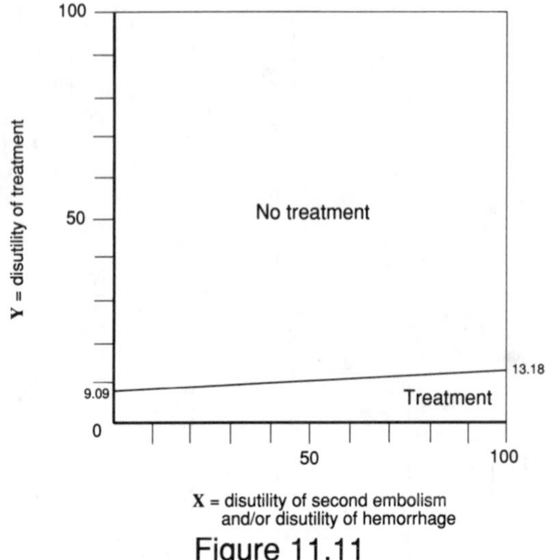

Figure 11.11

preferred to no treatment no matter what the disutility of a second embolism is. Furthermore, changes in the disutility of the side effect have almost no impact on the decision-theoretic recommendations; the indifference line is nearly horizontal. Roughly speaking, avoiding death swamps all other considerations. In any case, the disutility assigned to the treatment is not even close to a point where no treatment would be preferred. Even if the disutility of the treatment is only *roughly* 3, treatment is preferable to no treatment.

We can also do a sensitivity analysis of the probabilities. In the pulmonary embolism case most of the probabilities are taken directly from frequency data in the medical literature. The probability that the chest pain was caused by an embolism in the first place, however, was based on "educated intuition." Consequently, it is worthwhile to see how important this value is for the recommended decision. We can get a good idea of its importance from a shortened version of the pulmonary embolism tree shown in Figure 11.12. Here we have taken expectations and folded back the tree (see Figure 3.9) to the point where it is easier to assess the effect of the treatment on the utilities. Suppose the probability that an embolism caused the pain was p. Given the utilities in this shortened tree, for what values of p would treatment be preferable? In terms of expected utility, this question asks for what values of p is $[(1-p)100 + p72.5]$ greater than $[(1-p)96.5 + p88.5]$? We can solve this inequality:

$$[(1-p)100 + p72.5] \geq [(1-p)96.596.5 + p88.5]$$

$$\Rightarrow 100 - 27.5p \geq 96.5 - 8.0p \Rightarrow 3.5 \geq 19.5p$$

$$\Rightarrow 0.2 \geq p.$$

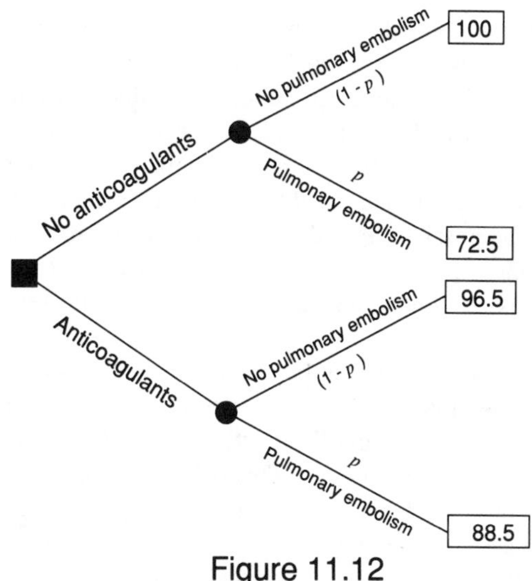

Figure 11.12

The value of 0.5 is considerably larger than 0.2. Thus for a wide spectrum of degrees of belief, treatment is preferable to no treatment.

7. REPRESENTING IGNORANCE

This Bayesian approach to induction advocates shifting probabilities in response to new information by means of Bayes' rule and the requirement that $\mathrm{P_{posterior}}(\mathbf{H}) = \mathrm{P_{prior}}(\mathbf{H}|\mathbf{E})$:

$$\mathrm{P_{posterior}}(\mathbf{H}) = \frac{\mathrm{P_{prior}}(\mathbf{H}) \times \mathrm{P_{prior}}(\mathbf{E}|\mathbf{H})}{\mathrm{P_{prior}}(\mathbf{E})}.$$

The new "posterior" probability of some hypothesis, **H**, in light of new evidence, or information, **E**, is proportional to the product of the "prior" probability of **H**, $\mathrm{P_{prior}}(\mathbf{H})$, and the likelihood of the evidence given the hypothesis, $\mathrm{P_{prior}}(\mathbf{E}|\mathbf{H})$. This way of shifting probabilities is sometimes called conditionalization because the posterior probability is given by the prior conditional probability, $\mathrm{P_{posterior}}(\mathbf{H}) = \mathrm{P_{prior}}(\mathbf{H}|\mathbf{E})$.

Finding new posterior probabilities requires knowing prior probabilities. But where do these prior probabilities come from? They could be the posterior probabilities of some previous use of Bayes' rule, but, eventually we need prior probabilities not based on earlier prior probabilities. Another way to ask this question is to ask how total ignorance can be represented.

Consider the baseball bets above. Consider a person, call him George, who knows nothing of team sports and certainly has never heard of baseball; George may not know how many teams compete in a baseball game. Suppose that we ask George what he thinks the chances are that the Red Sox will win the American League pennant. If we apply the "calibrating urn" approach to finding degrees of belief, we may find a number of red balls, *R*, such that George would prefer to gamble on drawing a ball from an urn with *R* or more red balls, than to gamble on the Red Sox, whereas for any urn with fewer than *R* red balls, George would prefer to gamble on the Red Sox. It may be possible to find such *R*s and thereby to find a "degree of belief" in a formal sense. It does not seem sensible, however, to interpret the ratio that follows, *R*/100, as an honest degree of belief. There are several reasons for this.

There is a problem of what might be called "faithfulness to mental states." Suppose, for concreteness, that *R*/100 turned out to be 0.5. George may know quite a bit about horse racing, and on careful reflection have a 0.5 degree of belief that "Fancy Dancer" will win a certain race. This 0.5 degree of belief corresponds to quite a different state of mind than does George's 0.5 degree of belief that the Red Sox will win. In one case 0.5 represents careful, informed judgment, in the other, utter ignorance. If we are to represent degrees of belief with numbers, we may want to have such different states of mind reflected in different numbers.

There is a problem of stability. George may have found a degree of belief of 0.5 because of ephemeral features of the context in which the hypothetical gambles with urns were presented. Had we done these thought experiments on some other day or in some other way, he may have found an entirely different ratio, 0.3 perhaps. Usually, when forced, people can state preferences between gambles. But it is not clear that such preferences have much to do with a person's *state of conviction*.

Finally, there is a problem of reasonableness. At the time of the play-offs, when all but two teams have been eliminated, it may make sense to have degree of belief 0.5 that the Red Sox will win—even when totally ignorant about baseball. This way one would have the same degree of belief that the other team will win. But early in the baseball season, when several teams are still in the running for the American League pennant, a degree of belief of 0.5 for the Red Sox will treat them differently from other competing teams—for no reason. Worse, when one is totally ignorant about baseball, one simply may not know how many possible winners there are. Thus, while one may want to treat each possible winner the same, one may not have enough knowledge to do so.

Several approaches have been pursued to deal with this problem of ignorance. Several Bayesians have tried to find "objective" prior probabilities. Here instead of treating probability simply as a degree of belief, it is treated as an objective feature of the relationship between evidence and hypotheses. This is analogous to deductive relationships. From **A** we can infer **A** or **B**, because there is the right kind of relationship between sentences which have these structures. The analogous move for Bayesians is to find relationships between certain kinds of sentences that can underwrite prior probabilities—and to suggest that a person's degrees of belief should agree with these objective probabilities.

For example, when we flip a coin, we usually think that there are exactly two possible outcomes. If we are entirely ignorant about which will occur, we should have prior probabilities that do not treat them differently: thus P(**H**) = P(**T**) = 1/2. That is, prior to any evidence, P(**H**) = P(**T**) = 1/2. According to this approach, this is an objective feature about coin flipping. When there is no evidence for bias either way, P(**H**) = P(**T**) = 1/2. As we flip the coin we may come to understand that the coin is indeed biased for heads; our probabilities would change to reflect this by means of Bayes' rule. But we start with this "ignorance prior."

This approach has substantial appeal, but it suffers from two difficulties. First, finding objective ignorance priors requires that we know how many possibilities there are. This frequently is not the case. An objectivist may retort that it is of no concern whether anyone *knows* how many possibilities there are, what matters is how many there are *in fact*. Objective prior probabilities do not depend on any person's knowledge of the world. This is still not fully satisfactory because, in order to *use* the Bayesian approach, we need prior probabilities, and thus must know how many possibilities there are.

Second, it is very difficult to find satisfactory criteria for ignorance priors which will produce unique priors. This is particularly a problem when there are an infinite number of possible outcomes. Consider a simple example. There is a cube, the dimensions of which we are entirely ignorant of, other than to know that its sides are between 1 and 3 meters in length. We could develop an ignorance prior in terms of all of the infinite number of different possible lengths the side of the cube might be. We treat each possible side length the same. We would adopt a "uniform prior probability density function" (see Chapter 9, Section 7) over side lengths from 1 to 3 meters. Alternatively, we could treat each possible *volume* the same. In this case we would adopt a uniform prior probability density function over volumes from 1 to 27 cubic meters. These two prior probability functions differ. In particular, for example, if we use the first side length prior, the probability that the cube in question has a side length between 1 and 2 meters is 1/2; if we use the second volume prior, the probability that the cube in question has a side length between 1 and 2 meters—a volume between 1 and 8 cubic meters—is $7/27 \neq 1/2$ (Figure 11.13). These two ignorance priors differ and so must the probabilities calculated from evidence when starting with one or the other of them. Serious and detailed attempts have been made to overcome these difficulties and find unique ignorance priors for such cases. But none has been fully persuasive or, alternatively, fully successful.

Another approach to the ignorance problem is to live with it. A thorough subjectivist may say that a person's prior, when ignorant, may not be stable. It may differ radically from another ignorant person's prior. Its actual values may have more to do with ephemeral issues than conviction. We should not be surprised; *the person really is ignorant*. But, after time, as information bearing on the issues at hand accumulates, this ignorance prior becomes unimportant. It does not matter so much where one's degrees of belief are at the outset. In the long run, degrees of belief are largely determined by the evidence.

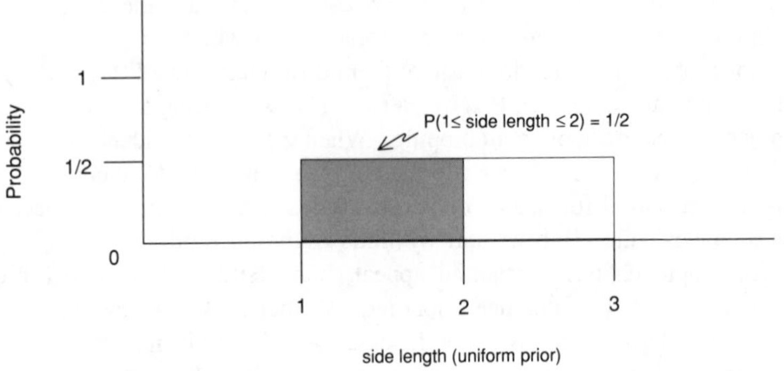

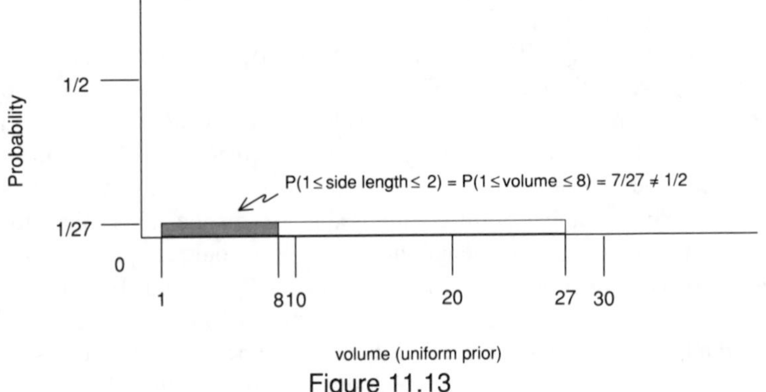

Figure 11.13

There is a theorem that can make this claim quite precise, and its sense can b nicely conveyed by a coin example. Suppose that one has a coin whose bias fo heads, call it θ, one is completely ignorant of, other than to know $0 < \theta < 1$. On can start with any prior probability density function for the possible values of θ. On can then flip the coin several times, observing the number of heads and tails and u this evidence to compute posterior probability density function by Bayes' rule. N matter what prior one started with, as the evidence accumulates—as the number flips gets bigger—the posterior density function will become very localized aroun values near the mean of the number of heads in the sequence of flips. Large diffe ences in prior probability density functions wash away as the evidence accumulate Degrees of belief, it seems, converge to the truth.

This theorem rests on certain assumptions that undermine some of its ability put aside the problem of ignorance. The theorem depends on no possibility bein assigned probability 1 or zero. Evidence can have no impact via Bayes' rule on hypotheses whose degrees of belief are either zero or 1. In a certain sense, this is nicely antidogmatic. But possibilities that are not imagined typically get probability zero. In the coin example, for instance, we started with a prior over possible values of the coin's bias for heads. Here we assumed—and assign probability 1 in doing so—that flips of the coin are independent and that there is a constant probability for heads. We did not even consider the possibility that the coin's behavior is controlled in some other way. We may not have the necessary language to describe such a possibility. If some such other possibility was true of the coin, degrees of belief could not converge to the truth as the evidence accumulated because the truth started with zero probability.

8. GLOBAL AND LOCAL PERSPECTIVES

The Bayesian approach provides a conceptually unified way to organize inductive learning about the world. Degrees of belief provide a very useful way to characterize attitudes that must fall short of complete conviction as we learn about the world. These degrees of belief can be nicely integrated into a decision theory which is useful and which also helps to characterize attitudes that fall short of complete conviction. Taken in its most grandiose terms, it provides a framework and prescriptions for how one's attitudes about the truth of anything should change as one learns about the world. Several philosophers of science have urged that the Bayesian approach can completely explain virtually every aspect of scientific progress.

This generality makes the Bayesian approach vulnerable to a variety of criticisms. One aspect of the ignorance problem urges that having degree of belief 0.5 may properly correspond to a variety of different mental states from utter ignorance to total confidence that "things could go either way." Another aspect of the ignorance problem urges that one must know of every possibility, so that something that turns out to be possible is not mistakenly assigned probability zero. Seen as an explanation of the development of science, this second problem can be quite a stumbling block, for it is understanding and describing new possibilities that is a hallmark of many significant scientific advances.

Seen in more local terms, however, the Bayesian approach is not easy prey to such problems. Given certain plausible assumptions taken from the context, sensible prior probabilities may be found which help us analyze the impact of a bit of evidence on a given collection of possible hypotheses. The frequency principle may be a good place to start finding probabilities. When such prior probabilities cannot be found, perhaps the Bayesian approach will not be helpful; other approaches may be necessary. Instead of seeing degrees of belief as the fully adequate framework for describing people's mental attitudes toward the truth, they can be seen as a useful and communicable way to describe the results of some inductions.

9. SUMMARY

1. The Bayesian approach provides a framework for describing appropriate attitudes to take toward fallible inductions.
   - (a) The framework of degrees of belief allows for attitudes that fall short of conviction, but do not correspond to complete ignorance either.
   - (b) Inductive learning from experience can sensibly be understood as the shifting of degrees of belief in response to evidence.
   - (c) The nature of degrees of belief can be understood in terms of preferred actions.

2. The Bayesian approach has a normative dimension.
   - (a) Actual people may have degrees of belief that do not obey the probability rules. This can be seen as a failing of these people instead of a failing of Bayesian theory.
   - (b) There are specific senses in which to argue that people whose degrees of belief do not obey probability are irrational.
   - (c) Given certain assumptions about betting, one can show that only those people whose degrees of belief do not obey probability are subject to books of bets where, no matter what happens, they would suffer a loss.

3. A more persuasive argument can be used to underwrite the Bayesian approach.
   - (a) Here one aims to show concurrently that people should have degrees of belief that obey probability and preferences that are measurable with an interval-valued utility scale.
   - (b) To construct an interval-valued utility scale for a given decision maker, one first arbitrarily assigns numerical utilities to the best and worst outcomes.
   - (c) A utility value for another outcome, ***O***, can be found by finding the probability, p, where the decision maker is indifferent between ***O*** for certain and a gamble with a p chance for the best outcome and a $(1-p)$ chance for the worst outcome. The expected utility of this gamble is the utility of ***O***.
   - (d) To find the probabilistic degree of belief the decision maker has for some outcome, ***O***, one seeks the probability, p, where the decision maker is indifferent between gambling on ***O*** and gambling on drawing a ball from an urn where the probability of winning is p. The utilities are the same for winning or losing either gamble. The probability of drawing a winning ball from the urn, p, is the decision maker's degree of belief in ***O***.
   - (e) These methods of constructing utility scales and probabilistic degrees of belief depend on certain assumptions about a decision maker's preferences.
     - (1) Transitivity: If gamble A is preferred to gamble B, and gamble B is preferred to gamble C, then gamble A is preferred to gamble C.
     - (2) Substitutivity: If the decision maker is indifferent between two gambles, A and B, they have the same value, and vice versa.

4. Bayesian probabilities are found from two other sources.
   - (a) In the absence of any reason to think a particular case differs from average, it is common to use the observed population frequency for degree of belief probability.
   - (b) Degree of belief probabilities respond to evidence according to Bayes' rule. Given prior probabilities, new posterior probabilities, given new evidence, can be computed: $P_{posterior}(\mathbf{H}) = P_{prior}(\mathbf{H}|\mathbf{E}) = [P_{prior}(\mathbf{H}) \times P_{prior}(\mathbf{E}|\mathbf{H})]/P_{prior}(\mathbf{E})$.

5. Exact numerical utilities and exact degrees of belief are not always necessary to find preferable courses of action.
   (a) By varying the values of degrees of belief and utilities with which the decision maker has the least confidence, one can determine the ranges of values for which the same course of action would be recommended. This is called sensitivity analysis.
   (b) In nice cases, the range of values for which a given course of action is recommended will provide a wide "margin of error" for troubling degrees of belief and utilities.

6. One central difficulty Bayesian degrees of belief suffer from is representing ignorance.
   (a) Although it may be possible to construct degrees of belief for some event about which the decision maker is ignorant, it is not clear that these degrees of belief provide a satisfactory representation of the decision maker's conviction that this event will occur.
   (b) "Ignorance degrees of belief" are difficult to distinguish from "knowledgeable degrees of belief," when both have the same numerical value.
   (c) Ignorance degrees of belief may not be stable, corresponding more to ephemeral features of the context in which they are elicited than to a person's state of conviction.
   (d) Ignorance degrees of belief may have difficulty treating every possible outcome the same—as one might wish to in a state of ignorance—when one is also ignorant of what possibilities there are.
   (e) One approach to coping with this problem is to seek objective probabilities that one should adopt when ignorant.
   (f) Another approach is not to worry so much about ignorance degrees of belief, and to rely on the fact that via Bayes' rule, degrees of belief based on evidence washes out the effect of ignorance degrees of belief.
   (g) Understood as a tool to help understand inductions in a local or circumscribed context, the Bayesian approach may have fewer difficulties representing ignorance.

10. REFERENCES

Thomas Bayes' original 1763 essay is reprinted in (Pearson and Kendall, 1970). The approach was quite popular during much of the early 1800s. (Venn, 1866) includes an early criticism of the Bayesian approach. (Fisher, 1956) includes a brief discussion of the early history of the Bayesian approach during the 1800s emphasizing the problem of prior probabilities—what is called here the problem of ignorance.

The Bayesian approach is enjoying a resurgence in popularity. Three modern classic sources for the derivation of Bayesian probabilistic degrees of belief and interval scaled utilities are (Ramsey, 1926), (de Finetti, 1937), and (Savage, 1954). (Davidson et al., 1957) is a philosophically and empirically careful examination of the difficulties of measuring degrees of belief and utilities. (Krantz et al., 1971) includes a detailed discussion of the measure-theoretic assumptions required by this Bayesian approach. (Raiffa, 1970) is a very readable and persuasive introduction to

Bayesian decision theory. (Iversen, 1984) provides an elementary introduction to Bayesian statistical practice; (Berger, 1985) is more elaborate on this topic.

(Glymour, 1980) attacks Bayesian claims to explain scientific progress; (Horwich, 1982) defends these claims. (Rosenkrantz, 1977) is a detailed, but demanding, development of Bayesianism with objective probabilities with an emphasis on the Bayesian explanation of scientific progress. (Jeffrey, 1983), (Kyburg, 1974, 1977, and 1983), and (Levi, 1977, 1980, and 1981) provide some of the recent philosophical debate over the Bayesian approach.

11. PROBLEMS

1. Suppose that Walter is interested in betting on who will win the next men's singles at Wimbledon. He offers the following odds: Becker, 0.4; Lendl, 0.3; McEnroe, 0.2; someone else, 0.4. Construct a dutch book of bets against Walter.
2. Suppose instead that Walter's betting rates on Becker, Lendl, McEnroe, and someone else are 0.3, 0.2, 0.2, and 0.1, respectively. Construct a dutch book of bets against Walter.
3. Suppose that Walter's betting rates obey the probability laws. Show that no set of three bets can be constructed so that Walter would lose money no matter what happens.
4. Attempt to carry out the "calibrating urn technique" for constructing personal probabilities with an unsuspecting friend. Pick some future event whose outcome is not certain and try, by offering various alternative urn gambles, to find your friend's degree of belief. Discuss the results of your experiment.
5. Do Problem 4, but pick some future event about which your friend is entirely ignorant. Discuss the results.
6. Consider Problem 5 from Chapter 3.
   (a) In terms of Bayes' rule, what is the probability that a baby who tested left-handed really is left-handed?
   (b) Suppose that the test developed by the psychologist was more accurate than stated in Problem 5 from Chapter 3; it will properly label 99% of all babies. In light of this change, what is the probability that a baby who tested left-handed really is left-handed?
7. Suppose that you have a coin whose bias for heads, θ, is unknown, except that you know it is either fair—$\theta = 1/2$—or strongly biased for heads—$\theta = 9/10$. You are certain that flips are probabilistically independent and have the same probability for heads, whatever that turns out to be. Suppose that you flip the coin 10 times and get 8 heads. Compute the posterior probability that the coin has a bias for heads 9/10 in each of the two following cases:
   (a) Your prior probabilities are equally distributed on the two possibilities: $P_{prior}(\theta = 1/2) = P_{prior}(\theta = 9/10) = 1/2$.
   (b) Your prior probabilities favor fairness: $P_{prior}(\theta = 1/2) = 3/4$; $P_{prior}(\theta = 9/10) = 1/4$.
8. Suppose that you continue flipping the coin from Problem 7.
   (a) In the next 10 flips, you get another 8 heads. Use the posterior probabilities computed in Problem 7(a) and (b) as two different sets of prior probabilities to compute new posterior probabilities.

(b) Suppose that you flip the coin another 10 times—for a total of 30 flips—and get another 8 heads. Using the two sets of posterior probabilities you computed in (a), compute new posterior probabilities.

(c) Discuss the impact of the different prior probabilities in Problem 7(a) and (b) on the final posterior probabilities computed after 30 flips with 24 heads in 8(b).

9. Consider yet again the coin example from Problems 7 and 8. Suppose that your prior probabilities rule out $\theta = 9/10$: $P_{prior}(\theta = 1/2) = 1$; $P_{prior}(\theta = 9/10) = 0$. Compute posterior probabilities after 8 heads in 10 flips, 16 heads in 20 flips, and 24 heads in 30 flips. Discuss the impact of the evidence in this case.

10. Consider the amniocentesis decision problem discussed briefly in Section 3 and in Chapter 3, Problem 7. Assume that the woman in question is 49 years old and has a 1/12 chance of carrying a Down's syndrome fetus. Assume that the test can detect 99% of all Down's syndrome fetuses and will mistakenly label a fetus without Down's syndrome as having Down's syndrome on no more than 0.1% = 1/1,000 of uses. Assume that 5 times in 1,000, the test will cause a spontaneous miscarriage, and that given a positive for Down's result from the test, the woman would elect to abort the fetus. Establish a utility scale from 0—baby born with Down's syndrome—to 100—baby born without Down's syndrome. Leave the utilities for miscarriage and abortion as variables, **M** and **A**. Compute the indifference equation in terms of **M** and **A**. That is, determine for what pairs of values of **M** and **A** the 49-year-old woman would be indifferent between having the test and not having the test. Discuss how this indifference equation can be used as part of a sensitivity analysis of the woman's preferences for having amniocentesis or not.

11. Suppose that I offer to flip a fair coin as many times as it takes for it to land heads once. It might land heads on the first flip, or it might take four flips, or any number of flips, N, to land heads once. I agree to pay you 2^N dollars however many flips, N, it takes for the coin to land heads. What is the expected monetary value of this game? Is this a fair price for this game? Why or why not? Discuss the implications of this problem for using expected monetary values as a measure of the fair price for some game.

12. Suppose that you and a second person each hold a sealed envelope. Both of you know that one envelope contains twice the amount of money as the other envelope, but neither of you know which envelope has more money in it.

(a) Suppose that you opened your envelope and found $10. You can choose to keep your $10 or trade it for the other person's envelope. Which option has higher expected monetary value?

(b) Suppose that you do not open your envelope and do not know how much money it contains. Still, you can choose to keep whatever your envelope contains or trade it for the other person's envelope. Which option has higher expected monetary value, or is it impossible to determine?

(c) Consider (a) and (b) from the other person's point of view. Would he or she rather trade or keep envelopes?

(d) Discuss this implications of this paradox for using expected monetary values as a measure of desirability.

CHAPTER

12

FACTOR ANALYSIS AND THE LOGIC OF DISCOVERY

1. FACTOR ANALYSIS AND FACTORIAL CAUSATION

Factor analysis does something different than either survey sampling or Bayesian decision theory. With survey sampling we generalize features we learn about a sample to the population it is drawn from. With Bayesian inference and decision theory we quantify our degrees of conviction so as to act sensibly despite our incomplete understanding. Factor analysis, in contrast, helps us generate new concepts.

Factor analysis helps generate new concepts by a computationally detailed examination of the pattern of correlations between known variables. Factor analysis seeks sensible possible causes for this pattern of correlations. To do this, factor analysis presupposes, what might be called ''factorial causation.'' At a rough level of approximation, this involves two assumptions. Factor analysis presupposes a general picture for the nature of causal relationships: Causal relationships are between variables and can come in varying degrees of closeness. We quantify this degree of causal relationship between variables with a scale that behaves very much like the correlation scale. Factor analysis also presupposes that correlations between observed variables are the result of causal relationships that these variables have in common with a smaller number of unobserved variables.

The results of factor analyses are subject to various sources of uncertainty. In the first place, only rarely can the correlations whose explanation is sought be assumed to be population correlations; almost always they will be sample correlations. Thus, these sample correlations must be generalized to population correlations. In the second place, factor analysis, by itself, cannot determine which causal system in fact is responsible for observed correlations. If the causal system responsible for observed correlations is not one embraced by factor analysis, if it is not an instance of "factorial causation," then whatever is produced by factor analysis will be a statistical artifact—predictively useful, perhaps, but not descriptively accurate. Finally, a factor analyst must make several decisions for how to proceed when running a factor analysis. Poor decisions can produce poor analyses. Nonetheless, when the assumption of factorial causation is met and when an analyst judges rightly how to proceed, factor analysis can provide detailed descriptions of particular causal systems that could give rise to a bewildering mass of correlational data.

A useful way to see how factor analysis works is to proceed backwards. Usually, factor analysis is used to find factors that can account for known correlations. Here we show how to find correlations from known factors.

Suppose we knew that students evaluated their teachers in terms of one basic characteristic: "*T*eaching Effectiveness," **T**. Initially, we may not know how to measure a student's evaluation of an instructor's "teaching effectiveness." But we can measure a variety of aspects of student's evaluation of an instructor. Suppose that questionnaires are prepared to allow students to rate an instructor on four scales.

C: On a scale from 1 (very little) to 5 (a whole lot), how much did the instructor *C*ommunicate about the subject?

E: On a scale from 1 (not at all) to 5 (very), how *E*nthusiastic was the instructor about teaching the subject?

A: On a scale from 1 (not a chance) to 5 (very likely), how inclined would you be to take *A*nother course from this instructor?

R: On a scale from 1 (would not recommend ever) to 5 (would strongly endorse), how strongly would you *R*ecommend this professor to another student?

Call these the "observed variables" (Figure 12.1). If students really respond to a single underlying characteristic, teaching effectiveness, student responses to these questionnaires should be determined, to a good extent, by this more basic evaluation of instructor. Teaching effectiveness, however, is an unobserved variable. This is all supposition. It may well be that students simply evaluate instructors in a variety of individual and idiosyncratic ways. There is no underlying variable of "teaching effectiveness." If, however, there was such a variable, and if values of this variable really were responsible for student responses to these questionnaires, this kind of causal path diagram would make a lot of sense.

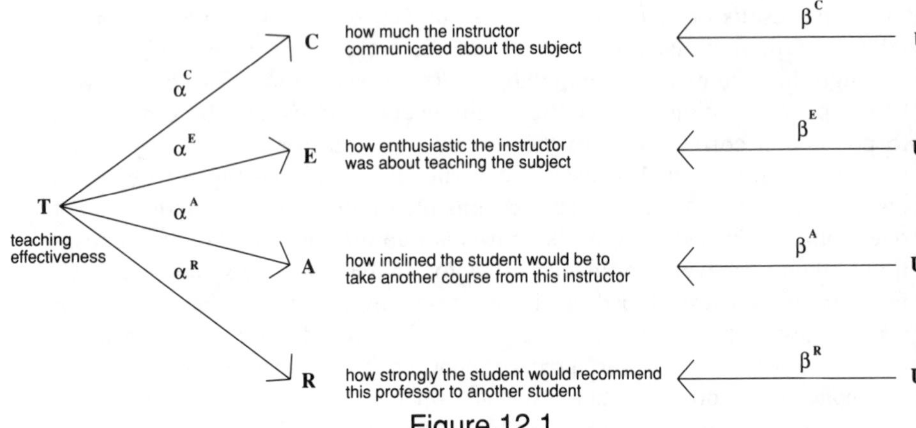

Figure 12.1

The idea behind this path diagram is that the correlations found between the observed variables are the result of relationships that each has to **T**. A high correlation between **E** and **A**, for example, would be the result of the common cause, **T**, not the result of a direct causal relation between **E** and **A**. In terms of the general presupposition of factorial causation, this means that values of the **C** variable, for instance, can be represented as a linear combination of values of **T** and a remaining "random fluctuation" variable $\mathbf{U}^C$, which is *U*nique to ***C***:

$$\mathbf{C} = (\alpha^C \times \mathbf{T}) + (\beta^C \times \mathbf{U}^C) = \alpha^C\mathbf{T} + \beta^C\mathbf{U}^C.$$

α^C and β^C are numerical coefficients, called "factor loadings," that weigh the relative importance of the values of **T** and of $\mathbf{U}^C$ in the determination of the values of **C**. If each of the observed variables is caused by **T** in this way, we get three more such equations:

$$\mathbf{E} = \alpha^E\mathbf{T} + \beta^E\mathbf{U}^E; \qquad \mathbf{A} = \alpha^A\mathbf{T} + \beta^A\mathbf{U}^A; \qquad \mathbf{R} = \alpha^R\mathbf{T} + \beta^R\mathbf{U}^R.$$

Factorial causation makes several additional assumptions about these variables. It assumes that there is zero correlation between **T** and any of the **U**-variables. The **U**-variables are supposed to represent "leftover," "random," and/or "nonsystematic" sources of variation in the observed variables. If these **U**-variables had a positive or negative correlation with **T**, they should be treated as an integral part of the causal system being analyzed. As we assume that they are nonsystematic sources of variation, they are supposed to have zero correlation with **T**. For similar reasons, every **U**-variable has zero correlation with every other **U**-variable.

From such a system of equations we can determine a variety of things about the original four variables. We can determine the correlation between each pair of the original variables from the factor loadings. We can also determine the amount of variation in each of the observed variables which **T** accounts for from the factor loadings. Doing these computations can be tedious, but it does show how factor analysis might uncover a causal account for observed correlations.

It is much simpler to do computations with these equations if we standardize each variable's scale to units based on its standard deviation (see Chapter 6, Section 8). That is, for each variable we translate the particular values measured to new values on a scale with mean, zero, and standard deviation 1. We can use a subscript i, $\mathbf{C}_i$, to help us refer to each of the students in our population. For each student, 1 to N, we obtain a value for the **C** variable; the value for the "*i*th student" is $\mathbf{C}_i$. We sum up all these values and divide by N to obtain their mean: $\overline{\mathbf{C}} = \Sigma[\mathbf{C}_i/N]$, and we sum up the squared deviations from the mean and divide by N and take the square root to obtain their standard deviation: $\sqrt{\Sigma[(\mathbf{C}_i - \overline{\mathbf{C}})^2/N]}$. We can then translate these "raw scores" into scores that reflect the number of standard deviations a raw score is from the mean:

$$\mathbf{C}_i \Rightarrow \frac{\mathbf{C}_i - \overline{\mathbf{C}}}{\sqrt{\Sigma[(\mathbf{C}_i - \overline{\mathbf{C}})^2/N]}.}$$

From now on we will assume that all variable values are already expressed in standard deviation units.

2. VARIANCES ARE ADDITIVE

The variance of a variable, **C** for instance, with values expressed in standard deviation units, is a simple function of the values. The variance is the square of the standard deviation. With variables expressed in standard deviation units, the mean, $\overline{\mathbf{C}}$, is zero. We can express the variance as the sum of the squares of each variable value divided by N:

$$\Sigma\left[\frac{(\mathbf{C}_i - \overline{\mathbf{C}})^2}{N}\right] = \Sigma\left[\frac{(\mathbf{C}_i - 0)^2}{N}\right] = \Sigma\left[\frac{\mathbf{C}_i^{\,2}}{N}\right] = 1.$$

Note that since we express values in standard deviation units where the standard deviation is 1, the variance must also be 1 ($1^2 = 1$).

When we assume that **C**'s values can be expressed as a linear combination of the values of **T** and $\mathbf{U}^C$, we can use this equation in the expression of **C**'s variance:

$$\mathbf{C} = \alpha^C\mathbf{T} + \beta^C\mathbf{U}^C \Rightarrow \Sigma\left[\frac{\mathbf{C}_i^{\,2}}{N}\right] = \Sigma\left[\frac{(\alpha^C\mathbf{T}_i + \beta^C\mathbf{U}_i{}^C)^2}{N}\right] = 1.$$

We can expand the square with a little algebra:

$$\Sigma\left[\frac{(\alpha^C\mathbf{T}_i + \beta^C\mathbf{U}_i{}^{C2}}{N}\right] = \Sigma\left[(\alpha^C\mathbf{T}_i)^2 + (2\alpha^C\beta^C\mathbf{T}_i\mathbf{U}_i{}^C) + \frac{(\beta^C\mathbf{U}_i{}^C)^2}{N}\right]$$

$$= \Sigma\left[\frac{(\alpha^C\mathbf{T}_i)^2}{N}\right] + \Sigma\left[\frac{2\alpha^C\beta^C\mathbf{T}_i\mathbf{U}_i{}^C}{N}\right] + \Sigma\left[\frac{(\beta^C\mathbf{U}_i{}^C)^2}{N}\right]$$

$$= (\alpha^C)^2\Sigma\left[\frac{\mathbf{T}_i^{\,2}}{N}\right] + 2\alpha^C\beta^C\Sigma\left[\frac{\mathbf{T}_i\mathbf{U}_i{}^C}{N}\right] + (\beta^C)^2\Sigma\left[\frac{\mathbf{U}_i{}^{2C}}{N}\right] = 1.$$

This messy result can be simplified by noting several convenient features of standard deviation units and factorial causation. First, when using standard deviation units, the sum of the squares of any variable is always equal to the number of units in the population, N (see Chapter 6, Section, 9). Thus, in particular we have $\Sigma[\mathbf{T}_i{}^2/N] = \Sigma[\mathbf{U}_i{}^{C2}/N] = N/N = 1$. Second, the correlation between two variables is the sum of the products of the variables divided by N. $\Sigma[\mathbf{T}_i\mathbf{U}_i{}^C/N]$is the correlation between **T** and $\mathbf{U}^C$, but we have assumed that there is zero correlation between **T** and the U-variables. So we have $2\alpha^C\beta^C\Sigma[\mathbf{T}_i\mathbf{U}_i{}^C/N] = 2\alpha^C\beta^C \times 0 = 0$. These facts simplify the foregoing equation considerably:

$$\Sigma\left[\frac{(\alpha^C\mathbf{T}_i + \beta^C\mathbf{U}_i{}^C)^2}{N}\right] = (\alpha^C)^2\Sigma\left[\frac{\mathbf{T}_i{}^2}{N}\right] + 2\alpha^C\beta^C\Sigma\left[\frac{\mathbf{T}_i\mathbf{U}_i{}^C}{N}\right] + (\beta^C)^2\Sigma\left[\frac{\mathbf{U}_i{}^{C2}}{N}\right]$$

$$= [(\alpha^C)^2 \times 1] + (2\alpha^C\beta^C \times 0) + [(\beta^C)^2 \times 1]$$

$$= (\alpha^C)^2 + (\beta^C)^2 = 1.$$

The variance of **C** is made up of two components, that due to **T** and that due to $\mathbf{U}^C$. The relative contributions of these two components is expressed in terms of the squares of the equation coefficients, or factor loadings, $(\alpha^C)^2$ and $(\beta^C)^2$. These contributions to **C**'s variance *add together* to equal **C**'s total variance—1. This is one reason that the variance, instead of the standard deviation, is a useful measure of variability; variances add together with linear systems like this. $(\alpha^C)^2/[(\alpha^C)^2 + (\beta^C)^2] = (\alpha^C)^2/1 = (\alpha^C)^2$ is the proportion of **C**'s variance that **T** accounts for. The remaining proportion of the variance, $(\beta^C)^2$, is accounted for by $\mathbf{U}^C$.

$(\alpha^C)^2$ is the proportion of **C**'s variance that **C** has in common with the other observed variables—through the common variable, **T**—and is known as the *communality* of **C**. For a given common factor, each observed variable will have its communality. The larger these communality values, the more the variance in the observed variables is accounted for by the common factor. Since we use standard deviation units, each observed variable has variance 1; the total variance of all the observed variables is just (1 × the number of observed variables) = (the number of observed variables). Thus, the sum of the communalities divided by the total number of variables is the proportion of the variance accounted for by the common factors. In this case, with four observed variables and one common factor, $(\alpha^C)^2 + (\alpha^E)^2 + (\alpha^A)^2 + (\alpha^R)^2$, is the sum of the communalities and $[(\alpha^C)^2 + (\alpha^E)^2 + (\alpha^A)^2 + (\alpha^R)^2]/4$ is the proportion of the total variance accounted for by **T**.

3. RECONSTRUCTING THE CORRELATIONS

The correlations between the four observed variables are also simple functions of the factor loadings. We can compute, for instance, the correlation between **C** and **E**. Again, since we are working with standard deviation units, the correlation between these variables is just the sum of the products of variable values for each student in the population divided by the number of students: $\Sigma(\mathbf{C}_i\mathbf{E}_i)/N$. But each of these variables can be expressed as a product of **T** and $\mathbf{U}^C$ or $\mathbf{U}^E$:

$$\mathbf{C} = (\alpha^C \times \mathbf{T}) + (\beta^C \times \mathbf{U}^C) = (\alpha^C\mathbf{T}) + (\beta^C\mathbf{U}^C);$$

$$\mathbf{E} = (\alpha^E \times \mathbf{T}) + (\beta^E \times \mathbf{U}^E) = (\alpha^E\mathbf{T}) + (\beta^E\mathbf{U}^E).$$

We can use these expressions in our computation of the correlation:

$$\Sigma\frac{(\mathbf{C}_i\mathbf{E}_i)}{N} = \Sigma\left[\frac{((\alpha^C\mathbf{T}_i) + (\beta^C\mathbf{U}^C{}_i)) \times ((\alpha^E\mathbf{T}_i) + (\beta^E\mathbf{U}^E{}_i))}{N}\right]$$

$$= \Sigma\left[\frac{(\alpha^C\mathbf{T}_i)(\alpha^E\mathbf{T}_i) + (\alpha^C\mathbf{T}_i)(\beta^E\mathbf{U}^E{}_i) + (\beta^C\mathbf{U}^C{}_i)(\alpha^E\mathbf{T}_i) + (\beta^C\mathbf{U}^C{}_i)(\beta^E\mathbf{U}^E{}_i)}{N}\right]$$

$$= \Sigma\left[\frac{(\alpha^C\mathbf{T}_i)(\alpha^E\mathbf{T}_i)}{N}\right] + \Sigma\left[\frac{(\alpha^C\mathbf{T}_i)(\beta^E\mathbf{U}^E{}_i)}{N}\right]$$

$$+ \Sigma\left[\frac{(\beta^C\mathbf{U}^C{}_i)(\alpha^E\mathbf{T}_i)}{N}\right] + \Sigma\left[\frac{(\beta^C\mathbf{U}^C{}_i)(\beta^E\mathbf{U}^E{}_i)}{N}\right]$$

$$= \alpha^C\alpha^E\Sigma\left[\frac{\mathbf{T}^2{}_i}{N}\right] + \alpha^C\beta^E\Sigma\left[\frac{\mathbf{T}_i\mathbf{U}^E{}_i}{N}\right]$$

$$+ \beta^C\alpha^E\Sigma\left[\frac{\mathbf{U}^C{}_i\mathbf{T}_i)}{N}\right] + \beta^C\beta^E\Sigma\left[\frac{\mathbf{U}^C{}_i\mathbf{U}^E{}_i}{N}\right].$$

Since we use standard deviation units, we have, $\Sigma[\mathbf{T}^2{}_i/N] = N/N = 1$. Since we assume factorial causation, there is zero correlation between **T** and any of the **U**-variables, and between pairs of **U**-variables: $\Sigma[\mathbf{T}_i\mathbf{U}^E{}_i/N] = \Sigma[\mathbf{U}^C{}_i\mathbf{T}_i/N] = \Sigma[\mathbf{U}^C{}_i\mathbf{U}^E{}_i/N] = 0$.

$$\alpha^C\alpha^E\Sigma\left[\frac{\mathbf{T}^2{}_i}{N}\right] + \alpha^C\beta^E\Sigma\left[\frac{\mathbf{T}_i\mathbf{U}^E{}_i}{N}\right] + \beta^C\alpha^E\Sigma\left[\frac{\mathbf{U}^C{}_i\mathbf{T}_i)}{N}\right] + \beta^C\beta^E\Sigma\left[\frac{\mathbf{U}^C{}_i\mathbf{U}^E{}_i}{N}\right]$$

$$= (\alpha^C\alpha^E \times 1) + (\alpha^C\beta^E \times 0) + (\beta^C\alpha^E \times 0) + (\beta^C\beta^E \times 0)$$

$$= \alpha^C\alpha^E.$$

The correlation between **C** and **E** is the product of the factor loadings for the path from **C** to **E** by way of **T**. Similar computations show that the correlation between any two of the observed variables is equal to the product of the factor loadings of **T** on each variable. The correlation between **A** and **R**, for instance, is $\alpha^A \times \alpha^R$.

If we knew the values for all the αs, we could calculate all of the correlations between the observed variables. Suppose, for example, that the four αs had the following values:

$$\alpha^C = 0.95; \quad \alpha^E = 0.89; \quad \alpha^A = 0.97; \quad \alpha^R = 0.85.$$

The correlation between **C** and **E** is $(\alpha^C \times \alpha^E) = 0.95 \times 0.89 = 0.84$. The correlation between **E** and **R** is $(\alpha^E \times \alpha^R) = 0.89 \times 0.85 = 0.76$. And so on. The results of all these computations can be tabulated in a correlation matrix (Table 12.1). Notice that the correlation between the observed variables depends only on the factor loadings they have with the common factors. Unique variable factor loadings play no role.

TABLE 12.1 Correlation Matrix

	C	*E*	*A*	*R*
C	1.00	0.84	0.92	0.81
E	0.84	1.00	0.86	0.76
A	0.92	0.86	1.00	0.82
R	0.81	0.76	0.82	1.00

These α-values also tell us about the variances of the observed variables. The variances for each of the observed variables are the sum of the squared factor loadings. Since these variables are measured in standard deviation units, each has a variance of 1. We have:

$$\text{for } \mathbf{C}\text{:}\quad 0.95^2 + (\beta^C)^2 = 1; \qquad (\beta^C) = \sqrt{0.10} = 0.31;$$

$$\text{for } \mathbf{E}\text{:}\quad 0.89^2 + (\beta^E)^2 = 1; \qquad (\beta^E) = \sqrt{0.21} = 0.46;$$

$$\text{for } \mathbf{A}\text{:}\quad 0.97^2 + (\beta^A)^2 = 1; \qquad (\beta^A) = \sqrt{0.06} = 0.24; \text{ and}$$

$$\text{for } \mathbf{R}\text{:}\quad 0.85^2 + (\beta^R)^2 = 1; \qquad (\beta^R) = \sqrt{0.28} = 0.53.$$

T accounts for a large proportion of the total variation in the four observed variables. It accounts for 90% $[= 0.95^2 = (\alpha^C)^2]$ of **C**'s variation and 79% $[= 0.89^2 = (\alpha^E)^2]$ of **E**'s variation. In total, **T** accounts for $(0.90 + 0.79 + 0.94 + 0.72)/4 = 3.35/4 = 84\%$ of the total variation in the four observed variables.

4. MORE COMPLICATED DESIGNS

Thus far we have assumed that the values for our four variables are largely determined by a single underlying common variable, **T**. The simplest extension is to suppose that there are two other variables, perhaps "*T*eaching effectiveness" and the "*P*ertinence of the topic"—**T** and **P**, respectively—that determine the correlations between **C**, **E**, **A**, and **R** (Figure 12.2). When two common factors are involved, we add a third term to the linear equations for **C**, **E**, **A**, and **R**:

$$\mathbf{C} = ({}^{T}\alpha^{C} \times \mathbf{T}) + ({}^{P}\alpha^{C} \times \mathbf{P}) + (\beta^{C} \times \mathbf{U}^{C}) = {}^{T}\alpha^{C}\mathbf{T} + {}^{P}\alpha^{C}\mathbf{P} + \beta^{C}\mathbf{U}^{C};$$

$$\mathbf{E} = ({}^{T}\alpha^{E} \times \mathbf{T}) + ({}^{P}\alpha^{E} \times \mathbf{P}) + (\beta^{E} \times \mathbf{U}^{E}) = {}^{T}\alpha^{E}\mathbf{T} + {}^{P}\alpha^{E}\mathbf{P} + \beta^{E}\mathbf{U}^{E};$$

$$\mathbf{A} = ({}^{T}\alpha^{A} \times \mathbf{T}) + ({}^{P}\alpha^{A} \times \mathbf{P}) + (\beta^{A} \times \mathbf{U}^{A}) = {}^{T}\alpha^{A}\mathbf{T} + {}^{P}\alpha^{A}\mathbf{P} + \beta^{A}\mathbf{U}^{A};$$

$$\mathbf{R} = ({}^{T}\alpha^{R} \times \mathbf{T}) + ({}^{P}\alpha^{R} \times \mathbf{P}) + (\beta^{R} \times \mathbf{U}^{R}) = {}^{T}\alpha^{R}\mathbf{T} + {}^{P}\alpha^{R}\mathbf{P} + \beta^{R}\mathbf{U}^{R}.$$

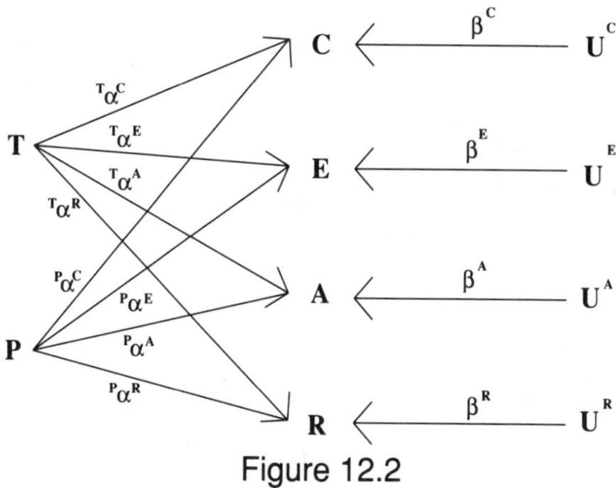

Figure 12.2

Again we assume that there is zero correlation between any of the **U**-variables, and that there is zero correlation between the two common factors, **T** and **P**.

We can do computations like those done in the preceding two sections. They are more tedious because of the third term involved, and for this reason, we will not pursue them. The results, however, are nice generalizations of the results in the preceding two sections.

The variance of each of the observed variables is the sum of three terms—the three squared factor loadings for the relevant factors. The variance of **C**, for instance, is the sum of

$$({}^{T}\alpha^{C})^2 + ({}^{P}\alpha^{C})^2 + (\beta^{C})^2 = 1.$$

The first two terms in this sum, $({}^{T}\alpha^{C})^2 + ({}^{P}\alpha^{C})^2$, represent the proportion of **C**'s variance that **C** has in common with the other observed variables—via the two common factors, **T** and **P**. Consequently, $({}^{T}\alpha^{C})^2 + ({}^{P}\alpha^{C})^2$ is **C**'s *communality*. The sum of all the communalities for all four observed variables divided by 4 is the proportion of the variance of the observed variables accounted for by these two common factors.

The correlation between two observed variables is the sum of two parts, one for "each way to get from" one variable to another via one or the other of the two common factors (Figure 12.3). Thus, for instance, the correlation between **C** and **E** is, $({}^{T}\alpha^{C} \times {}^{T}\alpha^{E}) + ({}^{P}\alpha^{C} \times {}^{P}\alpha^{E})$.

When more than two common factors are involved, these results generalize. The *variance* for an observed variable is the sum of the squared factor loadings for any factor that "loads on" the variable. The *communality* for this variable is the sum of squared factor loadings for all the factor loadings coming from common—as opposed to unique—factors. The sum of all the common-factor loadings—all the αs—divided by the number of observed variables is the proportion of the variance in the observed variables accounted for by the common factors. The *correlation* between two variables is the sum of the products of factor loadings for each route

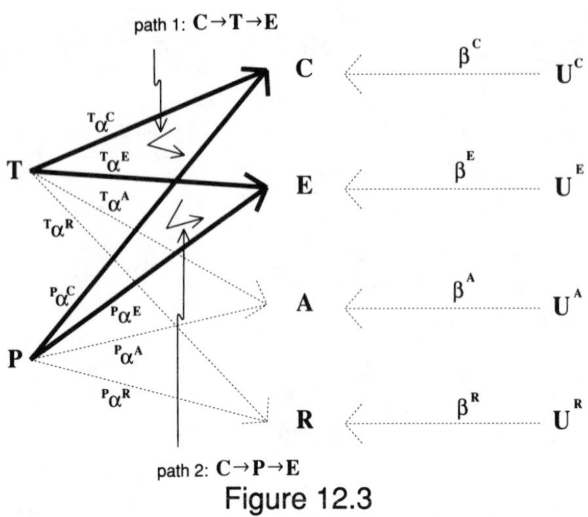

Figure 12.3

from one observed variable to another—via the various common factors successively.

Factor analysis also allows for the possibility that the common factors have nonzero correlations with each other. Suppose, for example, that there is a nonzero correlation between **T** and **P** of r^{TP} (Figure 12.4). This adds a new term in the formula for the variance of an observed variable, say **C**. We have the squared α- and β-terms as before, $({}^{T}\alpha^{C})^2$, $({}^{P}\alpha^{C})^2$, and $(\beta^{C})^2$. But here there is a fourth source of variability introduced through the correlation between **T** and **P**: the "closed path" from the variable back to itself via the correlation between the common factors $({}^{T}\alpha^{C} \times r^{TP} \times {}^{P}\alpha^{C})$ (Figure 12.5). The variance of **C**, for instance, is given in the following sum:

$$({}^{T}\alpha^{C})^2 + ({}^{P}\alpha^{C})^2 + (2 \times {}^{T}\alpha^{C} \times r^{TP} \times {}^{P}\alpha^{C}) + (\beta^{C})^2 = 1.$$

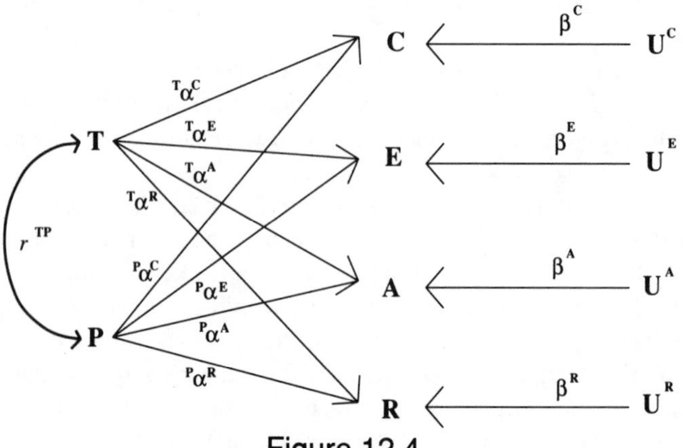

Figure 12.4

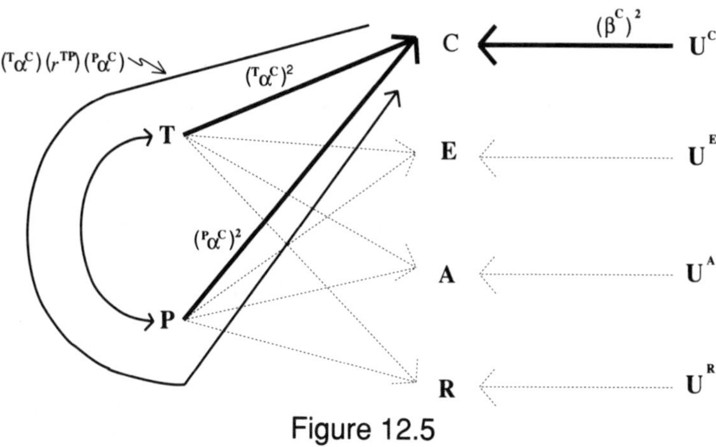

Figure 12.5

The first three terms in this sum—the α-terms again—are the source of variance due to the common factors. The sum of these three terms, $({}^{T}\alpha^{C})^2 + ({}^{P}\alpha^{C})^2 + (2 \times {}^{T}\alpha^{C} \times r^{TP} \times {}^{P}\alpha^{C})$, is the *communality* of **C**.

To compute the correlation between two variables, one considers all the paths from one variable to another. One computes the product of the factor loadings—and interfactor correlations—crossed on each path. The sum of these products is the correlation. For instance, the correlation between **C** and **E** is the result of four different paths from **C** to **E** (Figure 12.6). The correlation between **C** and **E** is:

$$({}^{T}\alpha^{C} \times {}^{T}\alpha^{E}) + ({}^{T}\alpha^{C} \times r^{TP} \times {}^{P}\alpha^{E}) + ({}^{P}\alpha^{C} \times {}^{P}\alpha^{E}) + ({}^{P}\alpha^{C} \times r^{TP} \times {}^{T}\alpha^{E}).$$

Two final remarks are worth making about the case where the common factors are correlated. In the first place, when common factors are correlated, the common factor correlations can be factor analyzed. In this way, "second-order factors" can be produced. In theory, this process could be carried out *ad infinitum*, although typically there is little prospect of making much sense of higher-ordered factors such as these.

Second, when there is zero correlation between each pair of common factors, the factor loadings—the αs and the βs—are just the correlations between the variables their paths connect. It is a fairly simple exercise to show, in the first, simplest version of the example we have been working with (Figure 12.1), that the correlation between **C** and **T** is just the factor loading of **T** on **C**: α^C. When there is a nonzero correlation between the common factors, however, this is no longer so. In the last version of this example, with a little more effort, one can show that the correlation between **C** and **T** is $({}^{T}\alpha^{C} + ({}^{P}\alpha^{C} \times r^{TP}))$. [Notice that when $r^{TP} = 0$, the correlation between **T** and **C** reduces to the factor loading again: $({}^{T}\alpha^{C} + ({}^{P}\alpha^{C} \times 0)) = {}^{T}\alpha^{C}$.] In terms of paths, the correlation between **C** and **T** is the sum of the two paths from **C** to **T**, the direct path with loading ${}^{T}\alpha^{C}$, and the indirect path via **P**, with loadings $({}^{P}\alpha^{C} \times r^{TP})$.

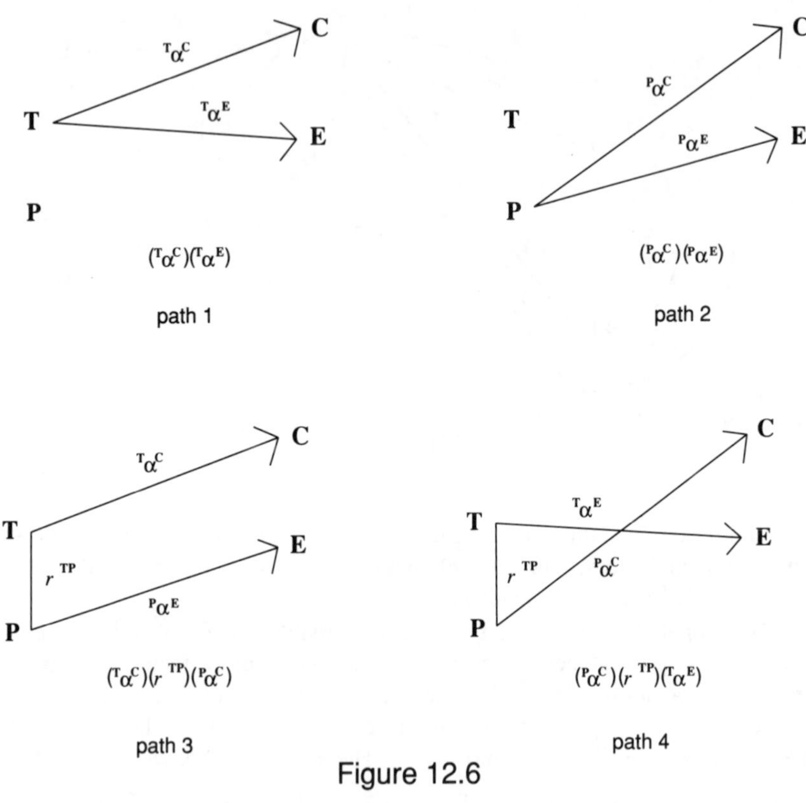

Figure 12.6

This second point is conceptual. Factor loadings cannot be understood simply as correlations between variables. They must bear something like a "causal weight" interpretation. They show how a common factor, alone, "influences" an observed variable—through its role in the linear equation that relates observed and common factors. When this common factor is correlated with another common factor, there is an indirect source of influence via this correlation.

5. FACTOR ANALYSIS FORWARDS

When done in the "right direction," a factor analysis starts with the correlation matrix for the observed variables and seeks common factors. There are a variety of procedures for iteratively seeking an initial factor analysis. The idea behind all these procedures is to find factor loadings such that the modified correlation matrix *computed* from these factor loadings is as close as possible to the observed correlation matrix. All of these methods require lots of computation and would not be feasible without computers.

One historically early approach was to guess the communalities and use these guesses to modify the correlation matrix. This will produce factors whose communalities can be determined. These communalities can then be used in place of the original guesses. The process can be repeated, and new—better—communalities can be determined. And so on. Eventually, results will settle down and very little change will occur, iteration to iteration.

Suppose, for example, that there are three observed variables, **A**, **B**, and **C**, and one common factor, **F**. We could compute the correlations between the observed variables in terms of the three factor loadings of **F** on **A**, **B**, and **C**: α^A, α^B, and α^C, respectively. A modified correlation matrix that includes all the correlations, expressed in "α-terms," is shown in Table 12.2. The matrix is modified by having variable communalities along the main diagonal instead of the correlations. **A**'s communality, for instance, is $(\alpha^A)^2$. **F**'s loading on **A** is α^A. From this modified correlation matrix, we can see that **F**'s loading on **A** can be expressed as the sum of all the entries in the "**A**-column" divided by the square root of the sum of all the entries in the matrix:

$$\alpha^A = \frac{\alpha^A(\alpha^A + \alpha^B + \alpha^C)}{\sqrt{(\alpha^A + \alpha^B + \alpha^C)^2}} = \frac{\alpha^A(\alpha^A + \alpha^B + \alpha^C)}{\alpha^A + \alpha^B + \alpha^C}.$$

This is the relationship that is exploited to iteratively approximate factor loadings.

Suppose that we found the correlations shown in Table 12.3 between three observed variables. From these correlations we want to find factor loadings, α^A, α^B, and α^C. We see in Table 12.2 that the factor loading for **A**, for instance, can be expressed as the sum of all the entries in **A**'s column divided by the sum of all the

TABLE 12.2 Modified Correlation Matrix

	A	*B*	*C*	Totals
A	$(\alpha^A)^2$	$\alpha^B \times \alpha^A$	$\alpha^C \times \alpha^A$	$\alpha^A(\alpha^A + \alpha^B + \alpha^C)$
B	$\alpha^A \times \alpha^B$	$(\alpha^B)^2$	$\alpha^C \times \alpha^B$	$\alpha^B(\alpha^A + \alpha^B + \alpha^C)$
C	$\alpha^A \times \alpha^C$	$\alpha^B \times \alpha^C$	$(\alpha^C)^2$	$\alpha^C(\alpha^A + \alpha^B + \alpha^C)$
Totals	$\alpha^A(\alpha^A + \alpha^B + \alpha^C)$	$\alpha^B(\alpha^A + \alpha^B + \alpha^C)$	$\alpha^C(\alpha^A + \alpha^B + \alpha^C)$	$(\alpha^A + \alpha^B + \alpha^C)^2$

TABLE 12.3 Correlation Matrix

	A	*B*	*C*
A		0.72	0.63
B	0.72		0.56
C	0.63	0.56	

entries in the matrix. The trouble is that we do not know **A**'s communality. So we guess. We could take the largest correlations for guesses, but any sensible value would do. Here values based on guesses are in curves (Table 12.4). From these guesses we can calculate totals and find approximate factor loadings from the quotient of a variable's column total and the square root of the grand total for the matrix. All this computation is done in Table 12.5. These new approximate factor loadings can be squared to give new approximate factor communalities for each of the variables, and the process can be done all over again. After four more such iterations, the approximate factor loadings for **A**, **B**, and **C** are 0.89, 0.80, and 0.70, respectively. More approximations produce no more change in these values to the second decimal place.

In fact, the correlations we began with were determined from the path diagram shown in Figure 12.7. **F**'s loading on **A**, **B**, and **C** are 0.9, 0.8, and 0.7, respectively. One can verify that these loadings will produce the correlations in Table 12.3. The correlation between **A** and **B**, for instance, is $0.9 \times 0.8 = 0.72$, as noted in the table. The values we found in the iterative process above, 0.89, 0.80, and 0.70, are virtually right on the mark. The process found the factor loadings from the observed correlations.

This is a simple example with few observed variables and only one common factor. This way the amount of computation has been kept manageable enough to be appreciated without a computer. The method of factor extraction used in this example has been superseded by computationally more demanding—but also more efficient—methods. Still the example gives the flavor of factor extraction.

TABLE 12.4 Modified Correlation Matrix—First Approximation

	A	*B*	*C*	Totals
A	(0.72)	0.72	0.63	(2.07)
B	0.72	(0.63)	0.56	(1.91)
C	0.63	0.56	(0.56)	(1.75)
Totals	(2.07)	(1.91)	(1.75)	(5.73)
	$\left(\frac{2.07}{2.39} \approx 0.87\right)$	$\left(\frac{1.91}{2.39} \approx 0.80\right)$	$\left(\frac{1.75}{2.39} \approx 0.73\right)$	$(\sqrt{5.73} \approx 2.39)$

TABLE 12.5 Modified Correlation Matrix—Second Approximation

	A	*B*	*C*	Totals
A	$[(0.87)^2 = 0.77]$	0.72	0.63	(2.12)
B	0.72	$[(0.80)^2 = 0.64]$	0.56	(1.92)
C	0.63	0.56	$[(0.73)^2 = 0.53]$	(1.72)
Totals	(2.12)	(1.92)	(1.72)	(5.76)
	$\left(\frac{2.12}{2.4} \approx 0.88\right)$	$\left(\frac{1.92}{2.4} \approx 0.80\right)$	$\left(\frac{1.72}{2.4} \approx 0.72\right)$	$(\sqrt{5.76} \approx 2.4)$

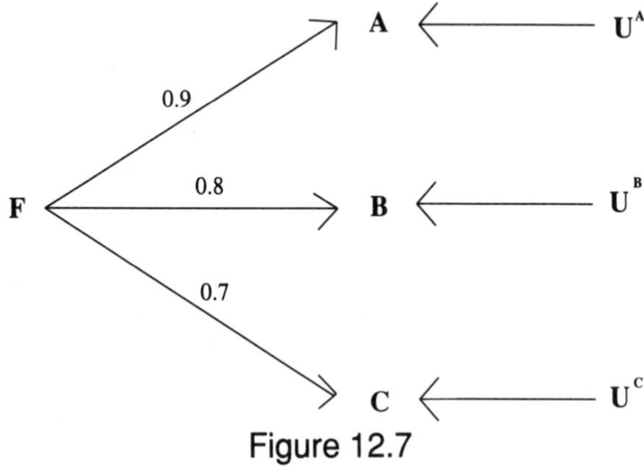

Figure 12.7

Once such a process of approximation has settled down, we can look to see if the correlations between observed variables are sufficiently well accounted for by this one common factor just uncovered. We compare the observed correlations with those that would be expected on the basis of the factor loadings found by this process of approximation. In this example observed correlations are very close to those computed from the extracted factor loadings. Table 12.6 shows both side by side. Predicted correlations are in brackets. If the results are in close agreement, as they are here, the one-factor model is sufficient. If not, a two-factor model is sought by the same kind of iterative process of approximation. Once two factors have been found, the correlations between observed variables are compared to those predicted by two factors. If they are near enough, one stays with a two-factor model; otherwise, a three-factor model is sought. And so on.

There is a difficult question of how close predicted values must be to correlations actually observed. A full answer to this question would take us beyond the technical expertise of this book. The kind of answer involved is discussed in some detail in the next chapter. Roughly, the idea is this. Suppose that the factor model is correct. Correlations that were used to recover it are sample correlations and thus may differ from the true population correlations, for the same reason that a random sample of balls taken from an urn with 50% green balls may include only 45% green balls. Thus, even if the factor model is right, we would expect some of the observed correlations to differ from those that are predicted on the basis of the model. A significance test is used to see if the amount of difference between observed and

TABLE 12.6

	A	*B*	*C*
A		0.72 [0.712]	0.63 [0.623]
B	0.72 [0.712]		0.56 [0.560]
C	0.63 [0.623]	0.56 [0.560]	

predicted values can be explained on the basis of chance fluctuations introduced by random sampling.

6. ROTATION

In almost all cases, the correlation matrix by itself is not sufficient to uniquely determine a common factor structure. For example, the two path diagrams shown in Figure 12.8 produce the same correlation matrix. The modified correlation matrix they produce is shown in Table 12.7—with the factor communalities along the main diagonal. Nor are these the only two common factor structures that produce this correlation matrix. In general, an infinite number of common factor structures can produce the same modified correlation matrix.

Such alternative solutions are related to each other. They differ in terms of rotations of the axes used to organize the space of correlations. We can express the factor loadings **F** and **G** have on the four observed variables (case **A**) in terms of a two-dimensional plot (Figure 12.9). Each of the observed variables, **A**, **B**, **C**, and **D**, corresponds to a point on this plot. The placement of a variable's point reflects **F**'s loading on the variable—with the horizontal scale—and **G**'s loading—with the vertical scale. **C**, for instance, has a loading of 0.1 with **F** and 0.7 with **G**. We can rotate these axes, pivoting on the origin, to produce new factors with different loadings (Figure 12.10). Here I have rotated the axes 45°. Factor loadings for these variables on these new common factors—or axes—are the coordinate values of the observed variables in this new coordinate system. Variable **A**, for instance, had coordinates <0.5, 0.0> in the original coordinate system; in the new system its coordinates are <0.35, 0.35>. With a little trigonometry, values for the other variable's factor loadings can be determined similarly. The results are the factor loadings in Figure 12.8, case **B**.

In these two cases, the axes have been kept perpendicular to each other. This orientation of the axes reflects the fact that the correlation between the common factors is zero. We can also organize points on a plane in terms of axes that are not perpendicular to each other. Such axes are called *oblique* (axes that meet perpendicularly are called *orthogonal*). When we rotate axes to an oblique orientation, we produce factor loadings for a case where the common factors are correlated with each other.

Changing common factors by rotation (oblique or orthogonal) does not alter the correlations between the observed variables. Nor does it alter the communalities of the observed variables. All such solutions have the same modified correlation matrix.

This kind of change in common factors changes the amount of variation in the observed variables accounted for by the different common factors. In case **A**, **F** accounts for 22.5%$(=0.5^2 + 0.8^2 + 0.1^2)/4$ of the variation in the observed variables; **G** accounts for 20% of the variation (the unique factors account for the

path diagram, Case A

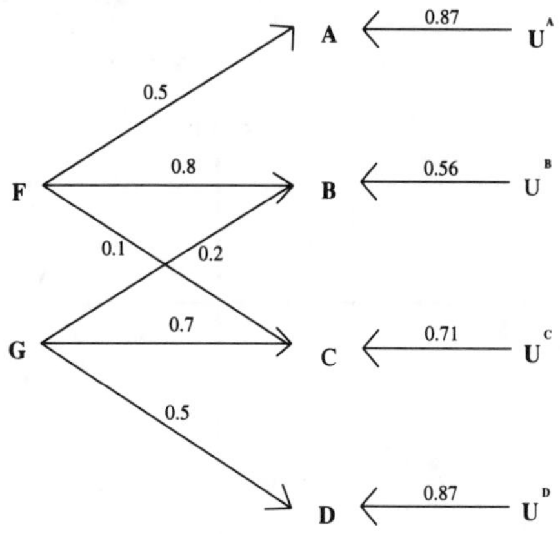

path diagram, Case B

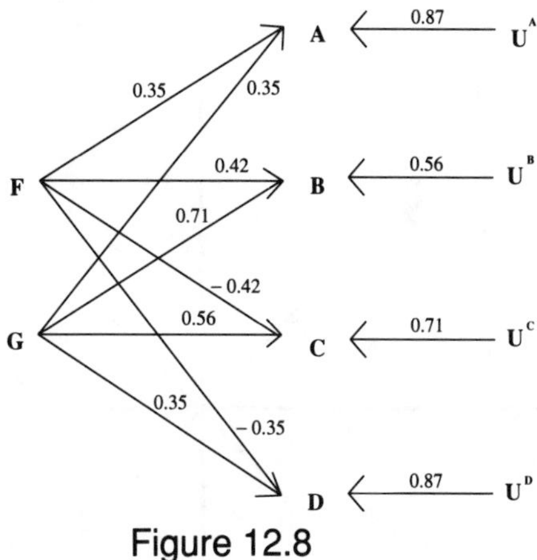

Figure 12.8

TABLE 12.7 Modified Correlation Matrix for Cases A and B

	A	*B*	*C*	*D*
A	0.25	0.40	0.05	0.0
B	0.40	0.68	0.22	0.10
C	0.05	0.22	0.50	0.35
D	0.0	0.10	0.35	0.25

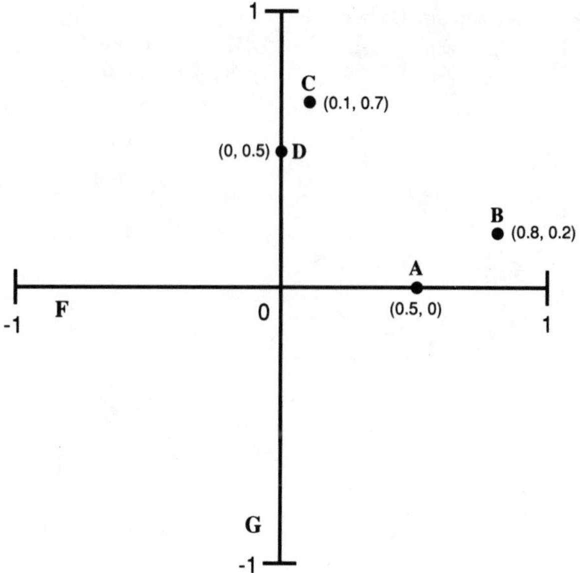

Figure 12.9 Factor loadings: case A.

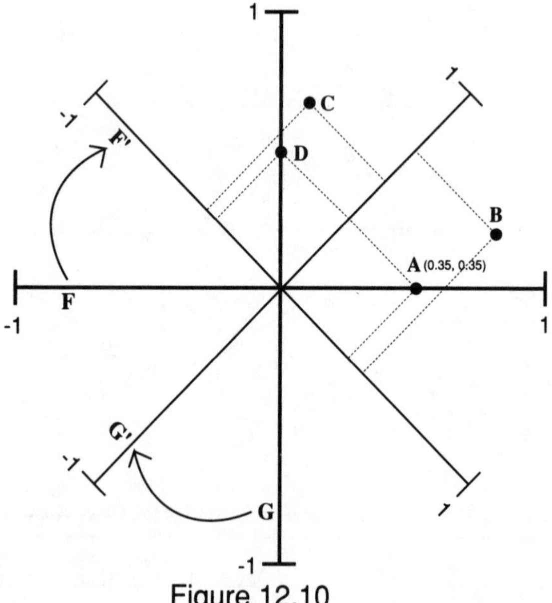

Figure 12.10

Factor loadings: case A, horizontal/vertical axes; case B, rotated axes.

remaining 57.5% of the variation in the observed variables). In case **B**, **F′** accounts for 15.25% of the variation, while **G′** accounts for 27.25% of the variation (the unique variables still account for 57.5% of the variation).

Procedures used to extract common factors from observed correlations seek factors in order of the amount of variation accounted for. Thus, the first factor extracted will account for more variation than any other single factor. The second factor extracted will account for more of the remaining variation than any other factor. And so on. When new factors are found through rotation, they need not have this property. Taken together, all the factors in any solution will account for the same amount of variation as the factors in any other solution. But in a rotated solution, the factor that accounts for the most variation may account for less than some other single factor—from a different solution—accounts for.

Thus, the correlation matrix—even with the correct communalities—generally is not enough to *uniquely* determine a factor solution. Other constraints are necessary to find a final factor solution. Such constraints typically have two kinds of sources, extrinsic and intrinsic.

The purpose of rotation is to find sensible, potentially meaningful, factors. Thus, typically, one rotates to try and find factors whose loadings on the observed variables make sense. Roughly, this means that one can "interpret" the nature of a factor from the observed variables on which it has large factor loadings. In Table 4.3, factor **I** has large loadings on just those tests that substantially involve upper body strength. It makes sense to interpret this factor as an "upper body strength" factor.

Researchers may know something about the topic under investigation, and this knowledge may help determine some of the factor's relationships to some of the observed variables. Here, information external to the analysis can help determine the final form of the solution. It is reasonable to think of upper-body strength as a distinct source of a person's physical abilities.

These extrinsic sources of constraint typically collaborate with intrinsic sources of constraint. A factor solution with "simple structure" is sought. Figure 4.9 presents the ideal of such "simple structure." Here one seeks factors with small—near zero—loadings on many observed variables, and large—near 1 or −1—loadings on other variables. One seeks a solution where each observed variable has only a few common factors with large loadings on it. There are a variety of ways to play these different desiderata off against each other. Each is instantiated through a different computer "simple-structure-optimization" program.

In the course of using factor analysis, an analyst may have to try several rotations before factors that make sense are found. Here we have an interplay between these extrinsic and intrinsic sources of constraint. Even then, these factors may turn out to be artifacts of the analysis. Further investigation into the reality and/or causal efficacy of such factors is necessary before one can confidently infer their existence.

7. THE LOGIC OF DISCOVERY

Factor analysis starts with a series of measurements of a variety of variables on a large population of units. Such measurements typically produce a bewildering array of correlations. While researchers may suspect that these correlations are the result of some smaller set of unobserved variables, there is very little that could be done about such suspicions without some means to analyze the correlations, looking for such unobserved variables. This is just what factor analysis provides. When it is successful, it uncovers such unobserved variables and helps to characterize them by reference to their effects on the observed variables. In this way, the barest of intuitions can be turned into a detailed picture of underlying processes responsible for observed correlations.

This seems just what a logic of discovery should do. Factor analysis seems to provide a means to convert raw correlational data into detailed hypotheses about underlying causal structures. Factor analysis instantiates, through factor analysis computer programs, certain cannons for inductively inferring a hypothesis about causal structure from correlational data.

This way of characterizing factor analysis is both common and troubling. It is troubling because, until the 1970s, it was common for philosophers of science (this century) to deny the possibility of a logic of discovery; factor analysis attempts the impossible. Echoing this kind of general philosophical critique, some factor analysts have argued against using factor analysis to discover new hypotheses. They urge, in contrast, that many of the factor analytic algorithms should be used as part of a process of testing previously postulated hypotheses. This is called *confirmatory*—as opposed to *exploratory*—factor analysis. Factor analysis should not be used to discover previously unknown hypotheses; it should be used to test previously known hypotheses.

One kind of argument against the possibility of a logic of discovery goes like this: Suppose that two scientists are curious about the way in which students evaluate their professors. One scientist collects data from students evaluating a professor on the four variables considered at the beginning of this chapter. She submits these data to a factor analysis and finds a single common factor, **T**, which explains the correlations in the data. The other scientist, while trying to disentangle four of his son's slinky springs, has a flash of inspiration. He sees how variation in one point, where the slinkys are tangled, produces variation at the four ends of the slinkys. He imagines that this must be the way students evaluate their professors: One central variable brings about variation in four (observed) variables that are used to measure the student's evaluation. He makes a wild guess and postulates four linear equations relating each of the four observed variables to the common cause. As it happens his equations are identical to those found by the first scientist. He then tests his model against the available correlational data (which he shares with the other scientist) and finds a good fit.

Intuitions differ about what to make of the difference between these two scientists' procedures. The first scientist's approach might be ruled out on grounds of opportunism: It is always possible to fit some model to data already gathered. Consequently, the fact that a model fits the data gives some people little confidence that the model accurately describes whatever underlying process produced the data. The second scientist, on the other hand, proposed a model, tested it against the data, and improbably enough, the model passed the test. Many people find this a much more persuasive reason to have confidence in the model. (Some reflection on the discussion of Bode's law in Chapter 1 can help intuitions here.) On the other hand, if logic has to do with atemporal relations between evidence and hypothesis, the order in which a scientist becomes aware of evidence and hypothesis should have no bearing on the strength to which the evidence logically supports the hypothesis.

Neither of these intuitions provides any reason to prefer the way the first scientist went about discovering the model. The first scientist used factor analysis; the second reasoned by analogy with slinkys. They both ended with a hypothesis about the causal structure underlying student evaluation of teachers. There is no advantage to taking the factor analysis route over the slinky route—and, on grounds of opportunism, there might be a disadvantage. What matters is the subsequent *testing* of the model. Roughly, while factor analysis may be a useful tool for provoking scientists to think up hypotheses, there is no special reason to think that these hypotheses are true, and certainly no reason to think that these hypotheses are more likely true than hypotheses that result from untangling slinkys.

At best, factor analysis—and any proposed method of discovery—might help with the psychology of discovery. This is not a matter of logic. Logic is concerned with *justifying* previously entertained hypotheses. How these hypotheses are thought up in the first place does not concern logic as much as the psychology and/or sociology of creativity.

Recently, there has been an attempt to revive the logic of discovery. Various arguments have been used. One focuses on the economics of research. It may be that the results of reasoning by slinky and reasoning by factor analysis are on a par with regard to reasons to believe their results. But factor analysis provides a set regimen for discovery. It was blind luck that the second scientist had to disentangle four slinkys. He could have been picking up Tinker Toys. The scientist who uses factor analysis, at least, will have an hypothesis to test. Perhaps the hypothesis will fail the test. Still this is some progress—a possibility has been ruled out—and the hypothesis might pass the test.

Even if one grants the merits of pursuing economical roads to discovery, it is not clear that this shows there is a *logic* of discovery. The scientist who uses factor analysis to think up hypotheses still has to test them, and this is where the logic lies. There is little comfort in knowing that a computer can quickly generate hypotheses if we have no reason to think that these hypotheses are probably close to the truth.

8. INSTRUMENTS AND DISCOVERY

It is possible that this controversy about the possibility of a logic of discovery—particularly as it bears on factor analysis—rests on an inadequate understanding of scientific progress. This controversy sees true hypotheses as the only unit of scientific advance. The data gathered by researchers has the single role to provide the evidence to ground our conviction that a hypothesis is true.

This picture of science is impoverished in many respects; two are important here. In the first place, true hypotheses are not the only important goals to scientific work. Finding an AIDS vaccine would be a great success for science—assuming that science is the responsible party. Here it is useful and important to know some true hypotheses about how the AIDS virus works and how the vaccine works. But an arguably more important aspect to such a success would be having the material itself. It would be nice to know that a vaccine exists; it would be nicer to have some of it in hand.

Second, this view of science makes data appear all too easy to obtain. It tends to make one forget that it takes hard work to get "nature to speak to us." Usually, data are hard won. Many people are aware of the apparatus of science; the chemist with test tubes is a common caricature. The point of all this apparatus is to help get the data. Thus, beside true hypotheses, two other goals of science are (1) to gather useful data and (2) to create new materials.

Microscopes are an instructive example. Scientists and glass craftspeople are properly proud of their successes with inventing and improving microscopes. These instruments have opened up a whole new world to wonder at. They have also provided a whole new source of data. Much contemporary biology rests on the evidence provided by the data from microscopes. If we did not have the microscopes, we would not have contemporary biology.

Factor analysis might similarly be seen, *not* as a method for discovering hypotheses, but as a method for discovering data. Microscopes allow us to see structures that are too small to be seen with the naked eye. Factor analysis might allow us to see structures in population data sets which are hidden in many confusing correlations. I say "might" because controversy remains over both the existence of such structures (and this depends on the source of the population data in the first place) and the ability of factor analysis to reveal such structures if they are there. Until roughly a century ago, people rightly worried about the evidence provided by microscopes. Not only have we significantly improved microscopes since their invention, we have learned much about what can and cannot be seen with microscopes as well. Factor analysis could have the same bright future that microscopes had 300 years ago.

Seen as an instrument for discovering data instead of hypotheses, criticisms that exploratory factor analysis attempts the impossible—to be a logic of discovery—are less compelling. Consider the two scientists again. As far as generating hypotheses, both scientists' work may be on a par. But the scientist using factor analysis has an advantage: She has access to an instrument that can help her "see" structure in correlational data. If slinkys were equally efficient at helping scientists see such structure, we would applaud the scientific contemplation of slinky tangles. But they are not. Consider the analogy with microscopes. If playing with baby rattles provided an equally detailed and intersubjective insight into cell structure, we would applaud the scientific contemplation of baby rattles. But it does not, while microscopes do.

Like microscopes, factor analysis should be seen as a tool that gives our minds access to a domain of structures otherwise beyond us. Some fertile imaginations may be able to imagine cell structure or population structure. But these tools of science allow access to these domains of structures for a wider audience—those trained to use the tools—and they mix elements from interaction with the real world with the products of fertile imaginations. This mixing is a central feature of a *logic* of scientific discovery.

9. SUMMARY

1. Factor analysis can help one discover new concepts, or variables, which are causally responsible for observed correlations.
  (a) It does this by a detailed examination of the patterns of correlations between observed variables.
  (b) It assumes that observed correlations are the result of factorial causation.
    (1) At a general level this means that causal relations occur between variables and come in degrees—much like correlations.
    (2) At a specific level this means that the relations between these variables can be expressed by linear equations, and that observed correlations arise from the action of unobserved underlying common variables.
  (c) Factor analyses are subject to various sources of uncertainty.
    (1) The correlations on which they are based are usually sample correlations, not population correlations.
    (2) There are causal systems other than those embraced by factorial causation which could be responsible for observed correlations.
    (3) The final form of an analysis depends on the judgment of the analyst to adopt a certain "factor rotation."

2. Variances provide an additive measure of variability.
  (a) The variance—the square of the standard deviation—of an observed variable can be expressed in terms of the factor loadings of a common factor model.
  (b) Suppose that an observed variable, **O**, is a linear combination of two other variables, a common variable, **C**, and a unique variable, **U**: $\mathbf{O} = \alpha\mathbf{C} \times \beta\mathbf{U}$. Suppose that **O**, **C**, and **U** are measured in terms of standard deviation units. **O**'s variance is the sum of the squared factor loadings on **O**: $\alpha^2 + \beta^2$.
  (c) If two common factors, with zero correlation between them, **C** and **D**, each have loadings on **O**, then **O**'s variance is the sum of $(\alpha^D)^2 + (\alpha^C)^2 + \beta^2$. This generalizes to as many common factors as have loadings on **O**.
  (d) If two common factors, **C** and **D** each have loadings on **O** and are correlated with each other, r^{CD}, then **O**'s variance is the sum of $(\alpha^D)^2 + (\alpha^C)^2 + (2 \times \alpha^C \times r^{CD} \times \alpha^D) + \beta^2$.
  (e) Contributions to **O**'s variance from the common factors, all the "αs," are **O**'s *communality*.

3. Correlations between observed variables in a factor model are simply expressed in terms of factor loadings.
   (a) When variables are measured in standard deviation units, the correlation between two variables, **C** and **O**, is the sum of the products of each variable's values divided by the number of values, N: $\Sigma[\mathbf{O}_i\mathbf{C}_i)/N]$.
   (b) Given a single common factor, **C**, the correlation between two observed variables, **M** and **N**, is the product of the factor loading of **C** on **M** and the factor loading of **C** on **N**: $\alpha^{M} \times \alpha^{N}$.
   (c) Given two common factors, **C** and **D**, with zero correlation between them, the correlation between two observed variables, **M** and **N**, is the sum of the products of the two paths between the two observed variables via **C** and, separately, via **D**: $[({}^{C}\alpha^{M} \times {}^{C}\alpha^{N}) + ({}^{D}\alpha^{M} \times {}^{D}\alpha^{N})]$.
   (d) Given two common factors, **C** and **D**, each with loadings on **O**, and correlated with each other, r^{CD}, the correlation between two observed variables, **M** and **N**, is the sum of the products of the four paths between **M** and **N**:

$$({}^{C}\alpha^{M} \times {}^{C}\alpha^{N}) + ({}^{C}\alpha^{N} \times r^{CD} \times {}^{D}\alpha^{M}) + ({}^{D}\alpha^{M} \times {}^{D}\alpha^{N}) + ({}^{D}\alpha^{N} \times r^{CD} \times {}^{C}\alpha^{M}).$$

4. Factor-analytic algorithms aim to produce a common factor structure that can reproduce the modified correlation matrix with as little error as possible.
   (a) By an iterative series of approximations, one can find a factor structure from correlations between observed variables. Several algorithms are available to do this.
   (b) Since observed correlations typically are sample correlations, one would not expect complete agreement between factor structure predictions and observed correlations. Significance tests are used to test whether the degree of difference could be expected on the basis of sampling variability.

5. Typically, more than one common factor structure will be able to account for observed correlations.
   (a) Factor extraction algorithms find the common factor structure with common factors which are not correlated. Furthermore, the ''first'' common factor extracted can account for more of the observed variation than any other single factor; the ''second'' common factor extracted can account for more of the remaining variation than any other second factor; and so on.
   (b) The different factor structures that equally well account for observed correlations are related to each other in terms of rotations of factor axes that organize the space of observed variable correlations.
   (c) When axes are perpendicular to each other, the common factors they represent have zero correlation between them. When they are not perpendicular, the common factors have nonzero correlation.
   (d) Rotated factor solutions account for the same amount of variation as the initially extracted solution; they also reproduce observed correlations equally well. The amount of variation accounted for, however, is not such that there is one factor that accounts for more variation than any other possible factor.
   (e) Factor analysts rotate solutions to find factors that make sense. This requires both that they be sensible in terms of what is known about the field under study, and that the factor loadings on observed variables be simple enough to allow for some insight into what the common factors could mean. Many different rotations may be attempted before these criteria are met.

6. Factor analysis is a good candidate for a logic of discovery.
   (a) Common factors are extracted from observed variables in a largely mechanical way. These common factors can provide insight into the underlying causes of observed correlations.
   (b) Some analysts have criticized factor analysis as attempting to be an impossible logic of discovery. Factor analysis might provide a psychologically useful aid in discovering common factor structure, but there is no reason to prefer factor analysis to other ways to gain insight about causal structure. Whatever means are used, the results must be checked against observed correlations. It is in the *testing* of factor structures that the logic lies.
   (c) By contrast, thought of as a method to re-present data in a useful form, factor analysis may be sensibly understood as a logic of the discovery of evidence, not hypotheses.

10. REFERENCES

(Kim and Mueller, 1978a and 1978b) are complementary concise and elementary introductions to factor analysis. (Harmon, 1976) is a more advanced treatment. (Joreskog and Sorbom, 1979) is a collection of advanced but marvelously clear papers on factor-analytic techniques. (Joreskog et al., 1976) also contains an advanced treatment of factor analysis and its application in geology.

(Curd, 1980), (Laudan, 1980), and (Nickles, 1985) contain recent philosophical discussions over the possibility of a logic of discovery. (Cattell, 1978) urges that factor analysis is an inductive method for the discovery of hypotheses. (Mulaik, 1985 and 1988) contains criticisms of the possibility of exploratory factor analysis as a logic of discovery. (Baird, 1987) defends factor analysis against such criticisms and urges that factor analysis be thought of as a logic of the discovery of data, not hypotheses. (Mulaik, 1991) replies to (Baird, 1987).

11. PROBLEMS

1. Suppose that the factor analysis for the four observed variables of teaching ability, **C**, **E**, **A**, and **R**, can be factor analyzed to a factor structure with a single common factor, **T**, and the factor loadings listed in Table 12.8.

TABLE 12.8

Observed Variable	Factor Loading on **T**
C	0.9
E	0.8
A	0.7
R	0.6

(a) Construct the correlation matrix between the observed variables.
(b) What loadings would each of the unique variables have on their respective observed variables?
(c) What are the communalities of the observed variables?
(d) What percentage of the total variance does **T** account for?

2. Suppose that the factor analysis for the four observed variables of teaching ability, **C**, **E**, **A**, and **R**, can be factor analyzed to a factor structure with two common factors, **T** and **P**, with zero correlation between them, and the factor loadings listed in Table 12.9.

TABLE 12.9

Observed Variable	Factor Loading on **T**	Factor Loading on **P**
C	0.7	0.5
E	0.7	0.6
A	0.6	0.7
R	0.4	0.7

(a) Construct the correlation matrix between the observed variables.
(b) What loadings would each of the unique variables have on their respective observed variables?
(c) What are the communalities of the observed variables?
(d) What percentage of the total variance does **T** account for? What percentage does **P** account for?

3. Suppose that everything is as given in Problem 2, except there is a correlation of 0.2 between **T** and **P**. Do Problem 2 under these conditions.

4. Given the same general set up as in Problems 1, 2, and 3, what is the correlation between **T** and **C** in the following three cases?
   (a) When the particular factor structure is as described in Problem 1.
   (b) When the particular factor structure is as described in Problem 2.
   (c) When the particular factor structure is as described in Problem 3.

5. Prove that when there is zero correlation between common factors, the correlation between an observed variable and a common factor is equal to the factor loading of that common factor on that variable.

6. Suppose that the factor analysis for the four observed variables of teaching ability, **C**, **E**, **A**, and **R**, can be factor analyzed to a factor structure with two common factors, **T** and **P**, with zero correlation between them and the factor loadings listed in Table 12.10.

TABLE 12.10

Observed Variable	Factor Loading on **T**	Factor Loading on **P**
C	${}^{T}\alpha^{C}$	${}^{P}\alpha^{C}$
E	${}^{T}\alpha^{E}$	${}^{P}\alpha^{E}$
A	${}^{T}\alpha^{A}$	${}^{P}\alpha^{A}$
R	${}^{T}\alpha^{R}$	${}^{P}\alpha^{R}$

(a) Show that the correlation between two observed variables is the sum of the products of factor loadings on the two paths from one variable to the other via the two common factors.

(b) Show that the variance of an observed variable is the sum of the squares of the factor loadings on that variable.

7. Suppose that the factor analysis for the four observed variables of teaching ability, **C**, **E**, **A**, and **R**, can be factor analyzed to a factor structure with two common factors, **T** and **P**, with nonzero correlation, r^{TP}, between them, and the factor loadings listed in Table 12.11.

TABLE 12.11

Observed Variable	Factor Loading on **T**	Factor Loading on **P**
C	${}^{\mathrm{T}}\alpha^{\mathrm{C}}$	${}^{\mathrm{P}}\alpha^{\mathrm{C}}$
E	${}^{\mathrm{T}}\alpha^{\mathrm{E}}$	${}^{\mathrm{P}}\alpha^{\mathrm{E}}$
A	${}^{\mathrm{T}}\alpha^{\mathrm{A}}$	${}^{\mathrm{P}}\alpha^{\mathrm{A}}$
R	${}^{\mathrm{T}}\alpha^{\mathrm{R}}$	${}^{\mathrm{P}}\alpha^{\mathrm{R}}$

(a) Show that the correlation between two observed variables is the sum of the products of factor loadings on the four paths from one variable to the other via the two common factors.

(b) Show that the variance of an observed variable is the sum of the squares of the factor loadings on that variable plus twice the product of the factor loadings of the two common factors and the correlation between them.

8. In Section 6 it was shown that the two factor structures for the four observed variables, **A**, **B**, **C**, and **D**, and the two common factors, **F** and **G** (in case A) and **F′** and **G′** (in case B), were related to each other by rotating the axes for **F** and **G** by 45°. Suppose that the axes were rotated 30° instead. What new factors would this produce? That is, compute the factor loadings for this new solution on **A**, **B**, **C**, and **D**. Show that the modified correlation matrix for this new solution is the same as for the original solution.

9. Why might one be suspicious of the logic of discovery? Should "economic considerations" be relevant to a logic of discovery? Why or why not? Discuss.

10. Why might using an microscope be considered part of a logic of discovery? Is this a sensible way to think about microscopes? About logic? About factor analysis?

CHAPTER 13

SIGNIFICANCE TESTS

1. SIGNIFICANCE TESTS AND INDUCTIVE INFERENCE

Significance tests are a deceptively simple—and perhaps for this reason widely used—kind of inductive inference. In essence, a significance test provides a measure of the fit between observed frequencies and frequencies that would be expected given some chance hypothesis, usually called the "null hypothesis." This measure is expressed in terms of probabilities—called *levels of significance*—computed on the assumption of the chance hypothesis: The lower the level of significance, the worse the fit. In a sense, given a low level of significance, of 0.01 say, one is faced with two alternatives, either the chance hypothesis, on the basis of which the level of significance computed is wrong, or a very improbable—probability 0.01—event occurred. When the level of significance—commonly called α—is low, the null hypothesis can be "rejected at the α level of significance."

Consider, for example, the polio vaccine study discussed in Chapter 5. The data show substantially lower polio rates among vaccinated children than among children who were not vaccinated. Evidently, the vaccine works (see Chapter 5, Section 2, and Table 13.1). But there was a legitimate worry that this difference might be the result of "chance fluctuations." That is, given the variable response of humans to the risk of polio, one could imagine that taking the vaccine had no effect on a child's chance of contracting the disease; the observed differences were simply the effect of "normal" variations in the children's susceptibility to the disease. A significance test can be used to show that observed polio frequencies do not fit frequencies one would expect if the vaccine had no effect. According to the chi-square significance test, the level of significance is quite small, much smaller than 0.001. Thus, researchers could "reject at better than the 0.001 level of significance" the chance fluctuations interpretation of the data.

A significance test can appear to extend to statistical hypotheses the method of "falsifying hypotheses." A hypothesis is falsified, in the deductive sense, if one of its deductive consequences is known (typically, on experimental or observational grounds) to be false. This follows a standard rule of deductive logic, "denying the consequent:"

A hypothesis → a consequence.	$\mathbf{A} \rightarrow \mathbf{B}$.
This consequence is false.	$\neg \mathbf{B}$.
So the hypothesis is false.	So $\neg \mathbf{A}$.

The null hypothesis of chance fluctuations, on the other hand, does not imply that data must not look as they do in the polio study. The polio data cannot *deductively* falsify the hypothesis of chance. Still, while the polio data are consistent with chance, it does not support chance; the data should not look the way it does if chance is the only source of difference:

Chance fluctuations "→" data should be like this ....

Data are quite different—to level of significance α—from this ....

So the chance fluctuations are rejected at the α level of significance.

At this general level of description, significance tests are fairly straightforward.

Significance tests pose two kinds of difficulties. Mathematically, it can be difficult to find level-of-significance probabilities in cases that matter. Conceptually, it is difficult to describe the detailed workings of significance tests on just those points where they must diverge from the simple deductive version of falsification. How *should* data look? How do levels of significance measure fit? What does it mean to "reject an hypothesis at an α level of significance"?

2. A SIMPLE COIN-FLIPPING EXAMPLE

We can better appreciate how significance tests by looking at examples. Computationally, coins provide the easiest entry to understanding significance tests. Suppose that we want to know whether a particular coin is fair or biased. We do not question the probabilistic independence of different flips, or that each flip has the same probability for coming up heads. We only want to know whether this probability is 1/2.

If the coin is fair, it *should* come up heads about half the time. Here is the beginning of a measure fit. We can rank the different outcomes in terms of how close the proportion of heads is to 1/2. Suppose, for instance, that we flip the coin 10 times. We can distinguish 11 outcomes corresponding to the 11 different proportions of heads that could arise. We can arrange these in order of how well each fits the hypothesis of fairness (Figure 13.1). Clearly, six heads in 10 flips fits the hypothesis of fairness better than eight heads in 10 flips.

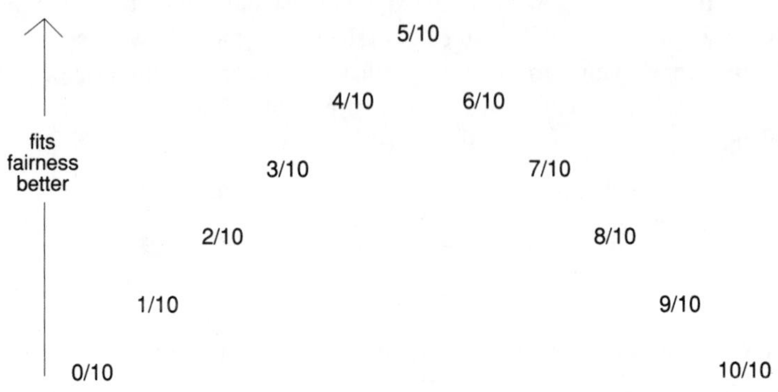

Figure 13.1

Level of significance probabilities provide a scale of how well or poorly data fit. The level of significance of an outcome is the probability—assuming that the hypothesis of fairness is true—of any outcome that fits the hypothesis of fairness as badly or worse than the given outcome. If the coin came up heads eight times in 10 flips, the level of significance is the probability of any outcome as bad or worse than eight heads (Figure 13.2). Six binomial computations are required to calculate the level of significance—one for each of the boxed results in Figure 13.2:

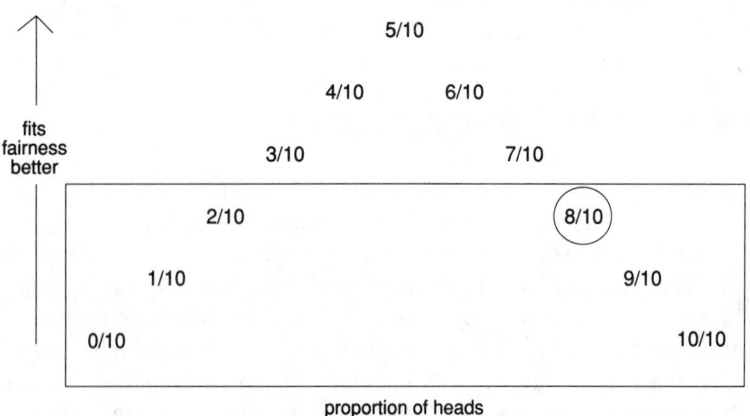

Figure 13.2

$$\frac{10!}{0! \times 10!} \times \left[\left(\frac{1}{2}\right)^0 \times \left(\frac{1}{2}\right)^{10}\right] + \frac{10!}{1! \times 9!} \times \left[\left(\frac{1}{2}\right)^1 \times \left(\frac{1}{2}\right)^9\right]$$
$$+ \frac{10!}{2! \times 8!} \times \left[\left(\frac{1}{2}\right)^2 \times \left(\frac{1}{2}\right)^8\right] + \frac{10!}{8! \times 2!} \times \left[\left(\frac{1}{2}\right)^8 \times \left(\frac{1}{2}\right)^2\right]$$
$$+ \frac{10!}{9! \times 1!} \times \left[\left(\frac{1}{2}\right)^9 \times \left(\frac{1}{2}\right)^1\right] + \frac{10!}{10! \times 0!} \times \left[\left(\frac{1}{2}\right)^{10} \times \left(\frac{1}{2}\right)^0\right]$$
$$= \left(\frac{1}{2}\right)^{10} \times (1 + 10 + 45 + 45 + 10 + 1)$$
$$= \left(\frac{1}{2}\right)^{10} \times 112$$
$$\approx 0.00098 \times 112$$
$$\approx 0.11.$$

The level of significance is (approximately) 0.11. We "reject the hypothesis of fairness at the 0.11 level of significance."

It is interesting to notice what would happen had we flipped the coin 20 times and gotten the same ratio of heads: 16/20 = 8/10. To calculate the level of significance of this result, we must do 10 binomial computations. The result is a level of significance of (approximately) 0.01. The fit is substantially worse. This is one reason why level of significance probabilities are a more useful scale of fit than simply the ratio of heads to tails.

3. TESTING AN INSTRUMENT FOR CALIBRATION

While the simplicity of the coin example makes it attractive for introducing significance tests, it is worthwhile to consider some more realistic examples. Suppose that we have an instrument designed to test the concentration of ozone in the atmosphere. Like any measuring instrument, we must expect some random error in its readings. Thus, were we to introduce several samples of air with a known concentration of ozone of, say, 200 "Dobson units" (a standard scale for measuring ozone concentration in the atmosphere), we would expect the instrument to produce readings spread around 200. If the instrument is properly calibrated, the average of this spread of readings should be 200. Unfortunately, the instrument tends to go out of calibration. Thus, it must be calibrated before it can be used and trusted.

Suppose that we use the instrument with five samples of air known to have an ozone concentration of 200 Dobson units. Suppose that the instrument reads 198, 195, 196, 201, and 195. Should we conclude that the instrument needs calibration because four of these five values are less than the true value? Alternatively, should we think that these values represent chance fluctuations from an instrument that is properly calibrated? We can use a significance test to argue that these values do not represent chance fluctuations.

To do so, we need a model of such chance fluctuations. The normal distribution is commonly used to model chance fluctuations—or errors. Indeed, the normal distribution has been called the "curve of error." It is a good model for several reasons. We can think of errors as being the result of many small independent disturbances, slight variations in the mechanical and/or electrical components of the instrument, for example. Sometimes a disturbance will cause a measurement reading to be too large, sometimes too small. If the probability of such tendencies is p, we have a binomial distribution of small disturbances pushing one way or the other of the true value. The normal distribution provides a good approximation to such binomial probabilities (see Chapter 9, Section 8).

Whatever the underlying justification, it is common to use the normal curve to model errors of measurement. Its mean, if the instrument is properly calibrated, should be 200. Its standard deviation gives us a measure of how precisely the instrument measures ozone concentration. Two cases might arise. In the simplest case, we would know the standard deviation of the instrument's readings. Here we suppose that when it goes out of calibration, its "average reading" slips one way or the other, while its basic precision remains the same. A harder case, which we discuss in the next section, is where we are unsure of the standard deviation of the distribution of readings provided by the instrument.

The measure of fit that is appropriate is the degree to which the average of our five readings differs from 200. This is a simple generalization of the coin example. There we compared the average number of heads with the number we "should expect"; here we compare the average instrument reading with what we should expect—200. The null hypothesis says that the instrument is producing readings that vary by a normal distribution with mean 200 and standard deviation of, we can suppose, 2 Dobson units.

We need to find level of significance probabilities to provide a *scale* of fit. In this case we need to find the probability distribution for the sample average when we take five observations. Again, there is a straightforward analogy with the coin example. There we sought probabilities for any value we might find for the proportion of heads in N flips. The result was the binomial distribution. Here we seek probabilities for any value of the sample average when we use the instrument N times (five times in our particular case). We assume that on each use the probability of a reading is given by the normal distribution with mean 200 and standard deviation 2, and we assume that different readings are independent of each other. It can be shown that the probability density function for the average of N observations from a population which is described by a normal distribution is also a normal distribution; it has the same mean as the underlying normal distribution, but its standard deviation is the standard deviation of the underlying normal distribution divided by the square root of the number of observations.

When we take five readings with our instrument, the average of our readings—if the instrument is well calibrated—should be distributed with a normal distribution with mean 200 and standard deviation $\sigma/\sqrt{N} = 2/\sqrt{5} \approx 2/2.24 \approx 0.89$. In precise terms we rank outcomes by the test statistic:

$$\frac{\overline{\mathbf{X}} - 200}{\sigma/\sqrt{N}} = \frac{\overline{\mathbf{X}} - 200}{2/\sqrt{5}} \approx \frac{\overline{\mathbf{X}} - 200}{0.89}.$$

The farther this value is from zero, the worse is the fit. Notice that the farther the average of our readings is from 200, the farther the numerator, $\mathbf{X} - 200$, is from zero; hence the farther $(\overline{\mathbf{X}} - 200)/0.89$ is from 0. Similarly, if the standard deviation, σ, of our instrument's errors, was smaller, the denominator, $\sigma/\sqrt{5}$, would be smaller as well, and holding the numerator constant, the test statistic value, $(\overline{\mathbf{X}} - 200)/(\sigma/\sqrt{5})$, would be farther from 0. This test statistic nicely combines information about the distance of the average of our readings with the standard deviation of the readings.

Another vital feature of this test statistic is that it allows us to determine level of significance probabilities. This statistic, $(\overline{\mathbf{X}} - 200)/0.89$, amounts to converting the average of the readings, $\overline{\mathbf{X}}$, to a scale of standard deviation units. When the values themselves are distributed normally, the distribution of standard deviation unit values is distributed normally with mean zero and standard deviation 1. Probabilities for this particular normal distribution have been calculated and can be found in widely available tables of "standard normal distribution."

Now we can run a significance test. The average of our five measurements is 197 Dobson units:

$$\overline{\mathbf{X}} = \frac{\Sigma \mathbf{X}_i}{5} = \frac{198 + 195 + 196 + 201 + 195}{5} = 197.$$

We need to find the probability of getting any average value as far or farther from 200 as 197, where the average of the five observations is distributed with a normal distribution with mean 200 and standard deviation 0.89. In standard deviation units, the average of our five measurements is $(197 - 200)/0.89 \approx -3.37$ standard deviation units. We need to find the probability of getting any average as far or farther from 0 as -3.37, where the average of the five observations is distributed with a normal distribution with mean 0 and standard deviation 1. This probability can be looked up in a table of standard normal probabilities; it is (nearly) 0.0008 (Figure 13.3). On this evidence we can reject at the 0.0008 level of significance the hypothesis that the instrument is properly calibrated. Very likely, we should recalibrate the instrument and test again.

4. STUDENT'S *t*-TEST

If we do not know the standard deviation of the instrument's distribution of errors, we cannot use the significance test from Section 3. In the preceding case, we compared the average of our readings against what it should be—200—and divided by the standard deviation to account for the fact that a difference would be more telling

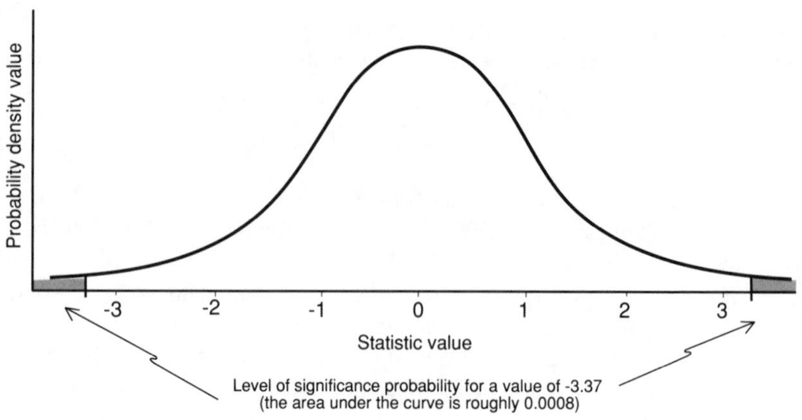

Figure 13.3 A standard normal distribution.

if the instrument was more precise. We used the statistic $(\overline{\mathbf{X}} - \mu)/(\sigma/\sqrt{N}) = (\overline{\mathbf{X}} - 200)/(2/\sqrt{5})$ to rank the outcomes. Here we cannot do this because we do not know the standard deviation of the errors produced by the instrument.

In 1908, W. S. Gossett, writing under the pseudonym "Student," suggested substituting an estimate for the standard deviation based on the spread of values in the sample. Specifically, he used the following estimate for the standard deviation:

$$SE = \sqrt{\frac{\Sigma(\mathbf{X}_i - \overline{\mathbf{X}})^2}{N - 1}}.$$

[Notice that if the "-1" were omitted from the denominator, *SE* would just be the standard deviation of the observed instrument readings. $(N - 1)$ is used in place of N alone because *SE* is an "unbiased estimator" of the population standard deviation—see Section 9.] The statistic that Gossett used to rank outcomes, known as Student's *t*-statistic, is just like the statistic used in the preceding section except that we replace the actual population standard deviation, which we do not know, with Gossett's estimate of it:

$$\frac{\overline{\mathbf{X}} - 200}{SE/\sqrt{N}} = \frac{\overline{\mathbf{X}} - 200}{\sqrt{(\Sigma[(\mathbf{X}_i - \overline{\mathbf{X}})^2/(N - 1)])}/\sqrt{N}.}$$

This statistic ranks the fit between observed outcomes and the chance model in a sensible way. The farther the average of the observations is from 200, the worse the fit—keeping the denominator fixed. The more closely the observations fall together, the worse the fit—keeping the numerator fixed.

The truly remarkable feat Gossett accomplished was to derive a probability density function for this statistic. Gossett showed that this statistic varied in a way that is described by one of a family of distributions, called Student's *t*-distributions, all of which are independent of the actual standard deviation, σ, of the population of errors. The particular *t*-distribution that applies in any particular case is determined by the number of observations, N. *t*-distributions are similar to normal distributions, but they have "fatter tails"; that is, a *t*-distribution falls off to zero more slowly than a normal distribution. Gossett's derivation is remarkable because, Gossett found exact probabilities in a case where the underlying probabilities are not known—because the standard deviation is unknown.

This fact allows us to find level of significance probabilities. First we need to calculate the value of the *t*-statistic for our particular case. The average of the observations is the same as in Section 3, $\overline{\mathbf{X}} = \sqrt{\mathbf{X}_i}/N = 197$. Gossett's estimate, SE, for the standard deviation is found as follows:

$$(198 - 197)^2 + (195 - 197)^2 + (196 - 197)^2 + (201 - 197)^2 + (195 - 197)^2$$
$$= 1 + 4 + 1 + 16 + 4 = 26.$$

$$\sqrt{\frac{\Sigma(\mathbf{X}_i - \overline{\mathbf{X}})^2}{N-1}} = \sqrt{\frac{26}{4}} = \sqrt{6.5} \approx 2.55.$$

Gossett's *t*-statistic value, then, is found to be -2.63:

$$\frac{\overline{\mathbf{X}} - 200}{SE/\sqrt{5}} = \frac{197 - 200}{2.55/2.24} \approx \frac{-3.0}{1.14} \approx -2.63.$$

The probability of a *t*-statistic value as far or farther from zero as -2.63 can be found from a table for a *t*-distribution for a sample of five observations. It is slightly larger than 0.05 (Figure 13.4). We can reject at nearly the 0.05 level of significance the hypothesis that these readings were chance fluctuations from a properly calibrated instrument. In this case, as in the preceding case, probably the instrument should be recalibrated, although the evidence supporting recalibration is weaker.

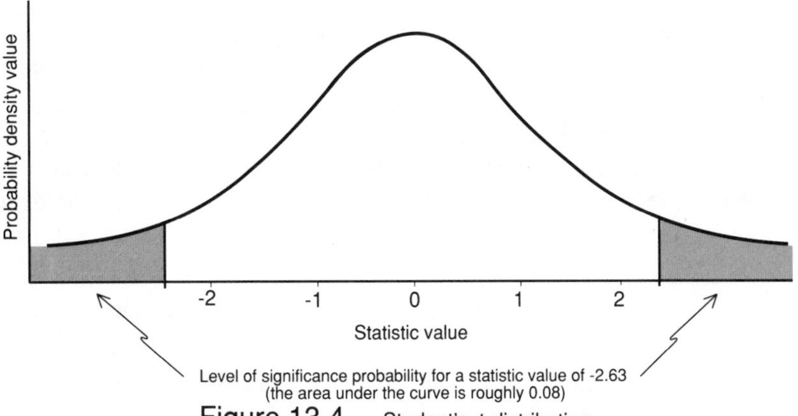

Figure 13.4 Student's *t*-distribution.

5. A CHI-SQUARE TEST OF THE POLIO DATA

For a final example, consider testing the data from the polio example. We have a 2×4 array of data. We "cross-classify" units according to whether they were vaccinated or not and what severity of polio disease they contracted (Table 13.1). Such tables are usually called "contingency tables." We would like to reassure ourselves that the differences between the polio rates for vaccinated and nonvaccinated children is not simply a matter of chance: Taking the vaccine does, in fact, alter a child's chance of contracting the disease. In more careful probabilistic terms, we would like to rule out the possibility that contracting polio is probabilistically independent of taking the vaccine.

TABLE 13.1

	Fatal	Paralytic	Nonparalytic	No Polio	Totals
Vaccinated	0	33	24	200,688	200,745
Nonvaccinated	4	115	27	201,083	201,229
Totals	4	148	51	401,771	401,974

Unfortunately, probabilistic independence does not completely constrain probabilities. Thus, it is not immediately clear how to compute level of significance probabilities. Indeed, it is not immediately clear what frequencies one would expect, given the hypothesis of independence.

The standard way to determine *expected* frequencies is to use the data to *estimate* from the observed data the best-fitting expected frequencies consistent with probabilistic independence. In terms of a contingency table, the best-fitting independence frequencies are those that are products of the observed "marginal totals." The marginal totals of a cross-classified table are the sums of a given row's or column's entries. Table 13.2 is a 2×2 contingency table. $P(\mathbf{A} \cap \mathbf{B}) + P(\neg\mathbf{A} \cap \mathbf{B})$ is the sum of the first row's entries, the row's marginal total. By the theorem on total probability, this sum is just $P(\mathbf{B})$. Similarly, the marginal total for the first column is $P(\mathbf{A} \cap \mathbf{B}) + P(\mathbf{A} \cap \neg\mathbf{B})$, or $P(\mathbf{A})$. When two events, **A** and **B**, are independent, the probability of their intersection is the product of the two individual probabilities: $P(\mathbf{A} \cap \mathbf{B}) = P(\mathbf{A})P(\mathbf{B})$. Independence requires that cell entries equal the product of their marginal totals.

Table 13.3 presents estimated cell values alongside observed cell values for the polio data. Here I express marginal totals as relative frequencies, while the cell

TABLE 13.2

	A	$\neg$**A**	Marginal total probabilities
B	$P(\mathbf{A} \cap \mathbf{B})$	$P(\neg\mathbf{A} \cap \mathbf{B})$	$P(\mathbf{B})$
$\neg$**B**	$P(\mathbf{A} \cap \neg\mathbf{B})$	$P(\neg\mathbf{A} \cap \neg\mathbf{B})$	$P(\neg\mathbf{B})$
Marginal total probabilities	$P(\mathbf{A})$	$P(\neg\mathbf{A})$	

values are still expressed as absolute frequencies. Estimated cell values are found by taking the product of the relative frequencies (the total frequency divided by the sample size, 401,974) of each marginal total for the cell with the sample size. For instance, the expected cell frequency for ''vaccinated and paralytic polio'' is the product of the marginal frequencies for this column and row with the number of children in the sample: $(0.4994 \times 0.00037 \times 401{,}974) = 74.2384$.

TABLE 13.3

	Fatal	Paralytic	Nonparalytic	No Polio	Marginal probabilities
Vaccinated					0.4994
Observed	0	33	24	200,688	
Expected	2.0074	74.2384	26.0970	200,643.4352	
Nonvaccinated					0.5006
Observed	4	115	27	201,083	
Expected	2.0123	74.4544	26.1597	201,125.5580	
Marginal probabilities	0.00001	0.00037	0.00013	0.99949	

We still need a measure of how well observed frequencies fit these expected frequencies. The chi-square statistic serves well in this capacity. It is a sensible measure of fit, for it is the sum of the squared differences between observed cell frequencies and expected cell frequencies divided by the expected cell frequency for all the cells:

$$\sum_{\text{cells}} \frac{(\text{observed - expected})^2}{\text{expected}}$$

The numerator measures deviations from expected values. The denominator serves to keep differences in cells where many observations are expected (in the polio study, the ''no polio'' cells) from swamping differences in cells where few observations are expected. In the polio study we have the chi-square cell values listed in Table 13.4. The sum of these chi-square cell values is 49.17.

The truly remarkable mathematical fact about the chi-square statistic is that—like Student's *t*-statistic—exact probabilities can be computed for it even though expected cell values have to be estimated from the data. That is, an exact probability density function can be determined even when the underlying hypothesis of probabilistic independence does not specify exact cell probabilities. This density function is known as the chi-square distribution.

TABLE 13.4 Cell Values for (Observed-Expected)^2/Expected

	Fatal	Paralytic	Nonparalytic	No Polio
Vaccinated	2.0074	22.9074	0.1685	0.0099
Nonvaccinated	1.9634	22.0799	0.0270	0.0090

Like Student's t-distribution, the chi-square distribution is a family of probability density functions. When testing for independence, the particular distribution that applies is determined by the dimensions of the contingency table. In the polio case, we have a 2 × 4 table. Probabilities for the appropriate chi-square distribution can be found in a chi-square table. We can find, for example, that the probability of finding a value larger than 16.27 is less than 0.001. The chi-square value we found with the polio data, 49.17, is much larger than 16.27. Thus the probability of getting a value this large, if contracting polio is independent of being vaccinated, is much smaller than 0.001 (Figure 13.5). We reject the hypothesis of independence at better than the 0.001 level of significance. As 0.001 is fairly small to begin with, and as there is good external, biomedical, reason to think that the vaccine does make a difference, we could—and the researchers did—discard the hypothesis that being vaccinated is probabilistically independent of contracting polio.

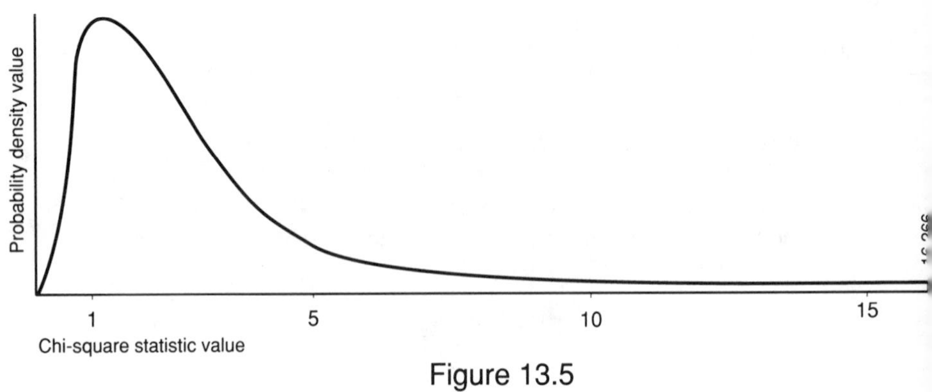

Figure 13.5

6. STRUCTURE OF A SIGNIFICANCE TEST

Here are four significance tests. Each tests a different hypothesis in a different context. But they share the following structure.

1. Stipulating a chance hypothesis. Significance tests are used in situations where the phenomena under investigation have a chance component. We recognize that people will differ in their reactions to polio and to polio vaccine. We say that this variability is caused by a *chance component*. This chance component creates the possibility of unusual and misleading experimental results similar to getting 70 heads in 100 flips of a fair coin. Significance tests provide operational bounds on the degree to which such unusual results can be attributed to the working of chance rather than to a systematic source—such as polio vaccine.

To provide these bounds, a model is used to describe the operation of chance effects. Within this model a particular chance hypothesis is formulated to express the proposition that observed differences are due to chance. If chance is the only source for the observed results, this hypothesis must fit the results. Significance tests aim to test the degree to which the hypothesis fits the observed results. The hypothesis is commonly called the *null hypothesis;* it represents the situation where *no* systematic source is needed to account for the observed results, as chance alone does an adequate job.

In the case of calibrating the instrument the normal distribution was used to model chance. The hypothesis that the instrument is well calibrated with some chance variation in readings was formulated as the hypothesis that the instrument readings would vary normally with a mean of the true value and a standard deviation of 2. If the instrument is well calibrated, this hypothesis would have to fit the data adequately. There is, of course, an important worry over how well the normal distribution does model chance variation.

2. Finding a test statistic. The different possible outcomes from the experiment are ranked according to how well they fit the chance hypothesis. This ranking is accomplished with a *test statistic* that provides a numerical ordering of outcomes. A test statistic is a means to arithmetically manipulate the data from the experiment. Different chance models require different rankings of outcomes, or test statistics. "Student's *t*-test" was the appropriate ranking when we did not know the standard deviation of the errors of the instrument. The standard normal value was appropriate ranking when we did know the standard deviation. Both statistics are such that the further the statistic value is from zero, for given data, the worse the fit. Both work by comparing the observed average with the average one would expect given the null hypothesis and dividing this difference by the spread in the values.

3. Computing levels of significance. Once the test statistic—or ranking—is chosen, we compute probabilities for the various outcomes on the assumption that the null hypothesis is correct. This is a problem in mathematical probability. Such computations can be quite involved, and fortunately, for practical purposes the results for most commonly needed cases are well tabled. The result should be a widely comparable measure of how well the chance hypothesis fits the observed outcome.

Once the experiment is run, we can calculate the value of the test statistic for the specific data obtained. The *level of significance* of the outcome is the probability of any result as bad or worse than that observed. The smaller this probability, the stronger the evidence against the null hypothesis.

In the polio study, we compute how likely it would be to get a chi-square value as large or larger than that found from the data—49.17. The probability of any chi-square value greater than 16.27 is 0.001. As 49.17 is considerably greater than 16.27, the probability of any result greater than 49.17 is considerably smaller than 0.001. We "reject the hypothesis of independence at better than the 0.001 level of significance."

4. Discarding the null hypothesis. When the chance hypothesis does not fit the observed results adequately, we discard it. Adequate fit reflects several features of the test situation, among them the strength of the evidence against the null hypothesis—measured in terms of the level of significance. If the level of significance is not low, we would not discard the null hypothesis. However, what is low enough depends on the context—how adequately the chance model is believed to work, how fully the underlying phenomena are understood, and so on.

Conclusions based on significance tests can be wrong. It is possible, but extraordinarily unlikely, for a truly fair coin to come up heads 12 times in 100 flips. Similarly, it is possible, but extraordinarily unlikely, that the vaccine had no effect in the polio study. But the implausibility of this possibility is measured by the level of significance of the result. The smaller this probability, the better.

7. OBJECTIVE AND SUBJECTIVE INFERENCES

Significance tests came into common use through R. A. Fisher's advocacy of them in the 1920s and later. There were precedents. The chi-square test, the first modern significance test, was developed by Karl Pearson in 1900. Student's *t*-test was developed in 1908. Fisher provided a general interpretive framework for these tests along with a variety of other tests capable of testing for the effects of chance in other contexts. Fisher wanted a measure of fit or ''negative support'' that would allow a researcher to communicate the import of his or her data to ''other rational minds,'' as he put it. If a researcher says that the hypothesis—that observed polio rates were the result of chance alone—may be rejected at better than the 0.001 level of significance, other researchers should then understand the strength of the evidence against this hypothesis.

We can better appreciate the nature of significance test inferences by contrasting them with confidence intervals—discussed in Chapter 10—on the one hand and the subjective Bayesian approach—discussed in Chapter 11—on the other hand. In a sense, which this and the following section should clarify, Fisher's justification for significance tests tries to walk a path between these two other approaches to induction.

On the subjective Bayesian view, the manner in which data bear on a hypothesis depends on the prior probabilities and utilities that a given Bayesian agent has regarding the hypothesis. There is nothing that forces two Bayesian agents to have the same prior probabilities. This is why this Bayesian view is *subjective*. Since the relation between data and hypotheses depends on this subjective component, there is nothing that forces two Bayesian agents to have the same regard for the relationship between data and hypothesis.

Consider the following artificial and exaggerated, but simple, coin example. Suppose that two different Bayesian agents are interested in the bias of the coin to come up heads, call it θ. They test the coin's bias by flipping it 10 times; eight flips result in heads.

One Bayesian agent thinks that there are only two possibilities: The coin is fair, $\theta = 0.5$, or the coin is biased for heads, $\theta = 0.75$. He assigns equal prior probabilities to both possibilities. His posterior probabilities follow from Bayes' rule (see Chapter 9, Section 4):

$$
\begin{aligned}
P_{\text{posterior}}(\theta = 0.5) &= P_{\text{prior}}(\theta = 0.5 | 8 \text{ heads and 2 tails}) \\
&= \frac{(P_{\text{prior}}(\theta = 0.5) \times P_{\text{prior}}(8 \text{ heads and 2 tails} | \theta = 0.5)}{P_{\text{prior}}(8 \text{ heads and 2 tails})} \\
&= \frac{(0.5)(0.044)}{(0.5)(0.044) + (0.5)(0.282)} \approx 0.135.
\end{aligned}
$$

For this Bayesian agent the evidence substantially diminishes the probability that the coin is fair.

The other Bayesian agent has different prior probabilities. She thinks that either the coin is fair, $\theta = 0.5$, or biased for tails, $\theta = 0.25$. Initially, she assigns the same prior probability to both of these possibilities. Calculating her posterior probabilities goes similarly:

$$
P_{\text{posterior}}(\theta = 0.5) \approx \frac{(0.5)(0.044)}{(0.5)(0.044) + (0.5)(0.000386)} \approx 0.991.
$$

In contrast to the first agent, her posterior probability that the coin is fair has gone up substantially.

Here we have a case with the same evidence. In Section 2 we found that this evidence analyzed in terms of a significance test allowed rejection of the hypothesis of fairness at the 0.11 level of significance. But for one of our Bayesian agents this evidence supports the hypothesis of fairness, while for the other it discredits the hypothesis of fairness.

The example shows that different prior probabilities lead to differences in how evidence bears on hypotheses. It is exaggerated because it depends on the two agents embracing different possible values for the coin's bias. It is not clear that someone running a significance test, who considered only two possible values for the coin's bias, 0.75 and 0.5 say, would discard the hypothesis of fairness because the evidence is "significant at the 0.11 level." Very likely, no significance test would be used in such a context.

A subjective Bayesian holds that any set of probabilities that obeys the probability axioms can describe a Bayesian agent's degrees of belief. This element of subjectivism is one of the aspects of the Bayesian approach that Fisher intended to avoid with his significance tests. In the interests of objectivity, the effect of data on a hypothesis should not depend on the beliefs that different "rational minds" may reasonably have.

Fisher did not have a difficulty with the Bayesian idea of "degrees of belief." Using probabilities to describe appropriate attitudes toward beliefs that fall short of complete conviction is an entirely appropriate goal for inductive inferences. Indeed,

Fisher's "fiducial argument" endeavored to take confidence intervals of the sort discussed in Chapter 10 and produce probabilities about particular intervals; for example, there is a 95% probability that the proportion of married couples who are childless, call it ***MCL***, is between 22 and 28%, P(22% ≤ ***MCL*** ≤ 28%) = 0.95. Such probabilities cannot be claimed for confidence intervals as they are understood by Neyman and Pearson (see Chapter 10, Sections 5 and 6). These probabilities, however, should not be different for different "rational minds." That is, they should be unique and, in this sense, objective.

In addition to disliking the subjective component to the subjective Bayesian approach, Fisher did not believe that *all* inductive inferences had to be constructed within the particular probabilistic structure the Bayesian approach employs. *Objective* Bayesians attempt to find criteria to uniquely constrain allowable prior probabilities, to thus drop the subjective component of the Bayesian approach. Fisher would have applauded the attempt to drop the subjective component, but he would have found such a project overly restrictive of the kinds of inferences that inductive logic can embrace. Significance tests are one simple alternative. They use probability as a scale of fit, not to make statements about the appropriate partial belief to have for some statement.

8. NEYMAN/PEARSON STATISTICAL TESTS

In the late 1920s and early 1930s, Jerzy Neyman and E. S. Pearson (Karl Pearson's son) developed an alternative justification for statistical testing that left much of the mechanics of Fisher's significance tests the same, but which supplied a different rationale. Neyman and Pearson claimed to be "patching up" some unclear aspects of the foundations of Fisher's significance tests. Fisher never accepted these patches because, in his view, they were based on an incorrect foundation.

Neyman and Pearson saw three related defects in Fisher's justification for significance testing. First, Fisher did not supply a sufficiently clear rationale for his choice of test statistic. Why use the chi-square statistic to measure "chance deviations" from independence? Why use the proportion of heads in testing a coin's fairness? Second, they saw no justification for measuring significance in terms of the probability of a result as bad *or worse* than the given result. When testing the calibration of the ozone instrument we measured the level of significance in terms of the probability of any result as far from 200 as 197; our measure of the significance of the actual result, 197, reflects results that are worse, but which did not occur (e.g., 204; see the shaded area in Figure 13.4). Why not measure significance in terms of the actual result alone? Third, Neyman and Pearson argued that the appropriate test of a statistical hypothesis depended on the alternative hypotheses that were considered. The exaggerated example in the preceding section should give some idea why they felt this way.

Neyman and Pearson agreed completely with Fisher's complaints with the subjective Bayesian approach. Indeed, Neyman and Pearson went further, to deny that there could be any sensible use of probabilities not based on observable frequencies in repeated trials. Probability is not an appropriate concept for describing degrees of belief. Neyman and Pearson sought to remedy the defects they found in Fisher's significance tests while maintaining an even more resolute frequentist approach to probability. While the underlying rationale for Neyman/Pearson tests is quite different from Fisher's for significance tests, the tests that result, formally, are virtually identical.

Neyman and Pearson's first claim was that a hypothesis is never tested in isolation. It is always tested with alternative hypotheses in mind. These alternative hypotheses allowed them to give a detailed statement of a rationale for the construction of statistical tests.

Consider a coin example. Suppose that we test the coin's fairness—the null hypothesis—against the alternative that the coin is biased 0.75 for coming up heads. We want to use the data to arbitrate between these two possibilities. As Neyman/Pearson see it, we want a rule that tells us which of the two possible hypotheses to adopt given the various outcomes from flipping the coin.

There are two different kinds of mistake we could make with any such rule. We could conclude that the coin is not fair—has bias 0.75 for heads—when in fact it is fair. That is, we could mistakenly reject the null hypothesis when it is true. Alternatively, we could conclude that the coin is fair, when in fact it is biased 0.75 for heads. That is, we could mistakenly accept the null hypothesis when it is false.

For Neyman and Pearson, the test that minimizes the probability of both kinds of error is the best test. A test, then, is a partition of the set of all possible outcomes into two parts, call them A (for accept fairness) and R (for reject fairness). The best way to partition the set of possible outcomes would minimize both kinds of error:

$P(\mathsf{R}|\theta = 0.5) = \alpha$; α is the probability of a "Type I error."

$P(\mathsf{A}|\theta = 0.75) = \beta$; β is the probability of a "Type II error."

Neyman and Pearson proved a fundamental theorem about tests of this kind. For a given, fixed probability of the first kind of error, $P(\mathsf{R}|\theta = 0.5) = \alpha$, there is a unique way to divide the set of outcomes which minimizes the second kind of error, $P(\mathsf{A}|\theta = 0.75) = \beta$.

Perhaps most important, Neyman and Pearson showed how to construct the rejection region for this "best" test. These tests are "likelihood ratio tests." This means that one compares the ratio of the likelihood of an outcome given the null hypothesis to its likelihood given the alternative hypothesis. If this ratio is smaller than some constant value, this outcome is in the rejection region. For example, the likelihood ratio for this particular sequence of 10 flips, $\{<h, h, h, t, h, h, h, h, t, h>\}$, is computed as follows:

$$\frac{P(\{<h, h, h, t, h, h, h, h, t, h>\}|\theta = 0.5)}{P(\{<h, h, h, t, h, h, h, h, t, h>\}|\theta = 0.75)} = \frac{(1/2)^{10}}{(3/4)^8 \times (1/4)^2}$$

$$\approx \frac{0.00098}{0.10011 \times 0.06250} \approx 0.156.$$

In principle, a similar computation would be done for each of the 2^{10} different possible outcomes. The rejection region is that collection of outcomes whose likelihood ratio is smaller than some particular constant value, chosen to ensure that the probability of a Type I error is the desired value.

There is a nice feature of likelihood ratios. Suppose that instead of computing the likelihood ratio for the particular outcome, $<h, h, h, t, h, h, h, h, t, h>$, we computed the likelihood ratio for a sensible summary of this outcome, 8 heads and 2 tails:

$$\frac{P(8\ h \text{ and } 2\ t|\theta = 0.5)}{P(8\ h \text{ and } 2\ t|\theta = 0.75)} = \frac{[10!/(8! \times 2!)] \times (1/2)^{10}}{[10!/(8! \times 2!)] \times (3/4)^8 \times (1/4)^2}$$

$$= \frac{(1/2)^{10}}{(3/4)^8 \times (1/4)^2} \approx 0.156.$$

The factorial terms—the "counting terms" in the binomial formula (see Chapter 9, Section 2)—cancel out. Consequently, the likelihood ratios for any two outcomes with the same number of heads and tails will be the same. To construct a likelihood ratio test we have only to compute a likelihood ratio for each binomial event instead of each simple event (Table 13.5).

Clearly, one would prefer the hypothesis of bias to the hypothesis of fairness when there was a preponderance of heads in the outcome. If we picked a rejection region, R, which included all results with a likelihood ratio of less than 0.157 (eight or more heads), we would have a test with the following two error probabilities:

TABLE 13.5

Outcome	Likelihood Ratio
0 heads, 10 tails	1,024.0
1 head, 9 tails	341.334
2 heads, 8 tails	113.778
3 heads, 7 tails	37.926
4 heads, 6 tails	12.642
5 heads, 5 tails	4.214
6 heads, 4 tails	1.404
7 heads, 3 tails	0.468
8 heads, 2 tails	0.156
9 heads, 1 tails	0.052
10 heads, 0 tails	0.017

$P[\mathsf{R}\ (= 8 \text{ or more heads}) | \theta = 0.5] = \alpha \approx 0.055;$ Type I error;

$P[\mathsf{A}\ (= 7 \text{ or fewer heads}) | \theta = 0.75] = \beta \approx 0.474;$ Type II error.

Although the probability of committing a Type II error is fairly large—0.474—the Neyman/Pearson lemma assures us that this test has the smallest possible Type II error for a test with probability of committing a Type I error of 0.055. We could reduce the probability of committing a Type II error, but only at the expense of increasing the probability of committing a Type I error:

$P[\mathsf{R}'\ (= 7 \text{ or more heads}) | \theta = 0.5] = \alpha \approx 0.172;$ Type I error;

$P[\mathsf{A}'\ (= 6 \text{ or fewer heads}) | \theta = 0.75) = \beta \approx 0.224;$ Type II error.

One remarkable feature about the Neyman/Pearson rationale for test construction is that it depends only on probabilities drawn from long-run frequencies. If we assume that this coin really is fair or biased, $\theta = 0.75$ for heads, these error probabilities are based on the actual frequencies which, in the long run, this coin must exhibit.

Notice how this approach to statistical testing deals with the defects Neyman and Pearson found in Fisher's rationale for significance testing. Fisher would have us test the coin's bias in terms of the ratio of heads to the number of flips, not in terms of the actual sequence of heads and tails. The use of likelihood ratios justifies this choice. Fisher measures the level of significance in terms of outcomes as bad *or worse* than those obtained. Such a collection of outcomes is analogous to Neyman/Pearson's *rejection region* for the null hypothesis. Fisher's level of significance probability is formally identical to Neyman/Pearson's probability of committing a Type I error. Finally, Neyman/Pearson tests are explicit about the need for alternative hypotheses. Indeed, they use these alternative hypotheses to construct the complete rationale for a test.

While Neyman and Pearson's theorem is quite general, a "best" test can be found whenever the two hypotheses involved each stipulate exact probabilities for all outcomes. It is not general enough to cover cases where the two hypotheses involved do not specify exact probabilities for all the outcomes, such as a test of the polio study data. Here the Neyman/Pearson rationale gets murkier. Neyman and Pearson advocated further constraints to find a unique rejection region that do not have the simplicity and intuitive appeal of the idea of minimizing error probabilities.

Even for the nicest cases, Fisher did not find the Neyman/Pearson rationale appealing. Neyman/Pearson error probabilities apply *before* the trial has been run—the very same point applies to Neyman and Pearson's approach to confidence intervals (see Chapter 10, Sections 5–7). Neyman and Pearson can say that if one were always to adopt tests based on considerations such as theirs, one could rest assured that one would make mistakes as infrequently as is possible—on average (see Chapter 10, Section 6). The problem, in Fisher's view, is that statistical tests are used to evaluate evidence *after* the trial has been run. Neyman/Pearson tests might have nice "long-run operating characteristics," but science needs a measure of support that particular evidence can offer particular hypotheses. Neyman and Pearson do not consider evaluating the support that actual evidence has for particular hypotheses (see Chapter 10, Section 7).

Neyman denied there could be a measure of the support particular data has for particular hypotheses. Instead, we could use empirical probabilities to our advantage. Given certain collections of data, if the underlying probability model supposed to apply is right, we can act in ways that have a high probability of being based on the truth. Statistical testing is not a form of *inference*, rather, it is a form of behavior optimization. Fisher complained that science needs cannons of inference—not rules of behavior (see Chapter 10, Section 6).

9. IN SEARCH OF GOOD STATISTICS

If we abandon the kind of rationale that Neyman and Pearson supply for statistical tests, we are left with the defects Neyman and Pearson found. Why adopt certain test statistics? Why use levels of significance measured in terms of a collection of outcomes most of which did not occur? What about the effect of alternative hypotheses? As an approach to these worries, Fisher conceived of the aim of statistics as finding the most succinct summary of the data's relevance for the hypothesis in question. The level of significance of the data—determined *after* the data are gathered—is supposed to supply this summary.

It is not enough to say that since data obtained are improbable, supposing that a given hypothesis is true, the given hypothesis should not be supposed true. Data are not simply probable or improbable. The probability of data depends on its description. Consider the coin case. There are 2^{10} (=1,024) different sequences of heads and tails that could occur. If the coin is fair, each of these sequences has the same probability, 1/1,024. Thus, no possible data, if they are described in terms of the exact sequence of heads and tails, are any more improbable than any other data. Still, the data, on the basis of which we run a significance test, must arise from one of these sequences.

Of course, Fisher did not advocate using the sequence of heads and tails to run a significance test of a coin's fairness. Instead, we use the proportion of heads and tails. There is a sense in which this contraction of the data—from the actual sequence of heads and tails to the proportion of heads and tails—contains all and only the relevant evidence the data have to offer regarding the hypothesis under test. Fisher's concept of a "minimally sufficient statistic" is aimed to spell out this idea in detail.

A statistic partitions the set of all possible results. For example, there are eight different sequences of heads and tails when flipping a coin three times (Figure 13.6). By using the proportion of heads, $H/3$, we ignore the order of heads and tails. The statistic $H/3$ allows us to distinguish only four different results. There is more information in the eight ordered sequences than there is in the four proportions. We can determine the value of $H/3$ given the sequence that occurred; we *cannot* determine

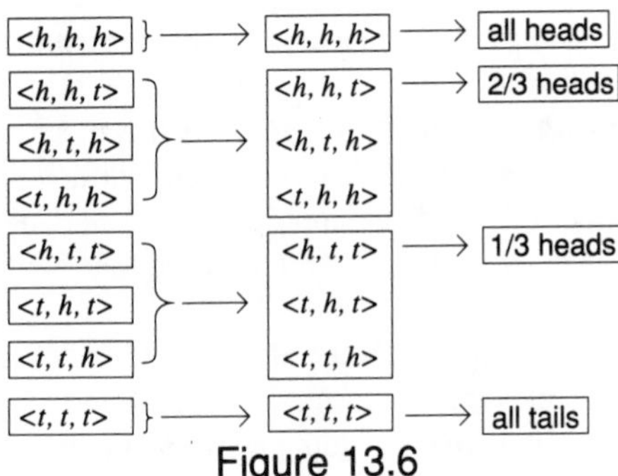

Figure 13.6

the sequence that occurred given the value of $H/3$. But we can show that none of the information that is lost is relevant to making inferences about the true bias of the coin.

At the very least, for evidence to bear on a hypothesis, the probability of this evidence arising, given this hypothesis, must differ from the probability of the evidence given some other hypothesis. If the evidence was equally probable given all hypotheses, this evidence would not distinguish between them. That is, for **E** to bear on **H** as opposed to **J**, the likelihood of **E** must differ for the two hypotheses:

$$\mathrm{P}(\mathbf{E}|\mathbf{H}) \neq \mathrm{P}(\mathbf{E}|\mathbf{J}) \quad \text{or, equivalently,} \quad \frac{\mathrm{P}(\mathbf{E}|\mathbf{H})}{\mathrm{P}(\mathbf{E}|\mathbf{J})} \neq 1.$$

This is the likelihood function encountered in the discussion of the Neyman/Pearson tests. One lesson from the Neyman/Pearson applies here as well. If we grant that flips of the coin are independent with a constant—unknown—probability for heads, no information is lost by only recording the ratio of heads and tails instead of the sequence of heads and tails. The factorial terms cancel out in likelihood ratios. No matter what hypotheses about the coin one entertains, the ratio of likelihoods does not distinguish between describing the data in terms of the ratio of heads and tails and describing it in terms of the sequence of heads and tails. In this sense, no information is lost when we only look at the ratio of heads and tails.

Fisher expressed this idea in a logically equivalent but somewhat different-looking way. For Fisher a statistic, **S**, is *sufficient* summary of the data for inferences about a certain parameter (e.g., a coin's bias for coming up heads, θ) if the outcomes are conditionally independent of the parameter's value, given the statistic's value. That is, for all possible outcomes, **O**, and all values of the statistic **S**, and all values of the parameter, θ,

$$\mathrm{P}(\mathbf{O}|\mathbf{S} \text{ and } \theta) = \mathrm{P}(\mathbf{O}|\mathbf{S}).$$

This is a generalization of independence to independence conditional on a third event (see Chapter 8, Section 2).

The fact that a statistic is sufficient is not enough to warrant its use in a test. The statistic must contain all *and only* information relevant to the parameter. The actual sequence of heads and tails from a coin is sufficient, but as we saw above, it is not a foundation for a test of significance of the coin's fairness. Appropriate test statistics must be *minimally* sufficient. Essentially, this means that the statistic provides the "coarsest" partition of the data that is still sufficient. The proportion of heads to the total number of flips is an appropriate test statistic because one cannot condense the data further without losing information that is relevant to hypotheses about the coin's bias.

Here, built into statistical tests, is the idea that inductive inferences can only be run with all and only the relevant evidence as premises. Inductive inferences, unlike deductive inferences, are sensitive to adding additional premises. Adding the additional information of the sequence of heads and tails undermines the significance test inference.

Alas, the requirement that statistics be minimally sufficient is not always enough to pick out uniquely preferable test statistics. Fisher advocated for a variety of other constraints. For instance, where appropriate, statistics should not be biased (see Chapter 10, Section 2). This is why we divide by $N - 1$ in Student's t-statistic estimate of the standard deviation instead of dividing by N. Fisher's criteria for statistic choice, beyond these considerations about information content, however, are less compelling.

Even setting aside issues about further criteria for selecting test statistics, one further point needs to be made about the criterion of sufficiency. One can only show that statistics are sufficient within a family of alternative hypotheses. In the case of the coin, for example, the proportion of heads to the total number of flips is only a sufficient statistic if one assumes that flips are independent and that there is a constant probability for heads on each flip. If the independence of flips is in doubt, the sequence of flips may be important to the consideration of hypotheses about the coin. We can say that sufficiency is a concept that applies within the context of a chance model. The model provides general constraints within which to characterize and test particular statistical hypotheses.

10. REJECTING AND FINDING FALSE

It is easy to see significance tests simply as methods of falsification brought to statistical hypotheses. *Rejecting* a chance hypothesis sounds like finding it false. Significance level probabilities are computed on the basis of probabilities introduced by the chance hypothesis. A low level of significance probability, then, arises when the outcome is unlikely given the chance hypothesis. These methods work by supposing that a hypothesis is true and showing that some consequence (deductive case) or probable outcome (statistical case) of the hypothesis is not true. Finding the hypothesis false seems the sensible conclusion to draw in either case.

But doing so misunderstands the point of significance tests. Significance tests try to establish a *measure* of fit between observed frequencies and those we would expect given some chance hypothesis. The fact that outcomes with poor fit are unlikely is *one* reason to trust such a measure of fit. But this is not a sufficient reason since the probability of an outcome depends on its description. Good test statistics need to measure fit *in the way we want chance models to fit data*. Typically, this means that expected values should be close to observed frequencies.

Rejecting an hypothesis is more of a decision to pursue alternative explanations for the data than a conclusion that the hypothesis is false. As such, rejection is sensitive to the context in which the test is run. In some areas of study, researchers may be able to express "chance" more carefully than in others areas. In some areas, researchers may be able to spell out detailed alternatives more carefully. Consequently, the level of significance at which one researcher in one field discards an hypothesis of chance may differ from the level at which another researcher in another field discards an hypothesis of chance. The test itself does not stipulate when to discard the hypothesis. The test merely summarizes the support for the hypothesis in a potentially misleading way: "Given the data, the null hypothesis may be rejected at the so-and-so level of significance."

There is another more important reason to distinguish finding an hypothesis false from rejecting an hypothesis with a significance test. Levels of significance violate a common rule of deductive logic central to the methodology of falsification, the consequence condition:

> If hypothesis **A** $\rightarrow$ hypothesis **B**,
>
> And if the evidence supports rejecting **B**,
>
> Then the evidence must at least as strongly support rejecting **A**.

A simple coin example can show that significance tests violate this principle. Let **A** be the hypothesis that a coin is fair and let **B** be the hypothesis that the coin is fair or biased for heads to some unspecified degree. Getting the evidence of four heads in 20 flips is sufficient to reject **B** at the 0.0059 level of significance. However, it is only sufficient to reject **A** at the 0.012 level of significance. This evidence is stronger against **B** than it is against **A**, despite the fact that **A** implies **B**.

The moral of the example is rejection at a significance level is not finding a hypothesis false. If it were, then, by denying the consequent, one would be able to find any other proposition, which implies a hypothesis found false, false as well. Thinking of rejection as finding false requires the consequence condition.

There is good reason to diagnose the violation of the consequence condition in terms of the informativeness of a hypothesis. The hypothesis that the coin is fair is more informative than the hypothesis that it is fair or biased for heads. More informative hypotheses are more desirable than less informative ones. Significance tests incorporate this desiderata right into their construction.

11. SIGNIFICANCE TESTS AND CHANCE MODELS

In a sense Fisher's significance tests do not avoid the problems that he found with both the subjective Bayesian approach and Neyman and Pearson's approach. Like the subjective Bayesian approach, the ultimate import of data is sensitive to the context in which it is gathered. Fisher sought to circumvent this fact by insisting that saying "data allow rejection at the α level of significance" is not finding the hypothesis false. It is simply a summary of the data. Whether a researcher discards the hypothesis may depend on contextual factors. But insisting this way is somewhat disingenuous. Fisher seeks to get some mileage out of the similarity between significance tests and the method of falsification, while carefully denying that such mileage can be had independent of context. The sense of "reject" is equivocated.

Similarly, Fisher criticized Neyman and Pearson's reliance on alternative hypotheses to provide a rationale for statistical tests. Fisher denied that tests should be thought of as a trial where one can know in advance that one of two candidates will win. Yet Fisher's concept of information depends on conceiving the hypothesis as one member of a family of possible hypotheses. H/N is only a sufficient summary of a coin's behavior if we assume independence of flips.

Fisher's concept of sufficiency requires that one confine one's attention to a family of statistical hypotheses, or a chance model. Fisher's levels of significance violate the consequence condition by making it harder to reject more informative hypotheses. These two features of significance tests are related to each other in ways that shed a little more light on the nature of this method of induction.

"Noise" contaminates statistical data. There can be little question that the advent of polio vaccine has dramatically reduced the number and severity of polio cases. Independent of any statistical test, the polio data are fairly convincing that there is a real causal relationship between being vaccinated and being protected from the disease. But because of human variability, the data are noisy: Some children who were vaccinated still came down with the disease; many who were not did not. Statistical tests are designed to extract as much of a clear message as is possible from noisy data.

Chance models allow us to distinguish message from noise—even if they are not wholly accurate. It probably does not make sense to think of chance models as literally true or false. Ultimately, of course, we would like to know the truth. But in many contexts, we can learn something about the world by supposing that it is *like* this .... Thus, we can think of errors of measurement as distributed *like* the normal distribution without supposing that the normal distribution is the absolute truth about errors of measurement. Similarly, we can think of human intellectual abilities as behaving *like* the common factor model without supposing that factorial causation is the absolute truth about causation in general and human ability causation in particular (see Chapter 12). The point of presupposing a general statistical model—be it factorial causation or a normal distribution of error—is to allow us to extract some information from data that would otherwise be meaningless.

Significance tests are not devices that tell us which of two hypotheses to believe. Rather, they help us determine, given a general chance model, whether a particular chance hypothesis is adequate to the data—whether the data can be understood to carry the message described by the chance hypothesis. The operation of a significance test acknowledges the fact that if enough latitude is left to adjust the particular hypothesis in light of the data, any hypothesis can be adequate to the data. Thus, significance tests penalize uninformative hypotheses and violate the consequence condition in so doing.

Seen in this light, Fisher's insistence that significance tests simply provide the best summary of what the data have to say about a hypothesis may make sense. It may not be possible to abandon the idea of a background chance model without abandoning the attempt to distinguish message from noise in statistical data. If the model is reasonably accurate, significance tests may help distinguish message from noise.

12. SUMMARY

1. Significance tests measure the fit between observed frequencies and those which would be expected given some chance hypothesis.
   - **(a)** Typically, the chance hypothesis, known as the null hypothesis, formulates precisely the claim that observed data are the product of random fluctuations alone.
   - **(b)** Significance tests are used to show the degree to which the evidence does not support the hypothesis that it arose by random fluctuations alone.
   - **(c)** The degree to which evidence does not support random fluctuations is stated in terms of a probability called the level of significance, frequently denoted α.
   - **(d)** Level of significance probabilities are computed on the assumption of the chance hypothesis. The level of significance of some evidence is the probability of evidence as bad or worse than that obtained.
   - **(e)** Significance tests bear a resemblance to the method of falsifying hypotheses.

2. Test statistics partition the set of possible outcomes into a smaller set of test statistic values.
   - **(a)** Test statistics rank the possible outcomes in terms of how well they fit the null hypothesis.
   - **(b)** It must be possible to derive a probability density function for test statistic values.
      - **(1)** The lower the probability of an outcome, the worse this outcome fits the hypothesis in terms of the test statistic ranking.
      - **(2)** Level of significance probabilities are computed on the basis of this probability distribution. The level of significance is the probability of any value as bad or worse than the observed value.
   - **(c)** Different chance models and null hypotheses require different test statistics.
   - **(d)** The right test statistic for a given chance model must contain all and only the information in the data relevant to the hypothesis under test.
      - **(1)** This concept of information presupposes he context of a family of possible hypotheses, where particular hypotheses are specified in terms of particular values of one or more parameters (e.g., a coin's bias, or the mean of a normal distribution).
      - **(2)** This concept of information requires that evidence not be conditionally independent of the parameter under test, given the value of the test statistic.

3. Fisher's interpretation of significance tests tries to provide the right alternative both to the subjectivism of the subjective Bayesian approach and to the purely empirical frequentism of the Neyman/Pearson approach.
   - **(a)** The subjective Bayesian quantifies our ignorance in terms of probabilities. Different Bayesian agents may reasonably differ in descriptions—their prior probabilities—of their quantified ignorance.
   - **(b)** The impact of evidence on hypotheses in the subjective Bayesian approach depends on the prior probabilities. It is possible for the same evidence to support a hypothesis for one agent and discredit it for another agent.
   - **(c)** Fisher has no quibble with quantifying ignorance in terms of probability, although he does not think that all inductive inferences need to be understood this way. Fisher does have a problem with the subjective aspect of the subjective Bayesian approach.
   - **(d)** The Neyman/Pearson approach thinks of statistical tests in terms of a competition between two hypotheses, the null hypothesis and an alternative. Test construction comes to stating a rule that says which of the two hypotheses to accept given the different possible outcomes.
   - **(e)** On this approach two errors are possible, incorrectly rejecting the null hypothesis when it is true and incorrectly accepting it when it is false. In Neyman/Pearson's view the best test is the test that minimizes the probability of both sorts of error.
   - **(f)** Neyman/Pearson show that when both hypotheses stipulate probabilities for all outcomes, there is a test that minimizes the probability of the second kind of error for a given probability of the first kind of error. These are likelihood ratio tests.
   - **(g)** Fisher did not think statistical tests should be thought of in terms of a competition between two hypotheses arbitrated by a rule. Statistical tests should measure the negative support that evidence offers hypotheses. Support is evaluated after the evidence is in. Thus the probabilities that Fisher employs for significance tests cannot be understood in purely empirical frequentist terms, as are Neyman/Pearson error probabilities. They have a frequency aspect, but they are epistemic in impact.

4. Significance tests are run in the context of chance models that probably should not be thought of as literally true or false.
   - **(a)** Typically, chance models provide an idealization of the effects of chance variation appropriate to our understanding of the particular context.
   - **(b)** Within the context of a chance model, one can state precise probabilistic hypotheses about the putative operation of chance in the genesis of the data.
   - **(c)** Chance models provide a means to distinguish "chance noise" from the message in data.
   - **(d)** Significance tests, used within the context of a chance model, show the degree to which the evidence does not support the hypothesis of "pure chance."
   - **(e)** Significance tests, used within the context of a chance model, are not appropriate tests of the model itself. Another chance model is necessary for such a test.
   - **(f)** Consequently, the measure of information that data have relevant to a given hypothesis is relative to the chance model in use.
   - **(g)** Another consequence is that rejecting an hypothesis at a given level of significance is not finding it false. Rather, it is stating the degree to which chance is not an appropriate genesis for the data, given the general validity of the chance model.
   - **(h)** Finally, significance tests violate the consequence condition.

13. REFERENCES

Virtually any standard statistics text will present some version of significance testing methodology. (Mood et al., 1974) and (Freedman et al., 1978) are examples. Typically, the interpretation that textbooks provide for significance tests is somewhat of a mix of Neyman and Pearson's ideas with Fisher's ideas. The chi-square test was first presented in (Pearson, 1900); Student's t-test was first presented in (Gossett, 1908). (Fisher, 1956 and 1970) provide Fisher's systematic efforts to state his rationale for significance tests. Neyman and Pearson's alternative rationale was set out in a series of papers (Neyman and Pearson, 1928, 1933, and 1936). (Hacking, 1965), (Seidenfeld, 1979), and (Johnstone, 1987) are three contributions that attempt carefully to state the rationale to significance tests. (Baird, 1983 and 1984) concern the violation of the consequence condition by significance tests.

14. PROBLEMS

1. Compute the level of significance for the hypothesis that a coin is fair with the evidence of 12 heads in 15 flips.

2. If we flip a coin 1,000 times to test for its fairness, how many heads would have to turn up to reject fairness at at least the 0.05 level of significance? *Hint:* Use a normal approximation to these binomial probabilities and find the interval on either side of 500 heads that includes 95% of all possible outcomes.

3. Suppose that the instrument in Section 3 produced the following readings: 202, 205, 204, 199, and 205.

   (a) Assume that the standard deviation on each reading is 2. Compute the value of the appropriate test statistic. Can you compute the level of significance as well? If so, do so.

   (b) As in part (a), except you must assume that the standard deviation is unknown.

4. Suppose that the instrument in Section 3 produced the following readings: 192, 199, 198, 202, 205, 204, 199, 205, 206, 200. Compute the t-statistic value for testing this instrument for proper calibration. If a table is available and you can figure out how to extract probabilities from it, find the level of significance of these data.

5. Compute a chi-square value to test the hypothesis that a die is fair when the following results have been observed in 600 tosses: one: 95; two: 103; three: 101; four: 96; five: 102; six: 103. If a table is available and you can figure out how to extract probabilities from it, find the level of significance of these data.

6. Suppose that the two Bayesian agents in Section 7 admit that all three biases $\theta = 0.25$, $\theta = 0.50$, and $\theta = 0.75$ are possible but the first agent assigns a prior probability of 0.02 to $\theta = 0.25$ and equal prior probabilities to the remaining two hypotheses. The second Bayesian agent does just the reverse. What posterior probabilities would each agent have concerning $\theta = 0.50$ given the evidence of 8 heads and 2 tails in 10 flips? Suppose that they got 16 heads in 20 flips; what would the posterior probabilities be? What does this say about the subjective component of the subjective Bayesian approach?

7. Construct the best Neyman/Pearson test of the hypothesis that a coin has bias $\theta = 0.25$, against the alternative $\theta = 0.75$, given 10 flips and a probability of Type I error of less than 0.05. What is the probability of the Type II error for this test?
8. Discuss Fisher's complaint that Neyman/Pearson tests ''only'' provide optimal rules of behavior, when science needs inference.
9. Given Fisher's interest in objective inference, why is it important that Fisher's concept of information requires the background concept of a chance model?
10. Discuss the difference between rejecting a hypothesis and finding it false. Is this a difference that makes a difference? Does it make sense?

BIBLIOGRAPHY

BAIRD, D. 1983. "The Fisher/Pearson Chi-Squared Controversy: A Turning Point for Inductive Inference." *British Journal for the Philosophy of Science,* Volume 34, pages 104–118.

BAIRD, D. 1984. "Tests of Significance Violate the Rule of Implication." In P. D. Asquith and P. Kitcher, eds., *PSA 1984,* Volume 1, pages 81–92.

BAIRD, D. 1987. "Exploratory Factor Analysis, Instruments and the Logic of Discovery." *British Journal for the Philosophy of Science,* Volume 38, pages 319–337.

BANVILLE, J. 1981. *Kepler: A Novel.* Boston, Massachusetts: David R. Godine, Publisher, Inc.

BAYES, T. 1763. "An Essay Towards Solving a Problem in the Doctrine of Chances." Reprinted in (Pearson and Kendall, 1970, pages 131–153).

BERGER, J. O. 1985. *Statistical Decision Theory and Bayesian Analysis.* New York: Springer-Verlag, New York, Inc.

BERRY, A. 1961. *A Short History of Astronomy.* New York: Dover Publications, Inc.

BHATTACHARYYA, G. K., AND JOHNSON, R. A. 1977. *Statistical Concepts and Methods.* New York: John Wiley & Sons, Inc.

BLOCK, N. J., AND DWORKIN, G., EDS. 1976. *The IQ Controversy: Critical Readings.* New York: Pantheon Books, Inc.

BOLTON, H. C. 1900. *Evolution of the Thermometer, 1592–1743.* Easton, Pennsylvania: Chemical Publishing Company, Inc.

BUNKER, J. P., ET AL., EDS. 1977. *Costs, Risks, and Benefits of Surgery.* New York: Oxford University Press, Inc.

Bureau of Labor Statistics Handbook of Methods. 1982. Washington, D.C.: United States Government Printing Office.

CARTWRIGHT, N. 1983. *How the Laws of Physics Lie*. Oxford: Oxford University Press, Inc.

CATTELL, R. B. 1952. *Factor Analysis: An Introduction and Manual for the Psychologist and Social Scientist*. Westport, Connecticut: Greenwood Press, Publishers, Inc.

CATTELL, R. B. 1978. *The Scientific Use of Factor Analysis in Behavioral and Life Sciences*. New York: Plenum Press.

CHUNG, K. L. 1975. *Elementary Probability Theory with Stochastic Processes*. New York: Springer-Verlag, New York, Inc.

CLEVELAND, W. S. 1985. *The Elements of Graphing Data*. Monterey, California: Wadsworth Advanced Books and Software.

COPI, I. 1961. *Introduction to Logic*. New York: The Macmillan Company.

COX, D. R. 1958. *Planning of Experiments*. New York: John Wiley & Sons, Inc.

CURD, M. 1980. "The Logic of Discovery: An Analysis of Three Approaches." In T. Nickles, ed., *Scientific Discovery, Logic and Rationality*. Dordrecht, The Netherlands: D. Reidel Publishing Company.

DAVIDSON, D., SUPPES, P., AND SIEGEL, S. 1957. *Decision Making: An Experimental Approach*. Stanford, California: Stanford University Press.

DE FINETTI, B. 1937. "Foresight: Its Logical Laws, Its Subjective Sources." Reprinted in (Kyburg and Smokler, 1980, pages 53–118).

EYSENCK, H. J. 1939. "Primary Mental Abilities." *British Journal of Educational Psychology*, Volume 9, pages 270–75.

EYSENCK, H. J., AND KAMIN, L. 1981. *The Intelligence Controversy*. New York: John Wiley & Sons, Inc.

FISHER, R. 1922. "On the Mathematical Foundations of Theoretical Statistics." *Philosophical Transactions of the Royal Society*, Series A, Volume 222, pages 309–368.

FISHER, R. 1925. "The Theory of Statistical Estimation." *Proceedings of the Cambridge Philosophical Society*, Volume 22, pages 700–725.

FISHER, R. A. 1935. *The Design of Experiments*. Edinburgh: Oliver & Boyd.

FISHER, R. A. 1956. *Statistical Methods and Scientific Inference*. New York: Hafner Press.

FISHER, R. 1970. *Statistical Methods for Research Workers*. New York: Hafner Publishing Co. This is the 14th edition; the first edition appeared in 1925.

FREEDMAN, D., PISANI, R., AND PURVES, R. 1978. *Statistics*. New York: W.W. Norton & Company, Inc.

GALLUP, G. 1978. "Opinion Polling in a Democracy." In (Tanur et al., 1978, pages 187–194).

GIGERENZER, G., ET AL. 1989. *The Empire of Chance*. Cambridge: Cambridge University Press.

GLYMOUR, C. 1980. *Theory and Evidence*. Princeton, New Jersey: Princeton University Press.

GNEDENKO, B. V., AND KHINCHIN, A. YA. 1962. *An Elementary Introduction to the Theory of Probability*. New York: Dover Publications, Inc.

GOSSETT, W. S. 1908. "The Probable Error of a Mean." Reprinted in (Pearson and Wishart, 1942).

GOULD, S. J. 1981. *The Mismeasure of Man*. New York: W.W. Norton & Company, Inc.

GROSSER, M. 1979. *The Discovery of Neptune*. New York: Dover Publications, Inc.

HACKING, I. 1965. *The Logic of Statistical Inference*. Cambridge: Cambridge University Press.

HACKING, I. 1980. "The Theory of Probable Inference: Neyman, Peirce and Braithwaite." In D. H. Mellor, ed., *Science, Belief and Behavior*. Cambridge: Cambridge University Press, pages 141–160.

HACKING, I. 1983. "Culpable Ignorance of Interference Effects." Center for Philosophy and Public Policy. Working Paper RC-7.

HALMOS, PAUL, R. 1970. *Naive Set Theory*. New York: Springer-Verlag, New York, Inc.

HARMON, H. H. 1976. *Modern Factor Analysis*. Chicago: The University of Chicago Press.

HILL, P. H., et al. 1979. *Making Decisions: A Multidisciplinary Introduction*. Reading, Massachusetts: Addison-Wesley Publishing Company, Inc.

HORWICH, P. 1982. *Probability and Evidence*. Cambridge: Cambridge University Press.

HUME, D. 1978. *A Treatise of Human Nature*. Oxford: Oxford University Press. First published in 1739.

IVERSEN, G. R. 1984. *Bayesian Statistical Inference*. Beverly Hills, California: Sage Publications, Inc.

JAEGER, R. M. 1982. *Statistics: A Spectator Sport*. Beverly Hills, California: Sage Publications, Inc.

JEFFREY, R. 1967. *Formal Logic: Its Scope and Limits*. New York: McGraw-Hill Book Company.

JEFFREY, R. C. 1983. *The Logic of Decision*. Chicago: The University of Chicago Press.

JENSON, A. R. 1980. *Bias in Mental Testing*. New York: The Free Press.

JOHNSTONE, D. J. 1987. "Tests of Significance Following R. A. Fisher." *British Journal for the Philosophy of Science,* Volume 38, pages 481–499.

JORESKOG, K., AND SORBOM, D. 1979. *Advances in Factor Analysis and Structural Equation Models*. Cambridge, Massachusetts: Abt Books.

JORESKOG, K., KLOVAN, J. E., AND REYMENT, R. A. 1976. *Geological Factor Analysis*. Amsterdam: Elsevier Scientific Publishing Company.

KALTON, G. 1983. *Introduction to Survey Sampling*. Beverly Hills, California: Sage Publications, Inc.

KIM, J., AND MUELLER, C. W. 1978a. *Introduction to Factor Analysis: What It Is and How to Do It*. Beverly Hills, California: Sage Publications, Inc.

KIM, J. AND MUELLER, C. W. 1978b. *Factor Analysis: Statistical Methods and Practical Issues*. Beverly Hills, California: Sage Publications, Inc.

KRANTZ, D. H., LUCE, R. D., SUPPES, P., AND TVERSKY, A. 1971. *The Foundations of Measurement*. New York: Academic Press, Inc.

KRIVINE, JEAN-LOUS. 1971. *Introduction to Axiomatic Set Theory*. Dordrecht, The Netherlands: D. Reidel Publishing Company.

KRUSKAL, W. 1978. "Taking Data Seriously." In Y. Elkana et al., eds., *Toward a Metric of Science: The Advent of Science Indicators*. New York: John Wiley & Sons, Inc., pages 139–169.

KYBURG, H. 1974. *The Logical Foundations of Statistical Inference*. Dordrecht, The Netherlands: D. Reidel Publishing Company.

KYBURG, H. 1977. "Randomness and the Right Reference Class." *The Journal of Philosophy,* Volume 74, pages 501–521.

KYBURG, H. 1983. "Rational Belief." *The Behavioral and Brain Sciences,* Volume 6, pages 231–273.

KYBURG, H., AND SMOKLER, H., EDS. 1980. *Studies in Subjective Probability*. New York: R.E. Krieger Publishing Co., Inc.

LAUDAN, L. 1980. "Why Was the Logic of Discovery Abandoned?" In T. Nickles, ed., *Scientific Discovery, Logic and Rationality*. Dordrecht, The Netherlands: D. Reidel Publishing Company, pages 173–183.

LEFTON, L. 1985. *Psychology*. Boston: Allyn and Bacon, Inc.

LEVI, I. 1977. "Direct Inference." *The Journal of Philosophy,* Volume 74, pages 5–29.

LEVI, I. 1980. *The Enterprise of Knowledge*. Cambridge, Massachusetts: The MIT Press.

LEVI, I. 1981. "Direct Inference and Confirmational Conditionalization." *Philosophy of Science,* Volume 48, pages 532–552.

LUCE, R. D. 1979. "Suppes' Contributions to the Theory of Measurement." In R. J. Bogdan, ed., *Patrick Suppes*. Dordrecht, The Netherlands: D. Reidel Publishing Company.

MOOD, A., GRAYBILL, F., AND BOES, D. 1974. *Introduction to the Theory of Statistics*, third edition. New York: McGraw-Hill Book Company.

MOORE, D. S. 1985. *Statistics: Concepts and Controversies*. New York: W.H. Freeman and Company.

MULAIK, S. 1985. "Exploratory Statistics and Empiricism." *Philosophy of Science,* Volume 52, Number 3, pages 410–430.

MULAIK, S. 1988. "Confirmatory Factor Analysis." In J. R. Nesselroade and R. B. Cattell, eds., *Handbook of Multivariate Experimental Psychology,* second edition. New York: Plenum Press.

MULAIK, S. 1991. "Factor Analysis, Information Transforming Instruments, and Objectivity: A Reply and Discussion. *British Journal for the Philosophy of Science,* Volume 42, pages 87–100.

NEYMAN, J. 1937. "Outline of a Theory of Statistical Estimation Based on the Classical Theory of Probability." *Philosophical Transactions of the Royal Society*, Series A, Volume 236, pages 333–388.

NEYMAN, J. 1950. *First Course in Probability and Statistics*. New York: Henry Holt and Company.

NEYMAN, J. 1957. " 'Inductive Behavior' as a Basic Concept of Philosophy of Science." *Revue de l'instutute internationale de statistique*, Volume 25, pages 7–22.

NEYMAN, J. 1977. "Frequentist Probability and Frequentist Statistics." *Synthese*, Volume 36, pages 79–131.

NEYMAN, J. AND PEARSON, E. S. 1928. "On the Use and Interpretation of Certain Test Criteria for Purposes of Statistical Inference." Reprinted in (Neyman and Pearson, 1967, pages 1–98).

NEYMAN, J. AND PEARSON, E. S. 1933. "On the Problem of the Most Efficient Tests of Statistical Hypotheses." Reprinted in (Neyman and Pearson, 1967, pages 140–185).

NEYMAN, J. AND PEARSON, E. S. 1936. "Contributions to the Theory of Testing Statistical Hypotheses." Reprinted in (Neyman and Pearson, 1967, pages 203–239).

NEYMAN, J. AND PEARSON, E. S. 1967. *Joint Statistical Papers*. Cambridge: Cambridge University Press.

NICKLES, T. 1985. "Beyond Divorce: Current Status of the Discovery Debate." *Philosophy of Science,* Volume 52, Number 2, pages 177–206.

NISBETT, R., AND ROSS, L. 1980. *Human Inference: Strategies and Shortcomings of Social Judgment*. Englewood Cliffs, New Jersey: Prentice Hall.

OTTE, R. 1985. "Probabilistic Causality and Simpson's Paradox." *Philosophy of Science,* Volume 52, Number 1, pages 110–125.

PAUKER, S. G. AND KASSIRER, J. P. 1975. "Therapeutic Decision Making: A Cost–Benefit Analysis." *New England Journal of Medicine,* Volume 293, Number 5, pages 229–234.

PAUKER, S. G. AND KASSIRER, J. P. 1978. "Clinical Application of Decision Analysis: A Detailed Illustration." *Seminars in Nuclear Medicine,* Volume 8, pages 324–335.

PEARSON, K. 1900. "On the Criterion That a Given System of Deviations from the Probable in the Case of a Correlated System of Variables Is Such That It Can Be Reasonably Supposed to Have Arisen from Random Sampling." Reprinted in (Pearson, 1948, pages 339–357).

PEARSON, K. 1948. In E. S. Pearson, ed., *Karl Pearson's Early Statistical Papers*. London: Cambridge University Press.

PEARSON, E. S. AND KENDALL, M. G., EDS. 1970. *Studies in the History of Statistics and Probability*. London: Charles Griffin & Company., Ltd.

PEARSON, E. S. AND WISHART, J., EDS. 1942. *Student's Collected Papers*. Cambridge: Cambridge University Press.

RAIFFA, H. 1970. *Decision Analysis: Introductory Lectures on Choices under Uncertainty*. Reading, Massachusetts: Addison-Wesley Publishing Company, Inc.

RAMSEY, F. P. 1926. "Truth and Probability." Reprinted in (Kyburg and Smokler, 1980, pages 23–52).

RANSOHOFF, D. F. AND FEINSTEIN, A. R. 1976. "Editorial: Is Decision Analysis Useful in Clinical Medicine?" *The Yale Journal of Biology and Medicine,* Volume 49, pages 165–168.

RESNIK, M. 1987. *Choices: An Introduction to Decision Theory*. Minneapolis: University of Minnesota Press.

ROLLER, D. 1957. "The Early Development of the Concepts of Temperature and Heat: The Rise and Decline of the Caloric Theory." In J. B. Conant and L. K. Nash eds., *Harvard Case Histories in Experimental Science*. Cambridge, Massachusetts: Harvard University Press, Volume 1, pages 117–214.

ROSENKRANTZ, R. 1977. *Inference, Method and Decision*. Dordrecht, The Netherlands: D. Reidel Publishing Company.

SALMON, W. 1967. *The Foundations of Scientific Inference*. Pittsburgh, Pennsylvania: University of Pittsburgh Press.

SAVAGE. L. J. 1954. *The Foundations of Statistics*. New York: John Wiley & Sons, Inc.

SEIDENFELD, T. 1979. *Philosophical Problems of Statistical Inference: Learning from R. A. Fisher*. Dordrecht, The Netherlands: D. Reidel Publishing Company.

SPEARMAN, C. 1904. " 'General Intelligence': Objectively Determined and Measured." *American Journal of Psychology,* Volume 15, pages 201–292.

SPEARMAN, C. 1927. *The Abilities of Man*. New York: Macmillan Publishing Company.

Statistical Abstract of the United States. 1986. Washington, D.C.: United States Government Printing Office.

STEVENS, S. S. 1951. "Mathematics, Measurement and Psychophysics." In S. S. Stevens, ed., *Handbook of Experimental Psychology*. New York: John Wiley & Sons, Inc., pages 1–49.

TANUR, J. ET AL., EDS. 1978. *Statistics: A Guide to the Unknown*. San Francisco: Holden-Day, Inc.

TAUREK, J. M. 1977. "Should the Numbers Count?" *Philosophy and Public Affairs,* Volume 6, Number 4, pages 293–316.

THOMAS, J. 1977. *Symbolic Logic*. Columbus, Ohio: Charles E. Merrill Publishing Company.

THURSTONE, L. L. 1938. *Primary Mental Abilities*. Psychometric Monographs, Number 1. Chicago: The University of Chicago Press.

THURSTONE, L. L. 1947. *Multiple Factor Analysis*. Chicago: The University of Chicago Press.

TUFTE, E. R. 1983. *The Visual Display of Quantitative Information*. Cheshire, Connecticut: Graphics Press.

TUKEY, J. W. 1977. *Exploratory Data Analysis*. Reading, Massachusetts: Addison-Wesley Publishing Company, Inc.

VENN, J. 1866. *The Logic of Chance*. London: Macmillan and Co. Reprinted in 1962 by Chelsea Publishing Co., New York.

WHEELER, M. 1976. *Lies, Damn Lies, and Statistics: The Manipulation of Public Opinion in America*. New York: Dell Publishing Company.

WOODROOFE, M. 1975. *Probability with Applications*. New York: McGraw-Hill Book Company.

YULE, G. U. 1911. *An Introduction to the Theory of Statistics*. London: Charles Griffin & Company Ltd.

INDEX